GEOLOGY: PRINCIPLES AND PROCESSES

GEOLOGY: PRINCIPLES
AND PROCESSES

WILLIAM H. EMMONS
Late Professor of Geology,
University of Minnesota

IRA S. ALLISON
Professor of Geology,
Oregon State College

CLINTON R. STAUFFER
Professor Emeritus of Geology,
University of Minnesota;
Research Associate,
California Institute of Technology

GEORGE A. THIEL
Professor of Geology,
University of Minnesota

McGRAW-HILL BOOK COMPANY, INC.

GEOLOGY: PRINCIPLES AND PROCESSES

FIFTH EDITION

NEW YORK   TORONTO   LONDON   1960

This book is set in Linotype Caledonia,

a type face designed by the American

graphic designer W. A. Dwiggins.

The boldface headings are Spartan Heavy and the

chapter titles are Venus Bold Extended.

PREFACE

The fifth edition of *Geology: Principles and Processes* provides, as did the previous editions, a sound basic introduction to physical geology for the student planning to major in earth sciences. At the same time it challenges the interest of the student seeking a cultural course in a natural science. Because many geology departments find it impractical to offer separate introductory courses, it is often necessary to give the same course to majors and nonmajors alike. Thus this course must be sufficiently comprehensive to acquaint students with the basic framework of a vast field of science. Because this field is an unfamiliar one to most students, this framework must be comprised of the essential major concepts of earth science, unobscured by a maze of details.

In preparing this revision we faced a dilemma common to every teacher of geology: Is it better to cover many topics in breadth or a fewer number in depth? Because the scope of physical geology has become so extensive with the advance of knowledge, there existed the twofold problem of how many topics to cover in the time and space available and how deeply to delve into each one. We hope that the organization of this text affords a partial solution to this problem.

In order to serve those holding different points of view, thoroughness has been combined with a considerable breadth of treatment, leaving the user free to make selections to fit his particular needs.

To this end we have included short treatments of fringe topics in meteorology, climatology, soils, oceanography, and seismology, which for exigencies of time or other considerations some teachers may prefer to omit. Furthermore, each chapter has been made a fairly complete and independent unit to allow greater versatility of presentation. Some teachers prefer to proceed from the simple to the abstruse, from the familiar to the less familiar. Others prefer to follow an order based on internal logic. Accordingly, the text is organized to make possible any sequence of chapter assignment.

The order of presentation in this edition differs in several ways from that of previous editions. Minerals, vulcanism, igneous rocks, and sedimentary rocks are treated early to prepare students for concurrent laboratory work on earth materials. Discussion of wind and ground water follows, rather than precedes, the more important topics of stream erosion, glaciation, and shore processes. The section on the effect of geologic structures upon stream erosion has been restored to the chapter on stream work. Special attention is given to rainwash, streams, and wind in dry-land areas. The geologic timetable and the measurement of geologic time by radioactivity have been removed from the Appendix and placed in Chapter 3.

One significant difference from previous editions is the treatment of the economic aspects of geology at appropriate places within the text instead of in a separate chapter at the end. Discussion in context of such practical considerations as the weathering of sulfide ores, the accumulation of iron-rich or aluminum-rich laterite, and the formation of placer deposits generally sharpens interest in the geologic process involved and gives point to an otherwise academic discourse.

We are aware that many students may have a limited knowledge of mathematics, chemistry, and physics. Nevertheless, we have unhesitatingly used some basic principles of these disciplines as tools in geology and have incorporated quantitative data freely. We trust that we have shown a proper sense of balance.

The fifth edition has been completely reset in two-column format for ease of reading. The contents have been extensively revised and brought up to date. This edition also includes some results from the International Geophysical Year investigations. As illustrations are such an important part of any geology text, all the line drawings have been redrawn by a professional scientific illustrator. The use of color in the line drawings gives greater visual clarity to contrasts and comparisons, which in turn makes the drawings more functional and meaningful to the student. The Glossary is a new feature with this edition and is located at the end of the book to give it greater reference value. Added to the Appendix are a reference list of chemical symbols and a set of keys to the identification of rocks.

Inasmuch as we exchanged our individual writing assignments as successive editions were revised, each of us at one time or another has had a hand in several different chapters. To a considerable degree, therefore, we all share a responsibility for them. However, the present chapters on glaciation, lakes and swamps, and rock deformation and mountain building were prepared by Professor Thiel, as was the Glossary. The remainder of this edition was prepared by Professor Allison.

We have endeavored throughout the book to acknowledge sources of all photographic illustrations and drawings. We realize, however, that it is impracticable to acknowledge all sources of the information we have acquired through the years. We wish especially to express our indebtedness to our colleagues and to scores of other persons for their many courtesies in connection with this revision.

Ira S. Allison
Clinton R. Stauffer
George A. Thiel

CONTENTS

GEOLOGY: PRINCIPLES
AND PROCESSES

Chapter 1

GEOLOGY—A SCIENCE

WE ARE naturally curious about ourselves, our fellows, and the world in which we live. We want to understand our world—how it originated and how it affects our life. Our interest extends to the earth, its lands and seas, its minerals, rocks, and fossils, which are the basic materials of geology, the science of the earth.

When natural science, at one time called natural philosophy, was in its infancy, man studied a wide range of natural phenomena. As he accumulated knowledge, however, he established many separate branches of more limited scope. Out of the broad field of the physical sciences, he developed mathematics, astronomy, physics, geology, and chemistry.

In the same way, geology has now branched off into separate, more limited fields. Meteorology, climatology, hydrology, geochemistry, geophysics, seismology, vulcanology, and oceanography are now considered more or less separate from geology proper. Yet these and other borderline sciences are still geologically significant, and we must consider them for a more thorough understanding of the earth.

Geology and Man

GEOLOGISTS AT WORK

Geologists work with minerals, rocks, ores, and fossils. Petroleum geologists seek deposits of petroleum and natural gas, which are our principal mineral fuels and our most valuable mineral products. Mining geologists search for ore deposits of iron, uranium, lead, and zinc or for nonmetallic deposits such as limestone, coal, salt,

FIG. 1.0. *Mount Robson, British Columbia, 12,972 feet high. This mountain has a long geologic history. It is composed of thousands of feet of sedimentary rocks that were deposited in the sea, subsequently elevated to mountainous heights, and then carved to their present form by glaciers and running water. (Harry Rowed, O'Neill & Associates, Ltd., and Canadian Government Travel Bureau.)*

gypsum, potash, and phosphate rock. Ground-water geologists assist in locating supplies of underground water for industrial and domestic use. Mineralogists identify minerals and study their physical and chemical properties. The study of gems is in their field. Petrologists specialize in the study of 'the composition and origin of various rocks. Paleontologists work with fossils, the remains or traces of past life naturally preserved in rocks. These remains show an orderly development from the most primitive forms in ancient rocks to remnants of modern life in recently deposited sediments. Fossils found in well cores in drilling for oil can be used to identify the relative ages of rocks.

Stratigraphers study the order in which the rocks were formed, so as to guide the search for such materials as petroleum and uranium. Structural geologists are concerned with the architecture, or arrangement, of the rocks of the earth's crust, important in oil fields and mining districts. Engineer-

ing geologists devote themselves to the application of geology to such projects as dam sites, tunnels, water reservoirs, highway and railroad construction, foundations, and construction materials. The work of geomorphologists, who study the nature and origin of landscapes, is important in the search for oil and gas, construction, land use, military operations, and other affairs.

The diversity of these activities indicates the broad scope of general geology.

Geologists receive assistance from exploration geophysicists, seismologists, geochemists, and such specialists as paleobotanists and, in turn, give assistance to engineers, miners, soil conservationists, and geographers.

MINERAL RESOURCES

Earth materials have long affected the activities and welfare of man. Primitive man made his first rude weapons and utensils from stone, wood, and bone. When he became more adept in working stone into various shapes, he entered the Stone Age. Overhanging cliffs and caves were his first dwelling places; the springs and streams furnished his water supply; and as he learned to fashion some kind of boat or canoe, the rivers served as highways for his travel. With the discovery of methods for isolating metals from their ores, man passed successively into the Copper, Bronze, and Iron Ages, and in each stage minerals assumed progressively greater importance.

In our modern industrial civilization, mineral resources play a role second only to that of agriculture, and consequently their mode of occurrence is of particular interest. Modern man has found thousands of uses for the various materials of the earth. Metals, fuels, fertilizers, structural materials, abrasives, fillers, chemicals, and almost countless other substances that affect our daily lives have been made available through geologic research. The importance of these materials is indicated by the fact that such activities as mining and well drilling furnish the raw materials for many industries. According to the U.S. Bureau of Mines, the total value of the mineral production of the United States in 1957 was more than 18 billion dollars (Fig. 1.1).

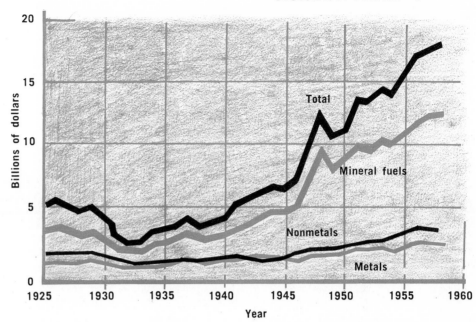

FIG. 1.1. *Value of the mineral production in the United States, 1925–1957. Mineral fuels now account for more than two-thirds of the total. (Data from Minerals Yearbook, U.S. Bureau of Mines.)*

More than two-thirds of the total value of the mineral production of the United States is supplied by the mineral resources known as the *mineral fuels* —coal, petroleum, and natural gas. Mineral resources other than fuels include the *metalliferous deposits,* from which metals are extracted, and the *nonmetallic deposits,* such as cement, stone, sand and gravel, clays, salt, lime, sulfur, phosphate rock, potassium salts, and gypsum. In 1957, the mineral fuels represented 70 per cent of the total mineral production, metals accounted for about 12 per cent, and the nonmetals (other than fuels) for about 18 per cent of the total value. Cement, stone, and sand and gravel supply nearly three-fourths of the nonmetallic fraction (other than fuels), because of their extensive use in construction.

INTANGIBLE BENEFITS

In addition to their practical value, the scientific discoveries of geology contribute greatly to our appreciation of our physical environment. When we learn that hills and valleys, lakes and streams are not permanent features of the landscape, they become more interesting and more fascinating to us, especially as we begin to understand the geologic processes that brought them into existence.

When we travel to such scenic features as the Grand Canyon, Painted Desert, Rainbow Bridge, Zion Canyon (Fig. 1.2), Niagara Falls, Mount Rainier, Crater Lake, and the Canadian Rockies, we can take pride and satisfaction in being able to analyze the changes and processes that produced them. Our enjoyment is increased by understanding. To those students who are not planning to become geologists, this cultural aspect of geology probably will be the most rewarding.

Changes in the Earth

LAW OF CHANGE

Although we are accustomed to thinking of the earth's crust as relatively stable, except in places where earthquakes or explosive volcanoes suddenly and visibly dislocate it, the earth is continuously changing. Streams erode the land and deposit large quantities of sand, silt, and clay onto lowlands (Fig. 1.3) or into the sea. Even the outer part of the solid earth, its crust, moves en masse. Careful observations on lake levels show that the land north of the Great Lakes has been rising at a rate of about 16 inches per century. Similarly, tidal-gauge

FIG. 1.2. *Zion Canyon, Zion National Park, Utah. The canyon walls are made of horizontal beds of sandstone. Geologic study of these rocks has shown that much of the sand originally accumulated as desert dunes. (Union Pacific Railroad.)*

records show that certain places beside the Baltic Sea have been rising at a rate of more than 3 feet per century. Fossil sea shells in rocks now thousands of feet above sea level indicate extensive movements of the same sort in the past.

Change, whether by slow internal movements, by volcanic activity, or by superficial agents, is the rule. A wag has said that the only fixed thing is the certainty of change. Yet change occurs in conformity with unchanging principles and processes.

PROCESSES OF CHANGE

The processes which are now in operation on the surface of the earth include gradation, diastrophism, and vulcanism.

Gradation. Rocks exposed at the surface of the earth are continuously subject to gradation (Fig. 1.4). Gradation can be either (1) degradation, the wearing down of rocks by water, air, and ice, or (2) aggradation, the building up of rock formations by deposition of the degraded material. Degradation usually occurs above sea level and aggradation below sea level. When rain falls, it eventually fills the creeks and rivers which go on to supply the lakes and seas. The water carries with it particles of rock, and these finally are dropped in lakes, along rivers (Fig. 1.3), and in the ocean, where they form beds of sand and mud. Waves beat upon the coasts and wear away the land. Winds carry rock particles and roll them along the surface of the earth, depositing them as sand dunes or as layers and films of dust. Sand and dust deposits of wind-blown origin are very thick in parts of China and the central part of the United States. Ice in motion carries rock fragments; and when the ice melts, these are deposited. The process of gradation is generally slow, but it is continuous, and over long periods of time its results are great.

Diastrophism. Diastrophism is the movement of solid parts of the earth with respect to each other. At many places rocks which undoubtedly were formed as sediments on the sea bottom, and which contain the remains of marine animals and plants, are now found high above the sea. Such rocks have been raised by diastrophism. A study of the rocks and their relation to each other shows that large areas of the earth's surface have been submerged below sea level and elevated above sea level many times.

Diastrophism commonly determines the nature of gradation. As we mentioned earlier, above sea level the dominant process is degradation, and below sea level the dominant process is aggradation. Degradation tears down the rocks and removes their particles to the sea, where new beds are formed from them. By diastrophism these beds are raised above the sea and exposed again to degradation.

When sediments are laid down in the sea, they are nearly flat-lying (Fig. 1.5); if they are found to be tilted (Fig. 1.6) or folded (Fig. 1.7), we can infer that they have been disturbed by diastrophic movements.

Vulcanism. Vulcanism includes all the phenomena connected with the movements of molten rocks and the formation of their products. Large parts of the earth's surface are made up of rocks that have solidified from a molten state. Such rocks are *igneous*. Some of them, called *extrusive* rocks, have been ejected from throats of volcanoes (Fig. 1.8); others, *intrusive* rocks, have been solidified at depths. The deep-seated intrusive igneous rocks are not exposed at the surface of the earth until erosion removes the material that formerly covered them. When igneous rocks are exposed on land, they are attacked by air and water and are broken down. Their fragments, together with other material, are carried away by streams and are deposited to form sediments.

HISTORY OF CHANGE

Interpretation of rocks. We are apt to consider rocks as dull and lifeless things, but in fact each rock carries within itself something of the record of

FIG. 1.3. *Stream deposits along the west side of Death Valley, California. These fan-shaped deposits occur where mountain streams descend from canyons onto broad, flat land areas. (Fairchild Aerial Surveys, Los Angeles.)*

FIG. 1.4. *Rocks called the Mormon Temple, in Bryce Canyon National Park, Utah. This type of structure is known as an erosional remnant because weathering and rainwash have removed the rocks that formerly surrounded it. (Union Pacific Railroad.)*

FIG. 1.5. *Horizontal bedding in sedimentary rocks near Hamlin, Texas. These rocks have evidently not been disturbed since their deposition in the sea. (N. H. Darton, U.S. Geological Survey.)*

FIG. 1.6. *Steeply tilted sedimentary rocks near Gallup, New Mexico. Diastrophism (earth movement) tilted them from their original horizontal position (see Fig. 1.5). (N. H. Darton, U.S. Geological Survey.)*

its origin and of the changes it has undergone. A coral-reef limestone in Illinois tells of its deposition in the warm, clear, shallow waters of a former sea; and steeply inclined layers of a common black lava rock (basalt) in Upper Michigan tell of the ancient volcanic activity there and of the earth movement that later tilted these lava flows.

To use the law of change to interpret the earth, we must first acquire a knowledge of the materials and of the structure of the earth, as well as proper concepts of the agents and processes which continuously alter it. In doing this, we make use of such sciences as chemistry, physics, mathematics, and biology.

The basic philosophic purpose of geology is to interpret intelligently the results of the natural processes acting on and within the earth during long ages of the past. Observations of present earth processes and their consequences enable geologists to determine the sequence of past conditions and events and thus to interpret the history of the earth and the development of its prehistoric plants and animals.

Methods of study. The methods of geology are very simple if the steps are taken one by one. As sediments are laid down in the lake or sea to which a stream has transported them, they are deposited over the bottom of the quiet water in sheets, or

FIG. 1.7. *Sedimentary beds in the Hastings district of Ontario that have been closely folded because of earth movements. (Canadian Geological Survey.)*

layers, one on top of the other, and obviously the lowest one was laid down first. If these beds are not disturbed over a long period of time, we can still be sure that the lowest was formed first and is the oldest of the series of sedimentary beds shown at this particular place. Moreover, the beds above it are successively younger toward the top. Therefore, the relative ages of the different layers can be established, even though these sediments may have been compressed and cemented into solid rock.

In rocks of sedimentary origin we sometimes find the remains of plants and animals that were living while the rocks were being formed. The remains in one set of beds may be different from those in other beds of the same group of rocks, but they may resemble the remains of organisms that are found in beds located far away. Thus a bed carries a "label" that states its age. By studying hundreds of sections of rocks and mapping them, we can establish the extent of the area over which a bed was deposited and can chart the ancient sea in which the bed was laid down many ages ago.

Where sediments are laid down in water, they are nearly flat and may remain so (Fig. 1.5); where beds formed from sediments have been disturbed by diastrophism, they are found to be tilted or folded (Figs. 1.6, 1.7). Where an igneous mass intrudes a group of beds, we know that it must be younger than the beds intruded. Thus, by studying large areas—the beds, their attitudes, and their relation to each other and to igneous bodies—we can ascertain the times at which the major events have

FIG. 1.8. *Paricutín Volcano, Mexico, as it appeared in 1943. In nine years it built a cinder and lava cone 1,350 ft high. This cone is an example of extrusive igneous rock. (American Museum of Natural History.)*

taken place in the area containing the rocks and interpret the geological history of the area.

Our conception of geologic time grows with our knowledge of earth's history. We realize that processes and forces that seem to have little effect when observed from day to day are capable of producing tremendous results when continued over long periods of time.

Summary

Geology, the science of the earth as recorded in rocks, is based on the fact that rocks are ever changing through processes of gradation, diastrophism, and vulcanism and that they thus register a decipherable history of the earth. This study has many ramifications, and its values are not only practical and economic, but also aesthetic and cultural. In addition to making important contributions to agriculture and industry, geology heightens our understanding and appreciation of the world in which we live.

Suggestions for Further Reading

Adams, Frank D.: *The Birth and Development of the Geological Sciences,* Dover Publications, New York, 1954. The beginnings of geology up to 1800 are covered in this well-known account.

Cloos, Hans: *Conversation with the Earth,* Alfred A. Knopf, Inc., New York, 1953. An interesting book which examines geographic regions of the earth.

Croneis, C., and W. C. Krumbein: *Down to Earth: An Introduction to Geology,* University of Chicago Press, Chicago, 1936. A nontechnical introduction to geology, dated but still useful.

Fenton, C. L., and M. A. Fenton: *Giants of Geology,* Doubleday & Company, Inc., New York, 1952. An interesting, well-illustrated book.

Geology, 1888–1938, fiftieth anniversary volume (a symposium), Geological Society of America, 1941.

Moore, Ruth: *The Earth We Live On,* Alfred A. Knopf, Inc., New York, 1956.

Technical and Teaching Careers in Geology, Chicago Institute for Research, 1956. An illustrated pamphlet for those interested in geology as a profession.

Voskuil, W. H.: *Minerals in World Industry,* McGraw-Hill Book Company, Inc., New York, 1955.

Chapter 2

EARTH AS A PLANET

THE STUDY of our earth may properly begin with an examination of its relationship to the rest of the universe. We are accustomed to thinking of our earth as the center of the universe. But how very far from the truth that is! Our earth is just one rather small planet traveling around one star, the sun. And our sun, with its planets, is only a small part of the Milky Way galaxy. This galaxy, joined with many others, gives us the universe.

Many of the physical aspects of the earth are affected by the interaction of the sun, moon, and earth. In this chapter, we shall see how the varying positions of these three spheres directly affect our day-to-day lives, and we shall learn just how much is known about the earth's size, shape, and density.

Stellar Systems

MILKY WAY GALAXY

The sun with its retinue of planets, including the earth, is one of billions of stars within our stellar system, or galaxy, which is known as the Milky Way system. This system of stars occupies a lens-shaped portion of space which has a diameter of about 70,000 light-years. One light-year is the distance light covers in 365¼ days, traveling at a velocity of approximately 186,200 miles per second. The average distance between stars is 8 to 10 light-years. Such great distances are

FIG. 2.0.   *Photograph of spiral nebula in Ursa Major taken with 200-inch Hale reflector. Nebulae are also known as stellar systems or galaxies. Our planets and sun are located in one of these systems, the Milky Way galaxy. (Mount Wilson and Palomar Observatories.)*

utterly beyond our comprehension, but to try to visualize the enormous distances in the Milky Way system, let us consider the group of stars known as the Great Cluster of Hercules, which is 36,000 light-years distant. The light which we receive from this cluster today left its surface 360 centuries ago. If a news dispatch could be flashed by radio from that cluster of stars, it would be ancient history before it reached the earth.

The millions of bright stars within the confines of our own galaxy are spheres of glowing gas. They vary in size from a globe as small as the earth to one 1,000 times larger than the sun, and their density ranges from 10,000 times rarer than our atmosphere to several hundred thousand times denser than water. The exceedingly dense stars are small and are called "white dwarfs." At the other end of the scale are the very large "red stars," which have a low density.

OTHER GALAXIES

Beyond our own galaxy are a large number of other systems of stars of approximately the same size. These systems, known as *extragalactic nebulae* (Fig. 2.0), are scattered fairly uniformly through space, the nearest to the earth being the nebula in the constellation of Andromeda at a distance of 1 million light-years.

The spectra of these extragalactic nebulae show a displacement of their lines toward the red end of the spectrum, which suggests that the nebulae are moving away from the solar system. This observation has led to the theory of the expanding universe, which proposes that all the matter in the universe was once concentrated into a smaller region and has expanded to its present proportions. With certain assumptions about the rate of expansion, the age of the universe has been computed to be several billion years.

Contrary to this concept of an exploding universe is the alternative view that atoms of hydrogen are continuously created in intergalactic space at a rate sufficient to condense into new galaxies of stars as fast as the old ones disappear by accelerating to the speed of light. The net result would be a steady state of equal input and outgo.

The cosmological problems of the origin of matter and energy, the origin and development of galaxies, the outermost limits (if any) of the universe, and the possible curvature of space lie beyond the scope of this book. Solutions to such problems as yet are mostly speculative. Nevertheless their contemplation induces within us a profound sense of awe and wonder.

SOLAR ENERGY

The sun and other stars shine because they have a certain mass and a certain composition. All stars contain abundant hydrogen, and the conversion of hydrogen into helium releases radiant energy in the form of heat and light. Thus a star cannot help shining; for if it did not, the mutual gravitation of its particles would cause it to contract, and the energy liberated by the contraction would soon heat the interior sufficiently to start the hydrogen-helium transformation. Once started, the radiation would maintain itself as long as sufficient hydrogen remained.

The hydrogen-helium transformation can take place at moderate temperatures (for stars). At high temperatures, as in the interior of the sun, a complex series of cyclic nuclear reactions is possible. These involve carbon, nitrogen, and oxygen, but the net result of all such reactions is to use up hydrogen and to produce helium. The making of other and heavier elements involves a similar transformation of part of the mass to energy. Conversely, on the earth, energy must be supplied to split heavy atoms.

At the present rate of radiation of energy, great though it is, 1 per cent of the sun's mass will suffice for about 1 billion years. This solar energy is essential to many geologic processes on earth. Directly or indirectly, it causes the winds to blow, water to evaporate and later to fall as rain or snow, streams to erode the land, and glaciers to carve their courses. The sun, therefore, makes gradational processes possible. Without solar energy the surface of the earth would be nearly inert, a lifeless and frozen waste. Such an eventuality, even if possible, is extremely remote, to say the least.

The Solar System

Let us now consider our solar system, which is just one insignificant part of our stellar system. The solar system consists of the sun, nine known planets and their satellites, and numerous asteroids, comets, and meteorites. The earth is one of the planets. Unlike stars, the planets do not produce light. They simply reflect part of the light they receive from the star we call the sun. The planets cannot produce radiation from atomic reactions because they do not have enough hydrogen, nor are they at a high enough temperature.

THE SUN

Although the solar system is of primary importance to us (Fig. 2.1), it is inconspicuous within our galaxy and insignificant in size in relation to the universe as a whole. The sun contains more than 99.8 per cent of the mass of the solar system. Spectroscopic analyses of its light indicate that it is composed of the same chemical elements as those found in the earth, although differences in surface temperatures doubtless cause different states and different combinations of these elements. Light from even more distant stars, some of which are hotter than the sun, is similar but shows much of the matter to be in a simpler atomic state. Hence the earth, although relatively small, appears to offer a fair sample of the matter composing not only the solar system but also our galaxy and perhaps even the entire universe. In geology we may well be dealing with the end products of matter as it exists under the temperatures and pressures of earth conditions; there may be no other *kind* of matter anywhere, but merely different *conditions* of matter.

Sixty-six of the more than ninety elements recognized on the earth have been identified in the sun's spectrum, and there is no reason to conclude that any element is really absent; for the others may be unobservable because of the small percentage present or because of the absorption of their wavelengths by the atmosphere of the earth.

Seen through the telescope, the sun appears as a yellowish disk, noticeably darker near the edge than at the center. The darkening toward the edge suggests that the material of the sun is gaseous for a considerable depth, since a solid or liquid surface would appear to have more uniform illumination.

All stars travel at very high speeds, and the sun is no exception. It rushes through space in the general direction of the bright star Vega at a rate of 12 miles per second. Since the planets and their satellites revolve around the sun, it follows that they are carried along with it.

THE SUN'S FAMILY

Traveling in orbit around the sun are 9 planets, 31 known satellites, or moons, which accompany certain planets, and more than 2,000 smaller bodies known as asteroids, or planetoids. All the planets revolve about the sun approximately in the same plane and in the same direction. Their average rate

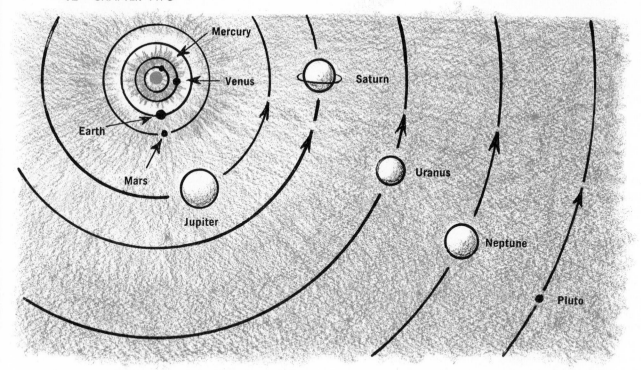

FIG. 2.1. *Diagram showing the planets of the solar system in the order of their distances from the sun. The distance from earth to sun is approximately 93 million miles. All the planets revolve about the sun in elliptical orbits that are in nearly the same plane.*

of speed is approximately 13 miles per second. The earth completes one revolution each year at an average velocity of about 18.5 miles per second. Since the outer planets move more slowly and have greater distances to travel, it takes them longer to revolve around the sun. All planets also rotate on their polar axes, with the earth rotating once every 24 hours.

The planets show a rather regular spacing in two contrasted groups: an inner group of small planets (Mercury, Venus, Earth, and Mars), which are called the terrestrial planets, and an outer group of large planets (Jupiter, Saturn, Uranus, Neptune, and Pluto), which are called the major planets. The small, terrestrial planets all have densities which indicate that they are composed of minerals and rocks closely related to those in the earth. Mercury has no atmosphere, but Venus, our nearest neighbor, has a very dense atmosphere, consisting almost entirely of carbon dioxide, which conceals its sur-

face. Mars has polar icecaps, which increase in size during its cold seasons and melt during its summer seasons; so its atmosphere must contain some water vapor. The major planets have low densities, with thick atmospheres that completely conceal their other features.

By various measurements the distance from the earth to the sun is shown to be about 93 million miles.. The distance from the sun to the outermost planet, Pluto, is approximately 4,000 million miles and from the sun to the nearest star, 27 million million miles.

To help us appreciate the relative distances in our solar and stellar systems, let us reduce the scale to distances we can visualize. To represent the sun, place a golf ball on a flat surface, and at a distance of about 12 feet from the ball place a grain of sand to represent the earth. On this scale, Pluto, the farthest planet, could be shown by another grain of sand placed 500 feet from the golf ball. All the other planets are within this distance. If the same scale were used to project the galaxy of stars, the nearest star would be represented by another golf ball at a distance of 600 miles from the one representing the sun.

The Earth

SHAPE

From early youth we are taught that the earth is spherical, and most of us accept the statement without giving further thought to any of the proofs. However, if we watch a ship at sea, we may note that, as it recedes farther and farther into the distance, it appears to sink slowly beneath the water level, until eventually even its funnels disappear below the horizon. The reason for the apparent submergence of the ship is the fact that the surface of the sea is curved. This curvature in itself does not prove that the earth is a sphere, but numerous observations in many different oceanic areas have demonstrated that the amount of curvature is nearly the same everywhere, as is true only of a spheroid. Furthermore, modern navigation methods are based on the assumption that the earth is a sphere, and the positions of vessels have been established correctly innumerable times thereby.

The shape of the earth's shadow, as seen against the face of the moon during all lunar eclipses, is another proof that the earth is a sphere. The edge of the shadow always appears as an arc of a circle, and it can be demonstrated geometrically that a sphere is the only body that will always cast a circular shadow upon another sphere.

Still another proof of the earth's approximate sphericity may be demonstrated from observations on the position of the North Star. Under ideal conditions, an observer at the equator can see the North Star on the horizon. If he travels northward toward the North Pole, the star rises higher and higher until he reaches the North Pole, where the star is directly overhead. Careful measurements show that the star rises 1 degree higher for about every 69 miles of northward travel. Since measurements on other stars and in other directions give approximately the same results, the surface of the earth must be nearly spherical.

The most recent and graphic proof of the earth's sphericity has been provided by extremely high altitude photographs, on which the horizon appears as a curved line.

SIZE AND WEIGHT

Since there are 360 degrees in a circle and each degree along a meridian equals a distance of about

TABLE 2.1 *The Solar System*

Sun and planets	Mean distance from the sun		Period of revolution, days	Diameter, miles	Density, water = 1
	Millions of miles	Earth = 1			
Sun	.....	.....	......	865,000	1.41
Moon	.....	.....	......	2,163	3.34
Mercury	36	0.387	88	3,030	3.80
Venus	67	0.723	225	7,700	4.85
Earth	93	1.000	365	7,918	5.52
Mars	142	1.524	687	4,230	4.01
Jupiter	483	5.20	4,333	86,500	1.33
Saturn	886	9.54	10,759	70,000	0.73
Uranus	1,782	19.19	30,686	31,500	1.22
Neptune	2,792	30.07	60,188	34,800	1.41
Pluto	3,666	39.50	92,611	3,600	?

69 miles, it follows that the earth's circumference is 360 times 69, or about 24,840 miles. Refined measurements have revealed that 1 degree is not exactly the same in all places and in all directions but that the true form of the earth is an oblate spheroid that bulges at the equator and is flattened slightly at the poles. This oblateness is caused by the earth's rotation. The amount of flattening is so slight that the difference between the polar and equatorial diameters is only about 27 miles (7,927 minus 7,900), which is equivalent to only about ½ inch on a globe 10 feet in diameter. The irregularities caused by the high mountains likewise mean a deviation from sphericity; but even the greatest of these irregularities, compared with the earth's diameter, amount to less, relatively, than the roughness on the skin of an orange.

If we ignore the slight flattening at the poles and the equatorial bulge and assume that the earth is truly spherical, with a diameter of 7,900 miles, its volume is a little more than 250 billion cubic miles[1] and its area nearly 200 million square miles.[2] Once these facts are established, we can calculate the mass, or weight, of the earth by the application of Newton's law of gravitation. By using a very delicate pair of scales, the Eötvös balance, physicists can compare the earth's attraction with that of a large ball of lead or quartz of known weight, and thus "weigh" the earth. Its weight by this method is 6,000 million million million tons; in digits, this figure would be written as a 6 followed by 21 ciphers (6×10^{21}).

DENSITY

Once the volume and mass of the earth are known, its density can be determined by dividing its volume into its weight. This calculation gives a density of 5.52, or about 5½ times heavier than water. Since the superficial layers of rock of the earth's crust are known, by direct observations, to have an average density of only 2.7, the inner core must be much denser. This increase in density at

[1] Volume = $(3.14/6) \times 7,900^3$ = 250 billion cubic miles (plus).
[2] Area = $3.14 \times 7,900^2$ = 196 million square miles (plus).

depth can be explained by a difference in composition and (if the materials are compressible) by the enormous pressures that the outer layers exert upon those inside (Fig. 2.2). At a depth of only 100 miles the pressure is already 300 tons per square inch, and at the center it reaches 20,000 tons per square inch. The inner core is thought to have a density of 10+ and to be composed mainly of metallic iron.

TABLE 2.2 *The Earth's Characteristics*

Shape	Very nearly spherical
Average circumference	Approx. 25,000 miles
Average diameter	Approx. 7,900 miles
Volume	250×10^9 cubic miles
Surface area	200×10^6 square miles
Mass or weight	6×10^{21} tons
Period of rotation	24 hours
Period of revolution	365¼ days
Inclination of axis	23½ degrees

FIG. 2.2. *Diagram showing the inferred nature of the interior of the earth. The outer shell or crust has a density of about 2.7, the inner layers are roughly twice as heavy, and the central metallic core has a density of at least 10.*

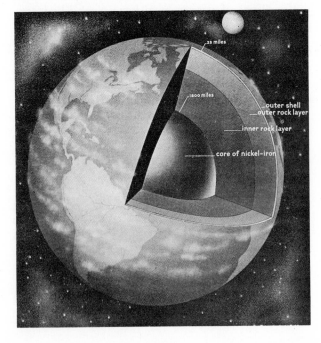

ROTATION

Our daily hours of darkness and light are produced by the earth's rotation around its polar axis. We can visualize the direction of rotation by imagining that we are looking down upon the North Pole of the earth. From such a position the direction of rotation is counterclockwise (Fig. 2.3). This direction is opposite that of the apparent daily motion of the sun, moon, and stars, which seem to travel westward across the sky because the earth is turning in an eastward direction.

The earth's rotation can be demonstrated simply by the Foucault pendulum. In this experiment, first performed by Foucault in Paris in 1851, a simple pendulum is made to swing. A pendulum swings along the same path until friction brings it to a stop. If the path along which the pendulum starts to swing is marked and the pendulum is allowed to swing undisturbed for several hours, the pendulum's path will appear to have turned through a small angle from its original direction. After each

successive hour the path will seem to have shifted farther and farther around. Since the pendulum maintains the same path in which it started to swing, we are forced to conclude that the earth beneath it is turning.

The velocity of rotation of the earth is such that a point on the surface at the equator travels about 1,000 miles per hour, for it completes 25,000 miles in 24 hours. At the 60th parallel the rate is half this amount, or about 500 miles per hour, and at the poles it is zero. Intermediate points travel at speeds determined by their distances north or south of the equator. The eastward velocity at a particular place may be easily computed by dividing the length of the parallel of latitude passing through the selected point by 24, the approximate number of hours required for rotation.

REVOLUTION

The earth makes one complete revolution around the sun in 365¼ days. The earth's axis of rotation is inclined to the plane of its orbital revolution at

FIG. 2.3. *Diagram showing the direction of rotation and revolution of the earth and its satellite, the moon: (a) earth's orbit, (b) moon's orbit.*

an angle of 66½ degrees, and it maintains this angle throughout the year. So for part of the year the North Pole is tilted toward the sun and for the remainder of the year it is tilted away from the sun. Because the vertical rays of the sun strike the area north of the equator for half of the year and south of the equator for the other half, the maximum of solar energy shifts from one part of the earth to another, thereby creating our seasons (Figs. 2.4, 2.5).

EARTH'S SATELLITE

The moon is the earth's satellite. It is approximately 2,160 miles in diameter and revolves around the earth at a mean distance of about 240,000 miles. Unlike the daily spinning of the earth, the rotation of the moon merely keeps pace with its revolution about the earth, so the moon turns completely around only once during each circuit of the earth.

Hence the same face of the moon is always turned toward the earth, and the other side remains hidden.

The moon is so close that we can clearly see the side facing the earth, and an ordinary telescope shows that much of the surface is covered by lofty mountains, wide plains, and very large pits which resemble volcanic craters on the earth (Fig. 2.6). The largest of these craters is 56 miles in diameter, and the height of its surrounding rim, as measured by its shadows, is 12,000 feet. Possibly these craters, or pits, have been formed by the infall of large meteorites rather than by vulcanism.

Because of its low gravity, the moon lacks both an atmosphere and water, and its surface is therefore dry, dead, and desolate, dazzling with light and sizzling with heat in the sunshine, but black and cold in the shadows.

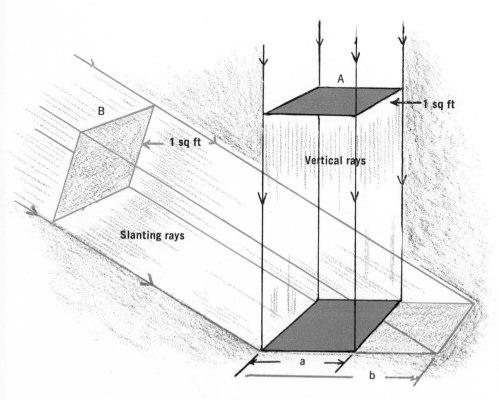

FIG. 2.4. *Diagram showing why the average temperature is higher at low latitudes than it is at higher latitudes. The vertical rays of the sun at A are concentrated in the square a, whereas the inclined rays coming from B are spread over the larger area b. Because the earth's axis is tilted, the incidence of the sun's rays at any one place changes with the seasons and modifies the temperature accordingly. (After Strahler.)*

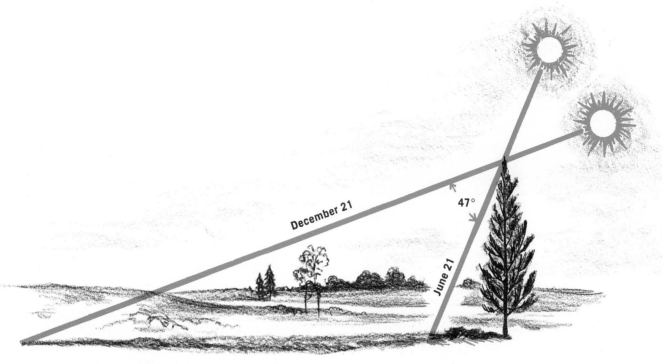

FIG. 2.5. *Sketch showing that the angle of the sun's rays at midday in June and December differs by 47 degrees, because the polar axis of the earth is inclined.*

The Tides

Even though its attractive power is low,[3] the moon is so near the earth that its gravitational attraction upon the earth is greater than that of all other heavenly bodies except the sun, which holds both in orbit.

The earth-moon pair, coupled by gravitation,[4] mutually whirl around a common center of gravity (*C* in Fig. 2.7), situated within the earth[5] because

[3] Only about 1/300,000 of the gravitational pull of the earth.

[4] Under Newton's law of gravitation,

$$f = \frac{m_1 \times m_2}{d^2}$$

the earth and moon may be considered to be "falling" toward each other at a rate which is directly proportional to the product of their masses and inversely proportional to the square of the distance between their centers.

[5] About 3,000 miles from the center of the earth.

of the preponderance of the mass of the earth over that of the moon. In this whirling system as a whole the total of the centrifugal forces exactly balances the centripetal forces of gravitational attraction. The moon's attraction, however, differs at different places on the earth because of the different distances involved (Fig. 2.7). The resultant of the forces is vertical and strongest along the line between the centers of gravity, but inclined and weaker elsewhere. On the side of the earth nearest the moon the gravitational attraction of the moon exceeds the centrifugal forces, whereas on the far side of the earth the centrifugal forces overbalance the pull of the moon. This imbalance produces faint tides in the atmosphere, the well-known tides in the ocean, and even tides of about 4 inches in the rocky crust of the earth.

As the earth rotates under this set of forces daily, points on its surface are alternately subjected to upward and downward pulls, twice each way in

FIG. 2.6. *Craters on the northern part of the moon, at last quarter, in the region from Coperni-cus to the limb. Although these craters resemble volcanic craters on the earth, their origin may be due to the infall of meteorites. (Mount Wilson and Palomar Observatories.)*

24 hours and 50 minutes. The 50-minute daily lag is caused by the forward motion of the moon in its orbit around the earth, which the earth has to overtake by continued rotation.

Tides are also raised by the sun, though only a third as much as by the moon, and these act as modifiers of the moon's tides. The sun, moon, and earth lie in nearly the same plane, but they constantly shift their positions with reference to each other. The pulls are therefore in different directions as their positions change, and the tidal effects change accordingly. Twice each lunar month, at the new moon and full moon, the earth, moon, and sun are aligned. Therefore, the tidal forces of the moon and sun are combined, and unusually high tides result, called "spring tides." Similarly, at the first and third quarters of the moon, the tidal forces of the moon and sun are at right angles to each other and hence opposed, so that lunar tides are reduced by about a third. These unusually low-ranging tides are called "neap tides."

Other variations in tides are caused by the moon's apparent north-south changes of position during the year, by effects of latitude, by the configuration of the coast line, and by other local factors. Tidal records therefore show complicated sequences of changing water levels.

FIG. 2.7. *Diagram illustrating the origin of tides. The distances AM, EM, and BM are approximately equal to 59, 60, and 61 times the radius of the earth, and so the gravita-tional forces at A and B are inversely proportional to the squares of 59 and 61, or 1/3,481 versus 1/3,721. The difference in favor of A is about 7 per cent. The arrows show the direction and relative intensity of the forces at different places.*

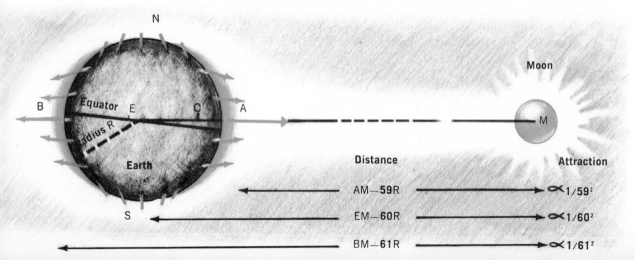

Summary

Now that we have studied the relationship of the planet earth to the rest of the universe, we are aware that the sun, a small star in the Milky Way galaxy, radiates heat and light, which are essential to the earth. This solar energy, derived from atomic reactions, supports life on the earth and actuates many geologic processes. Without it, the earth would be an inert and lifeless wasteland.

The earth is a minor planet revolving about the sun. It is a heavy, oblate spheroid about 7,900 miles in diameter. Its varying position with reference to the sun gives us the four seasons of the year, and the changes of the moon affect our ocean tides.

Suggestions for Further Reading

Gaposchkin, C. (Payne): *Introduction to Astronomy,* Prentice-Hall, Inc., Englewood Cliffs, N.J., 1954.

Kuiper, G. P.: *The Solar System,* University of Chicago Press, Chicago, 1953–1954. A two-volume study, more detailed than the following book.

Moore, Patrick: *The Solar System,* Methuen & Co., Ltd., London, 1958. A small, illustrated volume on the solar system.

Moore, Patrick: *A Guide to the Planets,* W. W. Norton & Company, Inc., New York, 1954.

Chapter 3

ATOMS, RADIOACTIVITY, AND GEOLOGIC TIME

SINCE WE NOW have some idea of the over-all character of the earth, we can begin to study it in detail. In this chapter we shall see that everything in and on the earth is composed of atoms and molecules. This atomic theory has led to that marvel of the twentieth century—the use of radioactivity.

In addition to its incalculable value in such fields as medicine and atomic energy, radioactivity is an important geologic tool. We all know that approximately 60 years ago the Curies discovered radium. This led to the knowledge that some of the chemical elements have radioactive properties and therefore disintegrate at a constant rate, unaffected by physical and chemical conditions. We shall see how this disintegration can be used to establish the age of rocks.

Atoms

ATOMIC THEORY

It is now accepted that all matter is composed of small particles called atoms. The original atomic theory, proposed by Dalton in 1805, held that atoms cannot be divided, created, or destroyed and that the atoms of any one element are all identical.

The discovery of radium by Pierre and Marie Curie in 1898, however, upset the theory of the indestructibility of the atom. We now know that some atoms continually give off small charged particles and radiant energy. The particles and energy have been shown to originate in the nucleus of the atom. The radioactive properties of the elements are not influenced by any external forces, temperature changes, or chemical reactions. Radioactivity is a natural process of disintegration.

ELECTRONS

The electron theory, evolved soon after the discovery of radioactivity, assumes that atoms are made up of a number of smaller particles. Each atom has one or more electrons, in addition to a nucleus consisting of protons and neutrons. The electrons are units carrying a negative electrical charge, the protons have a positive electrical charge, and the neutrons are electrically neutral. Therefore, the net charge of the nucleus is positive.

According to the theory of atomic structure proposed by the Danish scientist Niels Bohr, the electrons revolve in orbits about the nucleus, which contains all the protons and neutrons, in much the same manner as the planets of the solar system revolve about the sun (Fig. 3.1). Since the proton and neutron are relatively heavy, each being more than 1,800 times as heavy as the electron, the mass of an atom is largely in its nucleus. Most of the other properties of atoms, including their chemical behavior, can be ascribed to the electrons.

ELECTRONIC BEHAVIOR

In the simple atoms, such as hydrogen and helium, the electrons revolve in orbits, or "shells," close to the nucleus, but in the more complex atoms, with many more electrons, additional shells are present at varying distances from the nucleus (Fig. 3.2). We have found that the most chemically inert elements are those whose outermost electron shell contains eight electrons. The most active elements contain one to seven electrons in their outer shell. The outer shell may achieve its quota of eight either by borrowing from, or lending electrons to,

other elements or by sharing electrons with another atom. For example, sodium has one electron in its outer shell, and chlorine has seven. Both are highly active chemically. If sodium loses one electron and chlorine gains one, the atoms of both elements share an outer shell with a stable grouping of eight, thus forming sodium chloride, commonly known as table salt (Fig. 3.3).

ATOMIC WEIGHTS AND NUMBERS

The *atomic weight* of an element is approximately equal to the total number of protons and neutrons in the nucleus of an atom. If the elements are arranged in order of increasing atomic weight, the number of protons increases in the same order. Hydrogen, the lightest atom, has one; helium, the next to the lightest, has two; and lithium, which is next in weight, has three protons. Lithium, which has an atomic weight of 7, has four neutrons in addition to its three protons. The *atomic number* indicates the number of protons that are present (see Table 3.1).

As greater accuracy was introduced in determining atomic weights, it was found that they were not exactly whole numbers; for example, oxygen is in reality 15.876 times heavier than hydrogen.

FIG. 3.0. *An atom of helium, consisting of a nucleus and two electrons in orbit.*

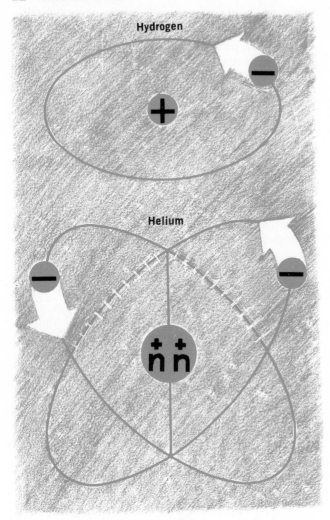

FIG. 3.1. *The relation of electrons (−), protons (+), and neutrons (n) in atoms of hydrogen and helium.*

TABLE 3.1 *Atomic Components*

Element	Atomic number	Number of protons	Number of neutrons	Number of electrons	Relative atomic weights
Hydrogen	1	1	0	1	1.008
Helium	2	2	2	2	4.004
Lithium	3	3	4	3	6.940
Beryllium	4	4	5	4	9.02
Boron	5	5	6	5	10.82
Carbon	6	6	6	6	12.01
Oxygen	8	8	8	8	16.00

rine, there are 76 grams of chlorine of atomic weight 34.98 and 24 grams of chlorine of atomic weight 36.98. The average weight of these two kinds of chlorine, when mixed in this proportion, is 35.46, the atomic weight of chlorine. Therefore, we see that isotopes are responsible for fractional atomic weights.

Since the number of protons in the atoms of any one element is always the same, it follows that the differences in weight are due to differences in the number of neutrons in the nuclei of the atoms. Uranium, which contains 92 protons, has three natural isotopes, weighing 234, 235, and 238 units, respectively. Thus uranium 238 has 146 neutrons in its nucleus, whereas the explosive isotope, uranium 235, has only 143 neutrons:

$$92 \ + \ 146 \ = \ 238$$
$$92 \ + \ 143 \ = \ 235$$

Protons   Neutrons

Atoms differ in size,[1] and this difference affects the process of replacement of atoms in various mineral crystals.

IONS

When an atom of an element loses an outer electron or gains an extra one, its electrical balance is destroyed, and it becomes electrically charged. For example, when an atom of sodium loses an electron, the atom then has one excess positive

Since oxygen entered into more compounds than hydrogen, it was agreed among chemists, purely for convenience, to call the atomic weight of oxygen 16.000. With that value standardized, hydrogen has an atomic weight of 1.008, carbon 12.01, etc.

ISOTOPES

An isotope is an atom which differs in atomic weight from other atoms of the same element. For example, in 100 grams of naturally occurring chlo-

[1] They are measured in *angstroms* (hundred-millionths of a centimeter). Many are about 2 angstroms in diameter, of which the nuclei occupy a very tiny fraction of 1 per cent.

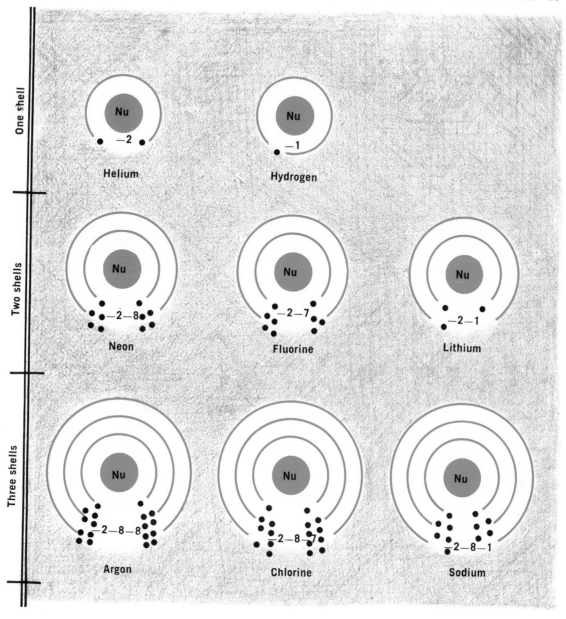

FIG. 3.2. *Diagrammatic sketches showing "shells" of electrons of atoms. The outer shells of helium, neon, and argon are complete, whereas the others are incomplete. Nu represents the nucleus of each atom. In reality, the orbits of the electrons are not equally spaced, nor are they all in one plane. The eight electrons in the second and third shells do not have equal energy values; instead, they form groups of two and six, with different quantum numbers, or energy values. Atoms of the heaviest elements have seven shells of electrons.*

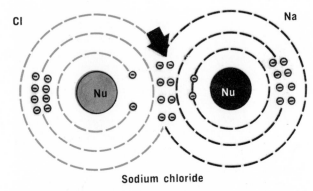

FIG. 3.3. *Diagrammatic sketch showing the transfer of an electron (indicated by arrow) from sodium to chlorine to form sodium chloride.*

charge, carried by the protons in the nucleus of the atom. Likewise, when an atom of chlorine gains an electron, the atom has one excess negative charge. Such electrically charged atoms are known as *ions*. Elements may be ionized by heating them or by exciting them electrically in a gaseous state, as in radio tubes and neon signs.

Many substances ionize freely in water solutions. In such solutions the chemical compounds separate into ions of their elements or groups of elements. These charged particles become dissociated in solution and move about in random fashion throughout the liquid. Such solutions are called *electrolytes*. Many chemical reactions of importance in geology depend upon the behavior of electrolytes.

ATOMIC COMBINATIONS

The atoms of various elements unite to form *molecules*. Some molecules contain only a few atoms which are arranged in relatively simple structures. Others are much larger and contain many atoms in very complicated arrangements.

Most of the ordinary materials of our everyday world are composed of molecules. Some materials, like oxygen, are gases; others, like water, are liquids; and still others, like sugar or steel, are solids. In gases the molecules are widely separated and move rapidly to and fro. In liquids, however, the molecules are closer together but still have considerable motion. In solids the mutual attrac-

tion of atoms is sufficiently strong to prevent unorganized motion. These three phases of matter—gaseous, liquid, and solid—are exemplified on earth as air, water, and rock, respectively.

Radioactivity

Certain chemical elements, such as uranium and thorium, have unstable nuclei, which undergo constant, spontaneous disintegration that eventually results in various more stable end products. Thus uranium gradually changes to radium. The radium in turn breaks down into helium nuclei (alpha particles), gamma radiation, and an isotope of lead. The lead formed in this way has a slightly different atomic weight from that of lead of other origin.

TABLE 3.2 *Radioactive Transformations (Uranium-Radium-Lead)*

Element	Group in periodic table	Atomic weight	Half-life	Particle emitted during transformation
Uranium	VI	238	4.56×10^9 years	Alpha
Uranium X_1	IV	234	24.5 days	Beta
Uranium X_2	V	234	1.14 min	Beta
Uranium II	VI	234	3×10^5 years	Alpha
Ionium	IV	230	8×10^4 years	Alpha
Radium	II	226	1,590 years	Alpha
Radon	0	222	3.82 days	Alpha
Radium A	VI	218	3.05 min	Alpha
Radium B	IV	214	26.8 min	Beta
Radium C	V	214	19.7 min	Beta
Radium C'	VI	214	10^{-6} sec	Alpha
Radium D	IV	210	22 years	Beta
Radium E	V	210	4.9 days	Beta
Polonium	VI	210	140 days	Alpha
Lead	IV	206		

The rates of atomic disintegration are well established. Regardless of the physical or chemical conditions under which the rate of change operates, it is constant for a given substance. We therefore can use it to determine the length of time during which the disintegration took place. The number of helium nuclei emitted by a measured amount of a radioactive element in a given unit of time can be determined accurately with the use of a Geiger counter, tabulated either manually or automatically.

The rate of disintegration is expressed in terms of *half-lives*. Half of any given quantity of U^{238} (i.e., uranium of atomic weight 238), for example, disintegrates in 4,560 million years, half of the remainder in another 4,560 million years, and so on. The half-lives of the radioactive elements most useful in geology are as follows:

TABLE 3.3   *Half-lives of Radioactive Elements*

Parent element	End products	Half-life, years
U^{238}	Pb^{206}, 8 He^4	4.56×10^9
U^{235}	Pb^{207}, 7 He^4	0.71×10^9
Th^{232}	Pb^{208}, 6 He^4	15×10^9
Rb^{87}	Sr^{87}	50×10^9
K^{40}	A^{40}, Ca^{40}	1.3×10^9
C^{14}	N^{14}	5,570

Dating Methods

URANIUM-LEAD

With a half-life of 4,560 million years, 1 gram of U^{238}, after 1,000 million years, will have decayed[2] to 0.116 gram Pb^{206}, leaving 0.865 gram U^{238}; in 2,000 million years, it will have decayed to 0.219 gram Pb^{206} and 0.747 gram U^{238}; in 3,000 million years, it will have decayed to 0.306 gram Pb^{206} and 0.646 gram U^{238}, and so on. The decrease in total weight represents helium and radiant energy.

Therefore, the ratio of the weights of radioactively derived Pb^{206} to U^{238} is a direct measure of the age of the rock in which the uranium-bearing mineral originally crystallized, if none of the lead or uranium has escaped.

Another isotope of uranium, U^{235}, changes to a different isotope of lead, Pb^{207}, at a considerably faster rate; and thorium, Th^{232}, a common associate of uranium, breaks down to Pb^{208} at still another

[2] Sir James Jeans, *The Universe around Us*, The Macmillan Company, 1929, p. 144.

(and slower) rate. Hence the ratios of Pb^{207} to U^{235} and of Pb^{208} to Th^{232} serve as checks on the Pb^{206}-to-U^{238} age determination. Moreover, the ratios of the different isotopes of lead to each other provide further internal checks on their consistency. Precise analyses, taking these isotopes and possible losses into account, have a high order of dependability. Thus a full set of analyses on uraninite from the Black Hills, South Dakota, gave the results shown in Table 3.4.

The near agreement of the first three figures makes them easily credible.

TABLE 3.4   *Analyses of Age of Uraninite, Black Hills, South Dakota*

Method of dating	Probable age, millions of years
Pb^{206}/U^{238}	1,580
Pb^{207}/U^{235}	1,600
Pb^{207}/Pb^{206}	1,630
Pb^{208}/Th^{232}	1,440

POTASSIUM-ARGON

One of the isotopes of potassium, K^{40}, is radioactive. It changes at a steady rate to argon, A^{40}, and to calcium, Ca^{40}, by electron capture, without much change in mass. This calcium cannot be distinguished from calcium of other origin. Since argon is an inert gas, most of it remains within the crystal lattice of the potassium-bearing minerals where it was formed. The minerals biotite, muscovite, orthoclase, and glauconite are possible sources of argon. After the complications of other isotopes, including atmospheric argon, are eliminated by careful analytical procedures, the ratio of K^{40} to A^{40} is also found to be a fairly dependable measure of age. Since potassium-bearing minerals are abundant, the method, though difficult in practice, is widely applicable.

RUBIDIUM-STRONTIUM

Since an isotope of rubidium, Rb^{87}, similarly disintegrates at a steady rate to strontium, Sr^{87}, the ratio of the weights of this pair also may be used to compute geologic time. Rubidium is generally

TABLE 3.5 *Samples Dated by Uranium-Lead Ratio*

Mineral	Locality	Geologic age	Probable age, millions of years
Pitchblende	Gilpin County, Colorado	Early Cenozoic	60
Pitchblende	Bohemia	Late Permian	215
Pitchblende	Oslo, Norway	Early Permian	230
Samarskite	Connecticut	End of Devonian	255
Cyrtolite	New York	End of Ordovician	350
Kolm	Gullhogen, Sweden	Upper Cambrian	440
Pitchblende	Katanga, Belgian Congo	Precambrian	610
Uraninite	Besner, Ontario	Precambrian	760
Bröggerite	Moss, southern Norway	Precambrian	860
Uraninite	Wilberforce, Ontario	Precambrian	1,035
Cleveite	Aust-Agder, Norway	Precambrian	1,075
Pitchblende	Great Bear Lake, Canada	Precambrian	1,400
Uraninite	Keystone, South Dakota	Mid-Precambrian	1,600
Uraninite	Northeast Karelia, U.S.S.R.	Early Precambrian	1,800
Pitchblende	Winnipeg River, Manitoba	Early Precambrian	2,300
Galena	Barberton, South Africa	Early Precambrian	3,380

dispersed in potassium-bearing minerals. The fact that the rubidium-strontium method and the potassium-argon method give approximately the same results tends to confirm the usually small losses of radioactively derived argon, and hence the computed age; otherwise the values are suspect. Micas give better agreement than do feldspars.

RADIOCARBON

Radiocarbon, C^{14}, is formed in the atmosphere by the collision of cosmic rays (neutrons) with atoms of nitrogen, N^{14}. It is then taken up by plants and passed on to animals. By continuous exchange during the life of the organisms, it remains in equilibrium in a fixed ratio with ordinary carbon, C^{12}. When the organisms die, however, exchange ceases, and the organic radiocarbon begins to operate as a clock as it reverts to nitrogen. Its half-life is only about 5,570 years (Libby), so its usable range in measuring time is limited to about the last 40,000 years. It is especially useful in dating charcoal from archaeological sites and wood, bone, or shells from Late Pleistocene (ice age) and Recent deposits.

Geologic Age

DETERMINED AGES

The ages of rocks, as determined by radioactive methods in widely scattered localities, range up to more than 3,300 million years. Some meteorites are more than 4,500 million years old, and the age of the earth as a whole may be approximately 4,000 to 5,000 million years. The earth is so old that geologists look upon the duration of geologic time as comparable with the vast expanses of space recognized by astronomers.

GEOLOGIC TIMETABLE

The combined efforts of several generations of geologists who have studied the petrology, stratigraphy, structure, paleontology, and other aspects of the rock record of the past have succeeded in establishing the geologic timetable shown in Table 3.6. We should keep in mind, however, that details of the table are subject to further refinement as additional data come to light, especially for the

Precambrian. The Paleozoic and later divisions, on the other hand, are well established. Although they cover only 500 million years, they span the spectacular rise of life on land.

TABLE 3.6 *Geologic Time Divisions for North America*

Eras	Periods	Some outstanding physical events	Life development
Cenozoic (70 million years)	Cenozoic	Postglacial changes	Advent of man
	Pleistocene	The Great Ice Age and Recent changes	Flowering plants dominate vegetation
	Pliocene	Formation of coast ranges	Primitive horses and other ungulates
	Miocene	Formation of the Alps and many mountain chains	
	Oligocene		Advent of apes
	Eocene	Extensive volcanic activity in Western United States	First placental mammals
	Paleocene		
		Laramide revolution	
Mesozoic (130 million years)	Upper Cretaceous	Early folding to form Rocky Mountains	Extinction of dinosaurs at close; climax of reptiles on land, air, and sea
	Lower Cretaceous	Central cordilleran disturbance	First flowering plants, trees, and grasses
	Jurassic	Beginning of Sierra Nevada uplift	First birds
	Triassic	Extensive volcanic activity in New England, Pennsylvania, and New Jersey	First dinosaurs and primitive mammals
		Appalachian revolution	
Paleozoic (300 million years)	Permian	Folding to form Appalachian Mountains, glaciation over wide area	Rise of reptiles
	Pennsylvanian	Extensive coal-forming swamps	Large nonflowering plants
	Mississippian	Paleozoic Alps	First land vertebrates
	Devonian	Acadian Mountains	Age of fishes
	Silurian	Caledonian Mountains	Rise of land plants
	Ordovician	Taconic Mountains	First known fishes
	Cambrian	Vermont disturbance	Age of invertebrate dominance
		Lipalian interval, peneplanation, glaciation, Killarney revolution	
Precambrian (1800+* million years)	Keweenawan	Extensive lava flows	Probable development of shells on invertebrates
	Huronian (Animikean)	Lake Superior iron ranges Oldest evidence of glaciation	Scanty record of primitive plants and animals
		Algoman revolution	
	Timiskamian		Algae fairly common
		Laurentian revolution	
	Keewatin	Rocks much altered and history obscured	Primitive life probable

* The total span of Precambrian time may be as much as 4,000 million years.

Summary

Now that we know something of the atomic nature of matter, we understand why atomic science has become so useful to geologists.

All matter is composed of atoms, which in turn are composed of atomic particles. Atoms have nuclei of protons and neutrons, surrounded by orderly shells of electrons. Atoms differ in weight according to the number of these particles. Different natural elements form a series ranging from atomic number 1 (hydrogen) to atomic number 92 (uranium). Thus each element, and each of its isotopes, has a characteristic atomic structure, which determines many of its properties.

Atoms become electrostatically charged (ionized) by gaining or losing one or more outer electrons. They combine chemically by sharing or exchanging electrons. Many substances ionize in water solutions and participate in reactions of geologic importance.

Several atoms, notably uranium, thorium, rubidium, potassium, and radiocarbon, have unstable nuclei which disintegrate at measurable rates. Even if a rock containing these elements has been weathered, crushed, metamorphosed, or otherwise subjected to the stress of time, its age can still be determined by means of the geologic time clock—radioactivity. The oldest rocks so dated are about 3,380 million years old.

Suggestions for Further Reading

Ahrens, L. H.: "Radioactive Methods for Determining Geological Age," *Repts. Progr. in Phys.*, vol. 19, pp. 80–106, 1956. A technical article.

Bowen, R. N. C.: *The Exploration of Time*, Philosophical Library, Inc., New York, 1958. A technical book on the science of dating, including both geological and other methods.

Evans, R. D. et al.: "Radioactivity: The Earth's Heat and Geological Age Measurements," *Geol. Soc. Amer. Spec. Paper* 36, pp. 267–277, 1936. A technical article, still useful, although dated.

Knopf, Adolph: "Measuring Geologic Time," *Sci. Monthly*, vol. 85, pp. 225–236, 1957.

Libby, Willard F.: *Radiocarbon Dating*, University of Chicago Press, Chicago, 1955.

Pauling, Linus: *General Chemistry*, W. H. Freeman and Company, San Francisco, 1953. An excellent basic chemistry text, with easily understood descriptions of atomic structure.

Semat, H.: *Atomic Age Physics*, Rinehart & Company, Inc., New York, 1959. An easily read book on atoms.

Zeuner, F. E.: *Dating the Past: An Introduction to Geochronology*, Methuen & Co., Ltd., London, 1946.

Chapter 4

LAND, SEA, AND AIR

WE USUALLY THINK of the earth as being divided into land, sea, and air. The more exact divisions are the lithosphere, or solid rock foundation; the hydrosphere, or water envelope, surrounding and penetrating the lithosphere; and the atmosphere, or gaseous envelope, completely surrounding both the hydrosphere and the lithosphere.

These three divisions depend on each other. The atmosphere contains much water and dust, sometimes exaggerated in the form of hurricanes or smog. The hydrosphere absorbs air and carries rock particles. The lithosphere absorbs both air and water and reacts with them. Water held in the rocks supplies much of the water we need.

THE LITHOSPHERE

The lithosphere is the solid, or rock, portion of the earth. Its mass is greater by far than that of the atmosphere and hydrosphere combined. As Table 4.1 shows, the mass of the air and water together constitutes only about 1/35 of 1 per cent of the total mass of the earth. However, their relative importance far exceeds their meager mass.

FIG. 4.0. *Wave erosion of the seashore near Brookings, Oregon, showing the interaction of the three spheres of the earth—air, water, and rock. The wind sets up waves, and the waves in turn pound the rock cliffs and cause them to crumble. The small islands are remnants isolated but not yet destroyed by wave attack. (Oregon State Highway Commission.)*

TABLE 4.1 *Relative Masses of the Three Divisions*

Division	Mass, metric tons
The whole earth (lithosphere, hydrosphere, and atmosphere)	$5,976,000 \times 10^{15}$
The atmosphere	5×10^{15}
The hydrosphere	$1,640–1,670 \times 10^{15}$

The lithosphere is not merely the land. An area of about 139 million square miles, or 71 per cent, lies below sea level; the land area is only 58 million square miles, or 29 per cent.

The Continents

SEA LEVEL

The surface of the ocean (sea level) is the datum, or reference plane, for all topographic and geologic work. Theoretically, all level surfaces are tangent to mean sea level, and that surface is assumed to be constant. It is, of course, not level, as it conforms to the spheroidal shape of the earth. The ocean's surface is further distorted many feet, because the gravitational attraction of high land masses draws the mobile waters of the sea toward them. The effect is greatest beside the Andes of South America and the Himalaya of India. Differences in salinity of the sea (and therefore in weight) probably affect sea level slightly. Temporary changes due to such influences as tides, winds, and excessive rainfall have no basic effect on sea level.

CONTINENTAL PLATFORMS

The continental platforms rising above the ocean basins are plateaulike features on which most mountains and valleys form relatively minor surface irregularities. They include not only the continents shown on conventional maps but also the gently sloping continental shelves, or margins, that lie below the shallow seas formed by the overlapping ocean (Fig. 4.1). These shelves extend over more than 10 million square miles. Beyond the continental shelves the edges of the continental platforms slopes comparatively steeply toward the ocean basins.

CONTINENTAL RELIEF

The continents have an average elevation of about ½ mile above sea level. Their major surface features are mountains, plateaus, and plains. Mountains are conspicuous elevations with small summit areas. Plateaus also rise high above their surroundings but have large summit areas. Plains are broad regions of low relief, commonly underlain by nearly flat-lying rocks. North American examples are the Rocky Mountains, Sierra Nevada, and Appalachian Mountains; the Colorado and Columbia Plateaus; and the Atlantic and Gulf Coastal Plains and the central plains of the Middle West.

The cores of the continents are low, rolling mountains or deeply eroded oldlands composed of complexly altered ancient rocks, which occur in areas that are oval or shieldlike in outline and are, therefore, known as *shields*. The Canadian Shield, the Brazilian Shield, and the Fenno-Scandian Shield (in northwestern Europe) are representative.

The maximum relief of the earth's lithosphere is approximately 12 miles (Fig. 4.2). The greatest elevation of land above sea level is Mount Everest, with an altitude of 29,028 feet, or 5.5 miles. The greatest depth below sea level known to date is in the Marianas Trench, which descends to 36,173 feet, or 6.85 miles below sea level.

The continent of North America has an average elevation of 2,360 feet; Europe averages about 1,150 feet; and Asia, with its high plateaus and the Himalaya, about 3,200 feet.

The Ocean Basins

Although the depressed oceanic area within which the ocean lies is called a basin, the bottom is the surface of a spheroid and is convex, like the surface of the sea itself. Water lies within it be-

cause the points on the bottom are nearer the center of the earth than are the adjacent points on land.

The ocean basin proper occupies about two-thirds of the earth's surface, but there is an excess of water, and so the basin is somewhat more than full. Its waters, therefore, spread over the low borders of the continental platforms, covering them to depths of a few hundred feet and to widths of as much as 100 miles. The whole ocean, including the deep basins and the shallow areas, covers 71 per cent of the earth's surface.

OCEAN DEPTH

Surveying. Mapping the depths of the sea involves two problems: (1) determination of the exact geographic position at which the observation is made and (2) measurement of the depth itself. Each of these has its difficulties.

Within sight of landmarks on shore, the position of a ship at sea can be found by ordinary trigono-

FIG. 4.1. *Photograph of a relief model of the continental shelf off the northeastern coast of the United States. Note the submarine canyon which seems to extend from the Hudson River southeast toward the ocean deeps. (Aero Service Corporation.)*

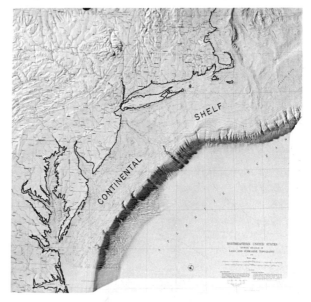

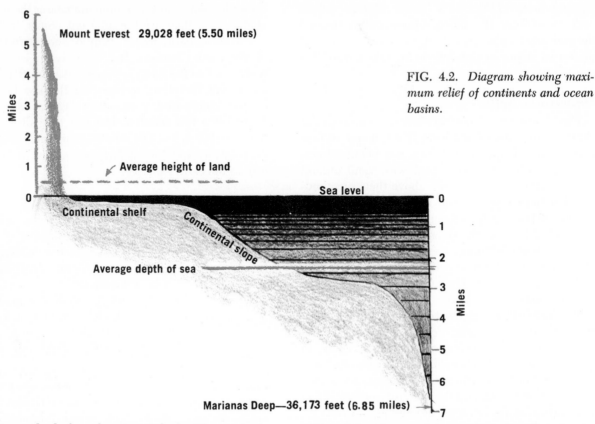

FIG. 4.2. *Diagram showing maximum relief of continents and ocean basins.*

metric methods from bearings taken with a sextant. When the ship is beyond sight of land, the methods used include dead reckoning, astronomical fixes, great lengths of taut wire, radio compass, radio acoustic ranging, radar, shoran, loran, and sofar. Shoran and loran utilize radio waves and special electronic equipment at shore stations and on board ship. Sofar uses the transmission of sound waves from a bomb exploded at a depth in the sea where sound waves travel horizontally at a uniform rate (about 4,800 feet per second) to geophones placed at the same depth near shore.

We can determine the depth of the sea by sounding. In shallow-water areas it is readily measured by a taut-wire sounding device, but in deep water the task is complicated by the length of time required, the difficulty of maintaining a vertical cast, the bulk of great lengths of wire, the heavy equipment needed to handle it, the possible error in measuring it on a wheel, its stretch, and other diffi-

culties. Therefore, echo sounding has largely replaced wire sounding, except in certain areas or for special purposes.

An echo-sounding instrument measures the time required for a sound to travel to the bottom and the echo to return to the ship. High frequency or audio frequency may be used. Based on the velocity of sound in sea water, the instrument automatically registers the depth as the ship continues along on its course. A recording device may be used to make a continuous record, which is convenient for later study (Fig. 4.3). The speed of echo sounding contrasts sharply with the time required for the old, laborious method of dropping a weight and line to the bottom. By the latter method the *Challenger* expedition made only 505 deep-sea soundings during its cruise from 1873 to 1876, and the locations of many of these soundings have been found to be in error by as much as 5 miles.

Sonic sounding, however, does not work well

near underwater cliffs, and in very deep water the velocity of sound (and hence the computed depth) is affected by differences in temperature and salinity. Despite these limitations, sonic sounding, coupled with good position fixes, promises to make possible ultimately a fairly accurate survey of the topography of the ocean bottom. Charts based on sonic and other soundings already have been prepared for much of the shallow sea around the continental margins, for the Gulf of Alaska, and for certain other regions. In many areas, however, the sea has still to be surveyed in detail, although the records of numerous traverses are now available.

Further study of the ocean bottom has been carried out with the aid of seismic refraction surveys, gravity meters, current meters, undersea photography (Fig. 4.4), and sediment-sampling devices,

FIG. 4.3. *A typical fathogram off San Diego, California. (Allan Hancock Foundation.)*

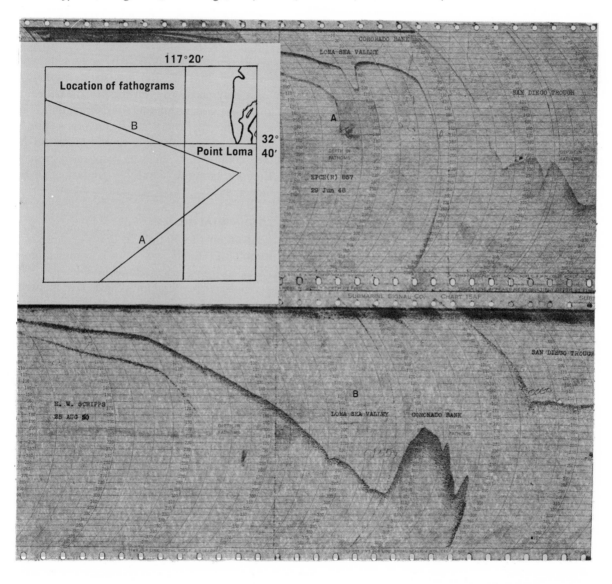

FIG. 4.4. *Underwater photograph of glauconitic, shelly foraminiferal sand. This was taken on the continental shelf at 192 fathoms off the northwest end of Santa Catalina Island, California. Note the abundant sea urchins and their trails. The bottom edge of the photograph represents a width of about 3 feet. (Allan Hancock Foundation.)*

including coring instruments capable of obtaining cores of bottom sediment as much as 70 feet long.

Distribution. The ocean has an average depth of about 12,450 feet (2.36 miles). About 4 per cent of the sea bottom descends to depths which range from 4 to more than 6 miles. The greatest depths lie in the western part of the Pacific Ocean, where several soundings have exceeded 30,000 feet (Figs. 4.2, 4.9). The greatest known depth was found in the Marianas Trench, where soundings showed nearly 7 miles (36,173 feet) of water. The relative percentages of the different depth zones is shown graphically in the upper part of Fig. 9.24.

CONTINENTAL SHELVES

The shallow part of the ocean bottom adjacent to the land is known as the continental shelf. A typical continental shelf slopes seaward about 12 feet per mile from the shore to about a 400-foot depth, where the bottom begins to descend more abruptly into the abyssal depths. The continental shelf varies in depth at its outer edge and even

more greatly in width along different parts of its extent. Its surface also is varied; in places it is fairly smooth, but elsewhere it is broken by channels, ridges, enclosed depressions, submarine benches, and other features. At some places the bottom material is solid rock; in others it is sand, mud, or even gravel. Along the coast of New England and adjacent parts of Canada the bottom in shallow water still retains many glacial features, among which are mounds of glacial deposits (drumlins), some projecting above water as islands.

Although the continental shelves are part of the continental masses and not merely an embankment of sediments, they are continually being built up and out by land-derived sediments discharged by streams or by the wind or by sediments worn from the coast line by the sea itself. Sinking of the coast may cause the sea to spread farther over the low coastal areas of the continents, and conversely a rise of the coast may convert a part of the continental shelf into a coastal plain on land. So the continental shelf is especially sensitive to changes brought about by gradation or by earth movements.

CONTINENTAL SLOPES

At about the 70-fathom line the slope of the sea bottom, as stated, generally becomes more abrupt. Even so, its average slope is only about 320 feet per mile off mountainous coasts and about 185 feet per mile off wide coastal plains. Its lower edge grades imperceptibly into the main floor of the deep sea. The continental slope thus defined varies in width upward from a few tens of miles, but it is nearly everywhere a feature of the border of the ocean basin and is one of the most marked changes of level on the sea bottom. Its area is a little more than twice that of the continental shelves.

The continental slopes are thought to be the margins of masses of relatively light continental-type rocks which give way seaward to heavier rocks underlying the ocean basin proper.

SUBMARINE CANYONS

At many places the continental slopes and the outer parts of the continental shelves are characterized not by a smooth, even descent from shallow water to abysmal depths but instead by deep, V-shaped, steep-walled, valleylike depressions called submarine canyons (Fig. 4.5). Some of these canyons have tributaries with a branchlike, dendritic pattern like that made by stream erosion on land. Some lie off the mouths of rivers, such as the Congo, Indus, Hudson, Delaware, and Columbia, whereas others have little or no counterpart on land nearby. Their lower reaches extend to depths of as much as 6,000 to 9,000 feet below sea level. Their walls in many places are rocky.

The origin of these submarine canyons is uncertain. They have been ascribed variously to erosion by turbidity currents of suspended mud, to mudflows and submarine slumping of recently deposited, highly water-soaked sediments on a steep outer depositional front, to erosion by rivers on land and subsequent submergence by downwarping and by rise of sea level, to erosion by tidal currents or by currents formed by giant sea waves, to fault-

ing, to sapping by submarine artesian springs, and to other causes.

Turbidity currents are known to occur in Swiss lakes and in Lake Mead and are thought to have broken telegraph cables at sea, but their ability to cut deeply into solid rock is questioned by many geologists. Certain of these gorges which have been under close observation, such as the Scripps Canyon off the Southern California coast, occasionally show sudden deepening that seems to indicate submarine slumping, but perhaps only in canyons already formed otherwise. On the other hand, the close resemblance of submarine canyons to valleys on land suggests that subaerial erosion may be a partial explanation. Erosion by streams during the Pleistocene glaciation's lowering of sea level may have extended to present depths of a few hundred feet, but hardly to depths of thousands of feet. The opinions of geologists are divided over the various possible causes, or combinations of causes, that have been proposed.

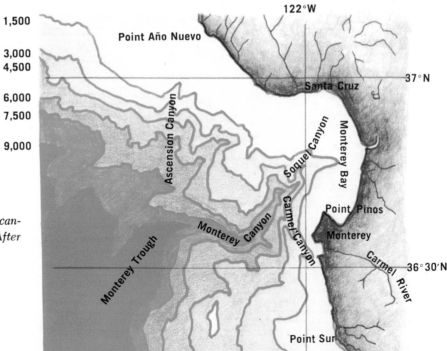

FIG. 4.5. *Monterey submarine canyon off the California coast. (After Shepard and Emery.)*

OCEAN-FLOOR RELIEF

The floor of the deep ocean is not a featureless plain; instead, it has a great variety of irregularities —both broad and narrow ridges, submerged plateaus, oval basins, elliptical and elongate depressions, submerged mountains, and flat-topped peaks (Fig. 4.6). The Mid-Atlantic Ridge, extending from Iceland almost to Antarctica, culminates in the Azores and other small islands, but most of it lies under about 9,000 feet of water and about 6,000 feet above the deeper areas on either side. The Hawaiian Islands, of volcanic origin, stand on another great ridge more than 2,000 miles long in the mid-Pacific. The Gulf of Mexico, the Caribbean Basin, the Mediterranean Sea, the Black Sea, the Red Sea, and the North Polar Sea, on the other hand, are examples of deep, almost landlocked basins on the sea floor.

Seamounts and guyots. A notable feature of the ocean bottom is a series of submarine mountains, aptly named seamounts. Some of those in the Gulf of Alaska are shown in Fig. 4.7. A large number of flat-topped seamounts, termed guyots (named for the geographer A. H. Guyot—pronounced gē-yō) have been charted in the central and western Pacific between the Hawaiian Islands and the

Marianas. Their summits, now submerged to a depth of about 4,000 to 6,000 feet, may represent volcanic peaks which were truncated by wave erosion in the geologic past or capped with broad coral reefs and subsequently drowned by subsidence of the ocean bottom or by rise of sea level (Fig. 4.8).

Trenches and deeps. Several deep elongate trenches occur on the floor of the Pacific (Fig. 17.49), especially at the foot of the continental slopes, as off the west coast of South America, or along the front of island arcs, as illustrated by the Aleutian Trench (Fig. 4.7). Other Pacific troughs are the Kurile Trench, the Japan Trench, the Mindanao, or Philippine, Trough (Fig. 4.9), the Marianas Trough, and the Kermadec-Tonga Trough (northeast of New Zealand). The Java Trough in the Indian Ocean and the Puerto Rico Trough in the Atlantic Ocean are other examples.

The deepest known soundings in the ocean have been found in these trenches—35,430 feet in the Philippine Deep by the German ship *Emden* in 1923, and 36,173 feet in the Marianas Trench by the U.S.S.R. vessel *Vityaz* in 1959.* In oceano-

* Added in proof: On Jan. 23, 1960, two men in the U.S. Navy bathyscaph *Trieste* reached bottom at 35,800 feet in the Marianas Deep 210 miles southwest of Guam.

FIG. 4.6. *Profiles across the United States and across the South Atlantic, using a similar spacing of reference points. The Mid-Atlantic ridge is a broad, plateaulike zone on the floor of the Atlantic. (After Shepard.)*

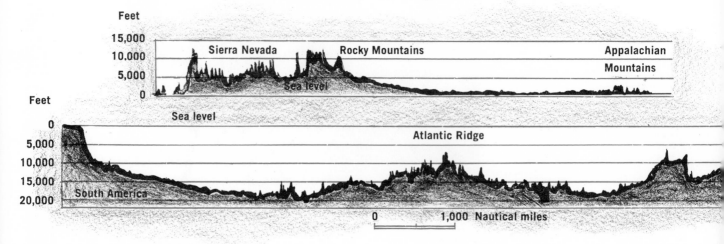

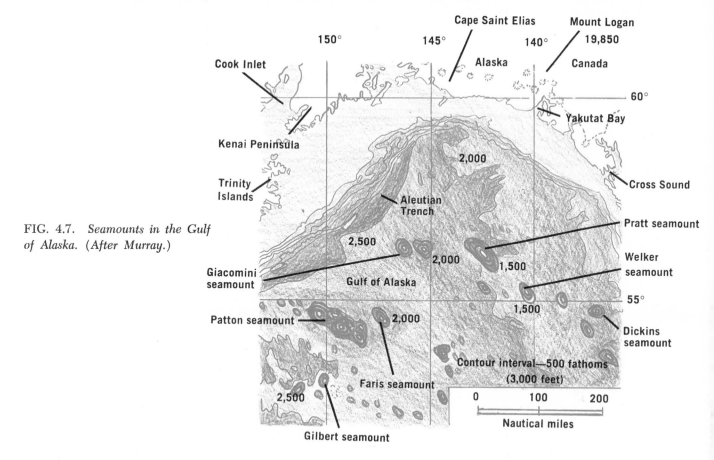

FIG. 4.7. *Seamounts in the Gulf of Alaska. (After Murray.)*

graphic usage a deep is any depression in the oceanic abyss that exceeds 6,000 meters (19,685 feet) in depth.

The origin of these deep-sea trenches is not known. Although a few straight ones resemble fault troughs on land, most of them are thought to be formed by downwarping or infolding. That they lie along active and mobile belts of the earth's crust is indicated by the fact that numerous earthquakes originate beneath these troughs.

Stability of Continents

PERMANENCY

Most geologists and geophysicists have long been convinced that the continental masses and the deep ocean basin have remained in the same general locations throughout recorded geologic time. In other words, the two have not exchanged places because of warping or folding of the earth's crust.

The evidence for this conclusion lies in the observation that nearly all the sedimentary rocks of past geologic ages that are exposed on the continents are of types that were deposited in shallow epicontinental seas, whereas sample cores from the deep ocean floor are composed of fine-grained clays and oozes which accumulate so very slowly that cores a few scores of feet long contain sediments that were deposited millions of years ago.

DENSITY

Another principle that is generally accepted by geologists and geophysicists is that the continents are composed of a lighter, or less dense, type of rock than that which underlies the ocean basins. Careful examination and classification of rock types have shown that rocks that approximate granite[1] in composition predominate under the continent,

[1] Granite is a common, generally pinkish-gray, coarse-grained rock composed of orthoclase feldspar, quartz, and other minerals crystallized within the earth.

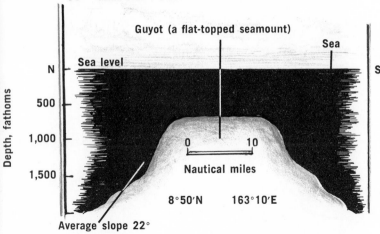

Depth, fathoms

Guyot (a flat-topped seamount)

Sea level

N

Sea

S

500

1,000

1,500

0 10

Nautical miles

8°50'N 163°10'E

Average slope 22°

FIG. 4.8. *North-south profile of a guyot south of Eniwetok Atoll, at a depth of 620 fathoms (vertical scale and slopes greatly exaggerated). The flat top and beveled edges sloping 2 to 3 degrees are characteristic. (After Hess.)*

whereas a heavier type of rock, essentially similar to basalt,[2] underlies the ocean basins.

The specific gravity, or density, of many types of rock has been determined with a high degree of accuracy, and granitic rocks are found to be about 10 per cent lighter in weight than basaltic rocks.

Geophysical investigations indicate that the light-weight (granitic) rocks composing the continents have the form of a discontinuous, curved plate, generally not more than 10 miles thick, which overlies a continuous substratum of heavy (basaltic) rock extending laterally beneath both land and sea.

[2] Basalt is a dark-gray to black, fine-grained, heavy lava rock.

Evidently the continents are high because they are light, and the ocean basins are low because they are underlain by heavy rocks.

Experiments demonstrate that rocks which are solid and brittle at the surface of the earth become plastic and flow when confined under great pressures corresponding to those encountered miles below the surface. Accordingly, we assume that the rocks at depth, though solid, are essentially plastic and that the continental masses of light material are buoyed up by the basaltic substratum so as to stand higher than the heavy materials beneath the ocean basins. Just as an iceberg floats with about seven-eighths of its mass submerged in water, so the light granitic continents, floating in the heavy basaltic substratum, have their crests, on the average, only about 3 miles above the floors of the ocean basins and extend their roots many miles downward.

ISOSTASY

The condition of balance, or flotational equilibrium, between continents and ocean basins (or between smaller areas) is called isostasy (Greek *isos*, equal; *stasis*, a standing still). At some depth beneath these areas of equal weight but unequal density, the pressures must be substantially the same. Any potential disturbance of isostatic balance, taking place at the surface (such as a lowering of weight by erosion of the lands or an increase in weight by the accumulation of a thick ice sheet, like that on Antarctica) presumably is met by slow flowage in the earth's plastic interior in order to keep the masses in equilibrium.

THE HYDROSPHERE

"Water, water everywhere, nor any drop to drink." This poetic plaint of the Ancient Mariner points up the vastness of the salty sea. The ocean covers 70.8 per cent of the earth's surface, contains nearly 3½ per cent salt, and constitutes by far the greatest part of the total waters of the earth. Its expanse and bulk are amazing.

DIVISIONS

The total hydrosphere includes (1) the ocean; (2) the inland lakes, swamps, rivers, and creeks; (3) ground water, or water that has soaked into the ground and occupies openings in the lithosphere; (4) water vapor in the atmosphere; (5)

water enclosed in sediments; and (6) masses of continental ice like those on Antarctica and Greenland. Ice is included because it is merely a passing stage in the transfer of moisture from sea to land via the air, and back again, in the hydrologic cycle. Water vapor is almost negligible percentagewise, but it is essential to that cycle.

The reserve of fresh water tied up as ice on land is variously estimated to be the equivalent of a layer of water about 75 to 200 feet deep over the present area of the ocean. The expected rise of sea level caused by hypothetical melting of all continental ice is difficult to estimate, because (1) the volume of ice is not known accurately, (2) its removal would alter the continents and ocean basins by allowing the areas freed of ice to rise, and (3) water added to the ocean would lap upon the continents landward from the present shores. After reviewing the uncertain estimates, Flint suggests that the net rise would be perhaps 66 to 165 feet.

The International Geophysical Year investigations found ice on Antarctica to exceed previous estimates by about 40 per cent (about 4.5 million cubic miles). At one place ice 14,000 feet thick rests on rock 8,200 feet below sea level.[3] These recent findings at least tend to raise the minima listed above.

WATER AND GEOLOGY

Water is an important geologic agent. Rain falls upon the land and gathers into rills, which unite to form brooks and creeks. These join to form rivers, which usually flow to the ocean. Since this running water carries with it rock particles, little by little the land is worn away. This wearing-away process goes on slowly but continuously. Ultimately the continents are reduced, and their material is carried to the sea and deposited as great beds of sediment. Thus the process of construction of new rocks goes on simultaneously with the destruction of the land. Air and water and vegetation work together to break down the rocks on land and

[3] Hugh Odishaw, "International Geophysical Year," *Sci.*, vol. 129, pp. 18–19, 1959.

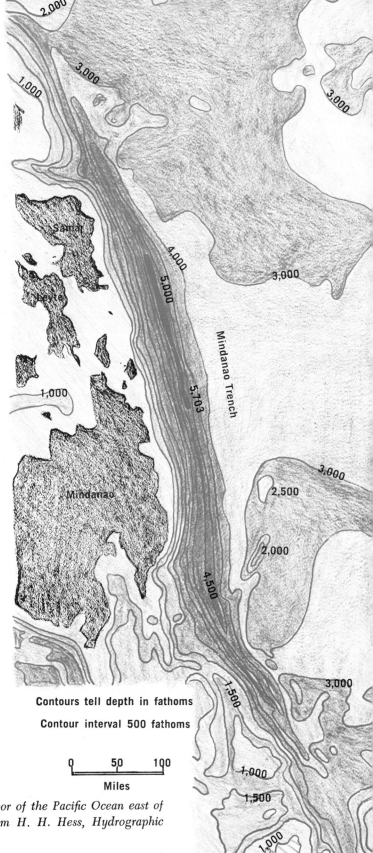

Contours tell depth in fathoms

Contour interval 500 fathoms

0   50   100

Miles

FIG. 4.9. *The great trench on the floor of the Pacific Ocean east of the Philippine Islands. (Redrawn from H. H. Hess, Hydrographic Office Chart 5485.)*

TABLE 4.2 *Data on the Hydrosphere*

Area of the ocean	361.16×10^6 square kilometers
Area of the ocean	139.44×10^6 square miles
Area of the ocean	70.8 per cent of earth's surface
Mass of the ocean	$1{,}420 \times 10^{15}$ metric tons*
Mass of the ocean	1/40 of 1 per cent of entire earth
Mass of fresh waters	0.51×10^{15} metric tons
Mass of continental ice	$20\text{--}50 \ (?) \times 10^{15}$ metric tons
Mass of water in sediment	200×10^{15} metric tons
Mass of water vapor in air	0.013×10^{15} metric tons
Total mass of the hydrosphere	$1{,}640\text{--}1{,}670 \ (?) \times 10^{15}$ metric tons
Maximum known depth of the sea	36,056 feet, or 6.83 miles
Mean depth of the ocean	12,465 feet, or 2.36 miles
Mean density of the ocean	1.03

* Metric ton = 2204.6 pounds.

render them incoherent and therefore more readily removable by running water. Loose material that is not removed constitutes soil and mantlerock.

We shall turn our attention first to the ocean, reserving ground water, streams, and lakes for consideration in subsequent chapters. The gradational work of ice and of waves and shore currents also will be taken up later.

The Ocean

FUNCTIONS

The energy source of running water is the sun. Ocean water is evaporated by the sun to form clouds, from which water falls as rain upon the earth's surface. The ocean is the ultimate source of the land waters which are so effective in carving the continents and which give life to terrestrial plants and animals. Its basin is the final resting place of all land detritus brought to it by streams. The ocean absorbs heat slowly and gives it up slowly. It is therefore a great regulator of climate. Extending from continent to continent, it is the route over which marine life migrates and the great highway of commerce, and its waters supply food for millions of people. From geologic, climatic, and economic standpoints, therefore, the ocean is of vital, often dominating importance. Its influence reaches nearly every part of the earth's surface.

DIVISIONS

The ocean occupies the depressed, basinlike parts of the earth's surface between and surrounding the continents. Although the partially separated water areas have different names (e.g., the Atlantic Ocean and the Pacific Ocean) and are somewhat independent, they are nevertheless connected at the surface to form a common ocean.

The outlying divisions of the ocean are commonly called seas, as the Red, the Mediterranean, and the Caribbean Seas; but a similar body of salt water may be called a gulf, as the Gulf of Mexico, or a bay, as Hudson Bay. The whole ocean, moreover, may be called the sea, and its surface is always called sea level. Some of its divisions, or seas, are almost completely surrounded by land; others are partly enclosed by island chains. Some are shallow; others are part of the deep ocean.

TEMPERATURE

The temperature of the ocean is dependent almost entirely on solar radiation. The slight heat received from the earth's interior and from the radioactivity of the sea bottom is negligible in comparison. The temperature varies greatly from equator to poles and from surface to the abysmal depths. At the equator the surface temperature averages about 80°F, whereas in the polar regions it is about 28°F, or near the freezing point of sea water. The water at the bottom of the deep sea varies from 28°F in the polar regions to about 35°F in the lower latitudes. The temperature of sea water in general changes rapidly from the surface to the 600-fathom line, where it is about 39°F, then less rapidly to the 1,000-fathom line, and below that it is relatively constant at or slightly below 35°F (Fig. 13.9). The great body of the ocean is therefore cold; and the heavy, cold waters that originate in polar and subpolar regions, creeping equatorward, dominate the circulation of the modern sea.

SALINITY

Sea water differs from land waters in that it carries in solution great quantities of mineral matter. One thousand parts of sea water contain 34.4 parts by weight of mineral matter, or 3.44 per cent (Figs. 4.10, 4.11). For 1 cubic mile of sea water this amounts to 151,025,000 tons. Murray estimates the total amount of sea water to be 323,722,150 cubic miles. Since each of these cubic miles contain 3.44 per cent of salts, the total in the sea is over 4,500,000 cubic miles of mineral matter, with a specific gravity of 2.2. This is equivalent to about 20 per cent of the volume of all rock masses above sea level and, if precipitated on the sea bottom, would make a layer about 175 feet thick over the entire ocean floor.

TABLE 4.3 *Salts Present in the Ocean*

Salt	Per cent
Sodium chloride, NaCl	77.758
Magnesium chloride, $MgCl_2$	10.878
Magnesium sulfate, $MgSO_4$	4.737
Calcium sulfate, $CaSO_4$	3.600
Potassium sulfate, K_2SO_4	2.465
Calcium carbonate, $CaCO_3$	0.345
Magnesium bromide, $MgBr_2$	0.217
Total	100.000

SOURCE: William Dittmar, *Challenger Rept., Phys. and Chem.*, vol. 1, p. 204.

About 50 elements have been found in sea water. In the order of amounts present, some of these are chlorine, sodium, magnesium, oxygen, sulfur, cal-

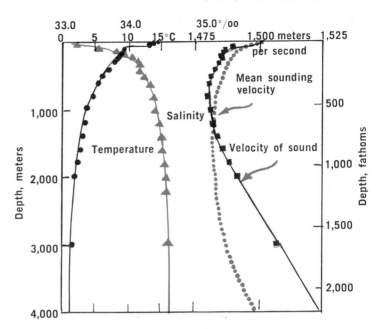

FIG. 4.10. *Changes in temperature, salinity, and computed velocity of sound with increasing depth off Southern California. The mean sounding velocity is the mean velocity from the surface to any specified depth. (After Sverdrup et al.)*

cium, and potassium. When the sea was originally formed, its waters may have contained some mineral matter in solution, and some may have been dissolved from the rocks of the area over which it spread, but probably the greater part of the solid matter has been contributed by streams, which obtain it by solution from the rocks of the land.

The mineral content of river water, however, differs considerably from that of sea water, as shown by Table 4.5. River waters contain relatively large quantities of calcium and bicarbonate but only moderate quantities of sodium, magnesium, and chloride. The relative percentages of these substances are changed drastically and almost completely reversed in the sea.

Mineral matter is constantly being removed from sea water by marine animals that use it in forming their shells, which are chiefly composed of calcium compounds. Still other parts of it are removed by precipitation, either when the temperature rises

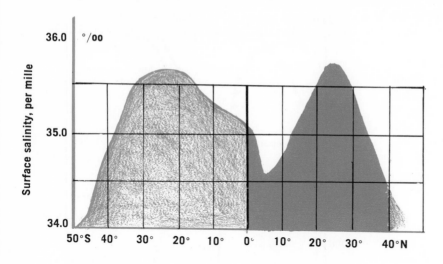

Surface salinity, per mille

FIG. 4.11. *Graph showing the average salinity of sea water in relation to latitude. Salinity is highest near Lat. 25°N and 20°S because of high evaporation and low precipitation there. It decreases toward the equator and toward high latitudes. (Data from Sverdrup, after Wüst.)*

and carbon dioxide escapes or when excessive evaporation takes place. Evaporation also causes the formation of salt and gypsum deposits, but this probably occurs only in shallow bays, coastal lagoons, and closed basins. Despite these removals, the mineral content of the sea is probably increasing. Common salt, NaCl, accumulates in the ocean more rapidly than the calcium salts, because it is rejected by organisms in the making of their skeletons or shells and is removed by evaporation only where unusual conditions prevail.

DISSOLVED GASES

Gases, as well as solids, are held in solution by sea water. Among the more abundant are nitrogen, oxygen, and carbon dioxide. The amounts of these gases can be suggested by some statistics on carbon dioxide. Assuming that air contains 3 parts of car-

TABLE 4.4 *Approximate Composition of Sea Water*

Constituent	Concentration, milligram atoms per kilogram of sea water	Constituent	Concentration, milligram atoms per kilogram of sea water
Chlorine	535.0	Nitrate	0.014
Sodium	454.0	Iron	0.0036
Sulfate	82.88	Manganese	0.003
Magnesium	52.29	Phosphorus	0.002
Calcium	10.19	Copper	0.002
Potassium	9.6	Barium	0.0015
Carbon dioxide	2.25	Iodine	0.00035
Bromine	0.81	Silver	0.0002
Strontium	0.15	Nitrite	0.0001
Aluminum	0.07	Arsenic	0.00004
Fluorine	0.043	Zinc	0.00003
Silicon	0.04	Hydrogen ion	0.00001
Boron	0.037	Gold	0.00000025
Lithium	0.015		

SOURCE: Compiled by T. G. Thompson and R. J. Robinson of the Oceanographic Laboratories, University of Washington. Taken from *Natl. Research Council Bull.* 85, p. 114, 1932.

TABLE 4.5 *Average Composition of Mineral Matter in River and Sea Waters*

Constituent	Percentage	
	River water	Sea water
Calcium	20.39	1.19
Silica, SiO_2	11.67	Trace
Sodium	5.79	30.59
Magnesium	3.41	3.72
Ferric and Aluminum oxides	2.75	0.00
Potassium	2.12	1.11
CO_3 radical	35.15	0.21
SO_4 radical	12.14	7.70
Cl radical	5.69	55.48
NO_3 radical	0.90	0.00
Total	100.01	100.00

SOURCE: Clarke, *U.S. Geol. Survey Bull.* 770.

bon dioxide per 10,000, it is estimated that the atmosphere contains 2,200 billion tons of carbon dioxide; and, according to T. Schloesing, the sea contains 18 to 27 times as much as the atmosphere. (The carbon in the carbon dioxide in the air is equivalent to about 1½ times that contained in the estimated coal reserves of the world.) Most of the gases in sea water have been absorbed from the atmosphere, although some probably have been derived from submarine volcanoes or from the disintegration of organic matter or have been liberated from compounds through life processes. Oxygen is essential to nearly all marine life and to the process of oxidation in putrefaction, and carbon dioxide is the chief food material of the green and brown algae in the sea. Cold water is capable of holding a greater quantity of gas than warm water. The gases absorbed from the atmosphere in the cold regions are diffused through the deep waters of the ocean and released in the warm regions of the earth or wherever these cold waters come to the surface and are warmed.

DENSITY AND PRESSURE

Because of its salinity, sea water has a normal specific gravity of about 1.025. In cold polar seas this increases to about 1.028, whereas in warm tropical seas it decreases to about 1.022. Changes in the density, along with changes in temperature, pressure, dilution, and concentration, are responsible for certain currents in the ocean (Fig. 13.9).

The pressure at any particular depth in the sea is equal to the weight of the water above it. One cubic foot of sea water from the surface weighs about 64 pounds. Accordingly, at a depth of 1,000 feet the pressure is about 64,000 pounds per square foot; at a depth of 35,000 feet, it is more than 1,100 tons per square foot. Although water is nearly incompressible, the pressure at great depths is enough to cause a slight increase in its density. Otherwise, sea level would be raised nearly 90 feet.

Life in the Ocean

ZONES

The marine environment has been divided into life zones (Fig. 4.12), each with a certain type of fauna and flora.

Littoral, or tidal, zone. The littoral, or tidal, zone includes the area exposed between high and low tides. In this zone the ebbing tide lays bare the sea bottom, and the high tide covers it with water. It is always within the influence of strong wave action. For these reasons living conditions are unusually difficult, and organisms must either be firmly attached to the bottom or burrow into the mud. Some find refuge in tidal pools, and others develop anatomical structures that enable them to survive periods of exposure to the air. Certain varieties of sea urchins occupy holes that they dig in solid rocks.

Neritic zone. The neritic zone extends from the lowest tide line to the outer edge of the continental shelf. It is probable that a greater abundance of life per unit area flourishes in this environment than in any other place on earth. Since the water is less than about 400 feet deep, the area is lighted by the sun, food is abundant, and vast numbers of different species or organisms thrive on one another and on the materials in solution in the sea water. Conditions in the shallow inland seas of the geologic past were similar in many respects to those on the continental shelves of today.

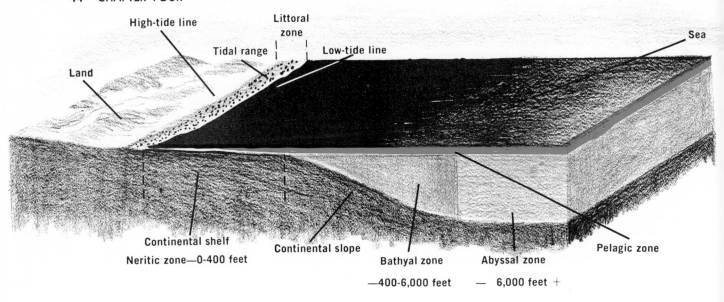

FIG. 4.12. *Life zones of the sea.*

Bathyal zone. The bathyal zone is that part of the sea bottom between the depths of about 400 and 6,000 feet. The higher parts of the area receive a little light, but even there plant life is rare. The floor of the sea in the bathyal zone has a prolific animal population, despite the fact that plant life is limited. Since the rate of deposition of sediments is slow, bottom-living scavengers destroy much of the organic matter. The calcareous sediment consists largely of planktonic shells, and the siliceous deposits are mainly diatoms and sponge spicules.

Abyssal zone. The abyssal zone includes that portion of the sea below a depth of 6,000 feet. This zone receives no sunlight, its temperature is near freezing at all times, and the pressure is greater than 1 ton per square inch. Since plants that require sunlight cannot live in this environment, the animals that depend on plant food must live on that which settles from the sunlit waters near the surface. The shells and bones of animals that live on abyssal bottoms indicate that only highly specialized creatures are able to live in these depths.

Pelagic zone. The pelagic zone includes the shallower section of the waters of the great, expansive sea that lies beyond the littoral zone. The life of this zone includes the floating planktonic forms as well as the free-swimming forms in the open ocean. Algae and diatoms are the most common plants, and many varieties of animals inhabit this realm. Their resistant, inorganic hard parts contribute abundantly to the formation of sedimentary rocks.

CORAL REEFS

Certain calcareous marine algae and many of the calcareous or lime-secreting marine animals, including the corals, live in colonies and are reef builders. Since the coral is a conspicuous form in the reef and is readily recognized, these structures are commonly called coral reefs, even though their major portions may be built by algae, Hydrozoa, Bryozoa, or other forms of marine life. A coral reef is a belt along which the algae, corals, and associated marine animals live, their skeletons building up a platform on which these forms continue to grow.

Reefs of this sort have been an important factor in the formation of limestone since very ancient (Ordovician) time, and they still are of common occurrence in the warm, shallow waters of the tropical and subtropical oceans. The total area covered by growing coral reefs is estimated at 500,000 square miles, and the detritus derived from them by wave action may cover more than twice that area.

Modern reef-building corals are confined to clear sea water with a temperature that does not fall below 68°F and a depth that varies from a little below mean sea level to about 150 feet. They are thus a shore phase of islands or of low shelving coasts of continents. The most vigorous growth of the reef is toward the open sea, where the waves bring food, oxygen, and the necessary calcium for the coral skeletons. Opposite the mouths of rivers, where quantities of fresh water and land detritus are discharged, there is a break in the coral growth; tidal movements may preserve such openings, so that the reefs form a disconnected belt along the coast.

Massive reefs built along the shore are termed *fringing reefs*. Those which are separated from the shore by a channel or a lagoon are called *barrier reefs*. Those which surround lagoons and are more or less circular in shape are called *atolls*.

Darwin suggested that an atoll is formed at a certain stage in the history of a fringing reef surrounding an island on a sinking sea bottom (Fig. 4.13). As the island sinks, the fringing reef, which grows chiefly to seaward, is changed to a barrier reef, separated from land by a lagoon; then, as the island sinks farther and disappears below sea level, the corals continue to build up the reef and it becomes an atoll. The waves break off fragments of the reef and pile them up above sea level on the lagoonward side. In time, land is thus formed,

FIG. 4.13.   *Diagrams showing how an atoll may be developed. (a) Island with a fringing coral reef. (b) After subsidence the fringing reef has grown upward and become a barrier reef. (c) After further submergence of the original island the barrier reef has become an atoll.*

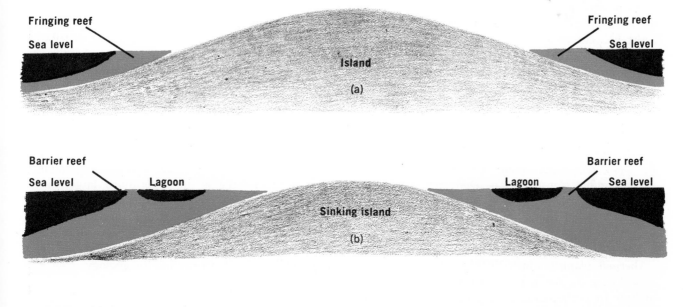

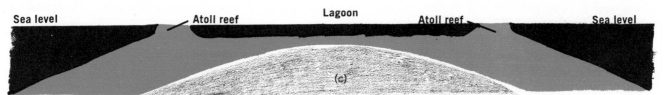

vegetation gets started, and a ringlike coral island results.

The most extensive coral reef of the present time is the Great Barrier Reef along the northeast coast of Australia. It is more than 1,000 miles long and varies from 10 to 90 miles in width. Behind this barrier is a channel 20 to 50 miles wide and 60 to 240 feet deep, which is thus protected and is used for coastwise shipping; the adjacent coast also is freed from the violence of the waves.

THE ATMOSPHERE

The atmosphere is the blanket of air that covers the rocks and waters of the earth. Its mass is less than a millionth part of that of the whole earth, but its activities and influences are far-reaching. Its presence, of course, is necessary to sustain the varied life of the earth, and it tends to equalize the temperatures of the earth's surface. It is one of the chief agents of rock weathering. It serves as a medium for the transfer of water, since water continually is evaporated into the atmosphere and subsequently precipitated onto the earth as rain or snow, which, gathered into streams and glaciers, assist in wearing away the rocks and transporting them to the sea.

The atmosphere itself is an important geologic agent. It reacts chemically with the rocks and oxidizes them, forming new minerals; it commonly breaks them up into smaller bodies and causes them to disintegrate. Disintegrated rock matter, being more finely divided, is more readily removed by wind and water. Wind—the air in motion—is an important transportation agent for dust and sand, as we shall see in a subsequent chapter. Moreover, wind causes the movement of water to form waves and certain ocean currents.

The atmosphere also serves in other ways. It is a thermal blanket which distributes the heat received from the sun and tends to prevent the escape of heat from the earth. Its gaseous molecules and suspended dust particles aid in the diffusion of sunlight. Furthermore, this gaseous envelope which surrounds the earth protects it from excessive ultraviolet radiation and from violent bombardment by meteorites. Several million meteorites fall into the earth's atmosphere daily, but most of them are disintegrated by the heat of friction that is generated as they travel through the air toward the ground. Their fragments settle harmlessly as fine cosmic dust. Occasionally, however, large meteorites do pass through the entire thickness of the atmosphere and may penetrate the ground several feet or more.

The daily weather of a place is the temporary state of its atmospheric conditions—temperature, air pressure, wind, humidity, cloudiness, and precipitation. Its climate is the composite of the weather over a long period of time. Climate is described in terms of mean annual temperature, temperature variations, humidity, amount and seasonal distribution of precipitation, storms, and winds. Since meteorology (the study of the atmosphere) and climatology are separate branches of earth science, we shall not study them in detail here, but some consideration of the atmosphere, weather, and climate is essential to an understanding and appreciation of the effects of the atmosphere upon geologic processes. Just as the soils and vegetation of a particular region are determined largely by climate, so geologic processes, especially the weathering of minerals and rocks and the erosion of land, differ greatly from place to place because of different climates. Hence the atmosphere as a climatic medium has great importance in geology.

General Features

ATMOSPHERIC COMPOSITION

Dry air, a mixture of gases, consists of about 78 per cent nitrogen, 21 per cent oxygen, and 0.94 per cent argon by volume; minute amounts of carbon dioxide, neon, helium, krypton, xenon, oxides of nitrogen, hydrogen, and ozone; and, locally, certain volatile organic substances, sulfurous gases, and chlorine from volcanoes and other sources.

Water vapor also is an important part of the atmosphere, probably averaging about 1.2 per cent of the total volume. Its abundance varies according to the temperature. It forms about 2.63 per cent at the equator, 0.92 per cent at Lat. 50°N, and 0.22 per cent at Lat. 70°N.

Fine earthy matter, salt crystals, smoke, soot, pollen, spores, bacteria, volcanic dust, and meteoritic dust may be spread as impurities through a considerable part of the atmosphere, sufficient at times to darken the sky and to reduce visibility. The presence of dust in the atmosphere increases the red colors at dawn and twilight. Dust particles (both terrestrial and meteoritic in origin) and salt crystals have an important function in that they serve as nuclei, or centers, around which water vapor condenses to produce cloud particles of water or ice.

AIR AND ALTITUDE

The air extends to great elevations above the land (Fig. 4.14). Mountain climbers have reached elevations of more than 29,000 feet on Mount Everest, and observers in balloons and airplanes have reached still greater heights. Artificial satellites carrying meteorological instruments have gone up tens of thousands of miles; indeed some rockets have gone beyond the earth's gravitational control. Meteors, white-hot from friction with the atmosphere, are generally observed at heights of 30 to 60 miles. Auroral discharges, giving evidence of ionized gases, are generally seen 50 to 80 miles high, and, exceptionally, as high as 190 miles (Fig. 4.14). Some extremely thin air certainly extends hundreds of miles aboveground and may extend 10,000 miles. Only the bottom portion, however, has much bearing on geology.

Air temperature decreases about 1°F for every 300 feet of difference in vertical elevation up to altitudes of 6 to 8 miles, above which a zone of nearly constant temperature (about −67°F) is reached. Differences in altitude account for the pronounced differences in temperature and the corresponding differences in climate, vegetation, and habitability of places having the same latitude. In general, a change in altitude of 1 mile is about equal to a change in latitude of 800 miles.

Dust and other earthy material in the air are confined essentially to the lower layers of the atmosphere. As one ascends into the air, he leaves the smoke and coarser dust behind. The water vapor becomes less and less, until at 6 or 7 miles above sea level in the middle latitudes it is so cold that practically no moisture can remain in the air. Consequently no ordinary clouds exist. This altitude marks the lower limit of the stratosphere, which we shall discuss in the following section.

About one-half the mass of the atmosphere occurs in the lower 18,000 feet. *Explorer II*, a United States Army balloon, reached an altitude of 72,395 feet, or 13.71 miles, above sea level. It was above 96 per cent of the mass of the atmosphere.[4]

ATMOSPHERIC STRATIFICATION

Studies of the air high above the earth have shown that the atmosphere may be divided into two main layers, or strata, and that each layer has its own peculiar composition and physical properties.

Troposphere. The region above the lithosphere, or solid earth, is known as the troposphere (Fig. 4.14). The prefix *tropo-* means a turning or overturning of the air due to convection currents set up by a difference in temperature. The height of the troposphere varies with latitude from about 11 miles at the equator to about 4 miles near the poles. There are also minor variations related to the seasons and to barometric pressure at the surface. The troposphere is higher in summer than in winter and higher when the surface pressure is high than when it is low.

Stratosphere. Above the troposphere, at about 6 or 7 miles above sea level in the middle latitudes, is the stratosphere, a region of cold, clear, thin, dry air, with a nearly constant temperature of −67°F

---

[4] Capt. Albert W. Stevens, United States Army, *Natl. Geog. Mag.*, vol. 69, p. 635, 1936.

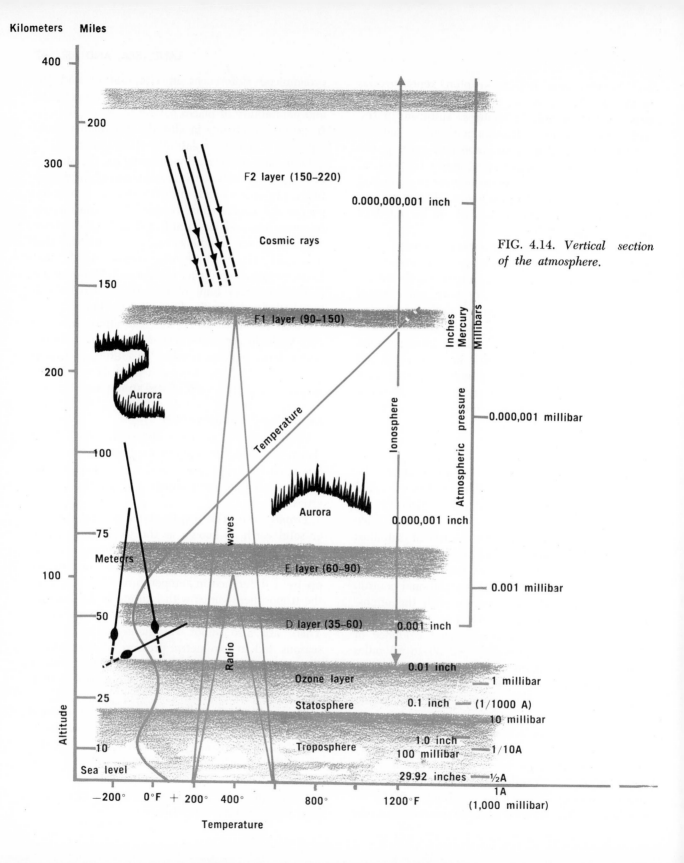

FIG. 4.14. *Vertical section of the atmosphere.*

for its lower portion. Unlike the troposphere, the stratosphere is characterized by a balance between absorbed and emitted radiation, and consequently there is no convection through it.

The temperature of the stratosphere partly depends on the troposphere; the higher the troposphere, the lower the temperature of the stratosphere. Since the troposphere varies with latitude, the temperature of the stratosphere near the equator is −80 to −100°F, or even lower; in polar regions −40 to −50°F; and in middle latitudes about −60 to −70°F. The general horizontal temperature gradient in the stratosphere is from relatively warm air at the poles to colder air at the equator, just the reverse of the gradient in the air near the ground.

The temperature of the stratosphere also depends on the altitude. At a level of about 20 miles or more above the ground, according to latitude and the season of the year, the temperature begins to increase slowly and continues that increase to a height of about 36 miles, where it reaches 150 to 170°F. At still higher levels the temperature decreases again, to about −28°F at 50 miles, and then, in the outermost levels, rises steadily again, with increasing altitude. It exceeds 2,000°F at the 250-mile level.

That there is an increase in the temperature of the upper air was first suggested by a study of meteors and has been confirmed by recent measurements and by investigations of the behavior of sound waves. A large explosion can be heard for a distance of 60 to 100 miles from its source, because of the direct travel of the sound waves through the lower air. Beyond this distance there is a belt about 125 miles wide in which the sound cannot be heard at all. Then, strangely enough, the sound again becomes audible in a zone of considerable width. This phenomenon may even be repeated, resulting in another zone of audibility beyond a second zone of silence. These outer zones of audibility can be accounted for only when we assume that the sound waves are refracted, or reflected, in the upper air and thus returned to the earth. Since sound travels faster in warm air than in cold, an assumption of increasing temperature in the upper stratosphere

accounts for the bending back of the waves. Such refracted sound waves appear to come mainly from a height of about 20 to 40 miles.

Within the stratosphere, at an elevation ranging from 12 to 30 miles, is a zone in which ozone is more abundant than at lower or higher elevations. Some ozone is found in the lower atmosphere, but the amount is extremely small. Ozone is similar to oxygen, except that three atoms are linked together to form the molecule, instead of two as in ordinary oxygen. The ozone layer in the atmosphere absorbs or intercepts a high percentage of the ultraviolet rays coming to the earth from the sun. It has been estimated that, if the ozone were decreased so as to allow even half the ultraviolet rays to reach us, they would destroy our skins and blind our eyes after a few minutes' exposure to the sun. However, if still more ozone were added to the atmosphere, it would absorb so many of the ultraviolet rays that animal life would suffer because of a lack of the essential "sunshine" vitamin. Absorption of radiant energy by ozone is also responsible for the high temperature found at that level.

Ionized layers. Above the ozone layer, starting at an altitude of about 37 miles, is a region of high electrical conductivity, called ionized layers. The conductivity results from the presence of free electrons and ions of gaseous atoms produced in the gases of the air by solar radiation. Three ionized layers have been identified: *D*, ranging from 37 to 60 miles aboveground; *E*, from 60 to 90 miles; and *F*, from 90 to 225 miles. These elevations, however, vary with day and night, the seasons, and other factors. The ionized layers cause radio waves to travel entirely around the earth within the atmosphere. If they were not there, the radio waves would spread out in straight lines radiating from their source. They can only be kept within the atmosphere and made to follow a path that has the curvature of the earth by being curved back to the earth in a way similar to that by which the sound waves are curved back.

AURORA BOREALIS

Auroral displays are an electrical phenomenon of the atmosphere in which the gases of the upper air are made luminous by electrical discharges, in somewhat the same way as neon is made luminous in the familiar neon street lights. Auroral glows occur most frequently around the magnetic poles of the earth and are closely related to magnetic disturbances on the earth. Since the greatest number of auroras occur at times of maximum sunspot activity, they are undoubtedly connected with electrical discharges from the sun. The heights of auroras above the earth correspond to the heights of the ionized layers, as shown by the reflection and refraction of radio waves. The displays of rapidly changing arcs, curtains, bands, and luminous patches in the Northern Hemisphere are called the aurora borealis, or northern lights; in the Southern Hemisphere they are known as the aurora australis.

ATMOSPHERIC TEMPERATURE

The air is heated mainly by the sun. Additional but minor sources of heat include radiation from the interior of the earth and eruptions of steam and other hot gases from inside the earth.

Of the total solar radiation received by the earth, averaging about 700 calories per square centimeter per day at the outer limit of the atmosphere, 42 per cent is reflected back into space, 43 per cent reaches the ground, and 15 per cent is absorbed by the air, especially by clouds. The average effective radiation, then, is about 400 calories per square centimeter per day—enough to melt a layer of ice about 2 inches thick. The tropical areas, of course, receive much more than average, and the polar areas much less; and the heat is unequally distributed over the seasons.

The short waves of the sun's radiant energy are converted to longer heat waves on the ground, which heat the air from the ground up. The lower part of the troposphere warms up more readily than the upper part because of this radiation from below and because of its greater density and water vapor. The most effective absorbents of heat in the atmosphere are water vapor and carbon dioxide. Retention of heat in this lower part of the troposphere gives the atmosphere a "greenhouse effect."

Barren rock surfaces absorb and later radiate heat more rapidly than areas covered with soil and vegetation or with snow and ice. The land also warms up and cools off faster than the sea because (1) rocks absorb and radiate heat more readily than water, since their specific heat is about one-fifth that of water; (2) they reflect less of the sunshine than water does; (3) they are less deeply penetrated by solar radiation; (4) they are less affected by cooling due to evaporation; and (5) they are not subject to mixing, as water is. Air temperatures over both land and sea are modified, however, by ocean currents and prevailing winds.

ATMOSPHERIC PRESSURE

The atmosphere weighs about 14.7 pounds per square inch at sea level, or enough to balance a column of water 33.8 feet high or to raise a column of mercury in a barometer to a height of 29.92 inches (760 millimeters). Atmospheric pressure rapidly decreases with increasing elevation, and at a height of 3.4 miles it is about half the pressure at sea level. Pressures in the lowest 6 miles are variable, but above that level they are almost uniform at all times and places for any particular elevation. One of the causes of pressure variation is temperature variation, since heat causes the air to expand and makes it lighter. Another cause is the differences in the quantity of water vapor in the lower atmosphere, since water vapor is relatively light.

Air pressures are measured by barometers which record the pressure of the atmosphere above the location of the barometer. A mercury barometer (Fig. 4.15) is a closed tube about 3 feet long, which is first filled with mercury and then inverted over a bowl of mercury. After the mercury settles in the tube (leaving a vacuum in the closed upper end of the tube), the weight of the column of mercury is balanced by atmospheric pressure on the mercury in the bowl. As the atmospheric pressure increases and decreases, the level of the mercury in the tube rises and falls accordingly. The tube is graduated so that the height of the mercury can be read easily.

An aneroid barometer (Fig. 4.16) is simply a sealed box of thin metal from which part of the air has been withdrawn and which responds by a system of levers to the varying pressures on the sides of the box.

In meteorological practice, air pressures are usually stated in *millibars* instead of inches or millimeters. One millibar is approximately one-thousandth of one standard atmospheric pressure (29.92 inches) at sea level. A pressure difference, or horizontal gradient, of only a few millibars (0.01 inch) is enough to induce movement of the air.

AIR MOVEMENTS

Wind is air moving essentially horizontally along the surface of the ground. Air currents are vertical movements of air, as in the thermal "air pockets" encountered in flying. The ultimate cause of these air movements is the pressure differences caused by the unequally distributed heat of the sun.

Air generally moves from high-pressure areas toward low-pressure areas under the pull of gravity, but the movement is modified by the earth's rotation, by turbulence and friction, and by centrifugal force (on curved courses). Water vapor serves as an important carrier of heat energy in air movements. Moisture evaporates into warm air. Subsequently, when the air cools, the latent heat is released by condensation, aiding in the transfer of the sun's energy from place to place.

Winds distribute heat over the earth and supply moisture for precipitation.

ATMOSPHERIC MOISTURE

The amount of water vapor in the air varies chiefly with temperature. The warm air of the equatorial region may contain 3 to 5 per cent water vapor, whereas that of the cooler middle latitudes may contain only 1 per cent or less. The average for all latitudes, according to Humphreys, is about 1.2 per cent. Because of its frigid temperature, the upper atmosphere, or stratosphere, contains practically no water vapor.

Condensation and precipitation. Condensation of moisture is caused by cooling and results in precipitation of dew, rain, snow, hoarfrost, hail, glaze, and sleet. Cooling may be caused by such factors as radiation, contact with cold surfaces, mixing of air masses of different temperatures, and expansion

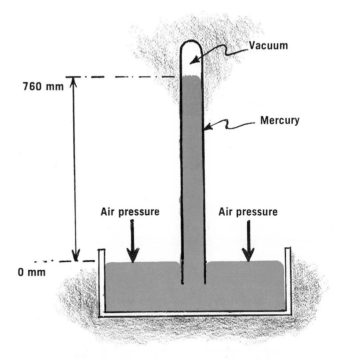

FIG. 4.15. *A simple mercury barometer. The height of the column of mercury in the inverted closed tube varies directly with changes in atmosphere pressure on the mercury in the bowl.*

FIG. 4.16. *An aneroid barometer with the cover removed; the dial is calibrated in millibars. (From Koeppe and DeLong.)*

due to movement of the air to places of lower pressure. Condensation to droplets of fog or cloud is facilitated by the presence of hygroscopic (water-absorbing) particles such as salt crystals and soot.

Rainfall. The average rainfall on the earth is about 30 inches a year, about 26 inches on land and considerably more over the ocean. About 20 per cent of the land receives less than 10 inches a year, and about 2 per cent receives more than 100 inches a year (Fig. 4.17).

The estimates on rainfall vary. Bruckmann estimates precipitation at 29.5 inches, 30 per cent of which falls on the land, or 26,679 cubic miles of water per year. Other estimates range from about 36 to 39 inches, with about 23 to 25 per cent on land.

The amount of rainfall is distributed very unequally over the earth as a whole. At certain places, as in parts of India, it is more than 500 inches a year, whereas in the Sahara Desert it is less than 10 inches. On the Atlantic Coastal Plain of North America it is approximately 40 inches a year. Farther west, in the northern part of the interior basin, it is 30 inches, and on the Great Plains it is 20 inches or less. In parts of the American Southwest, less than 10 inches of moisture falls per year. In some desert regions several years may elapse between showers, but these may be torrential.

These differences in rainfall on land are influenced mainly by (1) latitude; (2) nearness to the sea; (3) topography, especially the presence of mountain ranges, which intercept moisture-laden

FIG. 4.17. *Mean annual precipitation of the world. (After Koeppe and DeLong.)*

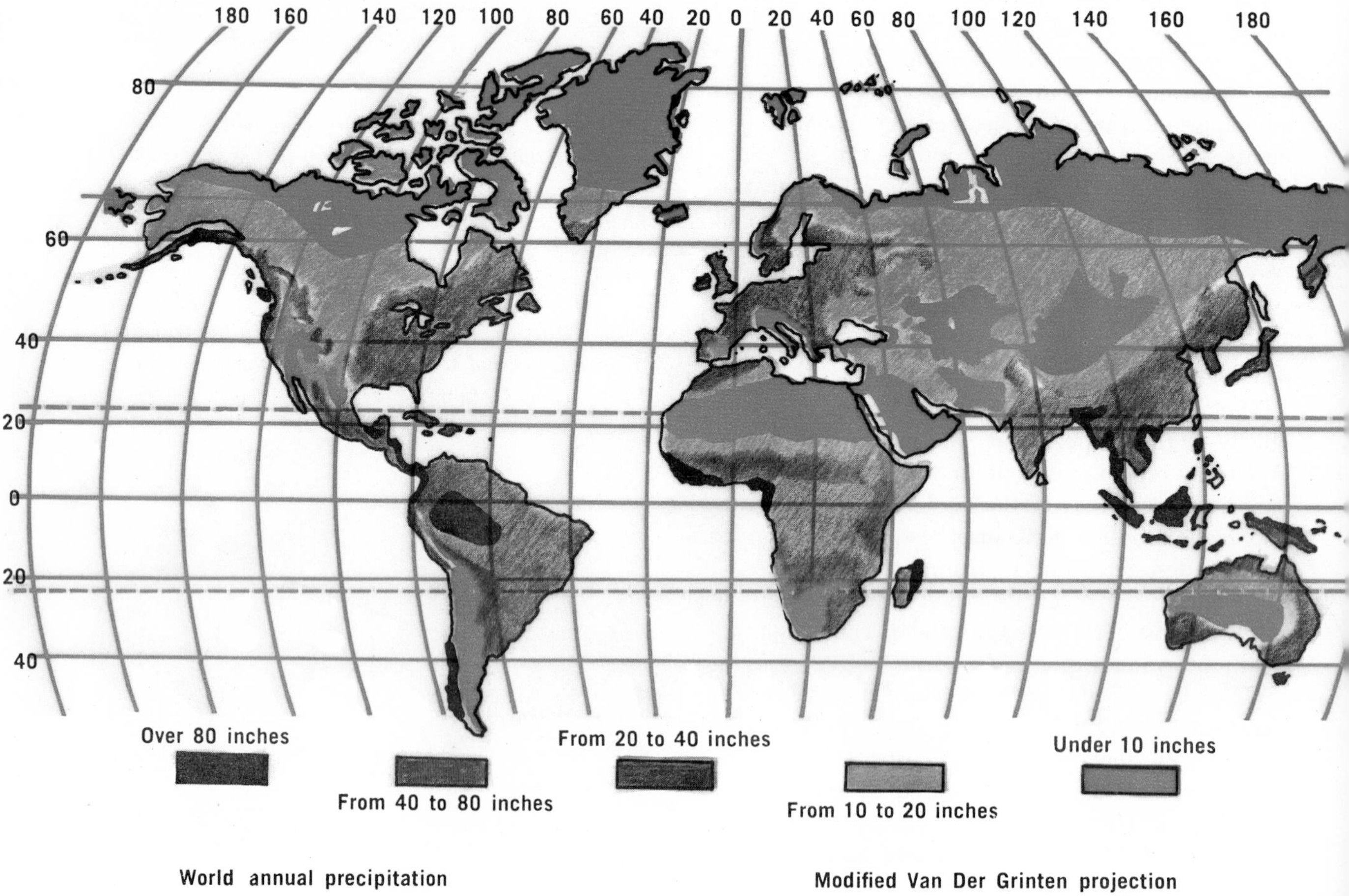

Over 80 inches

From 40 to 80 inches

From 20 to 40 inches

From 10 to 20 inches

Under 10 inches

World annual precipitation

Modified Van Der Grinten projection

winds; (4) prevailing winds; (5) seasons; and (6) frequency of cyclonic storms, hurricanes, and typhoons. Rainfall is heaviest in the tropical belt of calm, where warm, moist air rises abundantly and where daily showers are the rule, and on the windward sides of continents and mountain ranges. By contrast, many of the great deserts of the earth lie along the subtropical high-pressure belts or in the lee of mountains.

Hydrologic cycle. The principal source of moisture in the air is evaporation from the sea, lakes, ponds, streams, soils, or other moist surfaces. Such moisture is distributed widely by winds and ultimately precipitated. Of the water that falls upon the earth as rain, snow, hail, or sleet, a part enters the soil, mantle-rock, or solid rock to become ground water. Some is evaporated, even in mid-air; some is caught on the surface in snow fields, glaciers, ponds, and lakes and on vegetation; and some immediately runs off via streams toward lakes or the sea.

Of the fraction that enters the ground, much is returned to the air by evaporation from the soil or by transpiration of plants; a part later emerges as seepage or springs, to evaporate or join streams as part of the ultimate runoff; and a part goes into more or less extended storage underground.

Thus one route of circulation in the hydrologic cycle (Fig. 4.18) includes evaporation from the sea, distribution as vapor or as clouds over the lands by winds, precipitation, infiltration, emergence as seepage, and eventual runoff to the sea, ready for another round. However, several subsidiary cycles on land serve as short circuits, for only about one-fifth of the total precipitation on land returns to the sea as runoff.

FIG. 4.18. *The hydrologic cycle. The heat of the sun evaporates moisture from the sea or from lakes, ponds, reservoirs, streams, soils, vegetation, and falling rain. Moisture is also supplied by transpiration from plants and by sublimation from snow and ice. Precipitation results when relatively light, warm, moist, maritime air is blown landward and upward, and cooled (1) over the sloping front of a cooler and heavier continental air mass, (2) in the convectional system of a thunderstorm, or (3) in ascent over mountains. The precipitated moisture may be stored as snow fields, glaciers, ponds, lakes, soil water, or infiltrated ground water. Some water runs off immediately. Ground water returns to the surface to be evaporated or to join the runoff in streams that flow to the ocean. The runoff thus completes a cycle. (After Holzman).*

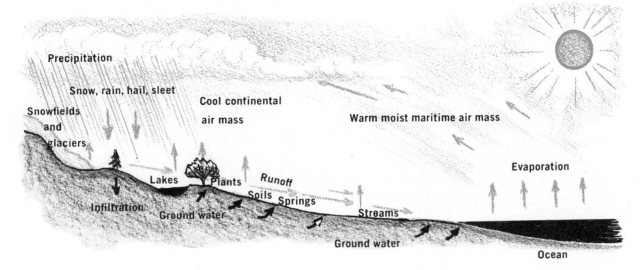

Atmospheric Circulation

PRESSURE BELTS

Because of the combined effects of unequal heating and the earth's rotation, alternating belts of low and high pressure encircle the earth parallel to the equator. The *doldrums belt* of low pressure along the equator, averaging 29.8 to 29.9 inches pressure, is caused by extreme heating. Pressures increase to the north and south of the equator to average maximums of approximately 30.0 to 30.1 inches along the parallels 30°N and 30°S (Figs. 4.19, 4.20), forming the *subtropical high-pressure belts,* or *horse latitudes,* where the air descends. The pressures then decrease north and south to form low-pressure belts, the *high-latitude* or *sub-*

polar lows (29.7 to 29.8 inches) in the region of 60°N and 60°S, where air rises. Finally, toward the poles, because of the extreme cold, the pressures gradually increase again to the *polar highs* (about 30 inches) over Antarctica and over Greenland–Arctic Canada. These seven pressure areas are parts of a complex convectional system.

The southern belt of low pressure, mainly over water, is continuous and fairly steady through the year, but the northern one is interrupted by relatively cold land areas to break the belt into two permanent lows, one near the Aleutian Islands and the other near Iceland. These lows wax and wane, and shift positions with the seasons. The equatorial low and the subtropical highs follow the apparent seasonal movement of the sun north and south.

FIG. 4.19. *Mean annual pressure at sea level. The subtropical highs and the Aleutian and Icelandic lows are especially noteworthy.* (After Koeppe and DeLong.)

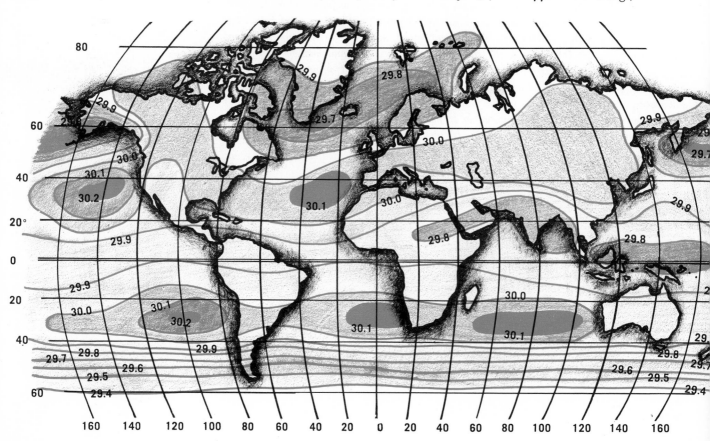

PREVAILING WINDS

Because of these permanent, though shifting, temperature and pressure differences, the convectional circulation between the equator and the poles embodies the following parts: (1) the doldrums belt at the equator, characterized by calm or by light winds and by rising moist air and frequent thunderstorms; (2) northeast trade winds in the Northern Hemisphere and southeast trade winds in the Southern Hemisphere, which are more or less steady; (3) the subtropical belts of dry, descending air; (4) the prevailing westerlies in middle latitudes; (5) cold winds spiraling out from the polar highs; and (6) a vagrant belt of cyclonic storms along the edges of surging masses of this cold polar air (the polar front).

Thus the circulation in each hemisphere is divided into three cells. (Recent research shows that the three-cell concept is oversimplified, though adequate as an approximation.) Although these cells (Fig. 4.21) are modified by differences between land and sea, by relief of the land, by seasonal changes, and by local factors, they persist as well-defined features of the atmosphere.

The trade winds, the westerlies, and all other winds are deflected by the earth's rotation (the Coriolis effect), to their right in the Northern Hemisphere and to their left south of the equator.

UPPER-AIR WINDS

Soundings by weather balloons reveal *antitrades*, the *jet stream*, and other strong winds, generally from the west, in the upper troposphere. The antitrades, found in limited areas, blow in directions opposite to those of the surface trade winds. The jet stream is a serpentine belt of swift wind 25 to 100 miles wide and 1 or 2 miles deep that rushes around the globe in middle latitudes at speeds of hundreds of miles an hour. Its course follows the cold polar front, and so its meanderings seem to have some bearing on the weather below. Its waves serve to exchange huge volumes of cold and warm air north and south, and thus to assist the latitudinal circulation.

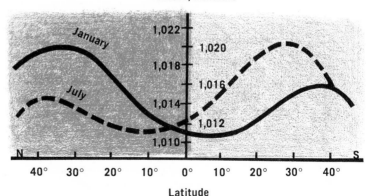

Pressure, millibars

FIG. 4.20. *North-south profiles of atmospheric pressure in January and July. Pressures are higher in winter than in summer, so they reciprocate with the seasons between the Northern and Southern Hemispheres. (After Riehl.)*

SECONDARY WINDS

In addition to these permanent movements, there are many temporary and local ones. These include cyclonic storms (which we shall study in later sections of this chapter), land and sea breezes, mountain and valley breezes, monsoons, hurricanes and typhoons, thunderstorms, tornadoes, chinook (or foehn) winds, and others.[5] Movements within the tropics also are more complex than the trades and doldrums alone imply.

Weather

AIR MASSES

Air masses are large bodies of air that have approximately the same temperature, pressure, and moisture content at any specific horizontal level. They form whenever a mass of air persists over a given area for a considerable time. *Continental* types form over land, *maritime* types over water. Some are warm and some are cold.

[5] Further information on these subjects can be found in standard works on meteorology.

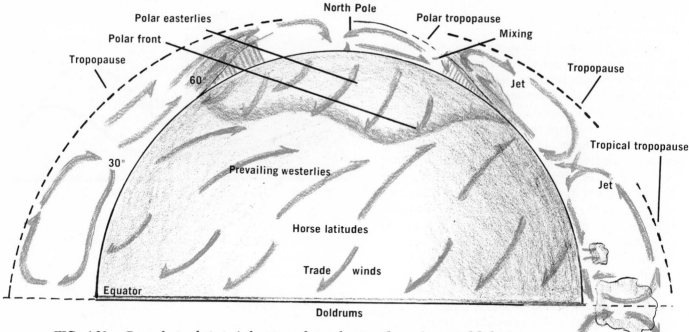

FIG. 4.21. *General circulation of the atmosphere, showing the surface wind belts in the Northern Hemisphere. One interpretation of the troposphere is shown in an exaggerated vertical section on the right, and a generalized, alternative concept is shown on the left. (Modified from Rossby et al.)*

Examples are (1) the cold polar continental air masses that originate over Canada, Alaska, or Siberia; (2) the cold polar maritime air masses formed over the North Pacific or the northwestern Atlantic Ocean; (3) the warm tropical maritime air masses that originate over the subtropical Pacific and Atlantic Oceans or the Gulf of Mexico; and (4) the warm tropical continental air masses that form over the Southwestern United States and northern Mexico or over North Africa.

As these air masses move away from the sites of their origin, they come into conflict with each other. Their interactions along their boundaries, the so-called *cold fronts* and *warm fronts*, are responsible for most of the weather changes of middle latitudes. The battle line between them surges back and forth as first a cold polar air mass and then a warm maritime air mass gains on the other. Cold surges occasionally reach as far south as Texas and Florida, and warm surges reach into Canada. The contest sets up storm waves, 500 to 3,000 miles wide, that travel eastward along the battle line, bringing a succession of temperature contrasts and wet and dry spells—with a change in the weather once or twice a week—especially over the Central and Eastern United States.

Eventually the air masses change their temperature and moisture content by rising or sinking, evaporation or condensation, heating or cooling from below, or mixing with other air.

CYCLONES AND ANTICYCLONES

A storm is a local disturbance in the general circulation. One type of storm, a cyclone, is a round or elliptical area of low atmospheric pressure toward which winds blow inward from all sides (Fig. 4.22). The earth's rotation deflects the incoming winds and causes them to curve to the right (in the Northern Hemisphere), so that they move in a counterclockwise direction around the storm center.

Many such lows are 500 to 1,000 miles in diameter; others range from about 100 to 2,000 miles. They are not to be confused with tornadoes or with tropical hurricanes and typhoons. They usually are attended by cloudiness and the precipitation of rain or snow.

The opposite of a cyclone is the *anticyclone*, or high-pressure area. It is a region in which the air moves spirally outward in all directions (Fig. 4.22).

In middle latitudes cyclones and anticyclones commonly alternate and move eastward across central North America with the general drift of the atmosphere, which moves at rates of 20 to 30 miles per hour according to the season. Cyclones and anticyclones cover large areas and seldom have winds of destructive velocity.

Cyclonic storms originate along the edge of the polar front where a mass of light, warm air brushes against a mass of heavy, cold polar air. Some irregularity along the boundary turns the warm air toward the cold, thus developing a warm front and a cold front. Once started, such a wave ordinarily grows by progressive stages and moves easterly. Southward surges of cold polar air form many of the anticyclones; other warm, sluggish anticyclones originate in the subtropics.

The warm, generally moist air of the warm front overrides the cold air along a gently sloping boundary that rises at a rate of about 1 mile in a distance of 100 to 300 miles (Fig. 4.23). Cloudiness and rain or snow usually result.

The cold front presses against the warm air mass on the west and northwest. The slope of its boundary is about 1 mile in every 50 to 150 miles. The wedge of cold air is usually only 1 or 2 miles thick, but it may be 1,000 to 2,000 miles wide. A narrow squall zone occurs along its front, but the main cold air mass ordinarily brings cool, clear, dry weather.

Occasionally the cold front overtakes the warm front and lifts the entire warm air mass off the ground. The cyclone is then said to be *occluded*.

Cyclones and anticyclones may wax or wane, accelerate or stagnate, and eventually lose their identity in a complex sequence of changes. Stagnant highs may lead to unseasonably warm weather, "Indian summer," or drought.

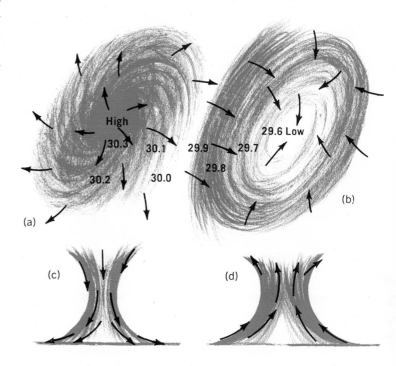

FIG. 4.22. *Sketches of an anticyclone, (a) and (c), and a cyclone, (b) and (d). (a) and (b) are map views, (c) and (d) are side views. Directions of air movement are indicated by arrows.*

WEATHER FORECASTING

Weather forecasting is based mainly on attempts to predict the direction and rate of travel of cyclones and anticyclones from a study of the conflicting air masses involved. By collecting simultaneous data from numerous stations, the Weather Bureau maps the daily positions of highs and lows, the fronts, the areas of precipitation, the humidity, cloudiness, winds, and temperature. The upper air is sounded by balloons. From the data thus assembled, meteorologists assess the changes in airmass and pressure conditions in progress, estimate the movements and alterations of highs and lows, and anticipate the changes in frontal conditions generally. These expected movements and changes are then translated into local and regional forecasts.

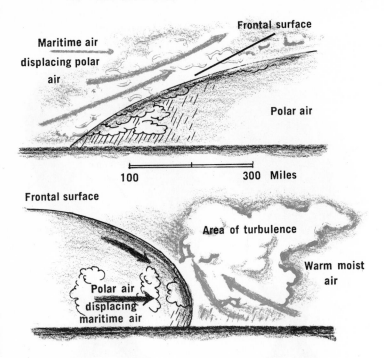

FIG. 4.23. *Sketches showing the relations and movements of air masses that produce a warm front (above) and a cold front (below). The frontal slopes are much exaggerated.*

Climates

The principal climates of the earth may be grouped as follows:

1. Tropical rainy climates
   a. Tropical rain forest (always wet), as in the Congo and Amazon Basins
   b. Tropical savanna (with wet and dry seasons), as in Burma and the veld and Sudan of Africa
2. Dry climates
   a. Low-latitude desert and steppe, as in the Sahara, Arabia, and Australia
   b. Middle-latitude desert and steppe, as in Iran, Mongolia, and the Great Basin of the Southwestern United States
3. Humid mesothermal climates (moderately warm)
   a. Mediterranean (dry-summer subtropical), as in Italy, Spain, and California
   b. Humid subtropical, as in southern China and the Southeastern United States
   c. Marine west coast, as in Western Europe and southeastern Alaska
4. Humid microthermal climates (moderately cool)
   a. Humid continental, as in North Central United States, Central Europe, and northern China
   b. Subarctic, as in Alaska, Canada, and Siberia
5. Polar climates
   a. Tundra, as on the borders of the Arctic Sea
   b. Icecap, as on Antarctica and Greenland
6. Highland climates
   a. Local climates of mountains and plateaus, varying mainly according to altitude and latitude, as in the Andes, Himalaya, Rockies, Tibet, and Mexico

The climatic types and geographic examples listed above illustrate the effects of the several climatic controls—latitude, the more or less permanent high- and low-pressure areas, prevailing winds, contesting air masses and storms, distribution of land and water, nearness to sea, mountain barriers, ocean currents, and altitude.

Summary

We have seen that the earth is composed of three overlapping and interpenetrating divisions—rock, water, and air.

The rock surface is characterized by (1) continents, with their mountains, plateaus, and plains; (2) continental shelves; (3) continental slopes, with their submarine canyons; and (4) the deep-ocean basin, with its ridges, swells, seamounts, guyots, trenches, and deeps. Land covers 29.2 per cent of the surface, and the sea 70.8 per cent. The maximum relief, from Mount Everest to Challenger Deep, is about 12.3 miles.

We have seen that the bulk of the hydrosphere is in the sea. Its surface waters in the tropics are warm, but deep waters are cold everywhere. The sea contains dissolved gases and nearly 3½ per cent dissolved solids. Its life zones are littoral, neritic, bathyal, abyssal, and pelagic. Algae and corals build fringing, barrier, and atoll reefs.

The atmosphere consists mostly of nitrogen, oxygen, water vapor, and argon. It weighs about 14.7 pounds per square inch at sea level, but only half as much 3.4 miles up. It is zoned vertically into the variable troposphere, cold stratosphere, and warmer ionosphere. The atmosphere has a profound effect on us as the medium of transmission of heat and light. Air in the troposphere circulates via the trade winds, prevailing westerlies, vertical air currents, jet streams, cyclonic storms, and various secondary winds. Conflicting air masses, continental or maritime in origin, warm or cold, and wet or dry, give us changeable weather along their interacting warm and cold fronts. Climates vary greatly from region to region, depending on such factors as latitude, altitude, and nearness to the ocean. Since climate affects the type and rate of rock weathering and land erosion, the atmosphere is an important geologic medium.

Suggestions for Further Reading

Bates, D. R.: *The Earth and Its Atmosphere*, Basic Books, New York, 1958. A very good collection of rather technical essays by various experts in geology. See especially pages 74–87, 97–112, 130–151, and 174–222.

Blair, T. A., and R. C. Fite: *Weather Elements*, Prentice-Hall, Inc., Englewood Cliffs, N. J., 1957.

Donn, W. L.: *Meteorology*, McGraw-Hill Book Company, Inc., New York, 1951.

Hambidge, Gove (ed.): *Climate and Man*, U.S. Department of Agriculture, 1941.

Jeffreys, Harold: *The Earth*, Cambridge University Press, New York, 1953.

Koeppe, C. E., and G. C. DeLong: *Weather and Climate*, McGraw-Hill Book Company, Inc., New York, 1958.

Kuenen, P. H.: *Marine Geology*, John Wiley & Sons, Inc., New York, 1950.

Ommanney, F. D.: *The Ocean*, Oxford University Press, New York, 1949.

Petterson, Hans: *The Ocean Floor*, Yale University Press, New Haven, Conn., 1954. A popular study of the ocean bottom.

Proudman, J.: *Dynamic Oceanography*, Methuen & Co., Ltd., London, 1954. An excellent technical book for those interested in oceanography.

Shepard, F. P.: *Submarine Geology*, Harper & Brothers, New York, 1948. A very good standard text by one of the foremost submarine geologists.

Sverdrup, H. U., M. W. Johnson, and R. J. Fleming: *The Oceans: Their Physics, Chemistry, and General Biology*, Prentice-Hall, Inc., Englewood Cliffs, N.J., 1942. A very useful standard text on oceanography.

Trewartha, G. T.: *An Introduction to Climat.*, McGraw-Hill Book Company, Inc., New York, 1954.

Trumbull, James, John Lyman, J. F. Pepper, and E. M. Thomasson: *An Introduction to the Geology and Mineral Resources of the Continental Shelves of the Americas*, U.S. Geol. Survey Bull. 1067, 1958.

Chapter 5

MINERALS

IN CHAPTER 4 we discussed some general features of the lithosphere; we are now ready to consider its rocks and their constituent minerals in more detail. In this chapter, we shall cover many of the minerals that make up the earth's crust, their chemical and physical properties, and methods of identifying them both in the field and in the laboratory. The chapter includes descriptions of the nine most abundant minerals, as well as of other minerals commonly found on the earth.

Important Facts

COMPOSITION OF EARTH'S CRUST

Many chemical rock analyses have established that 98 per cent by weight of the earth's crust consists of only 8 elements (see Table 5.1), out of more than 90 possible (Fig. 5.1). About a dozen other elements make up much of the remaining 2 per cent.

General Characteristics

DEFINITION

When we examine field samples of rocks, we notice different kinds of particles. These are not mixtures; rather, each is a distinct, homogeneous substance with definite chemical and physical characteristics. Some particles may be dull, earthy grains; others may be tiny, brilliant flakes that reflect sunlight; and still others may be dense, transparent grains that resemble bits of colored glass. Each of these particles is a mineral.

The geological term mineral should not be confused with other uses of the word. A nutritionist who suggests certain minerals for the diet or an advertiser who tries to sell water from a mineral spring is not referring to a constituent of rocks. Geologists use the word to mean *a naturally occurring inorganic substance with a characteristic internal structure and with a chemical composition and physical properties that are either uniform or variable within definite limits.* Most minerals are compounds of two or more elements, but a few,

FIG. 5.0. *Colorless hexagonal crystals of quartz, or rock crystal, with pyramidal ends. (American Museum of Natural History.)*

TABLE 5.1 *The 23 Most Abundant Elements in the Earth's Crust, in Order of Abundance*

Element	Per cent
Oxygen, O_2	46.60
Silicon, Si	27.72
Aluminum, Al	8.13
Iron, Fe	5.00
Calcium, Ca	3.63
Sodium, Na	2.83
Potassium, K	2.59
Magnesium, Mg	2.09
Subtotal	98.59
Titanium, Ti	0.440
Hydrogen, H	0.140
Phosphorus, P	0.118
Manganese, Mn	0.100
Fluorine, F	0.070
Sulfur, S	0.052
Strontium, Sr	0.045
Barium, Ba	0.040
Carbon, C	0.032
Chlorine, Cl	0.020
Chromium, Cr	0.020
Zirconium, Zr	0.016
Rubidium, Rb	0.012
Vanadium, V	0.011
Nickel, Ni	0.008
All others	0.286
Total	100.000

SOURCE: Brian Mason, *Principles of Geochemistry*, 2d ed., John Wiley & Sons, Inc., New York, 1958.

FIG. 5.1. *The relative abundance of the most common elements in the earth's crust. The figures indicate percentages.*

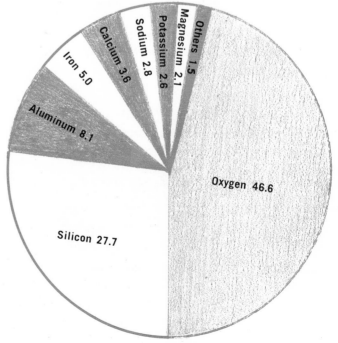

such as sulfur (Fig. 5.2), graphite, and native gold, are single elements. Coal and petroleum are not minerals, for they are organic in origin. They are, however, called "mineral fuels" and are included under the broad term "mineral resources."

CRYSTALS

The geometrical form of many solids suggests an arrangement of atoms in patterns of equally spaced rows and planes, like soldiers on parade (Fig. 5.3). Each particle is in a definite place, and the distances to its neighbors on all sides are determined by its attractive forces in various directions. This inner regularity is manifested in the smooth faces and sharp angles of crystals. According to the geometric shape of their crystals, crystalline minerals are classified into six systems: isometric, tetragonal, hexagonal, orthorhombic, monoclinic, and triclinic (Figs. 5.4, 5.5). Crystal size varies widely, and the microscope and X rays prove convincingly that many solids which do not show crystal faces nevertheless have a regular pattern in their inner structure. Solids of this sort, whether or not they recur in well-shaped crystals, are called

FIG. 5.2. *Rhombic opaque crystals of native sulfur. (American Museum of Natural History.)*

crystalline solids; common salt, diamond, calcite (Fig. 5.6), and most metals are familiar examples. Each type of crystal has a definite internal atomic structure (Fig. 5.3). Solids whose particles have no regularity of arrangement and which never show crystal forms are called *amorphous solids;* rubber, opal, and glass are typical examples.

ORIGIN

Most minerals are formed from various kinds of solution. Many have crystallized from (1) hot liquid-rock solutions, as the molten mass cooled, or (2) hot gases or hot-water solutions expelled into the rocks adjoining such a molten body. Others form at or near the earth's surface (3) by sublimation from cooling volcanic vapors, (4) by chemical reactions between air, ground water, and previous rock minerals, or (5) by evaporation of salt lakes or other surface waters.

COMPOSITION

The composition of minerals ranges from single elements to complex compounds containing 10 or more elements. Some relatively inactive elements occur in the free state, whereas the active elements form compounds. Soluble compounds occur as minerals only under cover or in arid regions, and easily oxidizable compounds occur in a fresh, unoxidized state only some distance beneath the surface. Highly reactive compounds, such as calcium and sodium oxides, never occur as minerals.

Silicate compounds are by far the most abundant minerals; feldspar and mica are familiar examples. *Carbonate* compounds, occurring most commonly as the mineral calcite (calcium carbonate), also are very important. Certain elements may unite with oxygen to form *oxides.* These include such common minerals as quartz (silicon dioxide); hematite (ferric oxide), the chief ore of iron; and bauxite (hydrated aluminum oxide), the chief ore of aluminum. Many other metals occur as *sulfides,* such as the major lead ore, galena (lead sulfide) (Fig. 5.7), and the zinc ore, sphalerite (zinc sulfide). Other chemical combinations form *chlorides, phosphates, sulfates, hydroxides, nitrates,* and *borates.*

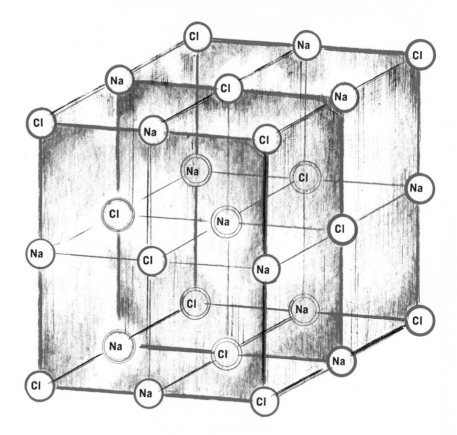

FIG. 5.3. *Diagram showing the arrangement of atoms of sodium and chlorine in a crystal of common salt (NaCl), the mineral halite. They alternate in three planes at right angles to each other.*

ISOMORPHOUS MIXTURES

The mineral sphalerite, zinc sulfide (ZnS), commonly contains some iron (Fe). The light-yellow variety is practically free from iron; the brown variety contains a little iron; and the black contains more. The formula for sphalerite may be written (Zn,Fe)S to show that some of its molecules are ZnS and others FeS. Despite this mixture, all the crystals of sphalerite may have the same form and essentially the same structure, and any particle of the dark sphalerite would show, on analysis, the same composition as any other part of it.

Such a mixture, in which one atom takes the place of another without changing the crystal form, is termed isomorphous. An isomorphous group is a series of compounds that have closely related chemical composition and nearly similar crystals. Thus calcite (calcium carbonate), magnesite (magnesium carbonate), and siderite (iron carbonate) all crystallize in the same system and, within certain limits, form isomorphous mixtures. Many calcites contain some magnesium carbonate;

others contain iron carbonate; and still others contain both. Isomorphous mixtures, notably plagioclase feldspars, pyroxenes, and amphiboles, constitute a large part of the earth's minerals.

NUMBER

Approximately 2,000 different minerals are known, but most of these are rare. Fortunately for the beginner in geology, the number of minerals which are important constituents of ordinary rocks is surprisingly small. A group of a few dozen includes all the minerals that are abundant in the rocks of the earth's crust.

IDENTIFICATION

Most minerals can be identified readily on sight if their ordinary physical properties are known. These include such properties as color, streak, luster, cleavage, hardness, specific gravity, and crystal form.

To distinguish the rarer minerals, we must use various laboratory tests. With the aid of a blowpipe and a few simple reagents, chemical tests may be

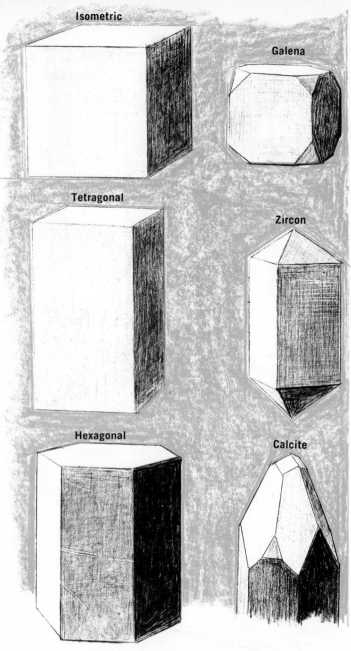

Isometric

Galena

Tetragonal

Zircon

Hexagonal

Calcite

FIG. 5.4. *Drawings of crystals in the isometric, tetragonal, and hexagonal systems, with common forms of minerals that crystallize in each (right). Isometric crystals have three axes of equal length and at right angles to each other. Tetragonal crystals have three axes at right angles, two equal in length and the third either longer or shorter. Hexagonal crystals have three equal axes in a common plane at 60° and 120° with each other, and a fourth axis perpendicular to this plane.*

made, and mineral powders or fine-grained mixtures may be investigated. Minerals differ in fusibility, in solubility in acids, and in their behavior with reagents.

Many silicates may be identified in the field, but exact determinations are most readily made with a polarizing microscope. This involves grinding the minerals or rocks into very thin slices and allowing polarized light to pass through them. Very exact determinations can be made in this way because the effect on light of every transparent mineral differs from that of every other one. Opaque minerals, such as the sulfides of the metals, are studied under the microscope by reflected light.

In still more difficult determinations, we can make use of (1) X-ray diffraction to determine crystal structure, (2) spectrographic analysis to identify the component chemical elements, or (3) differential thermal analysis to measure the temperatures at which diagnostic changes take place during heating.

Physical Properties

COLOR AND STREAK

Color is fairly constant in some minerals but not in all. Commonly the color is due to pigments or impurities in the mineral. Streak, the color of the powder of the mineral, is more nearly constant than the color. The streak is determined by marking unglazed porcelain with the mineral, by scratching the mineral with a knife and observing the color of the powder, or by crushing the mineral.

LUSTER

The luster of a mineral is its appearance in ordinary reflected light. Those with metallic luster look like metals, and most of them are dark and opaque. Those with nonmetallic luster are usually lighter-colored and transparent on their thin edges. Adamantine luster is brilliant, like that of diamond; vitreous luster is shiny, like that of glass or quartz; and dull luster is like that of chalk.

CLEAVAGE AND FRACTURE

Many crystals break readily along certain parallel planes, and thus the fragments have certain shapes determined by these planes. This property is called cleavage (Fig. 5.8). Some crystals, like mica, have perfect cleavage; others, like quartz and garnet, have none. Certain minerals have two or more good cleavages (Fig. 5.9).

Many minerals that have no cleavage may nevertheless fracture in a characteristic way. Some minerals have a conchoidal fracture like the fracture of glass. Certain fibrous minerals, like asbestos, break in minute threads (Fig. 5.10).

HARDNESS

The hardness of a mineral, or its resistance to abrasion, is a fairly constant quality. It is generally designated by a number indicating the relative position of the mineral on Mohs' scale, in which 10 representative minerals are arranged in increasing order of hardness as follows: (1) talc, (2) gypsum, (3) calcite, (4) fluorite, (5) apatite, (6) orthoclase feldspar, (7) quartz, (8) topaz, (9) sapphire (corundum), (10) diamond.

The minerals in the first five categories can be scratched with a knife. In the field a sharp-pointed penknife is very useful, since with a little practice it can be used to estimate the hardness and observe the streak. A few minerals, such as magnetite (iron oxide), are magnetic, and their particles are easily picked up by a small magnet. So, if the knife blade is magnetized, the test will be all the more easily made.

SPECIFIC GRAVITY AND HEFT

The specific gravity of a mineral is its weight in air compared with the weight of a volume of water equal to that of the mineral. The specific gravity of a small piece is easily determined by using a spring balance, weighing the mineral fragment first in air and then in a small pan suspended in a beaker of water. The specific gravity is its weight in air divided by its loss of weight in water. Since pure specimens of the same mineral generally have approximately the same specific gravity, the deter-

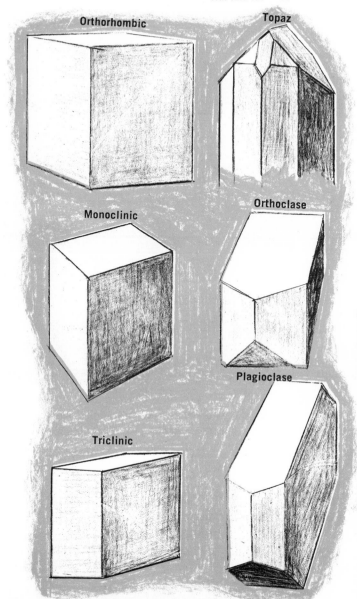

FIG. 5.5. *Drawings of crystals in the orthorhombic, monoclinic, and triclinic systems, with common forms of minerals that crystallize in each (right). Orthorhombic crystals have three axes at right angles to each other, but each has a different length. Monoclinic crystals have three unequal axes, two at right angles to each other and the third obliquely inclined. Triclinic crystals have three unequal axes, all oblique to each other.*

FIG. 5.6. *Colorless crystals of the variety of calcite (calcium carbonate) known as dog-tooth spar, showing their hexagonal form. (Ward's Natural Science Establishment, Inc.)*

FIG. 5.7. *Cubic crystals of galena (lead sulfide). (Ward's Natural Science Establishment, Inc.)*

mination of specific gravity is a useful aid in mineral identification.

Heft is the relative weight of the mineral as determined by raising or lowering a rock fragment in one's hand—a useful test in the field. Very heavy or very light minerals are recognizably heavy or light by their heft.

TENACITY

Certain minerals which powder easily are *brittle*. Others, like gold, are *malleable* and can be hammered into thin sheets. Still others, like horn silver, are *sectile;* they cut like cheese. A mineral, such as chlorite, that bends yet does not resume its original shape when pressure is released is said to be *flexible*. An *elastic* mineral, like mica, springs back to its original shape after being bent.

OTHER PROPERTIES

Minerals also differ in such qualities as magnetism, fusibility, and solubility.

Common Rock-forming Minerals

Although many hundreds of minerals have been identified, only a few of them commonly occur. The earth's crust is made up chiefly of nine: feldspars (orthoclase, microcline, and plagioclase), quartz, pyroxenes, amphiboles, micas (biotite and muscovite), and olivine. First we shall discuss the properties and uses of these common minerals, and then we shall take up certain other, less abundant ones.

FELDSPARS

The feldspars (Fig. 5.5) make up almost half the ingredients of the rocks of the earth's crust. They are generally light-colored and are characterized by two good cleavages. Feldspars are divided into three types, according to composition, cleavage, and crystal structure.

1. Orthoclase (Greek *orthos,* straight + *klasis,* fracture), in which the cleavages form angles of 90 degrees; hence the name. Orthoclase feldspar,

potassium aluminum silicate,[1] is commonly creamy white or pink and has a hardness of 6.

2. Plagioclase (Greek *plagios*, oblique + *klasis*, fracture), in which the cleavages make angles of about 86 degrees. Examples of plagioclase feldspar are albite (sodium aluminum silicate), which is usually white, and anorthite (calcium aluminum silicate), which is commonly gray-green.

3. Microcline, which has the same composition as orthoclase but a different crystal structure. Its color ranges from creamy and pastel to red or green.

Feldspar is used in the ceramic industry for making glass, porcelain, tile, enamel, and glazes.

[1] The formulae of the feldspars are as follows: orthoclase, $K_2O \cdot Al_2O_3 \cdot 6SiO_2$, hardness 6; albite, $Na_2O \cdot Al_2O_3 \cdot 6SiO_2$, hardness 6.5; anorthite, $CaO \cdot Al_2O_3 \cdot 2SiO_2$, hardness 6.5. Albite and anorthite molecules form a series of isomorphous mixtures or compounds: albite, oligoclase, andesine, labradorite, bytownite, and anorthite. From albite to anorthite, the sodium decreases and calcium increases. The physical properties of the isomorphous crystals vary with the composition, particularly the effect on light, as the light passes through the crystals under the microscope. The mixtures in the albite-anorthite series are generally striated, and with a small lens the striations often may be observed as very fine parallel lines closely set, like ruled lines on a sheet of paper.

FIG. 5.8. *Sketch showing the difference between cleavage and fracture of minerals.*

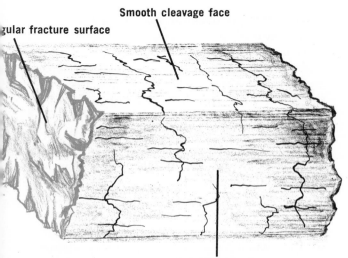

Smooth cleavage face

gular fracture surface

Smooth cleavage face

FIG. 5.9. *A cleavage fragment from crystalline halite, showing the perfect cubic cleavage.* (Ward's Natural Science Establishment, Inc.)

QUARTZ

Quartz, silicon dioxide, SiO_2, next to feldspar the most abundant material of the earth's crust, forms six-sided crystals. Quartz is colorless or white when pure, although it is commonly tinted (Fig. 5.11). Because quartz has no good cleavage, it rarely presents flat surfaces when broken, but breaks like glass, with a conchoidal fracture. With a hardness of 7, quartz cannot be scratched with a knife. However, its crystals do scratch glass.

Quartz grains are abundant, not only in granite, but also in most sands. In a granite in which the light-colored minerals are quartz and feldspar, the quartz may be distinguished from the feldspar by turning the rock so as to get a reflection from the cleavage planes of the feldspar.

Crystal quartz has a piezoelectric property; that is, it has an electric polarity resulting from the pressure used to form the crystal. Thin slices of it are used for accurate frequency control in radio and radar transmission, and it was also used in tuning the old-fashioned crystal radio set.

PYROXENES

The pyroxenes (Fig. 5.12) consist of diopside, calcium silicate, $CaMg(SiO_3)_2$; hypersthene, mag-

FIG. 5.10. *The asbestos type of mineral; note the fibrous structure.*

nesium silicate, $(MgFe)SiO_3$; and augite, which resembles diopside but contains aluminum and iron. They constitute an important group of rock-forming minerals and are generally recognized by their stout, usually four- or eight-sided crystals and their two good cleavages (Fig. 5.12a) almost at right angles to each other (87 and 93 degrees). Most pyroxenes are green or dark-colored, particularly those that contain much iron, with augite occurring most commonly. They are not especially useful in industry. As a rule pyroxenes have a dull luster, and this is an aid in distinguishing them from amphiboles (hornblende), which commonly have a silky sheen.

AMPHIBOLES

The amphiboles, consisting of calcium, magnesium, iron, and aluminum silicates, generally have complicated formulae. Some of the varieties are tremolite, $Ca_2Mg_5Si_8O_{22}(OH)_2$; actinolite, $Ca_2(Mg,Fe)_5Si_8O_{22}(OH)_2$; and hornblende, the most common amphibole, which also contains alumina and soda. The amphiboles may have stout, commonly six-sided crystals but more usually have long-bladed or fibrous ones, green to black in color. They have cleavage angles of 124 and 56 degrees (Fig. 5.12b). Unlike pyroxenes, which are dull, the amphiboles commonly have a glittering, silky sheen. Certain fibrous amphiboles serve as low-grade asbestos (see serpentine under Other Minerals below).

MICAS

There are two main varieties of mica: muscovite, hydrous potassium aluminum silicate, $KAl_3Si_3O_{10}(OH)_2$, which is white or colorless; and biotite, $K(Mg,Fe)_3AlSi_3O_{10}(OH)_2$, black mica, which resembles muscovite except in color. Biotite has a chemical composition similar to muscovite but contains some iron and magnesium. Other micas are phlogopite, a bronze-colored magnesium mica; and lepidolite, a lilac-colored lithium-bearing mica. The micas are distinguished from most other minerals by their one perfect cleavage, which makes it possible to separate them into extremely thin sheets.

Muscovite, in high-grade cleavage sheets, is used extensively for electrical insulation for irons and toasters. Mica in sheet form (once called isinglass) is used for glazing, and in flake or powder form for filler, heat insulation, decoration, and tire powder. Large sheets of clear quality bring several dollars a pound.

Sheet mica is obtained from pegmatites (very coarse-textured igneous rocks) in association with large crystals of feldspar and quartz. India, Brazil, and Canada are the leading foreign producers, and North Carolina is the chief domestic source.

OLIVINE

Olivine is a magnesium iron silicate, $(Mg,Fe)_2SiO_4$. The magnesium and iron form an isomorphous series in all proportions, but the magnesium usually exceeds the iron about two to one. Olivine is found in many basic (low silica) igneous rocks and usually occurs in stout crystals. It is glassy like quartz but is generally olive green or yellow. Its grain in a rock resembles that of granulated sugar. Peridot, a clear variety, is used for gems. Rocks composed of nearly pure olivine are used to a limited extent in the manufacture of refractories.

Other Minerals

APATITE

Apatite, a complex phosphate of calcium, has hexagonal crystals, a hardness of 5, and a vitreous to greasy luster. It occurs in a variety of colors, including red, brown, green, and yellow. It is a possible source of phosphorus and fluorine, but since it generally occurs in small quantities disseminated through rocks, it is not of economic value.

BARITE

Barite, a sulfate of barium, $BaSO_4$, is a white, gray, or variously colored mineral with a specific gravity of 4.5 and a dull, vitreous, or pearly luster.

FIG. 5.11. *Varieties of quartz. Top row: botryoidal (grapelike) chalcedony, rock crystal, and smoky quartz. Center: amethyst. Bottom row: quartz geode, agate, and tourmalinated quartz. (Ward's Natural Science Establishment, Inc.)*

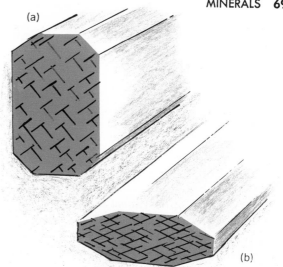

FIG. 5.12. *Outlines showing crystal forms and directions of cleavage (a) in pyroxene and (b) in hornblende.*

It occurs in granular or crystalline masses or nodules. Its main use is in heavy, oil-well drilling muds, but it is also used in the glass, paint, rubber, and chemical industries.

BAUXITE

Since bauxite is amorphous, or noncrystalline, it is not a true mineral. A soft, earthy substance composed of hydrous oxides of aluminum, it frequently occurs in tiny pellets. It is white or gray if pure, and red, yellow, or brown if iron-stained. It is the chief ore of aluminum and is formed by prolonged weathering of aluminous rocks in warm, wet climates. Some bauxite is mined in Arkansas, Alabama, and Georgia, but more is imported from Jamaica and British Guiana.

CALCITE

Calcite, calcium carbonate, $CaCO_3$, is colorless, white, or variously tinted and has a hardness of 3 (Fig. 5.8). It is characterized by good cleavage along three inclined planes. It is the chief constituent of limestone, chalk, and marble. Colorless "Iceland spar" is used in optical instruments (Fig. 5.13).

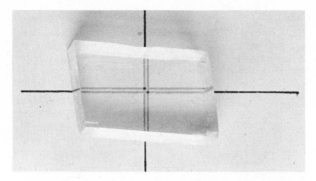

FIG. 5.13.   *A transparent cleavage block of clear calcite (Iceland spar) showing its property of doubly refracting light. The images of the spot and of the two lines that cross underneath the calcite are split in two by unequal transmission of light within the calcite crystal. For this reason calcite prisms are used in certain optical instruments. For example, such pronounced double refraction helps to identify many different minerals under a petrographic microscope. (Ward's Natural Science Establishment, Inc.)*

CHALCOPYRITE

Chalcopyrite, a copper and iron sulfide, $CuFeS_2$, is a golden-yellow, metallic mineral of medium hardness (3.5) and black streak. It is an ore of copper. Unlike pyrite, it can be scratched with a knife.

CHLORITE

Chlorites are hydrous magnesium iron aluminum silicates that have low hardness (1 to 2.5) and a green to dark-green color. The crystals resemble mica because they have one excellent cleavage. Unlike mica, however, the cleavage plates are only flexible and not elastic; when bent, they do not resume their original shape on release. Chemically, chlorite is much like biotite, but it contains less silica, more water, and no potassium.

CHROMITE

Chromite, a ferrochromite of iron and chromium, $(Fe,Cr)(Fe,Cr)_2O_4$, is a hard (5.5), brownish-black, submetallic mineral with a pitchy luster and a brown streak. It occurs as disseminated grains or as granular masses. The iron-chromium ratio varies. Chromite is used as refractory brick and as a source of metallic chromium and chromium chemicals.

CINNABAR

Cinnabar, mercury sulfide, HgS, the chief ore of mercury, is a soft (2), heavy (specific gravity, 8), scarlet or brownish-red to brownish-black mineral with a scarlet to reddish-brown streak.

CORUNDUM

Corundum, an aluminum oxide, Al_2O_3, is a very hard (9), fairly heavy (specific gravity, 3.9 to 4.1), usually gray, brown, or bluish mineral that forms striated, hexagonal, often barrel-shaped crystals with basal parting (Fig. 5.14). Ruby and sapphire are the gem varieties.

DIAMOND

Diamond is pure carbon crystallized in the isometric system. Its hardness is 10. It is the familiar, high-priced, colorless, and cleavable gem. However, it is also an important industrial mineral, much of it off-colored, gray, or black, used in drills, abrasives, and dies. Production is mainly from Belgian Congo, South Africa, Brazil, the Gold Coast, and Angola.

DOLOMITE

Dolomite is a double carbonate of calcium and magnesium, $CaMg(CO_3)_2$. Its hardness is 3.5. Like calcite, it has three good inclined cleavages. Dolomite is a little harder than calcite, however, and it effervesces only feebly in cold, dilute hydrochloric acid, whereas calcite effervesces freely. Although it is mainly found in dolomitic limestone, it also occurs as common white marble.

FLUORITE

Fluorite is calcium fluoride, CaF_2; it forms cubic crystals, has a hardness of 4, and shows a vitreous luster and octahedral cleavage. It may be colorless, green, white, purple, blue, or some other tint. It is used as a flux in steel furnaces and in smelters,

FIG. 5.14. *Striated, hexagonal, columnar crystals of common brown corundum. The flat ends represent parting along the basal planes of the columns. (Ward's Natural Science Establishment, Inc.)*

as a source of hydrofluoric acid and other chemicals, and for making glass and enamel.

GALENA

Galena, lead sulfide, PbS, the chief ore of lead, is a soft (2.5), brittle, heavy (specific gravity, 7.5), lead-gray, metallic mineral that occurs in cubes (Fig. 5.7) and other isometric crystal forms and has excellent cubic cleavage.

GARNET

The garnets are iron, calcium, or magnesium silicates. They include almandite, the common red garnet, $Fe_3Al_2(SiO_4)_3$; pyrope garnet, $Mg_3Al_2(SiO_4)_3$; glossularite, $Ca_3Al_2(SiO_4)_3$; and andradite $Ca_3Fe_2(SiO_4)_3$. Garnets are usually red or brown, with vitreous or resinous luster. They are about as hard as quartz, and since they have no good cleavage, they break like quartz or glass.

Garnet is used mainly as a coated abrasive on sandpaper and subordinately as a gem and watch jewel.

GRAPHITE

Graphite is a very soft, dark-gray mineral composed of crystalline carbon. It has a greasy feel, and its forms range from dull, earthy, or granular masses to high-grade, shiny, clean flakes.

Graphite has wide geographic distribution, and commercial deposits have been formed by several different geologic processes. The crystallized flake graphite of Alabama and Pennsylvania resulted from the alteration of carbonaceous matter in sedi-

ments, whereas the deposits of Quebec were formed by igneous emanations. Some of the deposits in Mexico and in Austria represent coal beds that have been altered by the intrusion of igneous rocks. The island of Madagascar is the leading producer of high-grade flake graphite. There it occurs as lenses, veins, pockets, and large masses in crystalline metamorphic rocks.

Much graphite is used to make crucibles for the manufacture of crucible steel and to melt brass and other nonferrous alloys. Such crucibles are composed of approximately 50 per cent graphite, bonded with clay and sand. Finely pulverized graphite is used in foundries to give the surface of molds a smooth finish. Graphite is also used in various types of lubricant and has many other uses. Recently a substantial tonnage has been used in the atomic pile as a moderator, that is, as a retarding agent for neutrons.

GYPSUM

Gypsum is hydrous calcium sulfate, $CaSO_4 \cdot 2H_2O$. It is usually white or colorless. Since gypsum is very soft, with a hardness of 2, it can be scratched easily with a fingernail. Most gypsum occurs in diamond-shaped crystals or in granular masses. The crystals have three cleavages—one perfect, one good, and one poor. One variety, having a fine fibrous structure, is called satin spar. The fine-grained, massive variety is alabaster, which is carved into ornamental objects. We shall discuss the uses of rock gypsum in Chapter 9.

HALITE

Halite is the mineral name for sodium chloride, or common salt, NaCl. Colorless to gray, it occurs as cubic crystals with perfect cubic cleavage, in three planes at right angles to each other (Fig. 5.9). Its hardness is 2 to 2.5. Beds of common salt occur interstratified with sedimentary rocks. At many places the salt is associated with gypsum. The origin and uses of salt will be treated in Chapter 9.

HEMATITE

Hematite, red iron oxide, Fe_2O_3, is the chief ore of iron. It has a blood-red streak, like rouge or red paint, and may be soft and earthy or compact and hard (about 6). Hematite forms shiny, platy, steel-gray crystals; submetallic reddish-brown to black masses; red granules; and dull, red ocher. It occurs as a primary mineral, as an oxidation (rusting) product of weathering, and in sedimentary beds. Bedded deposits supply the great bulk of iron ore.

KAOLINITE

Kaolinite (china clay), hydrous aluminum silicate, $Al_2Si_2O_5(OH)_4$, is a soft and usually light-colored mineral that occurs in minute particles. It is the main constituent of many clays and shales. It feels greasy between the fingers and is plastic when wet. Kaolinite is an important constituent of many soils and is used in making paper, china, brick, tile, and crockery.

LIMONITE

Limonite is the yellow, brown, or black hydrous oxide of iron, $Fe_2O_3 \cdot nH_2O$. It is a noncrystalline weathering product of various iron minerals and is responsible for the yellow or brown color of many soils. Its hardness ranges from 1 to 5.5, and its streak is always yellow-brown. Its forms include compact masses, nodules, porous bog iron ore, earthy yellow ocher, and rusty stains. Limonite is a minor source of iron.

MAGNESITE

Magnesite is magnesium carbonate, $MgCO_3$. It forms white or variously colored compact masses or crystalline deposits. Magnesite has a hardness of about 4 and a specific gravity of about 3. Much of it was formed through the alteration of dolomite or serpentine by magnesium-bearing solutions. Its principal use is in making refractory brick for open-hearth steel furnaces, cement kilns, and other furnaces. Magnesite is found in Washington, Nevada, and California.

MAGNETITE

Magnetite, black iron oxide, Fe_3O_4, is a dark, heavy (specific gravity, about 5) magnetic mineral that is present in small amounts in most igneous rocks and in black sands (Fig. 5.15). It is brittle, has no good cleavage, and is a little too hard to be scratched with a knife; its streak is black. Magnetite is an ore of iron.

MOLYBDENITE

Molybdenite, molybdenum sulfide, MoS_2, the chief ore of molybdenum (a metal used in steel), is a very soft (1 to 1.5), heavy (specific gravity, 4.75), blue-gray mineral that forms shiny, flexible scales or flat, hexagonal crystals with platy cleavage. It resembles graphite but differs in color and specific gravity.

PYRITE

Pyrite is a pale brass-yellow, hard (6 to 6.5), brittle iron sulfide, FeS_2, called fool's gold because of its slight resemblance to gold. However, gold differs from pyrite in being softer, heavier, and malleable. Pyrite's streak is greenish black, and scattered cubes and other crystal forms occur in many different rocks (Fig. 5.16). In a few places massive pyrite is mined for making sulfuric acid.

SERPENTINE AND ASBESTOS

Serpentine is a fairly soft (2.5 to 4), greasy-looking, green, yellow, brown, or black hydrous magnesium silicate, $H_4Mg_2Si_2O_9$. Massive serpentine forms serpentine rock. Verd antique is an ornamental variety. Chrysotile, a silky variety that can be separated into strong, flexible, infusible, thread-like fibers, is high-grade asbestos (Fig. 5.10). Such fibers usually range in length from less than $\frac{1}{8}$ to

2 inches, but exceptional fibers as much as 24 inches long have been found.

"Asbestos" is not the name of one specific mineral but a commercial term applied to any mineral separable into more or less flexible fibers. It was given originally to amphiboles, such as tremolite and actinolite, which may occur as long, silky fibers, but they usually are brittle and have little tensile strength. A soda-rich amphibole called crocidolite is highly fibrous like chrysotile, but it is less resistant to heat.

Deposits of asbestoslike minerals are widely distributed geographically, but there are only a few localities in which high-grade spinning fibers have been found in sufficiently large deposits to have become important commercial sources. Quebec produces more asbestos than any other area in the world. There it occurs as narrow veins in an area of serpentine rocks. The fibers extend across the veins from wall to wall, and most of the veins are less than 2 inches wide.

The main uses for asbestos are in asbestos yarns and papers, asbestos shingles and siding, and in heat-insulating materials. In addition, asbestos is used in automobile brake-band linings and various types of gaskets.

SIDERITE

Siderite, iron carbonate, $FeCO_3$, has a hardness of 4, brown color, a nearly white streak, and three good inclined cleavages like calcite. It is found mainly in sedimentary rocks, where it may be an ore of iron.

SPHALERITE

Sphalerite, zinc sulfide, ZnS, the chief source of zinc, has medium hardness (3.5 to 4) and medium specific gravity (about 4), a resinous luster, and a white or pale-yellow streak. Sphalerite is commonly yellow, green, or brown but occasionally white, red, or black. This color variation gave rise to the name sphalerite, which is taken from the Greek *sphaleros*, meaning treacherous or uncertain. Dark varieties of sphalerite contain isomorphous iron.

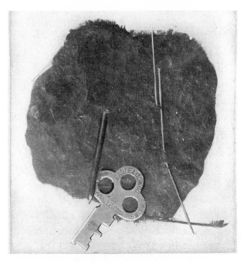

FIG. 5.15. *The variety of magnetite called lodestone. Since lodestone is naturally polarized, it acts as a magnet. Although all magnetite is strongly attracted and held by an artificial magnet, not much of it is found in the magnetized state.*

FIG. 5.16. *Striated cubic crystals of pyrite (iron sulfide), also called fool's gold. (Ward's Natural Science Establishment, Inc.)*

TALC

Talc is a hydrous magnesium silicate, $H_2Mg_3(SiO_3)_4$; it contains more silica and less water than does serpentine. Talc is very soft (1 to 2.5); generally white, gray, or pale green; soapy to the touch; and either massive or platy in form. It is the chief constituent of soapstone, which, when cut into slabs, is used for laboratory bench tops.

A massive variety of pure talc, called steatite, is used in paint, rubber, ceramics, roofing, insecticides, paper, plastics, refractories, and toilet preparations. It serves variously as filler, extender, coating and dusting agent, absorbent, polisher, and electrical insulator.

URANINITE

Uraninite, a complex uranium compound and an ore of uranium and radium, is a moderately hard (3 to 6), very heavy (specific gravity, 5 to 10), generally brown to black mineral with a greasy, pitchlike, or dull luster and a brownish-black streak. Pitchblende, in which radium and helium were first found, is an amorphous or dense form of uraninite. As we saw in Chapter 3, its radioactive elements supply data for measuring geologic time.

VERMICULITE

Vermiculite is a generic name for a group of hydrous micas which, upon heating, expand like an accordion to between 10 and 20 times their original volume. Vermiculite has approximately the composition of phlogopite, a magnesia mica. The expanded product is an excellent lightweight insulator against heat, cold, and sound in house walls, plasters, and various containers. Montana is the leading producer.

Minerals in Rocks

CONSTITUENTS OF ROCKS

A rock is any natural mass that makes up an essential and appreciable part of the earth's crust. Most rocks are physical mixtures of minerals. Chemical elements in minerals are combined *chemically* in definite proportions, but the minerals in rocks are merely collected *physically* in almost any proportion. The same mixture can occur over and over again in many different places; on the other hand, some mixtures are peculiar to only one or two localities. Some rocks are composed largely of one mineral. A few rocks are made of organic matter or volcanic glass instead of minerals, and some rocks contain all three.

CLASSES OF ROCKS

On the basis of their mode of origin, rocks are classified in three general groups.

1. *Igneous* rocks are those formed by solidification of molten matter which originated within the earth. They generally are made of minerals and have crystalline textures, although some, such as pumice and obsidian, are glassy. The principal mineral components of igneous rocks are the feldspars, quartz, pyroxenes, amphiboles, olivine, and micas. Granite and basalt are examples of igneous rocks. Granite is a formerly deep-seated, coarse-grained rock composed mainly of light-colored minerals, feldspar and quartz. Basalt is a fine-grained, variously colored but usually dark-gray or black lava rock, composed primarily of lime-rich plagioclase feldspar and pyroxene, with or without olivine.

2. Most *sedimentary* rocks are derived from the weathered waste products of older rocks. One group, called clastic or mechanical sediments, is deposited as broken fragments of earlier rocks and minerals, as in gravel, sand, silt, and clay. Upon consolidation, these become conglomerate, sandstone, siltstone, and shale. Another group is precipitated from solution and hence composed of new minerals, as in limestone (a rock consisting mostly of calcite or dolomite). Some rocks, such as rock salt and gypsum, are evaporites from salt lakes. Peat and coal are of organic origin.

3. *Metamorphic* rocks are made by the transformation of previous igneous or sedimentary rocks, changed either in mineral composition or in structure, or both, by recrystallization under the influence of high pressure, high temperature, and hot fluids within the earth. For example, granite may

change to gneiss (which differs from granite mainly in having a banded structure), fine-grained limestone may change to coarse-grained marble (still calcite), and shales to slate. In some metamorphic rocks, crystals of mica, hornblende, chlorite, or talc are lined up during metamorphism so as to give the rock ready cleavage along this foliated structure. Such rocks are schists.

Summary

The elements oxygen, silicon, aluminum, iron, calcium, sodium, potassium, and magnesium make up more than 98 per cent of the earth's crust. These and other elements combine in crystalline compounds as minerals.

Minerals are identified by color, luster, cleavage, hardness, specific gravity, tenacity, fusibility, solubility, magnetism, refraction of light or X rays, and other special tests.

The most abundant rock-forming minerals are feldspars (orthoclase, microcline, and plagioclase), quartz, pyroxenes, amphiboles, olivine, and micas (biotite and muscovite).

Most rocks are aggregates of minerals; some contain glass or organic matter. In origin, rocks are igneous, sedimentary, or metamorphic.

We have seen that rocks are composed of minerals, minerals of chemical elements, and elements of atoms; now we can go on to study many different processes which build rocks, break them down, and reconstruct them.

Suggestions for Further Reading

Dana, J. D.: *System of Mineralogy*, 7th ed., John Wiley & Sons, Inc., New York, 1944. A classic in the field, considered definitive.

Dana, J. D., and C. S. Hurlbut, Jr.: *Manual of Mineralogy*, John Wiley & Sons, Inc., New York, 1952. One of the classic textbooks of mineralogy.

English, G. E., and D. E. Jensen: *Getting Acquainted with Minerals*, 2d ed., McGraw-Hill Book Company, Inc., New York, 1958.

Fenton, C. L., and M. A. Fenton: *Rocks and Their Stories*, Doubleday & Company, Inc., New York, 1951. A popular account of rocks and minerals.

Kraus, E. H., W. F. Hunt, and L. S. Ramsdell: *Mineralogy*, 5th ed., McGraw-Hill Book Company, Inc., New York, 1959.

Pearl, R. M.: *How to Know the Minerals and Rocks*, McGraw-Hill Book Company, Inc., New York, 1955.

Pough, F. H.: *A Field Guide to Rocks and Minerals*, Houghton Mifflin Company, Boston, 1955.

Rogers, A. F.: *Introduction to the Study of Minerals*, 3d ed., McGraw-Hill Book Company, Inc., New York, 1937.

Wahlstrom, E. E.: *Igneous Minerals and Rocks*, John Wiley & Sons, Inc., New York, 1947.

Winchell, A. N.: *Elements of Mineralogy*, Prentice-Hall, Inc., Englewood Cliffs, N.J., 1942. A standard mineralogy textbook.

Zim, H. S., and P. R. Shaffer: *Rocks and Minerals*, Simon and Schuster, Inc., New York, 1957. A popular book about collecting rocks.

Chapter 6

VULCANISM

VULCANISM COVERS both the exterior and interior manifestations of the movement and solidification of hot, molten rock material. This fluid material, originating beneath the earth's surface, is the parent body for one of the three major rock types—igneous. Volcanoes and lava flows are formed when this subsurface material, called magma, erupts through the earth's crust and solidifies. Such an exterior eruption is called *extrusive*. In this chapter we shall also discuss *intrusive* vulcanism, or the emplacement of this material underneath the earth's surface, without eruption.

Generation of Magma

EARTH HEAT

Any explanation of volcanic activity involves the problem of heat. Many observations have demonstrated that the interior of the earth is hot. At points about 50 feet below the surface, in the intermediate latitudes, the ground temperature is constant at about 50°F. Nearer the surface the changes are caused by daily and seasonal temperature changes in the atmosphere, but at depths greater than 50 feet the temperature increases gradually with depth. Observations in deep wells and in mines show an average increase of 1°F for every 60 feet downward into the rocks of the crust. Boreholes have been drilled to depths of more than 20,000 feet, and the rise of temperature has been found to continue to their bottom limits. At greater depths the rate of increase may not be so high as it is nearer the surface, but extruded lavas and boiling hot springs indicate that at moderate depths the interior of the earth is very hot. An indication of the intensity of the heat is the fact that lavas issue from the earth at temperatures ranging from 600 to 1200°C.

The origin of the heat within the earth is not yet fully understood. According to an outmoded view long held by many geologists, this heat is simply a residue from the heat of an originally molten condition of the whole earth, which in spite of its great age is still intensely hot a few miles beneath the surface. Even if the earth were not constantly heated by the sun, it would lose its original heat at a very slow rate. The actual rate of loss is controlled by the heat conductivity of the rocks and by the temperature change with depth. Rocks are such poor conductors of heat that, if the internal heat were cut off entirely, the temperature 50 feet below the surface eventually would fall only about 0.01°C.

However, the earth may be becoming hotter day by day. When radioactivity was discovered in 1895, we learned that certain atoms disintegrate spontaneously to yield other atoms of less complex structure. This change is accompanied by the liberation of large amounts of energy in the form of heat. The most radioactive elements that occur naturally are uranium and thorium, which are universally present in all rocks in extremely small quantities. They are more concentrated in granites than in the dark-colored basic igneous rocks, and the amount of radioactive matter diminishes with depth. Computations based on the known content of radioactive matter and the thickness and area of the granitic foundations of the continents indicate that this granite alone would seem to be able to supply more heat from radioactivity than is escaping at the surface of the earth. If there are areas near the surface where the rocks are relatively rich in radioactive substances, the heat generated by radioactivity in those places would accumulate slowly and, because rocks are poor heat conductors, would remain localized. This localized heat might even-

FIG. 6.0. *Crater cloud of Mount Vesuvius, April 14, 1906. The cloud of steam and volcanic ash particles is ½ mile in diameter. (Photograph by Perret, courtesy of Chester A. Reeds.)*

tually, after the passage of much geologic time, become so great as to liquefy the rocks and produce bodies of magma.

More extensive sampling and measurement of radioactivity are needed before positive conclusions can be reached regarding the importance of radioactivity in the formation of magmas. The concept is significant, however, for it indicates a trend in geologic thought which differs from that of a century ago, when students of earth history concluded that the earth is cooling off because it is giving off heat.

MAGMA

Description. Magma is the parent material of igneous rocks. It is a natural, very hot fluid, formed beneath the surface of the earth and made up largely of mutual solutions of silicates with some

FIG. 6.1. *The volcano Ngauruhoe, New Zealand, sending out a plume of steam and volcanic ash. Gushing lavas and falling fragments blown out during its earlier eruptions have accumulated around the vent to build up a cone about 4,000 feet high. (Copyright by the National Geographic Society.)*

oxides and sulfides and usually with some steam and other gases held in solution by pressure. Magma has been defined as molten rock material, but this definition is not entirely satisfactory because it fails to point out that magma contains volatile constituents which are driven off as it

solidifies but which nevertheless are important prior to and during crystallization. In reality, magma, as such, has never been sampled, for it exists only beneath the surface. The molten matter which reaches the surface is called *lava*, which differs from magma in that most of the volatile materials and gases have escaped.

Magma is characterized by a composition that is predominantly silicate, by temperatures ranging from 500 to 1200°C, and by mobility that allows it to flow, even though it is part liquid and part gaseous. Some geologists once thought that magmas were essentially dry, but this opinion has been largely discarded, for water has been found to be universally present in volcanic fumes and also in gases evolved from crystalline igneous rocks when heated in the laboratory. Magma formed deep within the earth may contain an appreciable amount of hydrogen, which becomes oxidized when the magma nears the surface, thus producing water. Such formation of water within the earth is still conjectural, but current estimates suggest that magmas contain 1 to 8 per cent water.

Formation. Magma may be formed in any part of the earth where the temperature becomes high enough to melt or dissolve the rocks. Not all rocks melt at the same temperature, and furthermore many factors other than temperature influence the melting point. When magma forms, the liquid rock is lighter in weight than the adjoining solid rock, and the dissolved gases make it still lighter. Therefore, the magma is forced upward as it is subjected to the tremendous pressures of the surrounding heavier rock. The upward movement of the magma is aided by its mobility and by the expansive force and fluxing ability of the dissolved gases it contains. Some magma eventually reaches the outer part of the earth's crust, where the rocks are cracked and fissured, and makes its way through such openings to the surface. There the molten materials may be poured out as lava flows (Fig. 6.2), or great quantities may be broken and pulverized by explosive forces which eject it in solid form. These lava flows and fragments, ranging in size from great blocks weighing many tons down to particles as fine as dust, accumulate to form volcanoes.

ZONE OF MELTING

Experimental studies conducted by Tuttle and Bowen[1] at the Geophysical Laboratory emphasize that water vapor under pressure is essential to the formation of granitic melts at *moderate* temperatures, because water vapor under high pressure greatly lowers the melting temperature. These studies were carried out with synthetic mixtures of alkali feldspars, quartz, and water vapor and with natural minerals and rocks.

Tuttle and Bowen found that the amount of water present determines the depth at which melting of a granitic material takes place; a smaller amount of water calls for a greater depth, and therefore a greater pressure.

They outline an effective process whereby large masses of granite would be produced in a zone of melting ranging from a few to 13 miles, with most of the melting occurring at the greater depth and partial melting occurring at the lesser depth. This zone would have high enough temperatures to melt granite completely but would only partly melt more basic composition. However, the rate of tem-

[1] O. F. Tuttle and N. L. Bowen, "Origin of Granite in the Light of Experimental Studies in the System $NaAlSi_3O_8$-$KAlSi_3O_8$-SiO_2-H_2O," *Geol. Soc. America Mem.* 74, 1958.

perature increase as we descend into the earth, the water content of the rocks, and hence the depth of melting remain uncertain.

The melt formed at high temperatures and pressures can be intruded into higher levels in the crust, where either decreased pressure or lower temperature causes crystallization. In the zone of partial melting, recrystallization of the nonmelted fraction is also to be expected. Both partial melting and fractional crystallization of a melt, accompanied by crystal settling of the first fractions, contribute toward the segregation of unlike products. Thus we can account for the formation of granitic magma at depth by the melting of either deep-seated granite or sediments that have accumulated to great thicknesses in subsiding troughs in the earth's crust.

Sediments suitable in chemical composition to make granite after melting are derived mainly from earlier granites. It is not yet clear whether the previous granites necessary to begin the granite-sediments-granite cycle could have been formed directly by fractionization of partly melted basaltic material in sufficient volume to explain the sialic continents of high silica content in the early stages of earth history. The absence of granite from most of the Pacific Basin casts doubt on the matter.

FIG. 6.2. *Lava stream rushing pellmell downhill from a vent on the southwest rift of Mauna Loa, Hawaii, June, 1950. The white-hot lava is very fluid at this stage.* (Macdonald.)

Extrusive Vulcanism

VOLCANOES

A volcano is a conical hill or mountain formed around an opening in the earth's surface through which hot rock fragments, gases, and lavas are ejected. As the solid materials accumulate around the conduit, they build up a cone, which increases in size until a huge volcanic mountain is formed. A cone so constructed is called a volcano. However, the term includes both the vent in the earth and the mountain built around it (Figs. 6.1, 6.3). The name volcano was first applied to Mount Etna in Sicily and to some of the Lipari Islands north of Sicily. It is derived from the name of Vulcan, the Roman god of fire, who was supposed to dwell in the volcano.

Volcanoes vary in size from small conical hills to some of the loftiest mountains on the earth's surface. The Hawaiian Islands are volcanoes that reach a height of nearly 14,000 feet above sea level. Since they are built on a part of the floor of the Pacific Ocean which is 14,000 to 18,000 feet deep, their total height is approximately 30,000 feet. Some of the highest peaks in the Andes are volcanoes, and

FIG. 6.3. *Mayon Volcano in the Philippine Islands, 7,616 feet high. Its cone consists of both lava flows and pyroclastic fragments. (Chester A. Reeds.)*

in the Cascade Range of the Western United States, Mount Baker, Mount Rainier, Mount Adams, Mount Hood, and Mount Shasta are volcanoes which recently have become extinct (Fig. 6.4).

VOLCANIC ERUPTIONS

The eruption of a volcano is often preceded by earthquakes and by loud rumblings like thunder, which may continue on a gigantic scale during the eruption. The land rumblings of Tambora on Sumbawa Island, Indonesia, in 1815, were heard as far as 1,000 miles away. During this eruption, the greatest ever recorded, about 38 cubic miles of material was thrown out. The loud rumblings are probably due to the movement of gases and molten rock that are held in under great pressure. Before the actual eruption takes place, fissures often are opened, lakes are drained, and hot springs appear at many places.

The nature of a volcanic eruption is determined largely by the type of materials ejected from the vent—gases, molten rock, or solid fragments. A given volcano may emit all three types of product, but in many regions a certain product predominates. The Hawaiian volcanoes generally discharge very hot and highly fluid lava from which the enclosed gases escape readily. Such eruptions are nonexplosive. On the other hand, some volcanoes erupt with great explosive violence. Mount Pelée on the island of Martinique in the West Indies is a typical example. In May, 1902, it began to erupt in a series of violent explosions, but no lava was discharged during the eruption. A type of eruption intermediate in character between those on the island of Hawaii and Mount Pelée is that of the volcano Stromboli, located in the Mediterranean Sea north of Sicily. Stromboli erupts every 10 or 15 minutes with mild explosions that hurl small masses of partially solidified lava into the air. Most of the fragments, both large and small, fall back into the crater. Since the interval between eruptions is short, the magma in the crater does not have time to cool and solidify. Furthermore, heat is continuously being brought to the surface by gases streaming up from greater depths. Steam also issues from openings and forms a cloud which reflects the light from incandescent lava. This light, often visible at night, served the navigators of ancient times, and Stromboli came to be known as the "Lighthouse of the Mediterranean."

MATERIALS EJECTED

The solid fragmental material hurled from volcanic vents is called *pyroclastic debris*. Large solid pieces are referred to as *blocks*, and the more or less elliptical pieces with spirally twisted ends are known as *volcanic bombs* (Fig. 6.5). The smaller intermediate sizes are called *cinders* and *lapilli*, and the finer material is *ash* and *dust*. Some volcanic blocks are exceedingly large. In 1930, the volcano Stromboli hurled blocks weighing 2 tons a distance of more than 2 miles from its crater, and some of the solid fragments were only partially solidified when they were thrown. During their flight through the air, the trapped gases expanded and gave the fragments a vesicular or spongy appearance.

The liquid rock that issues from a volcano is *lava*. In many instances lava does not flow over the rim of the crater but issues through secondary vents, or fissures, in the sides of the cone. The character and appearance of lava vary with its chemical composition and temperature. When it comes up from the earth, it may be red- or white-hot, but it soon cools on the surface and becomes darker in color. In general, the more siliceous lavas are quite viscous, whereas iron-rich lavas are very fluid. The degree of viscosity determines the rate at which lava flows and the angle of slope at which it comes to rest before solidifying. Thus the nature of the lava determines the steepness of the slope of many volcanic mountains.

Large amounts of gas issue from the vents of most volcanoes. Of the many gases that escape, steam is by far the most abundant. Some of it is formed from ground water and surface water that have been heated by contact with the hot products of the volcanoes. Much of it, however, is believed to be steam that was dissolved in the magmas. Chlorine and sulfur gases issue with steam from certain volcanoes. Some of these may be the products of heated sea water, but most are probably of magmatic origin.

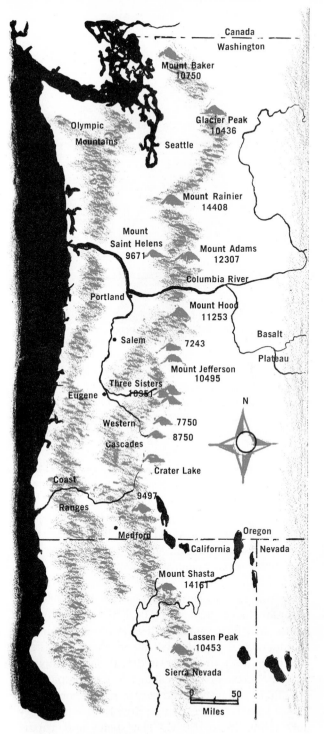

FIG. 6.4. *Map showing distribution of volcanic mountains in Washington, Oregon, and California. They are lined up atop the volcanic eastern or high Cascade Range. (After H. Williams.)*

FIG. 6.5. *Volcanic bombs. The characteristic spindle shape is caused by the ends being twisted during flight through the air while they are still soft; the spheroidal lumps are flattened upon landing. (Grout.)*

The gases arising from the Valley of Ten Thousand Smokes, a few miles northwest of Katmai, Alaska (Fig. 6.6), have been closely studied. An eruption in 1912 scattered ashes 6 inches deep as far as 150 miles away. This valley probably lies above a buried intrusive mass, for its hundreds of vents emit large amounts of steam, together with hydrochloric and hydrofluoric acids, sulfur, and boron compounds. Zies estimated that 1,250,000 tons of hydrochloric acid and 200,000 tons of hydrofluoric acid issue annually. The steam and chlorine compounds are probably not derived from sea water, for they are associated with large amounts of hydrofluoric acid, and fluorine is very sparingly present in sea water. The steam, which constitutes 99 per cent of the gas issuing from the vents, is very hot, about 97 to 650°C. The steam and vapors carry with them many metals in appreciable amounts, among them iron, lead, zinc, molybdenum, copper, arsenic, antimony, tin, and silver. These metals can be identified in the incrustations along the fissures through which the gases rise. The gases issuing from a vent of Mount Pelée in 1902 were examined by Lacroix and were found to consist of water vapor, hydrogen chloride, carbon dioxide, carbon monoxide, sulfur, methane, hydrogen, nitrogen, oxygen, and argon. These gases issued at a temperature of 400°C.

Measurements of the steam emitted at Paricutín in Mexico in 1945 showed that the weight of the water expelled was more than 1 per cent of the total weight of material erupted.

VOLUME OF MATERIAL

The volume of output of volcanic material varies greatly from place to place. Iceland leads all other districts in the total output of lava during the period of recorded history, and Indonesia leads the world in the total volume of fragmental deposits recorded.

In general, the oceans and subarctic regions are at present the great lava producers; the continental borders and equatorial belt provide most products of explosions. The output series are shown in Tables 6.1 and 6.2.

TABLE 6.1 *Production of Volcanic Fragmental Deposits*

Region	Total recorded output of fragments, cubic kilometers
Java belt	185.0
Central America	58.0
Alaska-Aleutian	30.0
Iceland	10.0
South America	9.5
Japan	8.2
Philippines-Molucca	6.5
Kamchatka-Kurile	6.0
New Zealand–Tonga	4.1
North America–Antilles	3.5
Mediterranean	3.5
Melanesia	3.1
Atlantic Ocean	2.2
Indian Ocean–Africa	2.0
Central Pacific	1.5

SOURCE: K. Sapper, *Vulcankunde*, Engelhorns Nachf., Stuttgart, 1927.

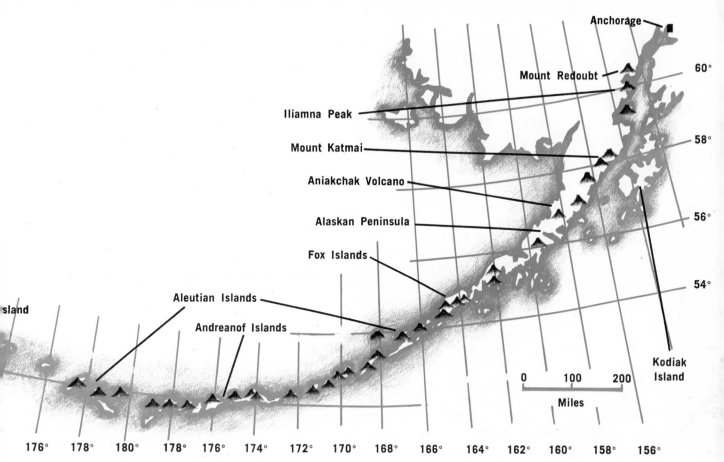

FIG. 6.6. *Map showing location of some volcanoes of the Alaskan Peninsula and Aleutian Islands. The Aleutians form a volcanic island arc along a curved zone of disturbance in the earth's crust. Katmai is near the base of the peninsula. (After R. R. Coats, U.S. Geological Survey.)*

LAVA FLOWS

Surfaces. Since the top of a lava flow is more exposed than the lower part, it cools more rapidly and, consequently, often forms a crust over the flow. Because of the movement of the lower part, the crust breaks into numerous blocks, largely of light vesicular material. These fragments floating on the lavas form great islandlike bodies, large parts of which project above the liquid. At certain places almost the entire surface of the flow is covered with these rafted blocks, hiding the liquid underneath. When the flow advances on land, it moves forward like a stone wall, with only solid matter visible (Fig. 6.7).

After cooling, the solidified fragmental crusts are called *flow breccias.* In the Western United States many lava flows are made up of flow breccias in which the total mass of the fragments is only slightly less than the lava matrix which cements them. Flow breccias are common in basaltic lavas, both recent, as in the West, and ancient, as at Keweenaw Point, Michigan. The voids between the fragments of flow breccias form great systems of openings which serve as important channels of movement of ground water.

In Hawaii the relatively rough lava surfaces are called *aa* (Fig. 6.7), and smooth, billowy, and ropy surfaces are called *pahoehoe* (Fig. 6.8). These names have come into general use to describe lavas from other localities.

Columnar jointing. A lava flow has a characteris-

FIG. 6.7. *The advancing front of the Zapicho lava flow at Paricutín Volcano, Mexico. The broken crust of the flow is pushed forward by the still-fluid lava in the interior. It topples and rolls down the front, as if shoved by a gigantic bulldozer, and is covered up as the front advances. Air-laid volcanic ash covers the foreground. (W. F. Foshag.)*

tic succession of structures from the top down. The crust is generally brecciated and full of bubble holes. Directly beneath it is a more compact section composed of slender, mostly five- and six-sided columns a few inches in diameter, which, on me-

TABLE 6.2 *Production of Lava*

Region	Total recorded output of lava, cubic kilometers
Iceland	15.5
Central Pacific	11.0
Indian Ocean–Africa	8.0
Atlantic Ocean	5.5
Mediterranean	5.1
Kamchatka-Kurile	5.0
Japan	3.5
Alaska-Aleutian	2.0
New Zealand–Tonga	2.0
North America–Antilles	1.5
South America	1.2
Philippines-Molucca	1.2
Central America	0.6
Java Belt	0.5
Melanesia	0.1

SOURCE: K. Sapper, *Vulcankunde*, Engelhorns Nachf., Stuttgart, 1927.

chanical weathering, break down into pieces resembling brickbats. Below that are other ranks of columns, each set consisting of larger columns than the one above, until near the bottom of thick flows the columns are 3 feet or more in diameter (Fig. 6.9). At the base there are again a few feet of breccia and bubble holes.

The columns are formed by shrinkage during cooling. They affect the storage and movement of ground water and the ease of weathering and erosion.

Some flows are composite, in that the mass is made up of *flow units* that resulted from separate gushes of lava. In such flows the arrangement of vesicular zones and columnar jointing is complex.

Driblet cones. As we have seen, a crust forms on the surface of a lava as it cools, and the moving of the lava causes the crust to fracture. If gases have accumulated below the solid crust, they may exert pressure on the portion still liquid. Thus the lava and gas are expelled through holes in the crust, and the molten lava builds up small, chimney-like "driblet" cones. Such cones commonly are only a few feet high. They are not connected with the main volcanic vents but are only minor features on the surface of lava flows.

Lava caves. Some lava flows show great caves that probably were formed by the flow of lava from below the solidified crust. Government Cave, 23 miles west of Flagstaff, Arizona, is a cavern in lava which flowed from the west side of San Francisco Mountain. The cave is about ¾ mile long and ranges in height from 20 to nearly 50 feet. A thick flow of lava poured out from a volcanic opening, and the upper part, being exposed to the air, cooled first. Later a low opening was formed, and the liquid lava flowed out from below the solid roof, leaving the cavity as it now is. Small pendants of lava hang from the roof.

Tumuli and pressure ridges. The surfaces of many lava flows display a series of domical, elliptical, or elongate ridges ranging in height from a few feet to 20 or more. In each ridge the lava crust has been buckled up, and tension has generally broken open the crust along the crest. The term *tumulus* is applied to a small ridge, and *pressure ridge* to one hundreds of feet long. Lava caves occur under many pressure ridges, where the lava drained out, but openings under others are small.

These raised and laterally compressed ridges are caused by doming of the crust due to the pressure of fluid lava beneath, by buckling of the crust from the drag of lava moving beneath it, or by unequal settling of a crust left unsupported after drainage of the still-fluid lava below. The subparallel, longitudinal orientation of many pressure ridges and their association with lava caves strongly suggest that the lateral compression resulted from collapse of a somewhat domed crust that became too large for a flatter profile when the fluid underneath moved on.

Pillow structure. In certain flows, lava forms pillowlike ellipsoids a few inches to a few feet in diameter. These pillows generally are glassy outside and finely crystalline inside. Some show both radial and spheroidal jointing. The upper ones fit over the lower ones like stacks of sacked grain (Fig. 6.10). The interstices between them contain volcanic ash, shale, or other sediment. Pillows are formed when the flow is extruded into some body of water, which suddenly quenches the repeated spurts of lava.

Other structures. Gas vents, lava pendants, squeeze-ups, lava blisters, tree molds (Fig. 6.11), and a host of other items appear with lava flows. Tree molds, either upright or prostrate, retain the form of the bark or other structures and may contain charcoal. Some hollow ones even extend, chimneylike, above collapsed lava flows.

VOLCANIC CONES

There are three main types of volcanic cone: cinder cones, lava cones, and composite cones.

Cinder cones. Cinder cones are steep-sided, symmetrical, cone-shaped volcanoes built up of angular fragments erupted from the earth in violent explosions. Where the material thrown out consists of large, solid fragments, the cone has steep walls with slopes of 30 to 40 degrees. If the material consists chiefly of finely broken rocks or dust, the wind and rainwash carry it farther away from the vent, so that the volcano develops gentler slopes. Volcanoes of this explosive type, such as Vesuvius,

FIG. 6.8. *Ropy pahoehoe lava, Kilauea, Hawaii. This type of structure is formed when smooth sheets of lava stiffen like taffy candy as they cool and finally freeze solid. (Mendenhall, U.S. Geological Survey.)*

FIG. 6.9. *Columnar jointing in a lava flow in central Oregon. Such columns are formed by shrinkage of the lava flow during cooling. (A. C. Waters.)*

FIG. 6.10. *Pillow structure in lava of the Precambrian age in the Northwest Territories, Canada. This type of structure is formed when lava flows into a body of water and is suddenly quenched. The flow has been tilted and beveled off at the present erosion surface. The rounded tops of the pillows and the way they fit together show that the base of the lava flow is toward the lower right. The hammer handle is 15 inches long. (Geological Survey of Canada.)*

Krakatao, and Mount Pelée, throw out both large fragments and dust and generally eject gases in considerable quantities.

Lava cones. Flatter than cinder cones, lava cones tend to be .dome-shaped. They are composed of many superimposed layers of lava which issued at a high temperature and therefore in a highly fluid state. Since basic lavas are more fluid (less viscous) than acidic lavas, they form volcanoes with gentler slopes. The nearly flat cones, such as those in Hawaii, are called *shield volcanoes* (Fig. 6.12).

Mauna Loa on the island of Hawaii is a shield-shaped dome about 60 miles long and 30 miles wide. It is one of the most prolific lava producers on earth. Its slopes near the base are only about 2 degrees, but they increase summitward to 10 degrees, and then flatten off again above an altitude of 10,000 feet. Its total elevation is 13,675 feet above sea level, but its base rests on the floor of the sea where the ocean is approximately 15,000 feet deep. Thus the mountain is really more than 28,000 feet high.

Vents are opened on the flanks of some volcanoes, and material is ejected from them to build up subordinate cones, called *parasitic cones,* with characteristic slopes and craters. The central vents on the main volcano probably become choked with the solidification of lava, and so molten matter rises in fissures radiating from the central vents. Since the openings on the flanks are lower than the central vents, lavas more readily escape from them. Parasitic cones are present on the flanks of Vesuvius and Etna.

Composite cones. Composite cones consist of layers of both lavas and cinders. Such cones are generally intermediate in steepness between cinder cones and lava cones. The presence of both lavas and cinders indicates that the volcano at times ejected fragmental materials and at other times discharged fluid lavas. The fragmental materials of successive explosions form layers of different textures and colors, thus producing a stratification that records the angle of rest of the material ejected. This stratification is made more conspicuous by the sheets of lava interbedded with the sloping layers of pyroclastic fragments. Volcanoes which

FIG. 6.11. *Mold of a fallen tree enclosed in lava of the aa type near Bend, Oregon. (Oregon State Highway Commission.)*

possess such well-marked stratification are called *stratovolcanoes* (Fig. 6.3). Those formed mainly by highly viscous lava are bulbous *volcanic domes* (Fig. 6.13) or *plug domes*.

CRATERS AND CALDERAS

The top of a recently or presently active volcano is generally marked by a pit, or crater (Fig. 6.14), which is usually funnel-shaped and which represents the vent through which material is ejected. The crater is widened near the top by explosions, by the sliding back of the volcanic matter of the rim, by the lava in the crater melting and dissolving the rock of the funnel, and by subsidence within the vent.

The explosion at Mount Katmai produced a crater more than 2 miles in diameter and 2,000 to 3,500 feet in depth. In a valley some distance northwest of the volcano, numerous fissures were opened, and rock debris was strewn over the valley floor. Gases still issue from these vents, and the area is now called the Valley of Ten Thousand Smokes.

A caldera is a huge circular pit resulting from an explosion or collapse of a former volcanic cone. Most calderas are of great size, and many are much wider than they are deep. However, there is no distinct line of demarcation in size between a crater and a caldera. The term caldera is taken from the huge pit in the Canary Islands, called La Caldera, which is more than 3 miles in diameter and is surrounded by cliffs nearly 3,000 feet high. Two excellent examples of this type of depression are the calderas at the summits of Kilauea and Mauna Loa in Hawaii. The caldera of Kilauea is 2½ miles long and 1¾ miles wide, and that of Mauna Loa is 3½ miles in length and 1¾ miles in width. Both these calderas were formed by the collapse of the summits of shield volcanoes. Such a collapse results when the lava column is withdrawn from below the shield-shaped cone, either by eruptions onto the surface or by movement of magma within the earth's crust. Evidence of the downward movement of the summit of the cones can be seen by the faults (rock fractures with movement) in scarps surrounding the pits. Furthermore, the steep inner walls of many calderas are marked by concentric

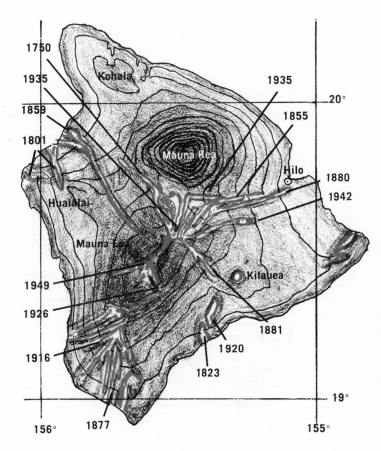

FIG. 6.12. *Map of Hawaii, showing its five coalescent lava cones and several recent lava flows. Contour interval is 1,000 feet. The island covers 4,021 square miles. Mauna Loa forms a broadly oval, dome-shaped lava cone astride a northeast-southwest rift. Lava pours out from fissures on the flanks as well as from the crater. (After Stearns and Macdonald.)*

or interweaving fissures, marking the slips and faults caused by the down-dragging core. Where magma is injected into the concentric fissures, ring dikes (page 99) are formed.

On the floor of a caldera, another cone may be built up of material ejected from the vent after the caldera was formed. Such a cone within a cone is said to be *nested*. An example is Wizard Island in Crater Lake, Oregon (Fig. 6.15).

Many of the known calderas are very large.

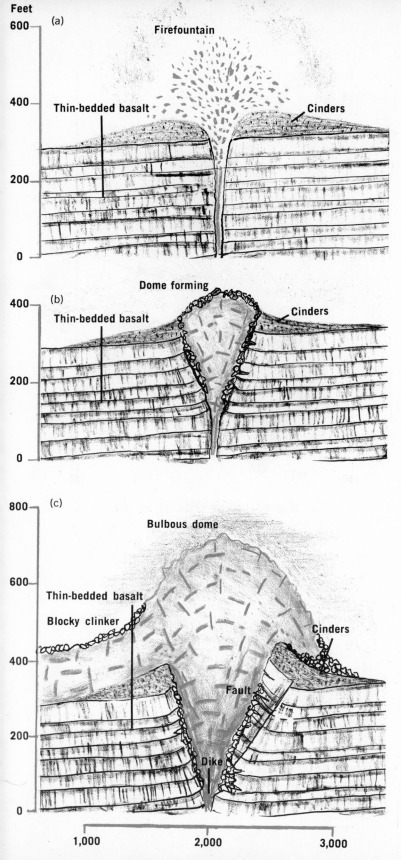

Feet

(a)

Firefountain

Thin-bedded basalt

Cinders

(b)

Dome forming

Thin-bedded basalt

Cinders

(c)

Bulbous dome

Thin-bedded basalt

Blocky clinker

Cinders

Fault

Dike

1,000   2,000   3,000

Possibly the largest in the world is the Valle Grande, 18 miles long and 15 miles wide, in the ancient volcanic field of northern New Mexico. Smaller pits, as much as 3 miles in diameter, were formed by gigantic explosions that blew away the summits of former cones. Subsidences on a much larger scale have occurred where lava erupted from fissures rather than central vents. Some of these *volcano-tectonic* depressions are enormous, like those of Lakes Tabo and Ranan along the rift zone of Sumatra, one of which is approximately 60 miles long and 20 miles wide.

At certain places, which may be distant from volcanic areas, low ridges occur around craterlike pits. The material in a given ridge consists largely of fragments of the country rock, but minor amounts of volcanic debris may be present. These structures are interpreted as embryonic volcanoes, in which the volcanic activity has been limited to the opening of a vent through the country rock. Such *explosion pits* are common west of the Rhine River in the part of Germany known as the volcanic Eifel. Since many of these pits, which range from ¼ to ½ mile in diameter, are filled with water, they are called moors, or maars.

NONVOLCANIC CRATERS

Meteor Crater near Winslow, Arizona, is a pit almost 1 mile in diameter and 500 feet deep in a region of recent volcanic activity (Fig. 6.16). The presence of abundant fragments of meteoritic iron found in and around the crater is interpreted as evidence that the crater was formed by the explosive impact of a large meteorite.

Chubb Crater, on the subarctic tip of Quebec Province, Canada, is believed to have been formed by the impact of a huge meteorite. Much larger than Meteor Crater in Arizona, it measures 11,500 feet from rim to rim; the lake in its bowl is more than 2 miles across and as much as 1,300 feet deep.

FIG. 6.13. *Stages in the formation of bulbous volcanic domes. The lava becomes too viscous to flow readily, and so it builds up and solidifies in and over the vent. (After Stearns.)*

FIG. 6.14. *Amboy Crater, San Bernardino County, California. This crater lies within the summit of a low cinder cone. (Spence Air Photos.)*

The rim of the crater stands 500 feet above the level of the lake and is composed of angular blocks of granite. By one estimate 5 billion tons of granite were shattered by the impact of the meteorite.

Other huge meteorites are known to have struck the earth, making craterlike depressions. One weighing more than 50 tons lies where it fell in South-West Africa, and one weighing nearly 37 tons was found by Peary near Cape York. It is now on display in the Hayden Planetarium of the American Museum of Natural History in New York City. Three meteorites ranging in weight from 11 to 27 tons have been found in Mexico.

TABLE 6.3 *Dimensions of Meteoritic Craters*

Crater	Width, feet	Depth, feet	Ratio of width to depth
Chubb Crater, Canada	11,500	1,800	6.4
Meteor Crater, United States	3,900	570	6.8
Wolf Creek Crater, Australia	2,800	170	16.5
Boxhole Crater, Australia	575	52	11.1
Texas Crater, United States	530	18	29.4
Henbury Crater, Australia	360	60	6.0
Henbury Crater, Australia	240	25	9.6
Henbury Crater, Australia	30	3	10.0
Wabar Craters, Saudi Arabia	328	40	8.0
Campo del Cielo Crater, Argentina	183	16	11.4
Siberian Crater, U.S.S.R.	164	13	12.5

MUD VOLCANOES

Gas issuing at the surface of the earth may carry with it particles of sand and clay which are deposited at the vent, and as the process continues, a cone is built up. If water is present, the sand and clay form mud, which dries and hardens at the surface of the mound. Gas then accumulates below the hardened surface until the pressure is sufficient to blow off the top of the cone, imitating on a small scale the eruption of a true volcano. Some of these mounds, or "volcanoes," are built to considerable heights. The famous Bog-Boga mud volcano in the Baku region near the Caspian Sea is more than 100 feet high. Many mud volcanoes are found in oil and gas fields, and some of these are far removed from true volcanic areas. They are formed by the gas that escapes from gas-bearing strata. Other mud volcanoes are found in areas where steam, probably volcanic, escapes through mud. Those at the southeast end of the Salton Sea, near the mouth of the Alamo River to the west of Niland, California, emit steam and gases that have a slightly sulfurous odor (Fig. 6.17).

VOLCANIC BELTS

Volcanoes may form on mountains or plateaus, on low plains, and on the bottom of the sea. They are widely distributed geographically and have been active during many periods in the geologic past, for their products are found in all the great rock systems. Although in many series volcanic products are only sparingly present, in others they are concentrated. Volcanic evidences are widespread in both the earliest-known rocks and in very late geologic time. In comparatively recent geologic time volcanoes existed at most places where they are active today, but in the intervening epochs there were periods of great igneous activity and other periods of relative quiescence over most of the earth's surface.

Locally, volcanoes are grouped in belts and are presumably located along fractures or along fractured zones. On the other hand, certain volcanoes seem to be independent of other volcanoes.

The Pacific Ocean is bordered by a nearly con-

FIG. 6.15.   *Crater Lake, Oregon. This lake, about 5 miles wide, occupies a caldera on the site of former Mount Mazama, now a beheaded volcano. Wizard Island (center), a later cinder cone with lava flows on the left and a hopper-shaped crater in its summit, rises about 780 feet above the lake. The layered arrangement of the lava flows and cinders is clearly seen in the wall of the rim. About 4½ miles distant on the right is Llao Rock, a lava flow of dacite 1,200 feet thick that overfills a U-shaped, glaciated valley. To the left of Wizard Island, a dike can be seen projecting from the caldera wall. (Oregon State Highway Commission.)*

tinuous volcanic belt which has been called the "circle of fire." Another belt extends westward from Baluchistan, a section of Pakistan, through Iran, through Asia Minor, the Mediterranean, the Canary Islands, and the Azores, trending toward the West Indies. In two other areas volcanic activity is notably concentrated. One of these includes the West Indies, northern South America, Central America, and southern Mexico. The other is on the opposite side of the Pacific Ocean and nearly west of the East Indies. It includes Sumatra, Java, New Guinea, and the Philippine Islands. In addition to

these volcanic areas around the Pacific Ocean, volcanoes are found at many places in the Pacific, where they are arranged in northwest-trending zones. Next in importance to the "circle of fire" surrounding the Pacific Ocean and the belt extending eastward through the Mediterranean Sea to Baluchistan is the great belt of the Atlantic Ocean, which includes West Spitsbergen, Jan Mayen Island, Iceland, the Azores, Madeira, and the Canary and Cape Verde Islands. Another belt extends from Israel southward through Saudi Arabia, the Red Sea, Ethiopia, and East Africa to

Madagascar. These belts include nearly all the active and recently active volcanoes of the world.

SUBMARINE VOLCANOES

Violent submarine eruptions repeatedly have been observed in the volcanic belt of the Aleutian Islands (Fig. 6.6) and elsewhere in the Pacific Ocean (Fig. 6.19), the Caribbean, and the Mediterranean. Cones may be built several hundred feet above sea level, but when volcanic activity declines, the small volcanic islands are soon destroyed by waves.

Pantelleria, a small island which lies between Sicily and Cape Bon, Africa, is wholly volcanic. A submarine eruption took place on Oct. 17, 1891, about 3 miles northwest of the island. Red-hot bombs were hurled high into the air, and an island 1,500 feet long and 9 feet high formed, which was soon washed away by waves.

In 1831, Graham Island rose from the sea between Pantelleria and Sicily where the water had been 500 to 600 feet deep. The water boiled, black clouds rose, and within 2 months a cone 200 feet high and about ½ mile in diameter was built above sea level. This cone also has been destroyed by wave action.

ACTIVE, DORMANT, AND EXTINCT VOLCANOES

About 450 volcanoes have been observed in activity. Hundreds of others that have been only slightly affected by erosion also must have been active in very recent times.

A volcano in eruption is "active." One that has ceased to erupt is "dormant." If the volcanic processes have subsided and the volcano does not seem likely to erupt again, it is said to be "extinct." An extinct volcano, however, can hardly be distinguished from a dormant one, and many volcanoes supposed to be extinct have erupted with great violence. Mount Vesuvius was regarded as extinct in A.D. 79, when its first eruption in historic time occurred.

FIG. 6.16. *Meteor Crater, near Winslow, Arizona. This crater, almost a mile wide and 500 feet deep, is believed to be of meteoritic rather than volcanic origin. Evidence includes the sedimentary rocks instead of lava around its rim, upturned beds, a jumble of limestone and sandstone blocks on the rim, and numerous small meteorites found in the vicinity. (Spence Air Photos.)*

FIG 6.17. *Mud volcanoes, 50 to 75 feet high, near the mouth of the Alamo River west of Niland, California. These cones were piled up by steam and other gases bubbling up through mud. Since the thin streams of mud on the slopes resemble lava flows, the cones are called mud volcanoes. (Frashers, Inc.)*

In the Phlegraean Fields, a densely populated area west of Naples, the eruption of Monte Nuovo took place in 1538. A new opening was formed, and in 3 days a cone was built up to a height of 500 feet. The eruption lasted a week, died down, and the volcano has not been active since.

Similarly, the volcano Jorullo in western Mexico, in 1759, built a cinder cone 1,300 feet high and three smaller ones, poured out three lava flows, and after a few years ceased to erupt.

Paricutín. In 1943, Paricutín Volcano, 65 miles northwest of Jorullo, broke out in a cornfield, made a 30-foot cinder cone overnight, and grew to about 350 feet in a week, 600 feet in 3 months, and

1,000 feet in a year. The cone later reached 1,350 feet, and tens of feet of ash spread for miles around. Lava flows broke out near the base of the cone, advanced irregularly (because of the uneven terrain) as much as 7 miles from the vent, and piled up in superimposed succession to a depth of several hundred feet near the sources. Fields, forests, and villages were overwhelmed and desolated by pyroclastic fragments and lava. After 9 years the action stopped.

The oval base of the completed cinder cone is about 2,000 by 3,000 feet, and the crater at its summit is more than 900 feet wide. The cone and surrounding lavas cover 9.6 square miles, and the ash beds cover many times that area. Their combined volume equals about $\frac{1}{3}$ cubic mile of magma.

Paricutín is perhaps unique among volcanoes in that its complete growth was observed and photographed from the third day on. Extensive data were obtained on the explosive eruptions, the behavior of the lavas and their temperatures (more than 1,900°F), the chemical and mineralogical composition of the products, the gases, the sublimates, the effects on vegetation, and the erosion of the ash beds.

Vesuvius. Vesuvius, the best-known volcano, is situated 7 miles southeast of Naples in a densely populated region. The height of the mountain varies, but it is about 4,000 feet above sea level. Before 1906, it was 4,275 feet high, but that year it was reduced several hundred feet by explosions. A great ridge known as Mount Somma half encircles the present active cone. This outer ridge partially encloses a huge prehistoric crater in which the present active cone is situated. In A.D. 79, the ancient crater had been quiet so long that trees were growing in it, but that year an explosion blew off a large part of the cone of Vesuvius, burying the cities Pompeii, Herculaneum, and Stabiae. Little or no lava was ejected, but much dust, ash, and steam issued, forming a pasty mud that flowed down the slopes and overwhelmed dwellings. Pompeii and Herculaneum were buried to depths of 25 to 50 feet. Gases from the volcano either poisoned or suffocated the citizens. Since A.D. 79, Vesuvius has erupted often. In 1631, a violent erup-

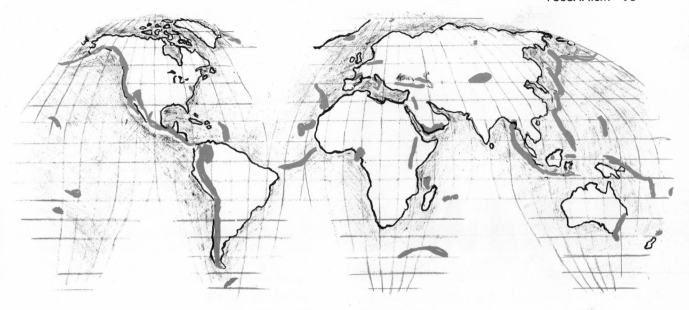

FIG. 6.18. *Map showing the distribution of volcanic areas in the world. The belt around the Pacific Ocean is outstanding. (Base map, University of Chicago Press.)*

tion of lava, dust, and steam killed many people. Lava streams flowed to the sea, and dust was carried as far as Constantinople, about 800 miles away.

Etna. Mount Etna, on the east shore of Sicily, rises to an elevation of about 10,758 feet and covers 460 square miles. The crater of the volcano is about 1,500 feet deep. Eruptions have been recorded as early as the eighth century B.C. A violent one, in 1169, overwhelmed Catania, and many eruptions have occurred since. In 1892, the temperature of a lava stream was found to be 1060°C at the depth of 1 foot.

Krakatao. One of the greatest eruptions recorded is that of Krakatao, a small island between Java and Sumatra. A great volcano existed in this area, and in prehistoric times its top was blown off, leaving a circular chain of islands around the crater. Subsequent eruptions built up small islands within the ring, one of which was Krakatao, with its summit 2,623 feet above sea level. In 1877, earthquakes were noted in this region, and in 1883 an eruption began throwing out pumice and dust. This increased in violence, and on Aug. 26, gigantic explosions began which lasted 3 days. Nearly all

the island was blown away, and a hole 1,000 feet below sea level was blasted out. Fragments were hurled 17 miles high, and in 15 days dust from the volcano had encircled the earth. Dust darkened the air so that lamps were used in daytime at Batavia 100 miles away. The sounds of explosions were heard hundreds of miles away. Sea waves 100 feet high were generated, which inundated many towns on the shores of neighboring islands.

Mount Pelée. Mount Pelée is situated at the north end of the island of Martinique, in the West Indies (Fig. 6.20). On May 1, 1902, its crater blew out, belching dust and cinders. Telegraph cables to the island were broken. On May 8, great explosions occurred and a great black cloud of hot gas and dust rolled down the mountainside like a hurricane and overwhelmed and destroyed the city of St. Pierre, killing nearly 30,000 people. The cloud was so dense with dust that it seemed to act like a liquid. Most of the deaths apparently resulted from the action of particles of hot dust on the membranes of the respiratory organs.

During the course of the eruption a "spine" rose from the crater, its top reaching an elevation of

FIG. 6.19. *Birth of a volcanic island off the coast of Japan. The island grew from the sea floor until it emerged. The heat generated caused the sea water to boil both underneath and at the surface, as shown here. (United States Navy.)*

5,276 feet above sea level and 1,000 feet or more above the level of the crater. The huge needlelike shaft of rock gradually rose almost vertically above the crater, pushed up by pressure from below. Its sides were scratched and slickensided (polished), and it was evidently composed of solid or nearly solid material that had formed in the vent. The spine soon disintegrated, and in 1907, a mere stump remained, surrounded by broken fragments.

Hawaii. Hawaii, the largest island of the Hawaiian chain, is built up of volcanic matter, which rises high above the level of the sea (Figs. 6.12, 6.21). Mauna Loa, in the southern part of the island, has an elevation of 13,675 feet and a crater 2 miles wide and 1,000 feet deep. Kilauea, only 4,050 feet high, is 20 miles away but is part of the same great mountain mass. The crater of Kilauea is about 1½ miles in diameter. It is crusted over in the main, but in part of the crater the vent, Halemaumau, is active (Figs. 6.22, 6.23).

The great difference in elevation between Mauna Loa and Kilauea seems to indicate that they derive their lavas from independent, and probably very deep, sources. Mauna Loa, the "summit" crater, is not drained by the lower one. It has been the more active volcano in recent times and is often violent at periods when the lower crater is only mildly active. Numerous flows have been expelled from fissures or from the summit crater, some of them reaching the sea (Fig. 6.12).

A new eruptive phase of Mauna Loa began in January, 1949. Lava broke out along a series of fissures extending part way across the summit caldera and a short distance down the southwest rift. Along the southwest wall of the caldera, and in the crater, lava fountains as much as 800 feet high built a large cone of pumice, fine cinder, and spatter. Lava flooded more than half the floor of the caldera and filled to overflowing a small pit crater adjoining the caldera on the south. A flow spilled out of the pit crater and moved 4 miles southward. The total volume of extruded lava was approximately 77 million cubic yards.

Mount Lassen. We know that in the western part of the United States there are many volcanoes that erupted in late geologic times. Their cones and craters are still intact and are little affected by erosion. Several of these volcanoes are reported to have erupted in historic time, but these reports have been questioned. Mount Lassen, in Northern California, is the only volcano in continental United States that has had eruptions in the present century (Fig. 6.4). These eruptions began in May, 1914, and in succeeding months several eruptions took place, during which a small crater formed at the top of the mountain, emitting gases, ash, and volcanic cinders. There were also explosions in 1915.

Katmai. Mount Katmai is situated where the Alaska Peninsula joins the mainland. It erupted violently on June 6, 1912; very few people lived anywhere near the volcano, but the explosion was heard 750 miles away at Juneau and even as far north as Dawson and Fairbanks across the Alaska Range. During the explosion, 3 to 5 cubic miles of dust and ash were thrown into the air. The dust continued to fall for 3 days, and when all had settled, it made a deposit 3 feet thick at Katmai, 12 miles from the volcano, and 10 inches deep at Kodiak, 100 miles away.

Ngauruhoe. The volcano Ngauruhoe is one of a group of three major volcanic mountains on North Island, New Zealand (Fig. 6.1). It is located about 80 miles southwest of the celebrated hot-spring district of Rotorua. Its cone rises 7,500 feet above sea level and nearly 4,000 feet above the surrounding hills. In 1949, it suddenly became violently active for a short period of time. The activity began with the blasting out of a plug of debris from one of the crater's two intermittently active vents, followed by avalanches of lava. At intervals during the eruption, huge red-hot blocks were hurled as much as 2,000 feet above the summit of the cone, and a plume of ash and vapor rose nearly 1 mile above it.

FUMAROLES

Fumaroles (Latin *fumariolum,* smoke hole) are vents in the earth's crust from which steam and other gases escape. They are common in regions of active volcanoes and also in areas of decadent volcanism. Many intrusives do not reach the surface but probably supply heat and gases to the regional ground water. Although the steam of fumaroles partly comes from heated ground water, some of

TABLE 6.4 *Volcanic Gases*

Steam, H_2O	Sulfur dioxide, SO_2
Oxygen, O_2	Hydrogen sulfide, H_2S
Nitrogen, N_2	Hydrochloric acid, HCl
Argon, A	Hydrofluoric acid, HF
Carbon dioxide, CO_2	Ammonia, NH_3
Carbon monoxide, CO	Sulfuric acid, H_2SO_4

it may come from the water in the same intrusive magma supplying most of the other gases. The temperature of the steam from certain fumaroles is well above the boiling point of water, and temperatures as high as 650°C have been measured.

Many of the gases escaping from vents are poisonous, such as hydrogen sulfide and carbon monoxide. Others, such as sulfur dioxide and carbon dioxide, are suffocating, the latter collecting at low places in the topography. Thus, we have places such as Poison Valley, Java, where, it is said, the bones of many men and animals killed by gases have been found.

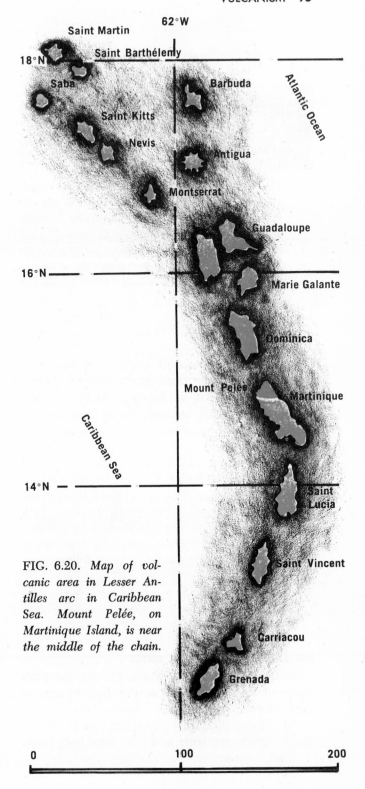

FIG. 6.20. *Map of volcanic area in Lesser Antilles arc in Caribbean Sea. Mount Pelée, on Martinique Island, is near the middle of the chain.*

FIG. 6.21. *Photograph of a lava fountain erupting from a vent, at an altitude of 8,500 feet, on the southwest rift of Mauna Loa, June 7, 1950. Molten lava flares up in irregular spurts; some solidifies as cinders or spatter, but the excess drains off as in the solidified, ropy rolls of lava in the foreground. (Macdonald, U.S. Geological Survey.)*

SOLFATARAS

Solfataras (Italian *solfo*, sulfur) are fumaroles which give off sulfur gases. At places the hydrogen sulfide gases oxidize on exposure to the air and form sulfur, which accumulates in considerable amounts, so that the rocks near the solfataras may contain commercial quantities of sulfur. One of the best-known vents yielding sulfur compounds is La Solfatara, west of Naples. The last eruption of this volcano occurred in A.D. 1198. Since then steam and sulfur compounds have issued. In places such as Mexico and Japan, deposits formed by volcanic emanations are worked commercially for sulfur. The chemical reaction can be given as follows:

$$H_2S \;+\; O \;=\; H_2O \;+\; S$$

hydrogen   oxygen   water   sulfur
sulfide

UTILIZATION OF VOLCANIC GASES

In the volcanic area of Tuscany, Italy, there are steam jets and pools of hot water boiling by natural heat. Notwithstanding the corrosive character of the hot gases, plants for generating electric power and for producing boric acid have been built there,

and boreholes cased with iron tubing allow steam to issue at an average pressure of 2 atmospheres and at 100 to 190°C. At Larderello, 150 metric tons of steam per hour is available from 135 boreholes and is used in turbine engines to generate electric power. Ammonium carbonate, sodium carbonate, and boric acid are recovered from the steam and hot water. Likewise, in an area of hot springs in the Coast Ranges of California, about 40 miles north of San Francisco, wells have been drilled to obtain steam for generating power.

FIG. 6.22. *Pools of liquid lava in the crater of Halemaumau, the fire pit within the Kilauea caldera in Hawaii. (T. A. Jaggar, Hawaiian Volcano Observatory.)*

EROSION OF VOLCANOES

After a volcano becomes extinct, destructive erosional forces dominate, and sooner or later the mountain disappears. On continental land, streams and glaciers are the most effective agents, and on volcanic islands, streams and wave action are most destructive (Figs. 6.24, 6.25). Sea cliffs and wave-cut terraces are developed around extinct volcanoes in the open sea, and all stages, from cones only slightly eroded to those almost completely obliterated, may be observed. The erosion of composite cones on land may leave the lava column of the throat of the volcano standing as an isolated rock shaft. Tabular masses of igneous rocks may radiate from the plug, and remnants of the volcanic material ejected from the volcano may occur in concentric zones around the former volcanic vent. Eventually these are all removed, and the intrusive masses are exposed at the surface. We shall discuss this more fully in later sections of this chapter.

FISSURE ERUPTIONS

Fissure eruptions are a form of extrusive igneous activity which does not produce volcanic cones. Lavas commonly rise along fissures, and at many places volcanoes also are arranged in lines which suggest a connection with hidden fissures. Great floods of very liquid (and, therefore, basaltic) lava have been discharged from such fissures far removed from volcanoes. Some of the flooded areas are covered by flows of basalt and other lavas which are, altogether, hundreds or thousands of

feet thick. Because volcanic cones are absent, we commonly assume that the lava issued from fissures. H. S. Washington, who studied many of these flows, suggests that they be called *plateau* flows, not because the lavas are all found high above sea level, but because the word implies flatness.

Some of these basaltic flows are very extensive. The Deccan flows of India cover an area of 200,000 square miles and probably average 2,000 feet in thickness. In the northwestern part of the United States, in Washington, Oregon, and Idaho, the Columbia River basalts cover about 225,000 square miles and have an average thickness of about 500 feet (Figs. 6.26, 6.27). Large areas of similar rocks are found also in northern Michigan and Wisconsin and along the north shore of Lake Superior. Washington studied the rocks from all these regions and has shown that they are characterized by high iron content, particularly ferrous iron, and therefore must have been formed from highly fluid lavas. Because of their lower viscosity, basic lavas move faster and farther than acidic ones. Some of them are known to have moved as fast as 10 or 12 miles

FIG. 6.23. *Small, circular lava lake, about 50 feet wide, at foot of the wall of Halemaumau Crater, September, 1920. The pool is kept liquid by superheated steam rising from fissures underneath it. (T. A. Jaggar.)*

FIG. 6.24. *Iliamna Volcano, Alaska. Although this volcano still emits steam, its cone is being eroded. Deep gouges caused by glaciers can be seen in the foreground and at right. (Spence Air Photos.)*

FIG. 6.25. *Shiprock in northwestern New Mexico is the remains of a deeply eroded former volcano. The central solid core of the volcano is more resistant than the rock into which it was intruded, as are the vertical dikes or lava-filled cracks that now form the wall-like ridges seen on the left and right. These resistant masses have been etched into relief by rainwash and stream erosion. Shiprock stands about 1,600 feet above the surrounding plain. The cone that formerly enclosed it is all but gone. (Spence Air Photos.)*

an hour. A basic lava in Hawaii flowed more than 40 miles, and one in Iceland flowed nearly 60 miles.

Intrusive Vulcanism

The underground movement of magma cannot be observed while it is in progress, but after the magma solidifies and is uncovered by erosion, we can see the shapes and forms it has assumed.

The term *pluton* is given to any body of intrusive igneous rock of any shape or size. Such masses differ greatly in composition and texture and in their relation to the enclosing rock. Furthermore, magmas are very different in their degree of fluidity or viscosity, and consequently a given intrusive mass represents the line of least resistance for that particular magma. On the basis of their shape or form and their structural relation to the enclosing rock, these masses are classified as dikes, sills, laccoliths, volcanic necks, stocks, and batholiths (Fig. 6.28).

DIKES

Dikes are rudely tabular bodies of igneous rocks that fill former fractures in the earth's crust (Fig. 6.29). They lie at angles to the bedding planes of the enclosing rocks. Dikes may cut across the structure of the intruded formations, or they may cut massive, structureless igneous rocks of older age.

They vary in width from less than 1 inch to many feet and in length from a few yards to many miles. Dikes 10 miles long are common in Iceland, and the Cleveland Dike in England is more than 100 miles long. The Great Dike in Rhodesia is 300 miles long and, in places, more than 5 miles wide.

Most dikes are formed by the injection of magma in preformed fractures, but some may be in fractures formed by the tensional forces produced by the intruding mass of magma. The pressure exerted by the magma may push apart the walls of the fracture, and the wedging action of the magma may play an important part in extending the fracture farther. Still other dikes are really dikelike replacements along fractures; these are produced by solutions moving through a fracture and altering its rock walls.

In certain areas dikes radiate from volcanic centers and are sometimes accompanied by concentric or curved dike patterns. In other localities they are parallel, or they may form intersecting systems. In the Sunlight area of Wyoming (Fig. 6.30), there are thousands of radiating dikes, averaging about 4 feet in width and extending 5 to 7 miles from the central area. Concentric systems are termed *ring dikes*. In the Belknap Mountains of New Hampshire, two distinct rings occur around a central core of older schists. The outer ring dike has a diameter of about 7 miles and a width of nearly 1 mile. An inner ring is smaller but nearly as wide.

Ring dikes that dip steeply inward toward the central core are called *cone sheets* (Fig. 6.31). If the dips of the cone sheets in Scotland are projected downward, they meet at a focus approximately 3 miles beneath the present surface. Such a focal point is believed to lie near the top of the magma reservoir from which the molten rock materials were injected upward into the fractures.

The original fractures into which the dikes are injected are caused both by tension and by compression. Some are produced by the pressure of magma as it moves upward toward the surface, and others result from compressive forces exerted by the magma in the conduit within the cone of the volcano. In either case, systems of fractures result.

In the Spanish Peaks district of Colorado, a

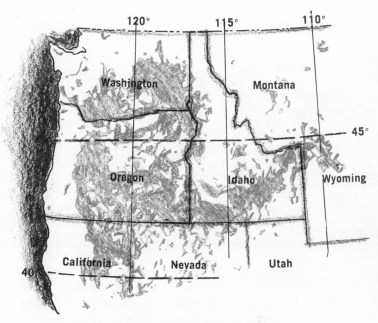

FIG. 6.26. *Map of the lava fields of the northwestern United States. Those near the Pacific Coast and in southwestern Idaho and vicinity are early Cenozoic in age; those of central and eastern Washington, north central Oregon, and the Western Cascade Mountains are middle Cenozoic; and those of northeastern California, northwestern Nevada, south central Oregon, and the Snake River lowland of Idaho are late Cenozoic in age. Nearly all are basalts. (After Geologic Map of the United States, U.S. Geological Survey.)*

system of dikes has been sculptured in relief by erosion. The dikes are 2 to 100 feet or more in thickness and dip at high angles. Some stand as wall-like masses as much as 100 feet above the surface and extend anywhere from a few hundred yards to 10 or 15 miles beyond the plutonic center.

SILLS

Sills, like dikes, are tabular intrusive masses. Sometimes called intrusive sheets, they differ from dikes in that they lie parallel, or nearly parallel, to the bedding planes of the enclosing rocks. Most sills are connected with dikes which are the feeding channels along which the magma reaches the bedding planes it invades. Some sills are small,

FIG. 6.27. *Exposure of lava flows along the valley of a Columbia River tributary, in central Washington. Piles of talus are seen at the bottom of the cliff. The layered arrangement in the cliff results from a succession of flows, each 50 to 100 feet thick. (Washington Department of Conservation and Development.)*

covering areas of only a few acres, but others are very extensive. They range in thickness from a few inches to a few thousand feet; most are less than 100 feet thick. Sills usually lie in an approximately horizontal position, like the sill of a door, except where they were intruded into tilted or folded strata or where the strata have been folded after the sill was intruded.

One of the best-known sills in the United States is the one that crops out along the west side of the Hudson Valley from Jersey City to Haverstraw. This thick sill with conspicuous columnar jointing forms the Palisades of the Hudson. The columns, similar to palisade structure, are the result of shrinkage cracking during cooling. Similar jointing occurs in sills at Mount Tom and Mount Holyoke, Massachusetts, at East and West Rocks at New Haven, Connecticut, and in the Trap Mountains near Orange, New Jersey. The great Whin Sill of northern England has an average thickness of about 160 feet and extends over an area of several thousand square miles. This sill intrudes nearly flat-lying limestone and in general is almost parallel to the beds it intrudes.

In some areas sills appear in great *swarms*. A typical example is the enormous sill swarm injected into the Karroo series of relatively flat-lying sedimentary rocks in South Africa. This swarm consists of many hundreds of sills ranging from a few feet to more than 1,000 feet in thickness. The total volume of magma that solidified to form these sills

and related dikes approaches that poured out to form the Columbia River lava plateau.

LACCOLITHS

A laccolith is a large lenticular mass of igneous rock similar in origin to a sill. If the injected magma lifts up the overlying beds or raises its cover into a domelike structure, the solidified mass of igneous rock is a *laccolith* (Fig. 6.32). The magma is supplied from below through a small pipe, or fissure, and the intrusive mass is inferred to have a flat base resting on sedimentary strata.

Laccoliths occur in a great variety of shapes and sizes. Many are oval, and some are quite irregular. The Henry Mountains in southern Utah have long been considered laccolithic domes. They range from ½ to 4 miles in diameter and from 2 to 10 cubic miles in volume. As a group, they show all stages of progressive erosion, but most of them are sufficiently eroded to disclose their igneous cores, or centers. Recent studies have shown that the igneous bodies forming the domes of the Henry Mountains may be *stocks* rather than laccoliths. A stock is a floorless, domelike intrusive, larger than a laccolith, with a roughly circular horizontal cross section (see page 106).

A group of domes less deeply eroded rises from the plain northwest of the Black Hills. Little Sundance Mountain, which is one of this group, is 3 miles in circumference at its base. This supposed laccolith has had only a part of the sedimentary

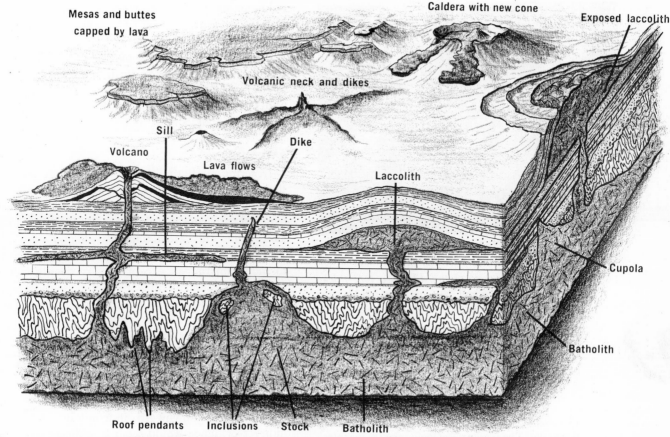

FIG. 6.28. *Diagram showing structural relations of various intrusive and extrusive igneous masses. (After F. P. Young.)*

strata of its roof removed by erosion, and the core has not yet been exposed.

LOPOLITHS

A lopolith is a large, floored, sill-like mass that is centrally sunken into the form of a basin.

VOLCANIC NECKS

The filled vents through which the magma moved that fed volcanoes are termed necks, or plugs. These cylindrical masses, with a subcircular cross section, are as much as several thousand feet in diameter. In volcanic areas where erosion has reached the late topographic stages, volcanic necks may rise 2,000 feet or more above the surrounding country. Such features develop where the rocks in the vents are more resistant to erosion than the pyroclastic materials of the cinder cones. In the plateaus of northwestern New Mexico and adjoining areas in Arizona, more than 150 plugs mark the sites of former volcanoes. The various volcanic buttes rise to different heights, and, furthermore, their bases stand at various altitudes, which indicates that each is a separate intrusive mass and not part of a single extensive lava flow.

The vents may be filled with heterogeneous brecciated material, or the magma in a vent may solidify to form crystalline intrusive rock. Where such fine-grained rocks are formed, vertical columnar jointing (Fig. 6.33) may develop in the upper part of the vent and curve outward toward the enclosing walls near the base of the volcano. The

FIG. 6.29. *A light-colored dike with offshoots, intruded along rock fractures in Cornwall, England. The main part of the dike is a foot thick. (Geological Survey and Museum, London.)*

FIG. 6.30. *Radiating dikes of the Sunlight area, Wyoming. The regional pattern indicates a central source of magma that spread outward several miles through diverging cracks. (After Parsons.)*

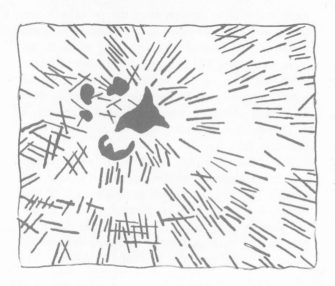

columns are the result of cooling, with the joints forming approximately at right angles to the cooling surface. At the top of the neck the cooling surface is the upper surface of the magma in the crater; and therefore the joints are vertical; but toward the base of the neck the cooling plane is the wall of the vent, and consequently a radial pattern of joints is developed in that portion of the intrusive mass.

BATHOLITHS

Description. Batholiths are the largest and the deepest intrusive bodies of igneous rock known. They are so large that they are never sufficiently exposed to permit measurement of all three dimensions. Some are 50 to 100 miles wide and more than 1,000 miles long. Most of them are aligned parallel to mountain ranges, except in very deeply eroded areas, where such alignment is not evident. In many cases, batholiths furnished the magma to form dikes and sills at higher levels.

Batholiths differ from laccoliths in that none is known to have a floor. They extend downward to great, but unknown, depths, and nearly all of them, where their contacts are exposed, are found to broaden downward. It appears improbable that they broaden downward indefinitely, and some indirect evidence would seem to indicate that they taper downward at depths of several miles.

Most batholiths occur as cores of folded mountain systems. They were emplaced either at times of crustal deformation or shortly thereafter. The Coast Ranges batholith of British Columbia, the Idaho batholith, and the Sierra Nevada batholith (Fig. 6.34) are each along a zone where mountain-building diastrophism took place. Of these, the largest is the Coast Ranges batholith, which is 1,250 miles long and 80 to 120 miles wide. Its surface area is about 100,000 square miles. The largest one wholly within the United States is the Idaho batholith, which is exposed over an area of 16,000 square miles. Similar great intrusive masses are exposed in the Patagonian Andes (Fig. 6.34) and along the cores of other great mountain chains. Most batholiths are composed essentially of granite or closely related granitoid rocks.

Structurally, batholiths are of two types, *con-*

cordant and *discordant*. An intrusive body, or pluton, is said to be concordant if the contacts are parallel to the bedding or schistosity of the older rocks, and it is discordant if the contacts cut across the structure of the country rock. Batholiths intruded during crustal deformation tend to have concordant contacts, and so the roof rocks arch over the top somewhat as the domelike beds arch over a laccolith. The discordant, or transgressive, types, which cut across trends of folds and other structures of their surrounding walls, were emplaced at the end of a period of intensive diastrophism.

The roofs, or upper surfaces, of batholiths are irregular and undulating (Fig. 6.28). The small domelike parts of their roofs that extend upward into the invaded rocks are *cupolas*, and the low sags of the invaded rocks that project or hang downward from the roof are *roof pendants* (Fig. 6.28). The walls slope steeply outward, but in many batholiths the contact that separates the granite of the intrusive mass from the wall rock is not sharp. Instead, the granite is surrounded by a zone, or aureole, of recrystallized rocks consisting of intimately penetrating masses of granite and small layers, or bands, of foliated metamorphic rocks known as *injection gneiss*. Beyond the margins of some batholiths the invaded rocks show a gradation from typical sedimentary and metamorphic characters to various mixed types and finally to granite. Such field evidence indicates that shales, sandstones, slates, and even basalts can be transformed into granite by partial replacement and the addition of materials from the invading magma. Still other batholiths have swarms of *inclusions* of wall rock near the margins. Some inclusions are sharply angular and fresh, whereas others appear partly assimilated and deformed, which indicates that they were softened by heat and stretched out in the direction of movement of the magma. Dark-colored, wavy streaks of half-assimilated hornblende- and mica-schist inclusions are called *schlieren*.

Formation. The manner in which such gigantic masses of magma make room for themselves is not yet fully understood. Some geologists believe that the very hot magma moves upward by engulfing and subsequently dissolving large quantities of the rock in its path. By such a process, called *magmatic stoping*, large blocks are loosened from the roof and chipped or crumbled by heating. They fall into the liquid magma and are partially dissolved or sink to great depths. In this way the magmatic chamber conceivably becomes enlarged, and the magma works its way upward into the earth's crust. The presence of large blocks of partly assimilated invaded rock in granite areas far from the margin of the batholith indicates that stoping actually takes

FIG. 6.31. *Concentric dikes, or cone sheets, intruded along curved fractures that converge downward. Above, map view; below, cross section along line MN. The inner ones dip (slant) more steeply than the outer ones. (After Billings.)*

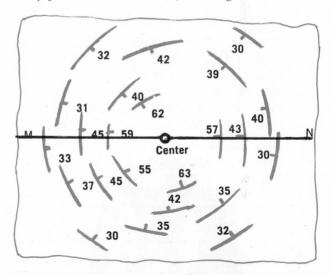

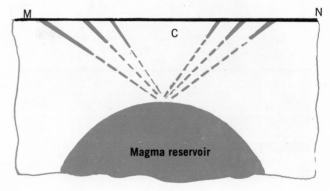

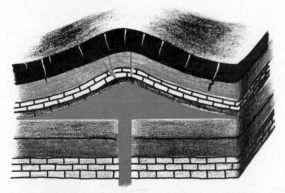

FIG. 6.32. *Ideal cross section of a laccolith. It has a feeder below, flat floor, domed roof, and small projecting dikes. The igneous rock is injected between the beds as a fluid and arches them up.*

FIG. 6.33. *Devils Tower National Monument, in northern Wyoming. Large-scale columnar jointing, formed by shrinkage during cooling, is seen in this exposed volcanic neck, 865 feet high. Although single columns average 7 or 8 feet thick, some reach 16 feet. (National Park Service.)*

place, but its quantitative importance is not known. Mechanical shattering may be as important as shattering due to heating, because the roof rocks are undoubtedly subjected to enormous tensional, compressional, and torsional forces.

Other geologists think that batholiths are emplaced by forceful injection. This is certainly a possible explanation for the positioning of concordant batholiths. The great mass of magma simply pushes its way into the older rocks, driving them aside or ahead as it moves upward. Where a lighter granitic magma rises through older, heavier rocks, the intrusive force may be entirely due to gravity, and since most large batholiths are related to zones of crustal deformation, the magma may also have been pushed around by diastrophic forces.

Still other geologists hold that granites are made *in situ* by "granitization," whereby deeply buried sediments, volcanic tuffs (consolidated volcanic ash), or lavas are first recrystallized to schists and then, through continued alteration by hot fluids or migrant ions, are supposedly converted to granular masses of batholithic form and granitic composition without ever having been entirely molten. In a mushy, structurally weak state, such masses conceivably might behave somewhat like magma. Certain injection gneisses, with their gradational boundaries, peculiar textures, and relic structures, support the hypothesis of granitization, at least on a modest scale; but in other places the sharp, transgressive contacts of granite, signs of stoping or of mechanical crowding, the relatively massive character of apparently intrusive units, and the composition and sequence of crystallization of the constituent minerals oppose the theory.

Because of the conflicting evidence, the relative importance of magma and of granitization in the origin of batholiths has been debated at length. If, however, granitic magma is made directly by partial or complete melting, with the aid of water vapor under pressure, as now seems likely under the proposal of Tuttle and Bowen, then displacement of other rocks is no longer a problem. Moreover, the evidences cited both for granitization and for magmatic intrusion find ready explanation under this scheme.

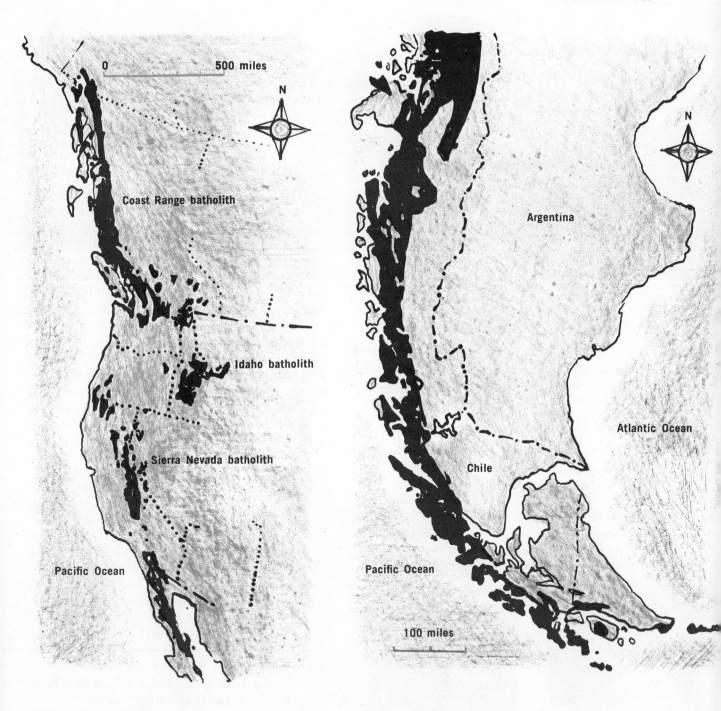

FIG. 6.34. *Batholithic intrusives of western North America and southern South America, intruded along the axes of ancient mountain ranges and subsequently unroofed by long-continued erosion. (After maps by Geological Society of America.)*

FIG. 6.35. *Diagram showing age relations of igneous rocks. The areas numbered 3 and 5 represent tilted and folded sediments; all others are igneous rocks numbered in chronological order.*

FIG. 6.36. *Diagrams showing relative ages of igneous and sedimentary rocks. In (a) the igneous rock (lower right) shows an intrusive contact, and so it is younger than the rock it intrudes. In (b) the igneous rock (lower right) was exposed by erosion, and sediments containing pebbles of it were deposited on an erosional contact, so the igneous rock is older than the overlying sediments.*

(a)

(b)

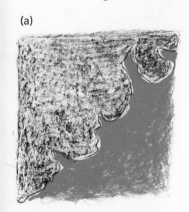

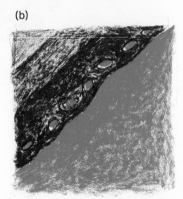

STOCKS

A stock is an igneous intrusion which has the essential features of a batholith but which differs in being smaller. If its areal extent is less than 40 square miles, the mass is called a stock. Some seemingly small intrusives which are called stocks may be cupolas of batholiths, not yet deeply eroded.

AGE RELATIONS OF INTRUSIVES

Except in rare instances, igneous rocks do not contain relics that may be used to determine the age of the rocks as fossils are used to determine the age of a sedimentary bed. The relative age of an igneous rock frequently may be determined, however, by observing its relations to associated rocks. If a rock intrudes another rock, it is younger than the rock invaded (Figs. 6.35, 6.36), and if it is covered by another flow or sedimentary bed, it is older than the overlying flow or bed.

The determination of the age relations of intrusives is an essential part of the systematic study of an area, and it is particularly important in areas containing mineral deposits, which commonly are related to the same magmatic reservoir that supplied the material of the intrusive. An intrusive that contains fragments of another rock is younger than the rock that supplied the fragments. When an intrusive alters another rock near its contact, it is younger than that rock. Certain intrusives are fine-grained or glassy near their contacts with other rocks, whereas a few feet away from the contact they are more coarsely crystalline. The chilled margin is evidence that the intrusive rock is later than the cooling surface that chilled it. If one igneous rock is regionally metamorphosed and another one nearby is not, the metamorphosed rock is the older; or if any regional change has taken place in one rock and the other rock is not affected, the altered rock is the older, for obviously both rocks would have been altered if both had been present when regional alteration took place.

Summary

We began our study of vulcanism by noting that the heat within the earth's crust, presumably of radioactive origin, increases with depth at an average rate of about 1°F per 60 feet. As rocks are poor conductors, the heat accumulates and eventually melts rocks, with the assistance of high-pressure steam, to form magma.

Magma solidifies within the earth's crust, forming dikes, sills, laccoliths, lopoliths, necks, stocks, and batholiths, or breaks through the surface in volcanic eruptions and fissure flows. Volcanoes eject gases (mostly steam), pyroclastics, and lavas and build cinder cones, lava cones, and composite cones. Fissure eruptions make extensive lava plains and lava plateaus.

Lava flows exhibit aa and pahoehoe surfaces, flow breccias, columnar jointing, driblet cones, lava caves, pressure ridges, pillow structure, tree molds, and other features.

Modern volcanoes, despite their terrifying and destructive behavior, must also be considered creative forces, for they make new mountains and provide us with highly spectacular scenery.

In this chapter we have considered the solidification both of magma below the earth's crust and of volcanic products above the surface. We shall now turn our attention to the various types of igneous rocks formed by these processes.

Suggestions for Further Reading

Coleman, S. N.: *Volcanoes New and Old*, The John Day Company, Inc., New York, 1946.

Cotton, C. A.: *Volcanoes as Landscape Forms*, Whitcombe & Lambs, Ltd., London, 1952. A well-illustrated study of volcanoes after erosion.

Foshag, W. F.: "The Birth of Paricutín," *Smithsonian Inst. Ann. Rept*, pp. 223–234, 1946.

Foshag, W. F.: "The Life and Death of a Volcano [Paricutín]," *Geog. Mag.*, vol. 27, pp. 159–168, London, 1954.

Jaggar, T. A.: *My Experiments with Volcanoes*, Hawaiian Volcano Research Association, 1956.

Jaggar, T. A.: "Origin and Development of Craters," *Geol. Soc. America Mem.* 21, 1947. A technical work on volcanic craters.

Russell, I. C.: *Volcanoes of North America*, The Macmillan Company, New York, 1924.

Stearns, H. T.: "Geology of the Hawaiian Islands," *U.S. Geol. Survey, Div. Hydrography Bull.* 8, 1946.

Tazieff, H.: *Craters of Fire*, Hamilton, London, 1952. A nontechnical book about volcanoes.

Williams, Howel: *Crater Lake: The Story of Its Origin*, University of California Press, Berkeley, Calif., 1941.

Chapter 7

IGNEOUS ROCKS

AND ASSOCIATED ORES

IGNEOUS ROCKS can solidify both above and below the earth's surface. In this chapter we shall study the rocks formed in both situations. A distinction is usually made between these two types of rock: deep-seated masses solidifying beneath the surface are called *intrusive,* and rock solidifying above the surface, such as volcanic lava, is called *extrusive.* Igneous rocks display different structures, textures, colors, and chemical compositions—all of which help to distinguish one from the other. In association with igneous rocks, we shall study the magmatic ore deposits that are formed by the related processes. Ores associated with sedimentary rocks will be discussed in the chapter on sedimentary rocks.

IGNEOUS ROCKS

Structures and Textures

STRUCTURE

The structure of igneous rocks refers to their gross features, such as form, occurrence, columnar jointing, and flow banding, and to the fabric of their components. Lava rocks commonly show banding, for as the lavas flow, they drag out the different kinds of material, and these form bands. Furthermore, the materials are rarely uniform but include colored spots and gas cavities. Columnar joints are present in many tabular igneous masses, such as sills and dikes. In these the joints are developed normal to the cooling surface. In flat sills the

FIG. 7.0. *A field of basalt, a dark-colored, fine-grained, extrusive igneous rock formed by solidification of basic lava. This ridged and blocky flow of lava issued from Belnap Crater (out of view on the right on the crest of the Cascade Mountains of Oregon). In the center, we can see that this flow surrounds an earlier hill, called a "steptoe." Since this lava flow overlies glaciated surfaces, we know that it dates from geologically recent time and may be only a few thousand years old. (Oregon State Highway Department.)*

columns are upright (palisadeslike) (Fig. 7.1), and in vertical dikes they are horizontal. Contraction resulting from cooling during solidification causes much of the jointing.

TEXTURE

The *texture* of igneous rocks refers to the size and shape of the mineral grains or crystals and to the pattern of their arrangement (Fig. 7.2). Most rocks contain mineral grains, but some are predominantly volcanic glass or mixtures of glass and mineral grains. The common textures are as follows.

Glassy. A glassy texture, as the name implies, is that of glass and slag, which have amorphous struc-tures, without definite crystals. It results when a magma is chilled so quickly that mineral crystals have no opportunity to form. Massive glass is called *obsidian* (Fig. 7.3).

Vesicular and scoriaceous. Porous, or vesicular, glass, called *pumice*, has fine, closely spaced pores. When the voids are fewer and larger, it is called *scoria*. The pores in pumice and scoria are the result of expanding gases, which tend to make a frothlike surface on the lava. When the lava solidifies, the frothy texture is retained (Fig. 7.4).

Pyroclastic. Pyroclastic (fire-broken) igneous rocks are made up of fragments of volcanic material of different sizes and compositions. The loose pieces

FIG. 7.1. *Devil's Postpile near Mammoth Lakes, California. This igneous rock shows columnar jointing, the result of shrinkage during cooling. The individual columns are 60 feet long and 2 to 3 feet thick. (Frashers, Inc.)*

range from fine dust or ash through volcanic sand, lapilli, cinders, and bombs to huge blocks. Rocks composed of consolidated volcanic dust and ash are called *tuffs*, whereas the term *breccia* is used if most of the fragments are more than 4 millimeters in diameter. Tuffs and breccia that have been partially remelted and fused by the collapse of pumiceous particles are known as *welded tuffs*. The extremely coarse explosive breccias are also commonly called *agglomerates*.

Aphanitic. An aphanitic rock is one in which the mineral constituents are so small that they cannot be distinguished with the naked eye. They are commonly less than 0.5 millimeter in diameter. The rock is crystalline but so fine-grained that it appears homogeneous. Such a texture results from rapid cooling, during which crystallization proceeds from many centers and small crystals form. Felsite (composed of feldspar and quartz) generally has an aphanitic texture; however, it may also be scoriaceous or vesicular.

Porphyritic. A porphyritic rock is composed of relatively large, isolated crystals enclosed in a groundmass, or matrix, of smaller crystals or of glass (Fig. 7.5). In some porphyritic rocks the matrix is a mixture of fine mineral grains and noncrystalline glass. The larger crystals, because of

their prominence in the rock, are called *phenocrysts* (apparent crystals). Phenocrysts may have sharp edges and well-formed crystal faces, or they may be corroded and somewhat irregular. They also range greatly in size; in some rocks they are several inches in diameter, and in others they are no larger than pinheads.

A porphyritic texture indicates two phases of crystallization: (1) the formation of the phenocrysts, which take shape early and remain suspended in the magma; (2) the formation of the groundmass, which may be finely crystalline or glassy or which may show both characteristics, because of a change in circumstances during solidification.

Amygdaloidal. When vesicular lava has been filled with secondary minerals, such as quartz, zeolite, epidote, and calcite, the fillings are called amygdules and the rock amygdaloidal. Amygdules

FIG. 7.2. *Simplified sketch of a magnified thin section of an igneous rock to illustrate the sequence of crystallization and solidification of magma to form rock. The ferromagnesian minerals crystallized first, then the feldspars, and finally the quartz, which fills the spaces between the grains of the other two.*

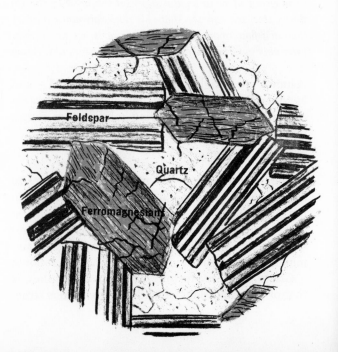

differ from phenocrysts in that the vesicles they occupy are almond-shaped or tubelike (Fig. 7.6), with irregular or oval cross sections, whereas phenocrysts have angular crystal outlines.

Phaneritic. A phaneritic, or coarse-grained, rock is one in which all the leading mineral constituents may be seen with the naked eye (Fig. 7.7). The grains are generally of nearly uniform size and may be quite fine or very coarse. The coarser the grain size, the more slowly the magma cooled. The average granite, which has grains 3 to 5 millimeters in diameter, is a good example.

Pegmatitic. Pegmatites are exceptionally coarse, crystalline aggregates, usually containing about the same minerals as a granite. Pegmatites are thought to have been formed from magmas with unusually high amounts of fluid.

VARIATIONS IN TEXTURE

The texture of an igneous rock reveals the manner of its formation. If cooling is slow, crystallization proceeds from few centers, and large crystals form. If cooling is rapid, it proceeds from many centers, and small crystals form. If fluids are present, they promote the diffusion, or movement, of material through the magma, thus lowering the temperature of crystallization, and permitting the growth of larger crystals. A magma may be fluid at a temperature so low that it would solidify readily if the gases were not present. If such a magma flows out upon the surface, the gases escape, and the molten matter solidifies quickly to form an aphanitic rock or a glass. If some crystals had formed at depth before eruption, phenocrysts would be present, and the rock would be porphyritic. In general, the basic magmas, which are low in silica and high in iron and magnesia, are much more liquid than the silicic magmas, and consequently the crystals or grains of minerals tend to grow to larger size in basic lavas than in the more viscous siliceous ones. This is not true in many deep-seated rocks, however, for pegmatites, which have the largest crystals, are of siliceous composition, but they formed in residual magmas high in fluids and gases.

Textural variations are influenced also by the

FIG. 7.3. *Obsidian, a glassy, extrusive igneous rock. This type of natural glass occurs when magma has cooled too rapidly to allow crystals to form. (Ward's Natural Science Establishment, Inc.)*

FIG. 7.4. *Scoria, a form of solidified lava, showing cavities formed by expansion of gases in the lava before cooling; natural size. (Ward's Natural Science Establishment, Inc.)*

mode of occurrence of igneous rock masses. Since the texture of an igneous rock depends mainly on the rate at which a magma or lava solidifies, it follows that large intrusive masses will form coarser-textured rocks than thin lava sheets or thin dikes and sills. In general, the rocks that occur as great

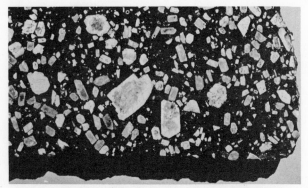

FIG. 7.5. *Trachyte porphyry from Bannockburn Township, Ontario. Large crystals of feldspar are set in a very fine-grained crystalline matrix. The two sizes of crystals were formed under different conditions and at different times. First the phenocrysts (large crystals) were formed in a deep-seated magma. Later the matrix crystallized after this magma was extruded as a lava flow; natural size. (Ward's Natural Science Establishment, Inc.)*

batholiths are of phaneritic texture, whereas dikes and sills are composed of fine-grained aphanitic rocks. Thin lava flows generally are glassy, as is much of the pyroclastic material.

Not all small bodies of rock, however, are fine-grained. Although the volume of a rock in a volcanic neck is not great, the rock commonly is

FIG. 7.6. *Drawings illustrating the development of bent-tube vesicles: (a) Gas bubbles rising through a liquid lava; (b) tubelike vesicles forming in partly viscous lava; (c) owing to movement of the viscous lava, the tubelike vesicles are bent in the direction of movement which is indicated by the arrow. Tube-shaped amygdules are formed by subsequent filling of the vesicles.*

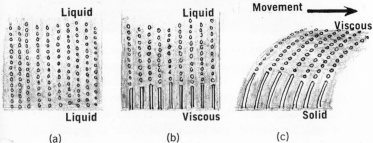

coarse-grained. The coarse texture in this instance is due to slow cooling; the constant upward passage of molten material heats the rocks surrounding the conduit of the volcano, so that when the magma in the conduit itself finally solidifies, it cools slowly, because of the warmth of the surrounding rocks.

Composition

The chemical composition of the magma from which an igneous rock is formed determines the mineral composition of the solidified product. Inasmuch as magmas vary in composition, the igneous rocks crystallized from them may grade into one another imperceptibly. Some rock types are so closely related that any rigid classification is impossible. Mineralogically, most igneous rocks are composed of the feldspars and one or more of the micas, pyroxenes, or amphiboles. Quartz or olivine may or may not be present.

Rocks of high silica content are called *acidic* or *silicic* because of their high proportion of the acid-forming radical, silica, SiO_2 (Fig. 7.8). They are, as a rule, light in color and of relatively low specific gravity. *Basic* rock, on the other hand, contains a predominance of bases such as lime, magnesia, and iron. They are dark-colored or green and heavy, because of their content of iron-bearing minerals. Since unbroken series of rocks have been found with a silica content ranging from 80 per cent down to 40 per cent, it follows that some are neither acidic nor basic. Rocks transitional between the two groups are called *intermediate*.

GRANITES

Granites are coarse-grained rocks consisting of orthoclase feldspar, quartz, and a small amount of mica or of some ferromagnesian mineral. Sodic plagioclase feldspar may be present. Since the proportions of minerals and rates of crystallization vary, many kinds and colors of granite have been formed. In some granites the mica is white (muscovite); in others it is black (biotite). In certain granites hornblende is present, and it may be more abundant than the micas. In a few granites the micas are absent altogether. The average granite contains 60 per cent feldspar, 30 per cent quartz, and 10 per cent dark minerals. Most granites contain pink or reddish orthoclase, and since it is the most abundant mineral, it gives the rock a pinkish color. In gray granites the feldspar is white or gray, and thus the dark biotite and hornblende show more plainly. This color combination gives a salt-and-pepper effect—a white area sprinkled with black.

Very coarse crystalline aggregates of the same minerals as granite occur in fractures near the borders of granite intrusions. Such rocks are called *pegmatites*, or "giant granite," and many of their crystals are perfectly formed and very large. The feldspars in pegmatites commonly are 1 foot or

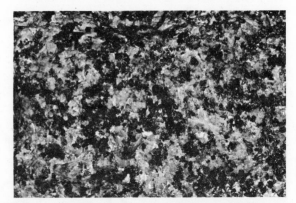

FIG. 7.7. *Granite, a coarsely crystalline, acidic, igneous rock formed deep in the earth's crust, where extremely slow cooling favored crystal growth. The light-colored minerals are feldspar and quartz, the dark ones hornblende and biotite.*

TABLE 7.1 *Igneous Rocks*

Mode of occurrence	Texture	Acidic rocks: light-colored minerals predominate		Basic rocks: dark-colored or green minerals predominate		
		Orthoclase, sodic plagioclase, and ferromagnesian minerals		Calcic plagioclase and ferromagnesian minerals		Ferromagnesian minerals only; no feldspar
		With quartz	Without quartz	With hornblende	With pyroxene	Olivine, with or without hornblende or pyroxene
Batholiths, stocks, and laccoliths	Phaneritic	Granite	Syenite	Diorite*	Gabbro†	Peridotite
Intrusive sheets, dikes, laccoliths	Porphyritic with many phenocrysts	Granite porphyry	Syenite porphyry	Diorite porphyry	Gabbro porphyry	
	Porphyritic with few phenocrysts	Rhyolite porphyry	Trachyte porphyry	Andesite porphyry	Basalt porphyry	
Surface flows	Aphanitic, some partly glassy	Rhyolite	Trachyte	Andesite	Basalt	
		Felsite group		Basalt group		
Volcanic cones, flow surfaces	Glassy	Dense: obsidian Finely vesicular: pumice Coarse pores: scoria		Basalt obsidian		
Beds, crudely stratified	Pyroclastic	Fine fragments: ash and tuff Coarse fragments: cinders and breccia				

* With quartz the rock is quartz diorite, and its aphanitic equivalent is dacite.

† With olivine the rock is olivine gabbro.

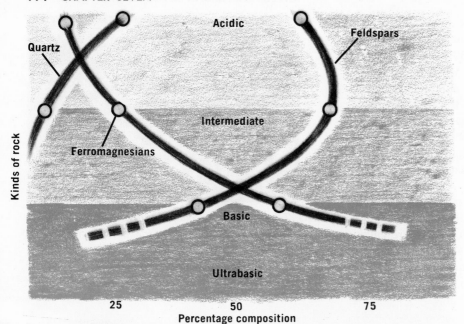

FIG. 7.8. *Diagram showing relative percentages of quartz, feldspar, and ferromagnesian minerals in acidic, intermediate, and basic igneous rocks. Acidic rocks are rich with alkali feldspars and quartz, basic rocks with calcic plagioclase and ferromagnesian minerals.*

more in length; some of those in Maine are as much as 20 feet across. The mica plates are 12 to 15 inches wide; some have been found that weigh many tons. In the pegmatite mines of the Black Hills, the mineral spodumene (a lithium-bearing silicate) occurs in the form of crystals 40 feet long and 4 feet thick.

In some pegmatites the feldspar and quartz have a curious intergrowth; on some of the cleavage faces of the feldspar the quartz makes patterns that resemble certain characters used in ancient writing. Such rocks, composed mainly of quartz and orthoclase, are called graphic granites (Fig. 7.9).

If a magma of the sort that solidifies at depth to form granite flows out upon the surface, the molten matter chills before there is time for the molecules to organize themselves to form crystals; or if crystals do form, they are generally small. The resulting rock is partly or entirely glassy and is called *rhyolite* (Fig. 7.10); if it is essentially all glass, it is called rhyolitic *obsidian*.

SYENITES

Syenites are formed from magmas that contain less silica than those which crystallize to form granite. In syenites the silica is almost or entirely taken up in the formation of silicate minerals, and little or none remains to form quartz. The average syenite is composed of orthoclase and hornblende, with plagioclase, apatite, and magnetite as accessory minerals. When plagioclase is present in larger amounts, the rocks are called *monzonites*, which represent a transition to the diorites (see below).

The aphanitic equivalent of a syenite is *trachyte*, which may be more or less porphyritic. Most trachyte porphyries have a groundmass, or matrix, of minute feldspar crystals and little or no glass.

The syenites are not very common rocks. They usually formed toward the edges of great bodies of granite where silica was scarce; some formed as small, independent intrusives near the margins of granite batholiths.

DIORITES

A diorite is a coarse-grained rock composed of plagioclase feldspar (intermediate in soda and lime content) and one or more of the common ferromagnesian minerals. The dark mineral is usually green hornblende, but augite and other pyroxenes and biotite occur in some varieties. The feldspar is more abundant than the dark minerals. Most diorites contain little or no quartz, but if quartz is present, the rock is *quartz diorite*.

The fine-grained equivalent of diorite is *andesite*. The andesites, which are generally dark gray, are transitional between the light-colored rhyolites on the one hand and the dark-green to black basalts on the other. An andesite with prominent phenocrysts of striated feldspar is an andesite porphyry. The rock may be glassy in part, but andesite obsidian is rare and can be distinguished from rhyolite obsidian only by chemical analysis. A quartz-bearing andesite is called *dacite*.

GABBROS

Gabbro is coarse-grained and is composed essentially of basic (lime-rich) plagioclase feldspars with varying amounts of dark minerals. Because the ferromagnesian minerals are abundant, the rock is dark gray to black and of high specific gravity (Fig. 7.11). Gabbros containing olivine are called olivine gabbros.

Basalt is the fine-grained equivalent of gabbro. The basalts are closely related to the andesites and connected with them by transitional forms. They are very common volcanic rocks formed by the rapid crystallization of basic-lava flows. Many are scoriaceous or amygdaloidal. Basalt porphyries have conspicuous phenocrysts of plagioclase or pyroxene or both in a dark basaltic matrix.

A *diabase* is similar in composition to a gabbro or a basalt. It is the name used for a texture in which the feldspar crystals are long, narrow, and lath-shaped, with the ferromagnesian minerals in the interstices. The term *dolerite* is used for a basic rock of intermediate grain size that does not have a diabasic texture.

The term *traprock* is a common field name for

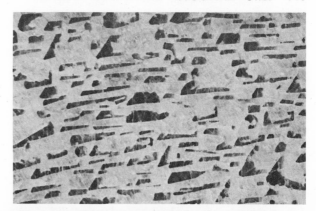

FIG. 7.9. *Graphic granite, from Hyble, Ontario. This type of granite is called "graphic" because the wedge-shaped quartz crystals, surrounded by orthoclase feldspar, resemble ancient cuneiform (wedge-shaped) writing. (Ward's Natural Science Establishment, Inc.)*

various kinds of dark, heavy, basic rocks which cannot readily be identified without a microscope. The term, first used in Europe, was derived from the stairlike appearance of the eroded edges of a series of flows (Anglo-Saxon, *treppe*, stairs).

Massive basalt glass, or obsidian, is relatively

FIG. 7.10. *Photograph of a fragment of a partly glassy rhyolite flow. The gray areas represent reddish-brown crystalline or stony rhyolite. The black bands are obsidian, or black glass. The dark gray areas of the upper part of the figure show cavities formed by expanding gases. Rhyolite is the extrusive equivalent of intrusive granite.*

1 Inch

FIG. 7.11.   *Gabbro, a coarse-grained, basic, intrusive igneous rock composed essentially of pyroxene and high-calcium plagioclase feldspar.*

rare. However, the vesicular basic glass called scoria is abundant at the surfaces of lava flows and in cinders. It differs from pumice in that the composition is more basic, the vesicles are larger and more irregular, and the color is reddish brown to black.

PERIDOTITES

Peridotites are coarse-grained, nonfeldspathic rocks consisting mainly of olivine, with or without other ferromagnesian minerals. Related rocks rich in hornblende are hornblendites; others, rich in pyroxene, are pyroxenites. The mineral chromite is common in some peridotites and, if abundant, may be an ore of chromium.

MAGMATIC DIFFERENTIATION

Why do igneous rocks have different chemical and mineralogical composition? Why are some granite and others gabbro, andesite, or basalt? One possible answer is magmatic differentiation.

Many thick basic sills and laccoliths have a higher percentage of heavy ferromagnesian minerals at or near their bases than throughout the bulk of their mass. The diabase sill, more than 900 feet thick, that forms the Palisades across the Hudson River from New York has a zone near its base containing nearly 65 per cent of ferromagnesian minerals and 35 per cent plagioclase, whereas the bulk of the sill is composed of approximately 60 per cent plagioclase. Apparently the heavy iron-bearing minerals crystallized early and sank to the bottom during the course of crystallization. Since narrow, chilled zones at the top and at the bottom of the sill have identical composition, it is inferred that they represent the composition of the injected magma before it had time to separate into gravitative differentiates.

Similar observations of differentiated zones have been made in certain laccoliths where the rock of the lower part of the intrusive mass is different from that in the middle and upper parts. The fact that heavy minerals, such as magnetite and pyroxene, generally are more abundant in the lower rocks, whereas quartz and feldspar predominate in the upper positions, suggests differential crystal settling. Furthermore, at many places, deep-seated igneous rocks are found to grade one into the other. Thus a light-colored granite may grade into a darker diorite or even into a gabbro. Neither rock intrudes the other, and therefore they are believed to be of the same age. Hence, some sort of separation must have occurred.

Doubtless, differentiation due to gravity also occurs in a volcanic conduit and in a volcano's reservoir of magma at greater depth. During a dormant period, the magma in the feeder, or neck, of a volcano may solidify, and, below this plug, the heavier minerals that slowly crystallize out first may sink and leave a lighter and more silicic magma near the top of the reservoir. When the volcano erupts again, the first flows, or pyroclastics, are highly silicic and the later ones more basic. As many as five different kinds of lava, presumably the products of such a separation, were erupted from San Francisco Mountain in northern Arizona. This extinct volcano, rising 5,000 feet above the plateau on which it was built, has been dissected by erosion sufficiently to expose to view the five kinds of eruptive rocks in its make-up.

On the other hand, eruptions of other volcanoes do not show much change in composition of the lavas. In its early stages, the originally basic lava at Paricutín brought up pieces of solid granite from the wall rock along the feeder. Later, such fragments were lacking, and the lava seemed instead to have been contaminated by assimilation (melting) of the wall rock. So the evidence for differentiation during the brief span of activity there was weakened.

In great batholiths, magmatic differentiation probably is carried out on a vastly larger scale than in sills, laccoliths, and necks, which have magmatic chambers of restricted size. The batholiths, however, are so large that the operation of the processes is more difficult to interpret, and, moreover, the floors of batholiths do not come under observation. The very predominance of granite in batholiths tends to support the theory of wholesale differentiation, unless the granite was formed by replacement (granitization) or the magma was highly siliceous at the outset. As we have seen, the origin of granite is still in dispute.

In any event, basalts, and possibly andesites, represent little modification in magma formed in the lower part of the earth's crust.

Economic Uses

In a later section we shall see that pegmatites supply feldspar, mica, graphite, gems, and lithium minerals and that certain intrusives were responsible for the formation of metallic ore deposits. At this point, however, we wish to consider the economic importance of the igneous rocks themselves, as rocks in bulk.

GRANITE

Granite is used both as dimension stone and as crushed stone. *Dimension stone* is a term applied to stone sold in blocks or slabs of specified shapes and sizes. It includes monumental stone, building stone, paving blocks, and rough-cut stone for various structural purposes. The requirements of a dimension stone depend on the use for which it is intended. The essential qualities are strength, durability, workability, color, and beauty. For bridge spans, great strength is essential; for monuments and other outdoor structures good appearance and resistance to weathering are required; and for interior decoration, pleasing color and adaptability to carving and polishing are the most important properties.

In the building trade the term granite is used to include nearly all coarse-grained, generally light-colored igneous and metamorphic rocks, as well as true granite. These rocks have low porosity and great strength and durability. In fact, most of them are much stronger than necessary to meet all demands likely to be made upon them.

Architectural and monumental granites are quarried extensively in Vermont, Massachusetts, and Maine in the East (Fig. 7.12); in Georgia in the Southeast; in Upper Michigan, Wisconsin, and Minnesota in the Middle West; and in Colorado and California in the West.

In some areas, such as parts of North Carolina and Georgia, granite is crushed for use in concrete aggregate, since, in the absence of gravel, it is the cheapest rock locally available for the purpose.

BASALT

Because of its dark color and toughness, basalt is little used as building stone, but where it is widespread, it supplies large tonnages of crushed stone. Andesites and other lavas locally serve as well. The principal basalt-using states are New Jersey, Oregon, Washington, Connecticut, and Pennsylvania.

PUMICE AND CINDERS

Pumice is used as an abrasive in scouring powders and, in the West, as aggregate in lightweight

FIG. 7.12. *Granite quarry, Stonington, Maine. Stone is removed in benches by utilizing the natural jointing in the rock. (Oliver Bowles.)*

concrete blocks. California, New Mexico, Arizona, Idaho, and Oregon are the leading producers of pumice. Cinders are used principally on roads near the source.

PERLITE

Perlite, a volcanic glass resembling obsidian, is found in several Western states. It contains con-siderable water and, when heated to a softening temperature, expands or "pops" suddenly, like pop-corn, to make an artificial, sand-sized pumice. It is used mainly as a lightweight aggregate and in plaster for heat and sound insulation. It is quarried in New Mexico, Colorado, Nevada, Arizona, California, and Utah.

ASSOCIATED ORES

An ore deposit is a concentration of one or more metallic minerals sufficiently rich in some metal to make its mining profitable. Some metals, such as gold and platinum, are found in the metallic state, but more commonly the metallic elements occur in chemical combination with other elements, in the form of such compounds as sulfides, oxides, and carbonates.

The ores of greatest monetary value produced in the United States yield iron, copper, zinc, lead, uranium, molybdenum, gold, silver, manganese, titanium, aluminum, mercury, tungsten, and chromium. The iron and copper ores together are worth more than two-thirds of the total (Fig. 7.13).

Composition of Ores

An *ore mineral* is one that contains a valuable metal. In most deposits the ore minerals are associated with large amounts of material consisting of gangue and country rock. *Gangue* is the value-less and usually earthy, or nonmetallic, material deposited along with the ore. Country rock is the rock that encloses the ore deposit. In many deposits the ore grades into the country rock, much of which is removed by mining the ore. Certain ore and gangue minerals are listed in Tables 7.1 and 7.2.

FIG. 7.13. *Value of mineral production in the United States in 1957. Mineral fuels, primarily petroleum, coal, and natural gas, account for two-thirds of the total. Cement, stone, and sand and gravel are the principal nonmetals, copper and iron the leading metals. (Data from Minerals Yearbook, U.S. Bureau of Mines.)*

Billions of dollars

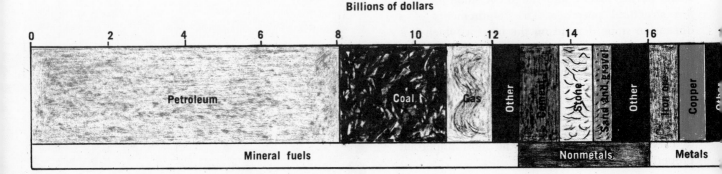

In some ores the valuable metal predominates, but in most deposits the ore minerals are present in subordinate amounts. An iron ore generally contains between 50 to 70 per cent iron, a zinc ore generally between 3 and 25 per cent zinc, and a lead ore between 3 and 15 per cent lead. Copper ores are generally low in copper, and the bulk of the metal is derived from ore that carries between 0.75 and 5 per cent copper. Silver ores carry between 8 and 30 ounces or more of silver per ton, and gold ores generally contain between $3 and $10 worth of gold per ton.

Many ores contain two or more metals. Thus the copper ores of Butte, Montana, carry important amounts of silver and gold, and there are few copper ores that do not contain small amounts of the precious metals. Lead and zinc are very commonly found in the same deposit, and lead and silver are common associates. In general, in the present practice of treating ores by milling and smelting, two or more metals are recovered from the ore, and ores that contain less than the amounts of the metals stated above often are utilized.

Deposition of Ores

Ore deposits are formed by the same processes that form other rocks, that is, by gradation and vulcanism. Like other rocks they are deformed by diastrophism and, where exposed at the surface of the earth, are weathered. Certain mineral deposits

TABLE 7.2   *Common Ore Minerals*

Metal	Mineral	Elements present	Percentage of metal	Formula
Iron	Hematite	Iron, oxygen	70	Fe_2O_3
	Magnetite	Iron, oxygen	72.3	Fe_3O_4
	Limonite	Iron, oxygen, hydrogen	59.8	$2Fe_2O_3 \cdot 3H_2O$
	Siderite	Iron, carbon, oxygen	48.3	$FeCO_3$
	Pyrite	Iron, sulfur	46.6	FeS_2
	Pyrrhotite	Iron, sulfur	60.4	Fe_7S_8
Copper	Native copper	Copper	100.0	Cu
	Chalcopyrite	Copper, iron, sulfur	34.6	$CuFeS_2$
	Chalcocite	Copper, sulfur	79.8	Cu_2S
	Cuprite	Copper, oxygen	88.8	Cu_2O
	Malachite	Copper, carbon, oxygen, hydrogen	57.4	$Cu_2(OH)_2CO_3$
Zinc	Sphalerite	Zinc, sulfur	67	ZnS
	Smithsonite	Zinc, carbon, oxygen	52	$ZnCO_3$
	Calamine	Zinc, silicon, hydrogen, oxygen	54.2	$Zn_2H_2SiO_5$
Lead	Galena	Lead, sulfur	86.6	PbS
	Cerussite	Lead, carbon, oxygen	77.5	$PbCO_3$
	Anglesite	Lead, sulfur, oxygen	68.3	$PbSO_4$
Tin	Cassiterite	Tin, oxygen	78.6	SnO_2
Silver	Native silver	Silver	100	Ag
	Argentite	Silver, sulfur	87.1	Ag_2S
	Cerargyrite	Silver, chlorine	75.3	$AgCl$
Gold	Native gold	Gold	50–100	Au
Uranium	Uraninite	Uranium, oxygen	. . . . . .	$UO_2 \cdot UO_3$
	Carnotite	Uranium, vanadium, potassium, oxygen, hydrogen	Variable	$2U_2O_3 \cdot K_2O \cdot V_2O_5 \cdot 3H_2O$
Aluminum	Bauxite	Aluminum, oxygen, hydrogen	30–40	$Al_2O_3 \cdot nH_2O$

TABLE 7.3   *Common Gangue Minerals*

Minerals	Elements present	Composition
Quartz	Silicon, oxygen	SiO_2
Calcite	Calcium, carbon, oxygen	$CaCO_3$
Dolomite	Magnesium, calcium, carbon, oxygen	$MgCO_3 . CaCO_3$
Barite	Barium, sulfur, oxygen	$BaSO_4$
Fluorite	Calcium, fluorine	CaF_2
Feldspar	Potassium, aluminum, silicon, oxygen	$K_2O . Al_2O_3 6SiO_2$
	Sodium, aluminum, silicon, oxygen	$Na_2O . Al_2O_3 . 6SiO_2$
Garnet	Calcium, iron, silicon, oxygen	$Ca_3Fe_2(SiO_4)_3$
	Magnesium, iron, silicon, oxygen, etc.	Many of complicated formulae
Tourmaline	Iron, silicon, aluminum, boron, oxygen, etc.	Variable

are igneous rocks in the strict sense. Other deposits are sedimentary beds that contain valuable materials. These include iron-ore beds, gold-bearing gravels, etc. The materials found in ore deposits are also present in other rocks, but in ores they are sufficiently concentrated to be of economic value.

Mineral Veins

In addition to being the most common type of mineral deposit, mineral veins are among the most valuable. Veins are formed as follows: water moves through fissures and other openings, deposits ore in the openings, and soaks into the wall rock, altering it. At places, ore is deposited by replacement in the wall rock near the openings. Veins exist in an almost infinite variety. They differ in structure, texture, composition, and arrangement.

STRUCTURE

The structure of a vein depends largely on the character of the openings that were prepared to receive the solution that deposited the ore. Some veins fill single openings (Fig. 7.14). Others fill closely spaced parallel openings. Still others, called fractured zones, fill irregularly fractured bodies of rocks. In many places the country rocks near the veins are partly replaced by ore. In certain irregularly fractured rocks small veins (veinlets) are closely spaced, and the rock is replaced between the fractures, so that the entire rock may be regarded as ore. Some veins occupy fault fissures (Fig. 7.15); others follow beds that are brittle and easily fractured and that therefore, after movement, offered favorable channels for waters. Certain beds are followed because they were easily replaced by the mineral-bearing waters that deposited the veins.

TABLE 7.4   *Kinds of Ore Deposits*

Type of rock	Form of deposit	Origin
Associated with intrusives	Veins and similar deposits	Formed by mineral-bearing waters moving along fissures and other openings
	Pegmatites	Formed by aqueo-igneous solutions derived from igneous intrusives
	Contact-metamorphic deposits	Formed by solutions from igneous intrusives replacing invaded rocks
	Magmatic segregations	Formed by consolidation of magmas
Sedimentary	Sedimentary beds	Formed by processes of aggradation

Many deposits along fissures replace limestone beds below shales but do not replace the shales, because the shales are relatively impermeable (Fig. 7.16). Because the contacts of two rocks commonly are planes of weakness, they are often fractured and mineralized (Fig. 7.17).

TEXTURE

Some veins are made up of one mineral or of two or more minerals so intergrown that the vein is essentially uniform throughout. Others consist of banded layers (Fig. 7.18). In certain veins these layers appear in the same order from the two walls to the center of the vein, that is, in symmetrical order. The waters moving through the fissure have deposited minerals layer upon layer on opposite sides of the channel. Where they do not come together, they leave an opening which is called a *vug*, or *druse*. Certain veins fill fissures without greatly altering the wall rock and without replacing it with ore. Such veins generally have sharp, regular contacts.

Many veins, however, do not have sharp, clean-cut walls but grade into the wall rock in such a way that it is difficult to determine where wall rock ends and vein begins. This is often noted where the vein-forming waters have soaked into the wall rock and replaced some of it with ore. The changes that are brought about in the wall rock by hot waters moving along fissures are due to hydrothermal metamorphism.

COMPOSITION

Veins are the chief sources of most of the metals. The veins and closely related deposits of ore formed in and along openings represent the most valuable sources of such metals as gold, silver, copper, lead, zinc, and mercury. Certain veins produce one metal; others produce two or more. In some veins the metals occur in the native state. This is true of most gold-bearing veins and of some copper-bearing ones. Many metals, however, occur combined with other elements. Thus lead is found mainly as the sulfide galena; zinc as the sulfide sphalerite; and copper as the sulfides chalcopyrite and chalcocite. Tin is found chiefly as the oxide

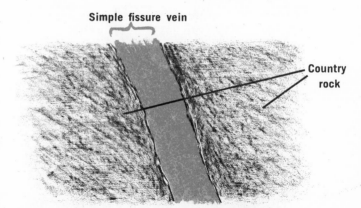

FIG. 7.14. *A cross section showing a simple fissure vein.*

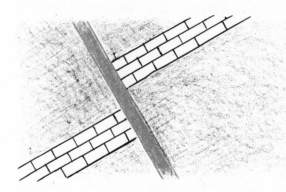

FIG. 7.15. *Cross section of a vein filling a fault fissure.*

FIG. 7.16. *Cross section of a vein replacing a bed of limestone.*

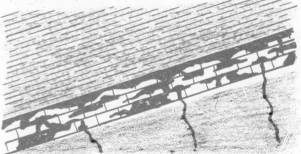

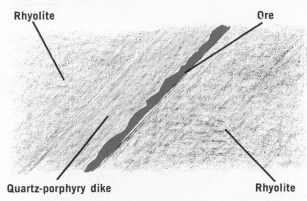

Rhyolite · Ore · Quartz-porphyry dike · Rhyolite

FIG. 7.17. *Diagram showing a vein at the contact between a rhyolite and a quartz-porphyry dike.*

cassiterite, and certain other metals often occur in compounds with arsenic. Iron ore is found in veins and beds. The iron-bearing minerals include the sulfides pyrite and pyrrhotite and the oxides hematite and magnetite. In the great majority of veins the metals are present as sulfides or in association with sulfides.

ZONAL ARRANGEMENT

As veins are worked out, we often find that a single vein changes in composition at successive depths. Certain lead veins change downward to zinc veins; certain zinc veins become copper veins with depth; and certain copper veins become tin veins. The order is essentially the same if the same

FIG. 7.18. *Section of a vein with symmetrical crustified banding, Creede, Colorado. The numbers indicate the order of deposition of the mineral bands.*

1 2 3 4 5 4 3 2

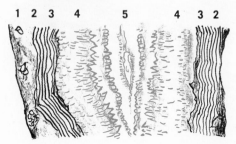

metals are present, and the reverse order is rare. A tin vein does not pass downward into a vein of copper, lead, or zinc, nor does a copper vein change to a lead vein with depth. The part of a vein in which one metal predominates is called a zone, and the zonal arrangement is characteristic of many veins. In some veins similar changes are found along the strike (the horizontal direction of the vein). Thus a vein can be followed along the surface through zones in which tin ore gives way to copper ore and copper to zinc ore. These arrangements are due to the fact that different metals are precipitated by solutions under the changing conditions of temperature and pressure associated with increasing distances from the magmatic source.

VEIN-FORMING WATERS

It is thought that ordinary ground water has deposited certain veins, such as the uranium deposits of the Colorado Plateau. However, the great ore veins are believed to have been formed mostly by ascending hot fluids that escaped from cooling igneous masses. When deposits are associated with shale, they generally are found below the shale (Fig. 7.19). Shales are relatively impervious to water and form the great natural barriers to solutions. Limestones are replaced readily by ore; and if the ores are in limestone near shale, they are nearly everywhere below the shale, which suggests that the ore-bearing waters rose in the limestone and were halted by the shale where the ores were deposited. At places the rocks are arched, and the ores occur at the top of the arches in limestone below the shales. The ascending waters apparently converged in the upfolds and deposited ore below the impermeable shale barriers (Fig. 7.20).

The waters that deposited the ore veins are believed to have been hot, for most veins are associated with igneous rocks; moreover, the wall rocks near the veins show alterations that are characteristic of hot waters (hydrothermal metamorphism). Steamboat Springs, Nevada, is a good example of metallic sulfides now being formed by hot-water deposition.

Although it is obviously not possible to observe the deposition of ores around deep-seated intrusives or to examine the whole of such intrusives and their associated ores, we may study many different intrusives and associated ores at many different stages of erosion. The study of these batholiths shows that their upper parts, called "roofs," are very irregular and generally broad. Their contacts with invaded rocks generally slope away from the mass, so that they become broader downward. Since many metalliferous veins are found in and around granitic batholiths, we believe that the solutions that deposited them were expelled from the cooling magmas that solidified to form the batholiths (Fig. 6.28).

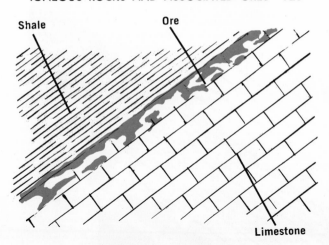

FIG. 7.19. *Replacement ore deposit formed at and below the contact of shale and limestone.*

Other Ore Deposits

PEGMATITES

Pegmatites are magmatic-differentiation products, but they represent, in general, the lighter rather than the heavier products of the magma. Generally they are composed of large crystals, and of these feldspar, quartz, and mica greatly predominate. They have been called "giant granites." Some have crystals of tourmaline (a boron mineral) and of apatite, which contains fluorine and chlorine. We believe that the boron, fluorine, and chlorine, probably as gases, aided the growth of the large crystals, for it is known that these substances, and also steam, tend to keep the magma liquid, thus allowing the crystals greater freedom of formation and promoting the development of larger crystals. Because the parent magmas of pegmatites probably contain much water, they are called *aqueo-igneous* solutions.

Pegmatites fill dikes in or near the roofs of batholiths. A few of them are associated with basic rocks. They are the chief sources of the micas, lithium minerals, and feldspars of commerce; they contain also such gems as tourmaline, ruby, and diamond. On the other hand, pegmatites are rarely important as metal sources. A few are banded, like quartz veins, and some of them grade into quartz veins, but they are very rarely found grading into veins that carry commercial amounts of the precious metals.

CONTACT-ZONE DEPOSITS

Metamorphic deposits in contact zones are replacements of invaded rocks formed by solutions that are expressed from the invading rocks. Although they are found in the garnet or other contact zones of both sedimentary and igneous rocks, they occur mainly in sedimentary rocks, particularly in limestones and calcareous shales (Fig. 7.21). Many of them lie against the intruding igneous rock, and they are rarely as much as 1 mile away from it. Contact-metamorphic deposits carry ores of copper, iron, zinc, and, more rarely, gold, silver, and lead.

FIG. 7.20. *Cross section showing ore near the axis of an arch-shaped fold (an anticline) replacing limestone below shale.*

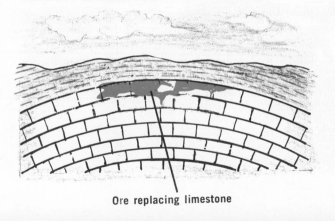

Ore replacing limestone

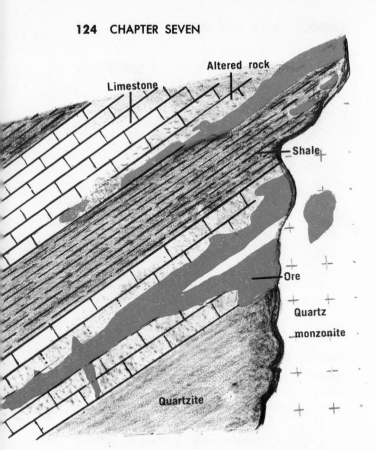

FIG. 7.21. *Section of contact-metamorphic ore deposit. The alteration was caused and the ore introduced by the intrusion of the magma that formed the quartz monzonite.*

The gangue minerals include garnet, amphiboles, pyroxenes, quartz, calcite, and dolomite. The sulfides, such as pyrite, chalcopyrite, and pyrrhotite; the oxides, such as hematite and magnetite; and the heavy silicates, such as garnet and amphibole, are mutually intergrown and were formed at about the same time.

Some contact-metamorphic deposits follow beds, and others cut across beds, but since they do not follow well-defined fissures, they differ from fissure veins. The ore-carrying solutions that moved out from the intruding masses and deposited material in the invaded rocks were at high temperatures and under strong pressures, so that they were able to penetrate minute joints and the cleavage planes of minerals. For this reason the contact-metamorphic deposits are generally irregular in shape and rarely tabular, like veins. As a rule, the minerals of contact-metamorphic deposits form coarse aggregates.

MAGMATIC SEGREGATIONS

Magmatic segregations are deposits formed by magmatic differentiation. The heavier minerals generally are found below the lighter ones. Differentiation is most easily discovered and studied in laccoliths and sills, because they have "floors," on which the heavier differentiates rest. The heaviest material sinks, the lightest material rises, and the constituents of intermediate weight occupy an intermediate position. Sometimes, however, after an igneous magma has formed a sill, the sill slumps down to form a lopolith (a basinlike sheet). After erosion, the lopolith presents at the surface a ring of the heaviest material, inside which is a ring of lighter material, and inside that a ring of still lighter material, such as granite. The Sudbury, Ontario, eruptive mass is said to show such relations, where a heavy ore consisting of sulfides of iron and nickel is found in the outermost ring below gabbro.

In certain regions dikes of iron ore fill fissures believed to extend downward to bodies of ore that were formed by the differentiation of a deeply buried and invisible rock magma. These dikes also are believed to be magmatic differentiations. Deposits formed by magmatic differentiation include ores of nickel, iron, titanium, chromium, platinum, and subordinate deposits of copper and gold. Diamonds and other gems also are formed in magmatic segregations.

SEDIMENTARY DEPOSITS

The mineral deposits associated with sedimentary rocks will be discussed in the following chapter.

Summary

In our study of the various types of igneous rocks, we have seen that some of them, because of the lack of clear-cut division, are difficult to classify. However, a sound background in mineralogy facilitates their identification.

Igneous rocks are either intrusive or extrusive. Their textures differ with the conditions of solidification, including the mode of occurrence and ease of crystallization, as determined by the rate of cooling, the presence of gas bubbles, and other variables. Common textures are glassy, vesicular, pyroclastic, aphanitic, porphyritic, amygdaloidal phaneritic, and pegmatitic.

Coarse-grained rocks include granite, syenite, diorite, gabbro, and peridotite. Their fine-grained equivalents are rhyolite, trachyte, andesite, and basalt. Glassy rocks are obsidian, pumice, scoria, and most pyroclastics. The pyroclastics include volcanic ash or dust, volcanic sand, lapilli, cinders, bombs, and blocks, and also their indurated products—tuff, breccia, and agglomerate.

Igneous rocks are of great importance to the construction industry as architectural and monumental stone, crushed stone, abrasives, lightweight aggregate, and insulation. Their associated ores are even more valuable to us. Igneous intrusives, especially stocks and batholiths, and their fluid emanations have formed many valuable mineral deposits in veins, pegmatites, contact-metamorphic deposits, and magmatic segregations.

Suggestions for Further Reading

Bateman, A. M.: *Economic Mineral Deposits,* John Wiley & Sons, Inc., New York, 1950. A textbook of economic geology.

Daly, R. A.: *Igneous Rocks and the Depths of the Earth,* 2d ed., McGraw-Hill Book Company, Inc., New York, 1933.

Fenton, C. L., and M. A. Fenton: *Rocks and Their Stories,* Doubleday & Company, Inc., New York, 1951. A well-illustrated nontechnical book.

Lindgren, W.: *Mineral Deposits,* 4th ed., McGraw-Hill Book Company, Inc., New York, 1933.

McKinstry, H. E.: *Mining Geology,* Prentice-Hall, Inc., Englewood Cliffs, N.J., 1948.

Pough, F. H.: *A Field Guide to Rocks and Minerals,* Houghton Mifflin Company, Boston, 1955.

Pirrson, L. V. (Adolph Knopf, ed.): *Rocks and Rock Minerals,* 3d ed., John Wiley & Sons, Inc., New York, 1947.

Shand, S. J.: *Eruptive Rocks,* T. Murby & Co., London, 1951. A very well known textbook on igneous rocks.

Turner, F. J., and J. Verhoogen: *Igneous and Metamorphic Petrology,* McGraw-Hill Book Company, Inc., New York, 1951. A comprehensive study, especially of the physical chemistry of petrology.

Wahlstrom, E. E.: *Igneous Minerals and Rocks.* John Wiley & Sons, Inc., New York, 1947.

Wahlstrom, E. E.: *Introduction to Theoretical Igneous Petrology,* John Wiley & Sons, Inc., New York, 1950. A standard textbook.

Williams, Howel, F. J. Turner, and C. M. Gilbert: *Petrography,* W. H. Freeman & Co., San Francisco, 1954.

Chapter 8

ROCK WEATHERING
AND SOILS

IN PREVIOUS CHAPTERS we have seen how some of the earth's rock is formed from magma originating below the surface of the earth. The rock thus created, however, is constantly subjected to further change. We are now ready to consider some of the forces responsible for this alteration—specifically, the weathering of rock by air and water and the chemical and mechanical means by which this is accomplished. Rock weathering eventually leads to the formation of soil, discussed in the second part of this chapter, and prepares material for a type of rock other than igneous—sedimentary rock, the subject of Chapter 9.

ROCK WEATHERING

The outer part of the solid earth, sometimes called the crust, is made up of various rock materials, which constitute the *bedrock*. The crust, or bedrock, is solid and resistant at depth but usually cracked and jointed near the surface, where the whole mass may be overlain or covered by loose rock fragments of various sizes, which compose the *regolith*. Moisture-laden atmosphere penetrates the cracks and pores of the bedrock, and this causes changes which lead to the formation of most of the regolith. So the crust is undergoing constant change. The rocks at or near the surface are subject to conditions that finally alter their physical form and chemical composition. Since the chemical and mechanical factors producing such results are associated with the weather, these processes are called weathering.

Rocks are attacked in this way largely because they come into contact with air and water, the weathering "elements." Thus weathering is related to the surface of the lithosphere, where rocks, air, and water come together. Water soaks into the rocks, dissolves and alters minerals, expands by freezing, and enlarges joints and fractures. The process begun on cracks (Fig. 8.1) ultimately affects the whole rock.

The weathering of rocks may be compared to the decay of a building. After a few centuries, even a house constructed of the strongest and most resistant stone decays and falls in ruins unless it has been repaired continually. Monuments, gravestones, roofing slates, roads, foundations, concrete buildings, and steel bridges are all subject to weathering in the same manner. Man is in a perpetual contest with the weather. He chooses resistant materials for buildings, and he paints exposed surfaces to delay disintegration, but ultimately all structures are destroyed by weathering and must be rebuilt.

Weathering is partly physical and partly chemical; the two phases are *disintegration* and *decomposition*. Disintegration is the physical disruption of rocks to form particles of smaller size without change in composition. The particles are of the same material, and the minerals are fresh. Normally, disintegration and decomposition go on at the same time, and physical disruption of rocks facilitates the access of the chemical materials involved in rock decay. In relation to erosion, weathering is but the first step—the preparation of the materials for removal. We shall first discuss physical weathering processes and then chemical weathering.

Physical Processes

FREEZING OF WATER

The formation of ice in the rocks causes ice wedging and frost heaving. The freezing of water in pores and cracks in rocks tends to disintegrate

FIG. 8.0. *Camel Rock, near Santa Fe, New Mexico. This irregular surface shows differential weathering of weak and resistant rocks. (New Mexico Tourist Bureau.)*

the rocks; for water, in freezing, expands about one-eleventh of its volume and exerts great pressure. Although the pressure is much less than that needed to crush most hard rocks, it is sufficient to disrupt soft rocks or rocks already weakened by cracks or partial decay. Highly porous rocks, such as sandstones, whose pore space commonly ranges from 10 to 30 per cent, are disrupted in this way, and so are jointed rocks, whose cracks become the loci of ice wedges. In the same manner the soils on fall-plowed lands in the north central part of the United States are made light, fluffy, and easily worked by repeated freezing and thawing during the winter and early spring. Frost heaving also brings boulders to the surface, and it pushes up such structures as stakes, posts, and foundations.

FIG. 8.1. *Venus Needle (on the left), more than 200 feet high, has been detached from the cliff (right) by crumbling of the intervening rock along vertical joints, near Gallup, New Mexico. (New Mexico State Tourist Bureau.)*

By the combined action of frost and other agents, unusual erosion forms may be produced. An outstanding example is the craggy features of the "Old Man of the Mountain" in New Hampshire's White Mountains.

HEATING AND COOLING

Just as steel bridges and concrete pavements expand when heated and contract when cooled, so rocks are affected by the alternate heating and cooling due to daily and seasonal temperature changes. In the daytime the air on mountaintops may reach a temperature of 120°F or more, and the rocks may become distinctly warm or even hot to the touch, but at night the temperature of the air drops below freezing and the rocks cool off.

Such repeated expansion and contraction seemingly should tend to develop cracks in rocks, but the extent to which these conditions promote disintegration remains uncertain. Laboratory experiments on repeated heating and cooling, even far beyond the temperature ranges encountered in the field, have thus far proved negative. Perhaps more time is needed, or other factors may operate. Certainly an increase in volume brought about by chemical changes, particularly hydration (recrystallization caused by addition of water), assists physical disruption in some measure.

In any event, most high mountain peaks which are unprotected by snow are much fractured and may be covered with boulder fields of angular blocks, many of which are on the move down slope. Some mountaintops have been reduced to domelike forms fringed by an accumulation of excess debris awaiting removal.

GRAVITY

Accumulations of rock fragments dislodged from cliffs by weathering and deposited below by gravity are called *talus* (Fig. 8.2). The slope of the talus pile is approximately the angle of rest of the material, generally about 25 to 35 degrees from the horizontal, depending on such conditions as the size and angularity of the fragments and the amount of subsequent rainwash.

EXFOLIATION

Smooth rocks exposed to weathering commonly chip off in thin slabs, sheets, or scales concentric with the surface. This process, called exfoliation, is caused by changes in the volume of a rock. The volume changes can result from ice wedging, alternate heating and cooling, expansion due to chemical changes in the rock, or all of these combined. The outer part of the rock pulls away from the inner part until it finally falls off and exposes a fresh surface to attack.

Exfoliation leaves smooth, rounded surfaces on most rocks, regardless of their composition. Rounded masses, such as Stone Mountain in Georgia or Half Dome in Yosemite Valley, California, are produced by the peeling off of slabs along curving secondary joints in the granite rock. These joints were formed by vertical expansion after erosion removed the overlying rocks and decreased the vertical pressure. In the case of Half Dome, the steep cliff in front is the result of splitting along nearly vertical major joints, mainly because of the wedging action of water freezing in the joints (Fig. 8.3).

SPHEROIDAL WEATHERING

Spheroidal weathering is the alteration of joint blocks progressively inward from their rims (Fig. 8.4). The rock on the edges of the fractures is partly or wholly converted to clay and other products, whereas the interiors remain relatively fresh and solid. Differential expansion of the weathered exteriors loosens them along concentric joints. The cores range in size from boulders to pebbles or even smaller particles. They are rounded by weathering in place, however, not by rolling. Continued weathering, mainly by hydration, may reduce their size by further exfoliation until the whole mass succumbs.

GRANULAR DISINTEGRATION

As the process of disintegration continues, the exfoliated slabs and chips of rock are subjected to

FIG. 8.2. *Talus cones at the foot of Tower of Babel, Banff National Park, Alberta, Canada. The light areas on the cliffs are sites of recent sloughing that has added to the piles below. (Canadian Government Travel Bureau.)*

other stresses, especially if the rock is composed of two or more minerals. In granite, for example, various minerals react differently. The dark minerals, such as hornblende and biotite, absorb heat more readily, and also give it up more quickly, than the lighter-colored feldspar and quartz. Furthermore, each mineral has its own coefficient of expansion and contraction, and each differs in its response to chemical attack. Consequently, in an intergrowth of minerals such as occurs in a granite, the stresses set up by the weathering processes tend to separate the minerals. Finally, the mineral grains fall apart and produce a sand of loose minerals.

This process of granular disintegration is in operation over large areas where coarse-grained rocks are exposed to weathering. Many of the slopes of Pikes Peak, Colorado, are covered with such products. The finer grains are transported by wind or water, and the coarser fragments remain until they are disintegrated more completely. At Dogtown Commons, Cape Ann, Massachusetts, large granite boulders have crumbled into heaps of crystalline sand; and at Medford, Massachusetts, the exfoliated slabs of a diabase dike are disintegrated and decomposed into a soft granular mass of dark minerals.

ORGANIC DESTRUCTION

Plants and animals also play a prominent part in weathering. Roots grow into cracks and crevices and push the fragments up and apart, often as much as several feet (Fig. 8.5). When the wind overturns well-rooted trees, the rock is fractured and exposed to destruction. The burrowing of animals such as earthworms, ants, and rodents and the tramping of larger animals, especially hoofed mammals, also contribute to the disintegration of rocks. Man likewise does his part, by excavating road cuts and tunnels, quarrying, mining, and cultivating the land. The "breaking" of the sod on the prairies, the clearing of brush and timber, and the destruction of forests by lumbering and by fire have upset the previous balance between weathering and erosion and indirectly have permitted rapid erosion and renewed weathering over large areas.

FIG. 8.3. *Half Dome, Yosemite National Park. Large slabs of rock peel along curving joints under the influence of frost and gravity. The loosened pieces tumble and slide to lower levels, fracturing and breaking on the way. The sheer cliff in front was formed by splitting along nearly vertical major joints. (Spence Air Photos.)*

Chemical Processes

Decomposition is a process of decay by which rocks are broken down by chemical alteration of minerals. Decomposition usually takes place at the same time as disintegration.

ROLE OF WATER

For chemical changes to take place, the atomic structure of minerals, especially the silicates, must be sundered. This is done by water and its ions. Water (H_2O) dissociates to a small degree into hydrogen (H^+) and hydroxyl (OH^-) ions. Natural waters ordinarily contain dissolved ions of several other substances. Since these ions are electrically charged atoms, they may replace or react with charged atoms in the crystals, thereby destroying the original crystal structure. Sodium, potassium, calcium, and magnesium ions tend to dissolve in the contacting solution. Aluminum and iron compounds hydrolyze to form relatively insoluble hydroxides. Silica is generally released as a colloidal suspension of silica in water. Many minerals are especially vulnerable to weathering because of weak links in their atomic structure, especially the oxygen bands in silicates.

Oxidation. Rocks decompose, or decay, when their component minerals are altered chemically by oxidation, hydration, carbonation, and solution. In the process of oxidation, oxygen is added to the rocks, especially to the iron compounds. The oxidation of rocks by air is aided by the presence of moisture; without water, oxidation is slow or nil. Air and water break down the ferrous silicates, such as pyroxenes, amphiboles, and olivine, and convert their ferrous iron to ferric oxide (hematite) or to hydroxides (goethite, limonite) with accompanying color changes from green or black to red, yellow, or brown. Hence many soils in warm, moist climates are colored red, yellow, or brown.

Local deoxidation, or reduction by organic matter, also may occur. Near the roots of trees and under peat bogs the bright colors may be changed to somber ones, or they may be bleached.

The oxidation of pyrite, which is composed of iron and sulfur, leads to the formation of sulfuric acid:

$$2FeS_2 + 2H_2O + 7O_2 = 2FeSO_4 + 2H_2SO_4$$

pyrite — water — oxygen — ferrous sulfate — sulfuric acid

Sulfuric acid attacks the rocks and develops solution pits and accompanying stains and discolorations, so that even small amounts of iron sulfides may be injurious in building stones. The change in color of certain roofing slates from green or gray to brown is caused largely by rusting of the component iron compounds, as in normal weathering. In the oxidation of pyrite, the sulfur as well as the iron is oxidized.

Carbonation. When crystals containing calcium, magnesium, sodium, or potassium ions react with carbonated waters, carbonates and bicarbonates are formed. This decomposition process is called carbonation. All surface waters contain dissolved carbon dioxide, which is derived from the atmosphere. The dissolved carbon dioxide reacts with the water in small quantities to form carbonic acid (H_2CO_3), which ionizes to form hydrogen (H^+), bicarbonate (HCO_3^-), and carbonate (CO_3^{-2}) ions. Carbonated water dissolves many substances more readily than pure water, and it is consequently an active agent of weathering.

Solution. Carbonated waters, although only feebly charged, are very abundant, and the carbonates of the alkalies and alkaline earths are soluble in such waters, so that solution of these materials goes on together with carbonation and plays an important part in the decomposition of rocks by removing certain constituents. In addition to calcium, magnesium, sodium, and potassium, even the less soluble alumina and iron are taken away in part. Dissolved sulfates and chlorides are less abundant than the bicarbonates.

Certain rocks are particularly subject to solution—notably, limestone and marble, both composed chiefly of calcium carbonate, which is soluble in solutions that carry carbon dioxide. Gypsum and rock salt are very readily soluble in water.[1] Exposed surfaces of limestone and gypsum generally become etched or pitted by solution. Rocks that are made up of two kinds of material, one readily dissolved and another less readily dissolved, develop pitted surfaces in which the less soluble material stands out in relief.

Hydration. Hydration is the chemical addition of water to the minerals of a rock to form new minerals, chiefly hydrous silicates and hydrous oxides. Carbonation frequently occurs together with hydration. Thus orthoclase feldspar, a mineral abundant in granite, is decomposed and converted largely to kaolin, the principal mineral in common clay. The potassium and excess silica are released at the same time:

[1] Commercial beds of gypsum, $CaSO_4 \cdot 2H_2O$, and rock salt, NaCl, commonly are protected from solution in humid regions by a cover of relatively impervious beds of clay or shale.

FIG. 8.4. *Spheroidal weathering converting jointed blocks of rock into rounded boulders, along the American River, near Riverton, California. (Eliot Blackwelder.)*

$$2KAlSi_3O_8 + 2H_2O + CO_2 = Al_2Si_2O_5(OH)_4$$

orthoclase   water   carbon dioxide   kaolin

$$+ 4SiO_2 + K_2CO_3$$

silica   potassium carbonate

Plagioclase feldspars are decomposed in the same way, and most of the alumina likewise is used to form kaolin:

$$2NaAlSi_3O_8 + 2H_2O + CO_2 = Al_2Si_2O_5(OH)_4$$

albite   water   carbon dioxide   kaolin

$$+ 4SiO_2 + Na_2CO_3$$

silica   sodium carbonate

In both of the above reactions, the kaolin is formed as the result of hydration, and the potassium and sodium carbonates are formed by carbonation. Solution of these two carbonates then takes place, and they are carried away with the water.

Other hydrous silicates formed by hydration of the primary silicates include such minerals as chlorite, serpentine, talc, and zeolites.

FIG. 8.5.   *A live oak growing in a crack and splitting a mass of limestone near Kerrville, Texas. (Elting H. Comstock.)*

ROLE OF VEGETATION

Plants and animals assist decomposition in several ways. Lichens, which are among the first plants to grow on freshly exposed rock, take certain chemical elements from the rock. The roots of other plants remove additional inorganic matter.

Also, vegetation can assist the power of water in decomposition. Decay of organic matter releases certain organic acids which increase the solvent power of water. The solubility of silica, alumina, and iron, for example, is much greater in the presence of these organic acids.

The chemical activity of the small but abundant and ever-present bacteria which produce ammonia, nitric acid, carbon dioxide, and other active chemical compounds is another factor in the alteration of rocks and the formation of soils. Indirectly, vegetation serves to retain moisture, to delay erosion, and hence to prolong chemical weathering.

DEPTH OF DECOMPOSITION

Rock decomposition may proceed to great depths. Granitic rocks in the District of Columbia are decayed to a depth of 80 feet, and near Atlanta, Georgia, similar rock is decayed to approximately 100 feet. In northwestern Georgia the depth of decay of limestones is nearly 200 feet, and in Brazil shales are decayed to a depth of 400 feet.

Climatic Influence

The nature and extent of weathering are controlled largely by climatic conditions. We shall consider the effects of four climatic types: (1) the hot and moist climate of the equatorial belt, (2) the hot and dry climate of desert areas, (3) the mesothermal moist climate of the temperate zones, and (4) the cold and dry climate of the arctic regions. In each of these regions, rock weathering is going on continually, but each region has its own peculiarities.

In a moist, warm climate, rock decay is rapid. In a dry climate, it proceeds more slowly. The effect of climate is well illustrated by the Egyptian obelisk that was presented to New York City. Although it had stood without apparent injury for many centuries in the mild, dry climate of northern Egypt, it began to disintegrate soon after its removal to Central Park, so that special protection had to be given to it.

EQUATORIAL REGIONS

In the equatorial regions, where the rainfall is heavy and the temperature is high, chemical processes are especially active, and the influences of organic agencies are pronounced. The chemical reactions are more rapid than in cooler latitudes, and consequently the decomposition of silicates is more complete, and much silica is removed in solution. The end product of such weathering is *laterite*, which consists largely of red hydrated oxides of aluminum and iron. This lateritic residue takes the place, to a large extent, of the clayey mantle-rock of the higher latitudes.

DESERT REGIONS

In desert regions peculiar conditions prevail, and the character of weathering differs from that found elsewhere. Rainfall is sparse, so that solution by downward-percolating water is of minor importance. Some water, however, is retained by capillary action (surface tension). Since the air is dry and the sun is hot, the capillary water drawn toward the surface evaporates so as to concentrate the salts that are in solution. These warm concentrated solutions react with the constituents of the rocks and tend to decompose them. The crystallization of new compounds takes place between the mineral grains, and this may cause splitting of solid rocks, in much the same way as the freezing of water does. Since water is constantly rising toward the surface by capillary action and depositing its dissolved contents, the surface materials become cemented, forming hardpan and irregular concretionary masses in the mantle-rock. Because of excessive evaporation, the soluble salts of sodium, calcium, and magnesium commonly occur as a powdery crust, or efflorescence, on the surface. This is especially true in depressions and over flat areas, where the salts remain, since there is insufficient rainfall to wash them out.

In many desert regions a brown or black shiny crust, called *desert varnish*, forms on the rocks. It consists mainly of oxides of iron and manganese. For some time desert varnish was thought generally to be the result of deposition of mineral matter from evaporated capillary water. Recent studies indicate, however, that in some instances the growth of lichens may be an important contributing factor.

TEMPERATE REGIONS

In temperate regions, there are marked seasonal variations in climate, and consequently the type of weathering that occurs in these areas is to a certain extent a combination of all the others. In winter, frost action is dominant, whereas in summer, spring, and autumn, percolating waters play a more important part. Elevation above sea level also is an important factor, especially where mountains extend above the timber line. Low-altitude temperate regions generally are not subject to extreme and sudden changes of temperature. In general, solution and other types of chemical decomposition are the dominant types of weathering in these areas.

ARCTIC REGIONS

In the subpolar regions, where a large part of the surface is covered with snow during most of the year, the underlying rocks are saturated with thaw water, which is repeatedly frozen and thawed. By far the most important weathering agent in such an environment is the expansion of water when it freezes. This process shatters the rocks and leads to the accumulation of a mantle of angular fragments. Essentially similar conditions prevail in the high, snow-capped mountains of the temperate and equatorial regions.

Weathering of Representative Rocks

Rocks weather in different ways, depending on their mineral composition.

GRANITE

When granite is fully disintegrated, it separates into its constituent minerals, for example, feldspar, quartz, hornblende, and mica, in sand-sized particles. Incomplete disintegration yields aggregates of these minerals in coarser pieces.

If the granite is decomposed in place, the feldspars will be changed to clay minerals and solutions, and the hornblende and perhaps the biotite will be altered to hematite or limonite, a little clay, and solutions. However, the quartz and muscovite will remain practically unchanged. Solutions take away potassium, sodium, calcium, magnesium, and silica. The residue then is a gritty, micaceous clay, more or less stained with hematite or limonite. If low in iron, such a clay may be used for ceramic purposes after the quartz grains and mica flakes have been washed out.

BASALT

Basalt breaks down mechanically to basaltic rubble, boulders, cobbles, pebbles, and basalt sand.

Even silt grains may result, because of the extremely fine size of the crystals in basalt.

As ordinary basalt contains high-calcium plagioclase feldspar, together with pyroxene and olivine, its chemical-decomposition products include clay, considerable hematite or limonite, and a substantial amount of soluble calcium, magnesium, sodium, and silica. A residual clay over basalt is therefore colored in deep tones of red, brown, or yellow.

LIMESTONE

The weathering of limestone is especially dependent on the climatic conditions under which it takes place. A medium to high temperature and abundant rainfall are the most favorable conditions. In warm, humid regions limestone weathers easily. Lowlands are produced, since the weathered products are carried away in solution or are transported by running water as fragments that have little resistance to mechanical wear.

In arid or semiarid regions, on the other hand, limestones and dolomites form resistant ridges or uplands. In such circumstances these rocks, already

FIG. 8.6.   *Weathered limestone block talus near head of Twelvemile Canyon, Utah. On such a steep slope residual soil is washed downhill and cannot accumulate. Although limestone is very susceptible to chemical weathering in humid climates, in arid regions it forms resistant ridges and is subject to mechanical weathering. (U.S. Forest Service.)*

jointed, may be further broken up by mechanical weathering (Fig. 8.6). Although limestone is soluble in carbonated waters and hence vulnerable to chemical weathering, which at best is a slow process even where water is abundant, bare surfaces of limestone in arid regions endure as cliffs or hill cappings for a long time.

Exposed, flat limestone surfaces in any climate may weather somewhat irregularly, for the purer portions are more susceptible to solution. However, surface water partly charged with carbon dioxide or organic acids, running down over the limestone face of a cliff or over a crack or cavity, may be especially effective. It dissolves the rock as it goes, the loosened insolubles drop from the surface, and eventually broad, more or less parallel furrows are developed, giving a fluted surface to the cliff or other limestone face. The fluted holes in the limestone capping of some of the hills along the Sacramento River, above the Shasta Dam, are good examples.

Through the widening of cracks or joints by chemical activity, chiefly solution, so much of the drainage of limestone areas may be transferred to underground passages that the weathering, as well as the erosion processes on the surface, will be greatly modified. In time the surface of such a region may be covered by an impure clay soil, generally red in warm climates, composed of the insoluble residue left by the disappearing limestone. In arid regions this residue is usually blown away as dust.

When water seeps down to limestone beds below the surface, they may be so decomposed and attacked as to form underground caverns. We shall discuss these caves, and the action of underground water, in Chapter 14.

ORES

Ores, like other rocks, are subject to weathering at the earth's surface. Where exposed to the action of air and water, the deposits break down and form new minerals. In certain deposits valueless materials are carried away by ground water, leaving the valuable material in a more highly concentrated state. In the Lake Superior iron-ore districts, sur-

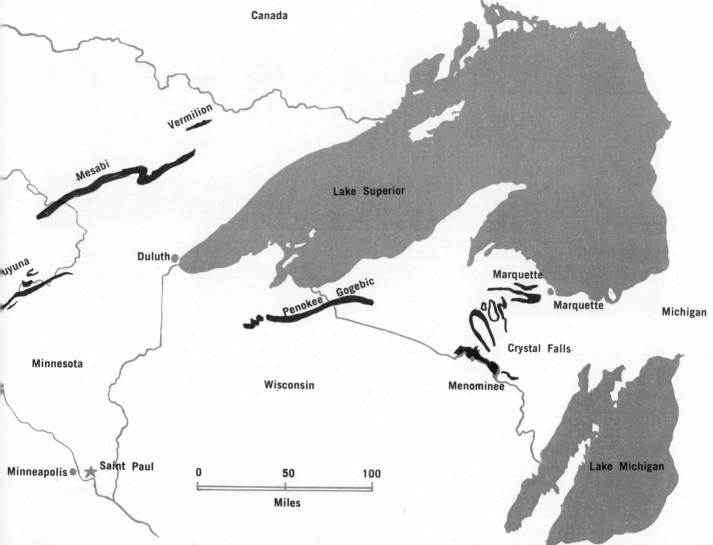

FIG. 8.7. *The distribution of iron ranges of the Lake Superior region. (After Leith, Lund, and Leith.)*

face waters have removed material other than iron, converting rocks with about 25 per cent iron into ores with 50 per cent iron or more (Figs. 8.7, 8.8). Near Little Rock, Arkansas, a highly aluminous igneous rock has been weathered and leached of silica, so that it is now a high-grade aluminum ore.

Nearly all the veins bearing ores of copper, silver, lead, zinc, and other metals contain sulfides. Pyrite (iron sulfide) is almost always present. Where the

veins are exposed at the surface of the earth, they are attacked by air and water and undergo a series of changes. Thus pyrite will be oxidized, forming sulfuric acid and iron sulfate:

$$2FeS_2 + 2H_2O + 7O_2 = 2H_2SO_4 + 2FeSO_4$$

pyrite   water   oxygen   sulfuric   iron
                         acid   sulfate

The sulfuric acid that is formed will dissolve cop-

FIG. 8.8. *In the Monroe open-pit iron mine, Mesabi Range, Minnesota, weathering removed the silica from ferruginous chert (taconite) along the outcrop of the iron-bearing formation. The iron thus was concentrated to form commercially valuable ore. (Oliver Iron Mining Company.)*

per, zinc, and certain other metals, which are carried downward. The iron sulfate will be further oxidized and will break down and form iron hydroxide, which is insoluble and will remain at the outcrop. Thus nearly all deposits that carry iron sulfides will be marked by iron hydroxide, which stains the croppings of the vein, giving it a rusty appearance. This altered iron-stained material is

called an "iron hat," or *gossan*. As a rule, the outcrops of copper sulfide veins carry very little copper. Gold, unlike copper, is not soluble in sulfuric acid, and gold-bearing veins are generally as rich in gold at the outcrop as at depth, or even richer. Copper is carried downward as copper sulfate, for in the presence of air and water copper is highly soluble in sulfuric acid.

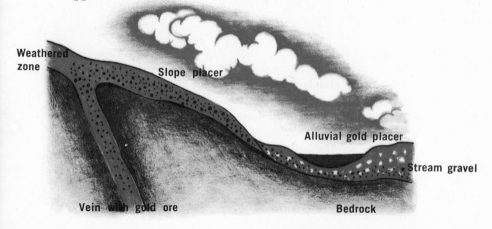

FIG. 8.9. *The origin of placer deposits. Weathering and erosion of the gold-bearing vein on the left release the heavy, insoluble gold particles, which then are carried down slope and deposited with gravel on stream bottoms.*

Where gold veins are exposed at the surface, the gold commonly will accumulate in the outcrop, to be washed away by running water. Thus the particles of gold will be strung out along the surface below the vein cropping and will be washed into the beds of the streams, as shown in Fig. 8.9. The stream gravels are washed into long wooden boxes, or sluices, and the gold, being heavier than rock, settles to the bottom of the box and is recovered. This method of recovering gold is known as *placer mining*, and gold-bearing gravels are *placer deposits*. All ore minerals that are heavy and not easily dissolved by ground water are likely to be accumulated in placer deposits. These include gold, platinum, tin oxide, diamonds, rubies, and other gems. Figure 8.10 illustrates the accumulation of a diamond placer by erosion of diamond-bearing material from a peridotite intrusive (Fig. 8.11).

SULFIDE ENRICHMENT

Sulfide enrichment is the process whereby ground water deposits ore minerals leached from a vein to form a secondary ore, richer than the first, or primary, ore. Many copper ores have been enriched in this way. The water containing sulfuric acid, which dissolves copper and other soluble metals from the outcrops of copper sulfide deposits, moves downward, carrying the copper with it as copper sulfate. When it reaches the water table, it enters a changed environment. The water table is the level below which the openings in rocks are filled with water. Although air is present in openings above the water table, it does not exist below that level, since the water seals it out. Copper is readily dissolved by sulfuric acid in the presence of air and water, but the solution in the absence of air loses its copper, which is precipitated by pyrite or by pyrrhotite or by many other minerals. Reactions forming copper sulfides are

$$FeS + CuSO_4 = CuS + FeSO_4$$

pyrrhotite | copper sulfate | copper sulfide | iron sulfate

$$ZnS + CuSO_4 = CuS + ZnSO_4$$

sphalerite | copper sulfate | copper sulfide | zinc sulfate

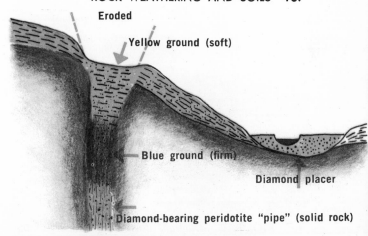

Eroded

Yellow ground (soft)

Blue ground (firm)

Diamond placer

Diamond-bearing peridotite "pipe" (solid rock)

FIG. 8.10. *A diamond-bearing pipe of peridotite and its associated placer deposits. Diamonds removed from the weathered and eroded yellow ground are washed downhill and deposited in gravels and sands along a stream near the pipe.*

FIG. 8.11. *The Kimberley Diamond Mine, South Africa. The mine is about 1,500 feet in diameter at the surface, and the main shaft is 3,520 feet deep. From 1888 to 1914, when operations were discontinued, about 16 million tons of diamond-bearing "blue ground" was taken from the mine and yielded 6,404 pounds of diamonds. (N. W. Ayer and Son, Inc.)*

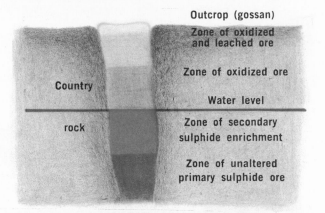

Outcrop (gossan)

Zone of oxidized and leached ore

Zone of oxidized ore

Water level

Zone of secondary sulphide enrichment

Zone of unaltered primary sulphide ore

Country rock

FIG. 8.12. *Diagram illustrating zones forming in a sulfide lode because of weathering and secondary sulfide enrichment. Valuable metals such as copper are dissolved in the acid zone near the surface and reprecipitated as an enriched zone of secondary sulfides in the alkaline environment just below the water level.*

The rich secondary copper ore appears just below the water table.

After oxidation and weathering, a copper vein shows a series of standard changes from the surface downward, as illustrated in Fig. 8.12. The gossan, or iron hat, which carries little or no copper, is found near the surface. Below that is a zone of oxidized copper ore with carbonates and oxides of copper found just above the water table. Then there are the water table and, below that, the secondary copper ore. At still greater depths the primary sulfide ore is found in its original state. It is reasonable to suppose, therefore, that the entire deposit from the surface downward had once been like the primary ore and that it was changed by ground water to the various types of ore that are found above it.

FIG. 8.13. *Solution pits formed by differential weathering of sandstone. The cement has been dissolved, and the softer parts of the sandstone have been washed out, leaving pits and lines of pits in the softer beds. The hammer handle near the center is a foot long. (C. E. Erdmann, U.S. Geological Survey.)*

Deposits of ores of other metals also show changes that are brought about by surface alteration, but each metal behaves in its peculiar way, depending on its chemical properties.

Differential Weathering

Neither all rocks nor all parts of the same rock weather evenly. Highly jointed portions break out and decompose more readily than massive ones, and some rock constituents are more soluble than others. In bedded rocks the different layers respond to weathering at different rates.

The net result of these various irregularities is differential weathering, whereby easily removed parts are taken away and less altered, resistant parts are left behind. On materials of differing mineral (and hence chemical) composition or of varying degrees of hardness, the more soluble or softer portions are weathered most readily, and the exposed surfaces become cellular, pitted, or recessed (Figs. 8.13, 8.14).

Grotesquely weathered resistant pinnacles of fantastic shapes are called *hoodoos* (Fig. 8.15). Other effects are "window rocks," natural bridges, widened joints, and variously ribbed and fluted surfaces (Figs. 8.16, 8.17). Removal of weak materials is assisted by gravity, rainwash, and wind.

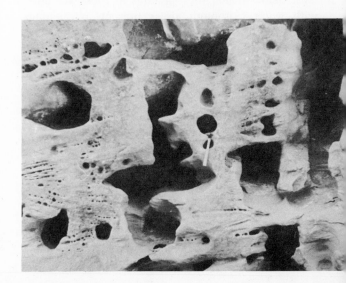

SOILS

Soil Formation

Soils are a complex mixture of inorganic mineral matter and partly decomposed organic residues. They are formed from disintegrated or decayed rock, which is a product of weathering. From man's point of view the formation of soil is by far the most important result of weathering. Soils differ greatly from area to area, not only in quantity, but in quality and in the capacity to support the growth of plants. The same agencies of weathering which produce the mantle-rock are continuously at work breaking it up into finer and finer particles and causing its further decay. Soil proper is the thin upper portion of this mantle, which is decomposed and altered sufficiently to support plant life. It usually contains more or less dark, carbonaceous organic matter called *humus*. The decomposed rock below the humus layer of the soil is sometimes spoken of as subsoil.

The texture, or size of grain, of the soil particles, as well as certain other physical characteristics, has much to do with the soil's ability to produce crops. The size of the mineral grains determines the amount of free surface exposed, and this, in turn, influences the quantity of water that can be retained by capillary and molecular action. Fine-textured soils have larger surface areas than do coarse-grained soils. Since it is from the surface areas of soil particles and from the film of solutions and colloids around them that plant roots obtain most of their mineral matter for plant food, texture is an important physical property of all soils.

The chief factors in soil formation are (1) action of living organisms, (2) parent rock material, (3) time, (4) climate, and (5) slope of the land surface.

Organisms. The bulk of most soil is composed of mineral grains of various sizes, but the presence of organisms and organic matter, the source of soil

FIG. 8.14. *Montezuma Castle, a national monument near Camp Verde, Arizona. Prehistoric tribes carved their homes into the shelter and protection of the solution pits in the weathered cliffs on the Verde River bluff. (Santa Fe Railway.)*

FIG. 8.15. *Hoodoos developed by differential weathering of a breccia, Yoho National Park, British Columbia. They are so named because of their grotesque shapes. (Canadian Government Travel Bureau.)*

FIG. 8.16. *Pink Cliffs at Bryce Canyon, Utah. Differential weathering and rainwash erosion have attacked the horizontally bedded, vertically jointed, soft limestone. (Union Pacific Railroad.)*

nitrogen, makes soils essentially different from most mantle-rock. Organic matter is derived from plant and animal tissues, which are made up largely of carbon, nitrogen, and water. Nitrogen is essential to plant growth. The air contains an inexhaustible supply of it, but plants cannot use atmospheric nitrogen. Instead, plants must have it in soluble form in soil solutions. Some of the bacteria in the soil are able to take nitrogen gas from the air and transform it into soluble nitrates. A number of leguminous plants play an important role in the so-called nitrogen cycle, since their roots act as hosts to various types of nitrogen-transforming bacteria.

Parent Rock. Any of the three principal kinds of rock—igneous, sedimentary, and metamorphic— may supply soils with the bulk of the parent rock material. However, the character of the ultimate soil derived from a given rock depends to a considerable extent on the other factors of soil formation. Some rocks that contain the minerals essential to plant growth may still produce very poor soil, whereas, under favorable conditions of climate and vegetation, a fertile soil may be produced from parent material relatively low in the minerals that contain the raw materials for plant food.

Time. Through weathering, most partly indurated shales, sandstones, and volcanic ashes are easily changed into soils, whereas the formation of soils from igneous and metamorphic rocks usually requires a longer time.

Climate. The influence of climate on weathering has been discussed earlier. It affects the type of weathering, the percolation of water through the soil, and the removal and redeposition of materials by such agents as wind and water. In general, the soils of humid areas are more thoroughly leached than those of arid and semiarid regions. Leaching removes lime and other soluble minerals and leaves a more acid soil. High temperatures promote rapid chemical changes in the soil, both by direct chemical action and by reactions induced by living organisms. In humid regions the organic acids produced by the decay of plant tissue hasten the soil-leaching process.

Land Slope. The soils of steep slopes differ from those on flat surfaces because of variations in drainage, rate of runoff, and erosion. Where the slopes are considerable, solid rock may crop out at the surface, for although mantle-rock is produced, the loose material is removed by rainwash, wind action, or other agents of erosion as rapidly as it is formed.

RESIDUAL SOILS

Soils which rest upon the bedrock from which they are derived are residual soils. Such soils show a gradual transition downward into subsoil, and this in turn grades imperceptibly into rotted rock, which crumbles readily when exposed at the surface. The thickness of the subsoil varies greatly, for the depth to which rock is decayed is greater at some places than at others.

TRANSPORTED SOILS

Transported soils are those which are derived from the regolith or from previous soils and which

FIG. 8.17. *Window Rock, northwestern New Mexico. Differential weathering of sandstone has produced this natural window. (New Mexico State Tourist Bureau.)*

have been carried to their present positions from their places of origin. Transported soils are made up largely of material that is not weathered or that is only partly weathered. They owe their present positions to some agent of transportation, such as running water, wind, moving ice sheets, or gravity. Since these agents accomplish different degrees of sorting, transported soils vary in texture from fine silts to coarse gravel. They vary also in chemical composition; certain transported glacial soils are very fertile, since they are made up largely of ground-up rocks that have not been leached by water of certain valuable mineral foods that plants require.

Soil Characteristics

SOIL PROFILES

Soil scientists have found that soils developed for a long time under a given set of climatic conditions have acquired fairly uniform characteristics over wide areas. Such well-developed soils are said to be *mature.* They exhibit a well-marked soil profile, consisting of three main horizons, designated *A, B,* and *C.* These differ in color, texture, and structure and vary in thickness (Fig. 8.18).

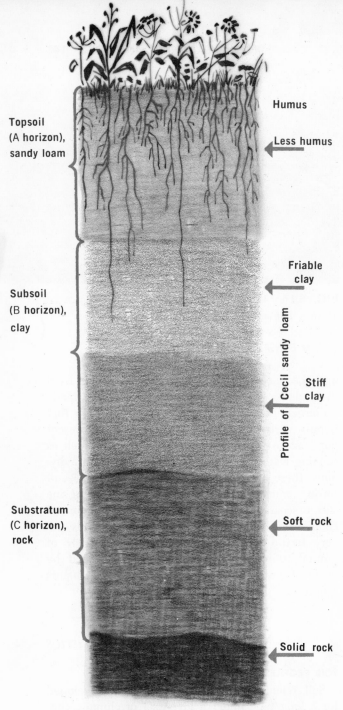

Topsoil (A horizon), sandy loam

Humus

Less humus

Subsoil (B horizon), clay

Friable clay

Profile of Cecil sandy loam

Stiff clay

Substratum (C horizon), rock

Soft rock

Solid rock

FIG. 8.18. *A mature soil profile, including a humus-rich sandy loam A horizon, a clayey B horizon, a somewhat weathered rock in the C horizon, and fresh solid rock below. (U.S. Soil Conservation Service.)*

The *A* horizon is the topsoil, generally rich in organic matter and in soil organisms. The intermediate, or *B*, horizon, sometimes called subsoil, has an accumulation of clay or iron minerals. It is more or less oxidized and leached. The secondary mineral deposits may constitute a continuous clay pan or iron pan. The *C* horizon is the unconsolidated, weathered parent material. Youthful soils lack good profiles.

SOIL CLASSIFICATION

The mature soils are grouped into classes determined by the prevailing climate and associated vegetation (Fig. 8.19).

Laterite (Latin *later*, brick) soils are developed by intense weathering in hot, humid climates under the rain forest. The material is high in iron and aluminum oxides and hydroxides, red or yellow in color, and leached of bases and silica.

Chernozem (Russian, black earth) soils are formed in temperate, subhumid climates, typically under tall-grass vegetation. The soil is black, granular in structure, fertile, and only moderately leached.

Podsol (Russian, salting, saltness) soils are developed in subarctic to cool, moist climates under a cover of coniferous or mixed hardwood and coniferous forest. The soil is ash gray, low in organic material (except for partly decayed surface matter), acid, leached, and underlain by a secondary clayey subsoil.

Desert soils are formed in arid regions under scanty vegetation. They are variable but are mostly low in organic matter, unleached, and light-colored.

These soil groups grade into each other through a complex series of intermediate or transitional types (see Table 8.1). In addition, special types of soils occur in peat bogs, on wind-blown sand, on alluvial plains, and in other local situations where the effects of the parent rock, youthfulness of the weathering, poor drainage, or erosion on steep slopes dominate over the effects of climate and vegetation. The U.S. Bureau of Soils recognizes more than 1,500 different soil types, but in many instances the differences are slight.

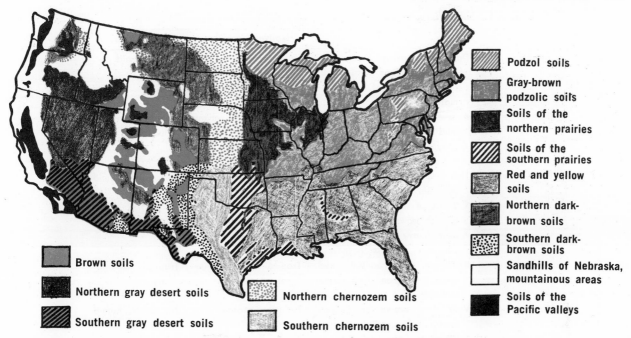

FIG. 8.19. *Climatic and vegetational soil groups of the United States. (After Marbut.)*

Soil Replenishment

Year by year soils are blown away by the wind, swept away by torrential downpours, or carried away by creeks and rivers to the sea. Farmers often provide small dams and earthworks to prevent their rich, dark soil from being gradually washed away. Soil on flood plains is so rich that many farmers risk repeated floods in order to work the land. For centuries, the Nile flood plain in Egypt has been noted for its continued fertility.

When topsoil is washed away, the new rock material exposed to weathering helps offset the loss and provides additional mineral substances necessary for plant life. Plants utilize a large number of materials for their growth. Derived from the atmosphere and from the soil, these substances include carbon, hydrogen, oxygen, nitrogen, phosphorus, sulfur, potassium, and calcium. Carbon, hydrogen, and oxygen are obtained from the air and water, and nitrogen may be taken from the atmosphere and developed in the soil by proper crop rotation. Clover, beans, peas, and similar crops add nitrogen compounds to the soil. In general, the phosphorus present in soils is derived from the mineral apatite (calcium phosphate) found in igneous rocks and from a quite similar substance found in sedimentary rocks. Potassium is present in orthoclase and in many shales and other sedimentary rocks. When soils are cultivated continually for many years, however, and particularly when grain is harvested and removed from the land, there is a steady decrease in fertility.

When soil has been exposed to weathering for ages with very little erosion and very little removal of rock matter to expose new minerals to decay, it must be enriched with mineral fertilizers —chiefly nitrates, phosphates, potash salts, and calcium salts. All these are added to certain soils in large amounts. Natural nitrates are obtained from the desert regions of Chile, where they have formed by the drying up of waters containing sodium nitrate and other salts. In recent years much nitrate has been made artificially from nitrogen of the air. Potash salts formerly were imported largely from Germany, where they are found with salt and

TABLE 8.1   *Soil Characteristics*

Soils	Profile	Native vegetation	Climate
Tundra	Dark-brown peaty layers over grayish horizons mottled with rust. Substrata of ever-frozen material	Lichens, moss, flowering plants, and shrubs	Frigid, humid
Podsol	A few inches of leaf mat and acid humus. A very thin, dark-gray A horizon, a dark-brown B horizon. Strongly acid	Coniferous or mixed coniferous and deciduous forest	Cool temperate, humid
Gray-brown	Thin leaf litter over mild humus over dark-colored surface soil 2 to 4 inches thick over grayish-brown leached horizon over heavy B horizon. Less acid than podsols	Mostly deciduous forest with mixture of conifers in places	Temperate, humid
Laterites	Red-brown surface soil. Red, deep B horizon. Red parent material	Tropical savanna vegetation	Tropical, wet-and-dry
Prairie	Very dark brown or grayish-brown soil grading through brown to lighter-colored parent material at a depth 2 to 5 feet	Tall-grass prairie	Temperate, humid
Chernozems	Black or very dark grayish-brown friable soil to a depth ranging up to 3 or 4 feet, grading through lighter color to whitish lime accumulation	Tall- and mixed-grass prairie	Temperate, sub-humid
Chestnut	Dark-brown friable and platy soil with lime accumulation at a depth of 1 to 4 feet	Mixed-grass prairie	Temperate to cool, semiarid
Sierozems	Pale-grayish soil grading into calcareous material at a depth of 1 foot or less	Desert plants, scattered short grass, and brush	Temperate to cool, arid

SOURCE: Adapted from *Agricultural Yearbook, 1938*, pp. 996–999, U.S. Department of Agriculture.

gypsum in beds evaporated from the ancient seas, but large amounts of potash salts have recently been found in West Texas, New Mexico, and Canada. The calcium phosphate of commerce is obtained chiefly from "rock phosphate," which is found in sedimentary beds. The phosphate is made more readily available by treatment with sulfuric acid. Calcium is added to the soil as calcium sulfate (gypsum) and calcium carbonate (powdered limestone). Often these substances are mixed to-gether as a fine powder and worked into the soil as the crop is planted, so that only a small amount may be required annually.

In agricultural regions the distribution and prosperity of the people are directly related to the fertility of the soil. Government agencies have been formed to give assistance to farmers by furnishing soil analyses and suggesting means of improving local soils by proper management, cultivation, and use of fertilizers.

Summary

We have seen how solid rocks are broken down to mantle-rock by various physical and chemical means, including freezing of water in pores and cracks, differential expansion and contraction from alternate heating and cooling, plant wedging, and animal activities. Boulder fields, talus piles, spalled surfaces, and granular debris result.

Many rock-forming minerals are chemically altered to clay minerals, more or less stained by iron oxide or hydroxide. At the same time, ions of calcium, sodium, magnesium, and potassium are released and carried away in solution.

Warm, wet climates favor decomposition, whereas cool, dry climates tend to limit weathering to disintegration.

Granites, basalts, limestones, ores, and other materials weather differently because of their different mineral contents. Unequal weathering produces hoodoos, pitted surfaces, natural bridges, and other irregularities.

Soils develop on residual, weathered rock or on loose transported material. When mature, they show characteristic profiles which reflect the influence of climate and vegetation. The depletion of elements essential to plant growth may be offset by the use of mineral fertilizers.

The alteration of rocks by weathering and the soils that result from this process are of prime importance to man. Not only are soil type and fertility important to agriculture, but weathering also enriches many ores. The upgrading of iron ores, the release of gold for concentration in placers, and the secondary enrichment of copper sulfide ores illustrate some of the important consequences.

Suggestions for Further Reading

Baver, Leonard David: *Soil Physics,* 3d ed., John Wiley & Sons, Inc., New York, 1956.

Bennett, Hugh Hammond: *Elements of Soil Conservation,* 2d ed., McGraw-Hill Book Company, Inc., New York, 1955.

Blackwelder, Eliot: "Exfoliation as a Phase of Rock Weathering," *J. Geol.,* vol. 33, pp. 793–806, 1925.

Jenny, Hans: *Factors of Soil Formation,* McGraw-Hill Book Company, Inc., New York, 1941.

Kellogg, C. E.: *The Soils That Support Us,* The Macmillan Company, New York, 1944. An introductory study of man's dependence on the soil.

Lyon, T. Lyttleton, H. O. Buckman, and N. C. Brady: *The Nature and Properties of Soils,* 5th ed., The Macmillan Company, New York, 1952.

Millar, C. E., L. M. Turk, and H. D. Foth: *Fundamentals of Soil Science,* John Wiley & Sons, Inc., New York, 1958.

Reiche, Parry: *A Survey of Weathering Processes and Products,* The University of New Mexico Press, Albuquerque, N.M., 1950. A very good study on weathering.

Thompson, L. M.: *Soils and Soil Fertility,* McGraw-Hill Book Company, Inc., New York, 1957. A study of the agricultural aspects of soils.

Chapter 9

SEDIMENTATION AND SEDIMENTARY ROCKS

SEDIMENTARY ROCKS are composed of rock particles (the products of weathering) and other materials; they form an extensive part of the earth's rocks and contain economically valuable deposits of such resources as coal, oil, and iron. In addition, they supply an excellent record of geologic age and history. Sedimentary rocks, unlike igneous, contain fossils, which can pinpoint a rock bed on the geologic time-table. Knowledge of the composition and structural characteristics of sedimentary rocks enables us to determine their origin and the conditions under which they were formed.

Sedimentation

SEDIMENTS AND SEDIMENTARY ROCKS

Sedimentary rocks are derived from the waste products of older rocks. Under the combined effect of atmospheric agents and processes, solid rocks constantly are decomposed and disintegrated. The resulting material, transported by such agents as running water, wind, and glacial ice, is ultimately deposited as sediment. Most of it is in the form of solid particles, but some is dissolved mineral matter carried in solution. Every stream, whether a small brook, a larger creek, or a great river, carries unconsolidated debris downstream. The coarser materials are rolled along the stream bed, the finer materials are carried in suspension, and the dissolved mineral matter is carried in solution.

FIG. 9.0. *The Grand Canyon of the Colorado River. The stratified sedimentary rocks in this beautiful gorge were laid down over a span of more than 200 million years. Although the beds immediately above the river level are tilted (center), the upper ones are nearly horizontal. (Fairchild Aerial Surveys.)*

Millions of tons of sediment are carried to the lakes and ocean basins every day. The Mississippi River alone transports and deposits on its delta more than a million tons every 24 hours. Much of the sand and gravel transported by a river is dropped temporarily in the form of sand bars or of beds in the slack-water parts of the stream's channel, but it is picked up again at the time of floods, when both the volume and velocity of the stream are greater.

During transportation, the solid rock fragments, such as gravel, sand, silt, and clay, tend to be sorted on the basis of size. Where a stream discharges into a body of quieter water, gravel is deposited near

the shore, sand is deposited farther out, and mud is deposited still farther out. Beyond the mud, or in clear water anywhere, the remains of organisms are deposited as calcareous matter. Thus, ideally, the belts of sediments are roughly parallel to the shore.

However, the orderly process of sedimentation may be modified by currents and bottom conditions that control wave action or interfere with the movement of the water shifting the sediment. Hence the different types of sediment are rarely pure, for the gravels generally contain sand, the sands generally contain mud or clay, the muds

FIG. 9.1. *Conglomerate, a sedimentary rock composed of gravel cemented together.*

contain fine sand or some calcareous matter, and the calcareous rocks may contain both clay and sand.

Because the conditions of sedimentation are not uniform or continuous, muddy sands may alternate with mud. Likewise, muds may be deposited with calcareous rocks. This alternation, or layering, of material, called *stratification,* is a feature of nearly all sedimentary rocks.

When deeply buried below younger beds, some sediments, such as mud, become consolidated by pressure as water is squeezed out of them. Others become coherent by *cementation.* Gravels become conglomerates (Fig. 9.1), sands become sandstone, muds become shales, and calcareous oozes become limestones.

Well-compacted sedimentary rocks or loose sediments not yet cemented or consolidated underlie approximately three-fourths of the area of the continents and much of the ocean floor. At some places they are many thousands of feet thick, and most of the continental landscape is sculptured out of such stratified rock formations. In the great chasms of the Grand Canyon and Zion Canyon, they are in their original, nearly horizontal position, but in many mountainous areas they are inclined at various angles. Some of these eroded areas are strikingly beautiful.

As noted above, sedimentary rocks are of great importance in geology because they furnish a historical record. Past life can be studied through the fossils sealed and preserved in the strata. Some fossil varieties are found only in beds that were formed at certain times, and thus serve to indicate the relative ages of the beds containing them. Other features of the rocks, such as their composition, color, and position, furnish information concerning the climate and other geographic features of the geologic past and the many changes that have occurred in and on the earth's crust. Rocks may contain a record of the area of former seas, their advance and retreat over parts of the continents, the time and degree of uplift of continental areas, and the time of formation of mountain ranges.

ORIGIN

On the basis of the origin of their components, sediments may be classified as (1) land-derived, or terrigenous; (2) organic; (3) volcanic; (4) magmatic; and (5) extraterrestrial, or meteoritic. Of these the land-derived materials are by far the most abundant.

Terrigenous. Large quantities of gravel, sand, and silt have their sources on the continents. In addition, land-derived solutions yield various chemical precipitates, including sodium chloride; calcium and magnesium carbonates; and iron, manganese, phosphatic, and barite concretions and nodules. Some of these inorganic precipitates are difficult to separate from those of biochemical origin. These terrigenous materials, both solids and solutions, are formed by the disintegration and decomposition of rocks of all kinds and represent the end products of erosion.

Organic. Organic sediments are those formed from constituents that were once dissolved in water and later extracted through the activity of plants and animals. Many organisms use inorganic substances in the development of their protective and supporting structures, such as bones, shells, and tests (the external shell of many of the invertebrates). These structures contain, in varying amounts, such constituents as phosphates, sulfides, iron oxides, calcium and magnesium carbonates, and silica, which accumulate as sediments when the organisms perish. Other organisms bring about chemical reactions that lead to the precipitation of sediments. Peat and coal are composed of the altered remains of plants.

Volcanic. Sediments of volcanic origin include the fragmental materials ejected from volcanoes and deposited in beds on land or in water. They consist of fine volcanic dust, ash, sand, and possibly stream-borne cinders and other coarse particles.

Magmatic. Sediments of magmatic origin are not extensive. They represent dissolved substances that were transported from within the earth by the heated waters associated with magmas. Much of the material reaches the surface in hot springs, which may make deposits on land, as in Yellowstone Park, or may discharge on the floor of the sea, adding their dissolved load to the sea water.

Meteoritic. The extraterrestrial materials come from outer space and result largely from the oxidation, or burning up, of meteorites in passing through the earth's atmosphere. The material from the meteorites then falls as very fine dust on land and sea alike.

As shown in Fig. 9.2, most sedimentary material is derived by the weathering and erosion of earlier rocks and the transportation and redeposition of the products so formed. Locally the volcanic contributions may be large. The principal agents of trans-

FIG. 9.2. *Derivation of sedimentary rocks.*

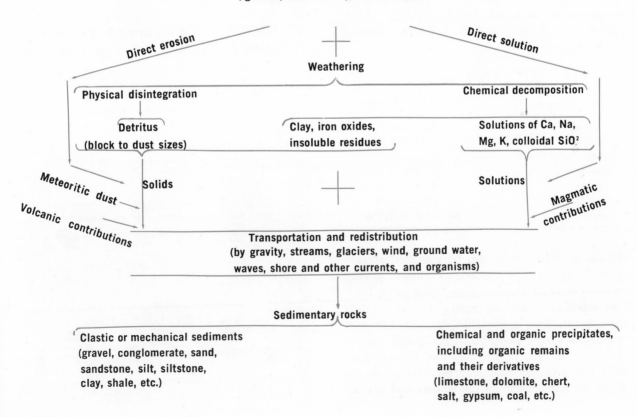

portation are gravity, streams, glaciers, waves and shore currents, wind, ground water, and organisms. In transit, the fragmental materials are subject to attrition, rounding, and sorting by size, shape, and specific gravity.

CLASSIFICATION

Sedimentary rocks have two main divisions: (1) *clastic*, or mechanically formed rocks; and (2) *nonclastic*, or chemically or organically formed rocks. Mixtures of both types, however, are very common, such as sandy shale, shaly limestone, carbonaceous shale, and gypsiferous shale. Since clastic sediments are solid and nonclastics are in solution, they are transported by different methods, which further segregate them.

Clastic. Clastic rocks result from the breaking up of other rocks. They include loose gravels, sands, and muds, as well as consolidated conglomerates, sandstones, and shales. The clastic sediments are classified further, according to the size of the constituent fragments, as boulders, cobbles, pebbles, granules, sands, silts, and clays. Several size classifications have been proposed, but the following is commonly accepted:

TABLE 9.1 *Classification of Fragments*

Name of fragment	Diameter, millimeters
Boulder	256 or more
Cobble	64–256
Pebble	4–64
Granule	2–4
Sand	1/16–2
Silt	1/256–1/16
Clay	Smaller than 1/256

Clastic sediments may also be classified according to the agent of deposition, as follows: gravity deposits (residual accumulations, talus piles, landslides, mudflows); aeolian, or wind-blown, deposits (dune sands, loess); fluviatile deposits (channel gravel, sand bars, flood-plain silt); and marine deposits. This type of classification, however, requires interpretation that may be difficult or uncertain. In some instances the shapes and surface markings of the pebbles and even of the sand grains may serve as clues to their history (Figs. 9.3, 9.4).

Nonclastic. Nonclastic rocks are derived only indirectly from the decomposition, solution, and redeposition of other rocks. In general, they are formed through the agency of some form of life or by chemical precipitation. These sediments are even more difficult to classify than the clastic sediments, for they differ widely in texture, composition, and conditions of deposition. The simplest scheme is to classify them on the basis of their chemical or mineralogical composition, as follows: calcareous (limestone of many varieties), ferruginous (bog iron ore, hematite rock), phosphatic (phosphorite), and siliceous (chert, flint, diatomite, geyserite). Many of them are marine; others are products of fresh-water lakes, salt lakes, springs, or other geologic settings.

MINERAL COMPOSITION

Because the minerals of sedimentary rocks have undergone alteration and sorting, they differ considerably from those of the parent igneous rocks. The differences are summarized in part in Table 9.2. Quartz is abundant in most sandstones; clay

FIG. 9.3. *The sizes and shapes of pebbles are varied and often give clues to their history. A, rounded, as worn away by water; B, subrounded; C, angular; D, disklike; E, faceted and striated glacial; F, dreikanter, faceted by wind-blown sand. About one-fourth natural size. (After Grout.)*

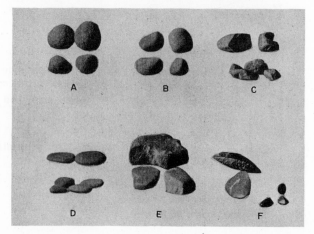

TABLE 9.2   *Mineral Composition of Average Igneous and Sedimentary Rocks*

Igneous rocks		Sedimentary rocks		
Minerals	Per cent	Minerals	Shale, per cent	Sandstone, per cent
Quartz	12	Quartz	22.3	66.8
Feldspar	59.5	Feldspars	30.0	11.5
Pyroxenes and amphiboles	16.8	"Clay"	25.0	6.6
Micas	3.8	Limonite	5.6	1.8
Other minerals	7.9	Carbonates	5.7	11.1
Total	100.0	Other minerals	11.4	2.2
		Total	100.0	100.0

SOURCE: F. W. Clarke and H. S. Washington, *U.S. Geol. Survey Prof. Paper* 127, 1924, p. 31.

minerals become prominent in shales; and calcite and dolomite are abundant in limestones. As compared with the parent igneous rocks, sedimentary rocks show a noteworthy decrease in feldspars, pyroxenes and amphiboles, and micas.

PROPORTIONS

It is estimated that the crust, or outer 10 miles, of the earth is composed of 95 per cent igneous rocks and 5 per cent sedimentary rocks. Of the sedimentary rocks on the continents about 58 per cent are shales, about 22 per cent sandstones (and conglomerates), and 20 per cent limestones (Pettijohn). However, calculations of the chemical composition of sedimentary rocks with relation to igneous rocks (the ultimate source) show that 70 per cent should be shales, 16 per cent sandstones, and 14 per cent limestones (Holmes). Despite the abundance of shales on land, it is clear that part of the shaly material must have been lost to the deep sea. In any event, the preponderance of shale, about two-thirds of all sedimentary rock, is striking. The minor types of sediment, such as coal, gypsum, phosphate rock, and chert, make up less than 1 per cent of the total volume.

CONSOLIDATION

As sediments increase in thickness, the lower beds are pressed together by the weight of the overlying beds and are rendered more compact. Lateral pressure or any other movement may bring the rock particles closer together, driving out water, decreasing the pore space, and consolidating the rock, especially a shale. Nevin[1] estimates that compaction reduces pore space in mud from 50 per cent at a depth of 100 feet to 33 per cent at a depth of 500 feet, to 18 per cent at 4,000 feet, and to 10 per cent at 6,000 feet.

Nonclastic sediments are consolidated partly by compaction and partly by recrystallization into

[1] Charles M. Nevin, *Structural Geology*, 4th ed., John Wiley & Sons, Inc., 1949, p. 210.

FIG. 9.4.   *Photomicrograph of quartz sand grains somewhat battered and worn during their transportation.*

strongly coherent masses. In medium- and coarse-grained clastic sediments, however, the most important consolidating process is cementation. The ground waters percolating through the sediments carry calcium carbonate, silica, iron oxides, or other cementing materials into the pore spaces between the fragments. There they are deposited, and the grains or larger fragments are cemented into a solid mass. The common solid clastic sedimentary rocks are the results of this process (Fig. 9.5).

In general, the older sediments are more highly consolidated than the younger ones. However, exceptions occur where the older material was never consolidated or where the cementing material has been dissolved and removed, so as to restore the sediments to a loose condition.

TEXTURES

The textures of most sediments may be described as (1) fragmental, (2) crystalline, (3) oölitic (including pisolitic and spherulitic), or (4) colloform.

Forms resulting directly from the activities of organisms—shells, bones, teeth, fragments of coral, siliceous skeletons of diatoms and radiolarians, calcareous tests of foraminifera, amorphous or replaced pellets of excrement, and so on—usually are classified as organic structures rather than as tex-

tures. The particles range in size texturally from microscopic grains through silt and sand grades upward to very coarse pieces. These organic forms will be more fully discussed later in this chapter, in the section on structure.

Fragmental. Fragmental textures range from very fine-grained clays to coarse boulders or blocks. They occur in clastic or mechanical sediments such as mud, sand, gravel, sandstone, and conglomerate.

Crystalline. Crystalline textures occur in evaporites and other rocks precipitated from aqueous solutions. The crystals may be microscopic, as in chert; fine-grained, as in common limestone; or coarse-grained, as in some rock salt and in certain limestones. The grains in crystalline rocks, instead of having definite crystal outlines, are commonly so crowded together that they interlock irregularly in a sort of mosaic. In some sedimentary rocks, however, well-formed crystals have developed later by crystallization or by replacement (Fig. 9.6).

Oölitic. The term oölitic means egglike (Greek *oion*, egg). An oölitic sedimentary rock is made up almost entirely of small shotlike bodies crowded together into a solid mass. The individual spherules are composed of concentric shells of calcite deposited about some minute grain, such as a grain of sand or a fragment of a shell (Fig. 9.7). When the spherules are about the size of peas, the rock is said to be pisolitic (Greek *pison*, pea). Particles showing a radial internal structure but lacking the

FIG. 9.5. *A quartz sandstone cemented with calcite, as seen in a magnified thin section. This type of rock is formed when ground water deposits cementing material in the pore spaces between the sand grains.*

FIG. 9.6. *Rhombic dolomite crystals in the Oneota formation, as seen in thin section.*

concentric laminations of oölites and pisolites are called spherulitic.

Oölites are found among the rocks of all geologic ages, and in many instances the evidence suggests that the small spherules were formed by accretionary growth during the deposition of the material that later was consolidated. Oölitic sands are now forming on the shores of Great Salt Lake, Utah, and off some of the coral islands of the Pacific. These modern oölites are calcareous (limestone), but in some older rocks the oölites are composed of chert, hematite, or other substances, which apparently replaced the original calcite. Other oölites and pisolites, less regular in structure, have been found in bauxite, phosphorite, and some iron ores, and these also were presumably formed by replacement of earlier substances.

Since oölites are about the size of sand grains, they are readily subject to transportation and redeposition, and so some oölitic rocks are crossbedded.

Colloform. Particles with colloform (Greek *kolla*, glue) texture result from the coagulation of bits of colloid, or gel, which subsequently lose water, shrink, and harden. Their roundish forms, amorphous internal structure, and shrinkage cracks help to identify them. In some cases, however, their colloidal origin has been obscured by later crystallization.

COLOR

Sedimentary rocks vary in color according to their composition. They may be white from relatively pure quartz, kaolinite, calcite, or other light-colored minerals; green from ferrous iron silicates; red from hematite (or less often from red feldspar, garnet, or red cinders); yellow or brown from limonite; black from organic matter, black minerals, dark rock fragments, or finely divided iron sulfide; or gray from a mixture of light and dark ingredients. Colors depend upon such factors as purity, degree of oxidation of iron compounds, and amount of organic matter.

The color of a sedimentary bed is characteristic only over limited areas and may differ with the degree of weathering to which it has been subjected. Thus limestones that vary widely in original

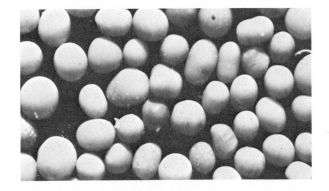

FIG. 9.7. *Photomicrographs of oölites from Great Salt Lake, Utah. Above, loose oölites from the southeast shore, enlarged 15 diameters; below, thin section of cemented oölites, enlarged about 35 diameters. The more or less complete radial and concentric structures are shown.* (A. J. Eardley.)

color may all weather to buff, and the residual clays resulting from their solution may be red. Gray or black shales may weather to a red clay. The red iron oxide which colors the clay may be the oxidation product of pyrite, disseminated through limestone or shale so finely that its presence is scarcely detected in the fresh rock.

Common Sedimentary Rocks

CONGLOMERATE

Conglomerates are rounded gravels (pebbles, cobbles, or boulders) that are held together by some kind of cement (Fig. 9.1). In many conglomerates the pebbles are chiefly quartz, since quartz is the most common mineral that possesses great resistance to disintegration and wear. Other siliceous minerals, such as flint, chert, and jasper, also are common, but the pebbles of a conglomerate may be made up of any kind of rock fragments. Thus, for example, there are limestone conglomerates and basalt conglomerates.

BRECCIA

Breccias are rocks composed of the cemented angular fragments of other rocks (Fig. 9.8). It is evident that the angular constituents of breccia have not been transported by water far from the source of the material. Breccias may be made from talus accumulations or any other angular rock debris. They grade into conglomerates when the fragments show signs of rounding as a result of transportation by water.

SANDSTONE

A sandstone is a bed of sand cemented to form a coherent mass. The cement may be the light-colored silica or calcium carbonate or the red, yellow, or brown iron oxide. If quartz sand is thoroughly cemented by silica, the rock is quartzite. Sand grains may be angular, subangular, or well-rounded. Their surfaces may be pitted, owing perhaps to impact in transit, or frosted, like the surface of ground glass. Thus the grains tell something of their history.

Most sands are made up chiefly of quartz fragments, but sands made of fine grains of olivine are found along the Bay of Naples, sands of calcium carbonate are found at Bermuda, and sands composed of gypsum are found in New Mexico. Certain sands are composed of magnetite, and others partly of tin oxide or of gold, but all such sands are unusual.

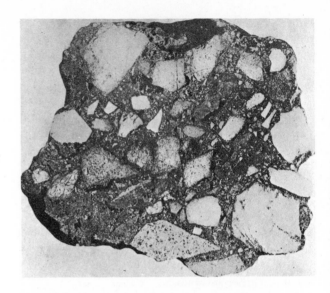

FIG. 9.8. *A breccia consisting of angular fragments cemented together. The angularity of breccia fragments shows they have undergone little, if any, water transportation.*

Sandstones grade through coarse-grained sands into conglomerates and through fine-grained sands into shales. Sandstones that contain an appreciable amount of calcium carbonate are calcareous sandstones (Fig. 9.5); if they contain clay, they are argillaceous sandstones. Occasionally a sandstone contains pebbles, sometimes strung along a bedding plane or scattered randomly in the sand. Such a rock is not a conglomerate, however, but a pebbly sandstone. A coarse sandstone, especially if the grains are sharp, is a grit.

GREENSAND

Grains of glauconite may be common or abundant in a sandstone. If they are more abundant than quartz grains, the sandstone is called greensand, or glauconitic sandstone. It is frequently found among some of the older sediments and is now forming in the ocean.

ARKOSE

Arkose is a clean sandstone composed principally of quartz and feldspar (especially orthoclase), indurated by chemical cement. Since the feldspar grains are largely unaltered, the grains evidently come mainly from disaggregated, but not decomposed, granite. Their derivation can be attributed to the high relief and rapid erosion of a granitic terrain, possibly in a cool or semiarid climate, where disintegration exceeds chemical decomposition.

GRAYWACKE

Graywackes are sandstones that contain considerable quartz, feldspar, and rock fragments, set in an originally muddy matrix (more than 15 per cent) that has usually recrystallized to muscovite mica, chlorite, and quartz. Graywackes are associated with marine shales, volcanic tuffs, cherts, and submarine lavas, or their metamorphosed equivalents. Their graded bedding suggests that they were deposited by submarine turbidity flows of sand and mud.

SHALE

Shale is composed of compacted or cemented beds of mud or clay. It includes the finest products of rock decay, which are swept farther out to sea than any other clastic sediment. Shales usually are thin-bedded, showing frequent changes in the fineness of materials composing them. Such variations in grain may be due to seasonal changes, or they may represent differences in rainfall or some other change that affected the amount or character of the sediment brought down by streams. Shales that contain sand are arenaceous; those that contain calcium carbonate are calcareous; those containing iron are ferruginous; and those containing large amounts of organic matter are carbonaceous. The carbonaceous shales usually are black, and sometimes they grade into beds of coal. Some of the ancient shales remain as beds of clay and differ from the deposits originally formed only in that they have been pressed together slightly.

Thin-bedded limestones or sandstones often are referred to as shaly, and many of them grade into shale. The weathering of limestones may give rise to beds of clay, which represent the insoluble residue of the limestone. Red-clay beds may be formed in this way. When covered by later sediments, these residual clays mark ancient erosion surfaces.

LIMESTONE

Limestone, the most abundant nonclastic sediment, is solid rock composed of calcium carbonate and formed mainly by the shells and skeletal materials of lime-secreting plants and animals. Such organisms extract this material from sea water to form their hard parts. The spaces between the shells are filled by fine calcareous materials resulting from the grinding action of waves.

Limestones are formed in relatively clear, shallow water where life is abundant and where the neighboring land areas are too low or too distant to contribute large quantities of clastic sediments. Living bacteria may cause the precipitation of calcium carbonate in sea water, and under some conditions limestone may be deposited by chemical precipitation. However, many limestones, whether fossiliferous or not, are composed of material that probably once formed organic remains (Fig. 9.9).

Limestone grades into shale when more clay is added to the calcareous sediments. When sand is added, the limestone grades into calcareous sandstone; with more sand, it may further grade into ordinary sandstone.

FIG. 9.9. *A slab of fossiliferous limestone from western New York. (Hardin, U.S. Geological Survey.)*

DOLOMITE

When a fourth to nearly a half of the calcium in a limestone is replaced by magnesium, the rock is dolomite (Fig. 9.10). If less than a fourth has been replaced, the rock is a dolomitic limestone. Dolomite is common in limestones of all ages. It is formed either during the process of sedimentation or by later substitution of magnesium for calcium. Dolomites and dolomitic limestones are less soluble than ordinary limestones and hence endure longer on exposure.

CHALK

Chalk is a special type of limestone usually composed of small shells or shell fragments cemented together. Foraminifera tests constitute a large part of the material, but shells of other organisms also are commonly present.

Chalk usually is soft, porous, and white or gray; some of it is massive in appearance. The chalk cliffs of Dover, England, are an example. Some of the chalks of the Southwest, particularly of Texas, grade into resistant beds that are as well indurated as ordinary limestones, and such beds are found capping the buttes and mesas of the region.

FIG. 9.10.   *Massive bedded dolomite (calcium-magnesium carbonate) along Stockton Hill in the Gilmore Valley at Winona, Minnesota.*

MARL

The porous masses of shells and shell fragments that accumulate on the bottoms of many freshwater lakes are shell marls. Large amounts of marls are formed by the lime-secreting alga *Chara;* the best-known example of Chara marl occurs at Pyramid Lake, Nevada. The term marl is used also to designate certain marine sediments, presumably formed at the outer margin of the shale mud, which contain a mixture of clay and finely divided shell fragments. Marine muds composed chiefly of calcium carbonate are sometimes called marls, but this practice is not general. The greensands of New Jersey usually are called greensand marls. Soil in which clay and calcium carbonate are present in about equal amounts is also termed marl.

COQUINA

Coquina is a limestone composed of loosely aggregated shells and shell fragments. This term usually is applied to relatively recent deposits of cemented shell heaps, such as those forming off the coast of parts of Florida, but it is also used to designate similar shell masses belonging to much older formations in which the mass is well consolidated.

OÖLITE

An oölite is a rock consisting of small concentrically built-up particles resembling fish roe (Fig. 9.7). The term oölitic generally is applied to the texture of the rock only; in composition, oölites may be siliceous, calcareous, phosphatic, or ferruginous. Commonly a sand grain or a shell fragment forms the center of the accretionary growth.

TUFA AND TRAVERTINE

Tufas are calcareous deposits formed about the mouths of springs; they are generally earthy, porous, or spongy. *Travertines*, deposits of calcite in limestone caves, are commonly banded (as in Mexican onyx), laminated, or stalactitic.

CHERT AND FLINT

Chert is a compact, dense, siliceous material that occurs both as distinct layers and as roundish nodules distributed through beds of other rocks, chiefly limestones. Either the silica was deposited in colloidal form as a primary precipitate, or silica-bearing waters partially replaced the associated sediments. Replacement is indicated when earlier textures and structures, including organic forms, are preserved. The secondary silica for such replacement may have come from re-solution of the primary silica of colloids or of hard parts of sponges or other siliceous organisms or from water squeezed out of other sediments during their consolidation. Both primary and secondary methods of chert deposition are known.

Flint, a dark-gray to black variety of chert, is essentially silica with some water, but the names chert and flint commonly are used interchangeably. In the Stone Age, man used flint (or chert) to fashion arrow points, and later he used it with steel to kindle fire. Agate is a banded variety of chert generally used for ornamental purposes, but also for laboratory mortars and pestles. Taconite is a granular ferruginous chert (15 to 35 per cent iron) found in the Lake Superior region.

DIATOMACEOUS EARTH

Diatoms are minute plants that have siliceous skeletons. They live in great numbers in the sea and in fresh-water lakes. When they die, their skeletons accumulate to form diatomaceous earth. At many places their accumulations form papery gray to white layers interbedded with shales. Such beds have high porosity and may contain much water, but, when dried, they will float on water. At Lompoc, California, and elsewhere, thousands of feet of diatomaceous shales are found.

COAL

Occurrence. Coal is the familiar, dark-colored, organic rock derived from peat. It occurs in lenses or continuous beds, interbedded with other sedimentary rocks (Fig. 9.11). The beds of coal range in thickness from a fraction of an inch to many tens of feet. Most of them are less than 3 feet thick and not workable. Some of them extend over large areas. An example is the Pittsburgh coal bed, which is workable over an area of more than 6,000 square miles and reaches a maximum thickness of 13 feet.

Origin. Coal was formed by (1) the accumulation and partial decomposition of vegetation in ancient peat bogs or swamps, (2) burial under a thick cover of other rocks, and (3) conversion of the peat to coal by heat and pressure.

Old stumps with roots still penetrating the former soil below the coal, the preservation of delicate plant structures such as fern fronds, and the common lack of a mixture of sand indicate that the coal usually was formed where the original plants grew. A few coals, however, were formed from vegetation that drifted into bays and estuaries.

Accumulation of peat. Peat accumulates in swamps or bogs whenever the rate of growth of the swamp plants exceeds the rate of decay. Ordinarily the dead vegetation reverts to water, carbon dioxide, and other products of decay through the action of molds and bacteria. Decay may be arrested or inhibited, however, by the development of toxins in the swamp water or by the smothering effect of burial under additional vegetation or sediments. The preservative effect of swamp water upon buried logs is well known.

FIG. 9.11. *Section showing typical relations of coal beds to associated strata in the eastern interior coal basin.*

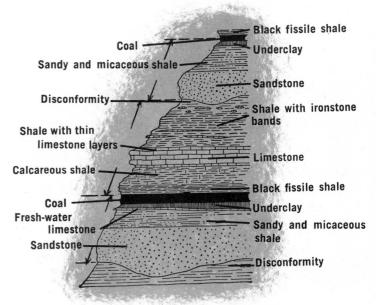

Humid temperate climates favor the formation of peat. Hot and wet tropical climates promote plant growth but also speed up decay, so tropical swamps contain little peat. Cold climates, on the other hand, retard plant growth and therefore restrict peat thicknesses.

Peat in present-day swamps and lakes ranges in texture from coarse woody or fibrous types through disintegrated, partly rotted bits, to a soft, nearly structureless, cheeselike mass, because of differences in the former plants, the degree of decay, and the depth of water. Pollen grains usually persist and may be used to identify the former flora.

Burial. Burial of peat virtually stops decay. Almost any type of sediment may bury peat, but most coal beds lie under shale, sandstone, and limestone (Fig. 9.11). The sediments now covering the coal were deposited by streams overflowing the swamps or by the sea after marine submergence of the swamp sites. The tops of subsiding deltas were especially favorable places for widespread peat accumulation and subsequent burial.

That the swamps stood relatively near sea level is suggested by the fact that coal-bearing strata ordinarily include many alternations of marine and nonmarine beds. In some coal fields a half-dozen or more coal beds lie one above another, separated by various thicknesses of other sedimentary rocks.

Conversion of peat to coal. Where the beds never were deeply buried or crumpled by earth movements, the coal is lignite. Where they were both deeply covered and highly folded, the coal is anthracite. In between come intermediate ranks of coal. The coal series is lignite (brown coal), subbituminous, bituminous, and anthracite. These ranks reflect the degree of chemical change caused by the weight of the overlying beds and by earth movements. In this series, in the order named, water and volatile gases decrease, and the percentage of carbon increases correspondingly. Lignite contains 30 or 40 per cent water, subbituminous coal 10 or 20 per cent, bituminous coal 5 or 10 per cent, and anthracite less than 3 per cent. Anthracite is high in carbon (90 per cent or more on an ash-free basis). The ash content of coals increases from a few per cent in clean, low-rank coals to 8 or 10 per cent in anthracite. Many coals, however, contain foreign mineral matter, and so their ash content is high. With increase in such impurities, coal grades into "bone coal" and black shale.

Coal as a fuel will be discussed later in this chapter, in the section on mineral resources.

PHOSPHATE ROCK

Most igneous rocks contain small amounts of the mineral apatite, a calcium phosphate. Ground water dissolves the phosphate, and plants and animals utilize it in their life processes. Small amounts of phosphate are carried to the sea and are deposited there in beds. Such beds, raised above the sea, have become available to man, and the phosphate rock is used in large amounts for fertilizer. The largest deposits of rock phosphate in the United States are found in Montana, Idaho, and Wyoming, where they are associated with limestone and cover extensive areas. Valuable deposits are found also in Florida, South Carolina, Tennessee, and Kentucky.

Some phosphate deposits have formed by replacement of coral or other limestone. In particular, this takes place when phosphate is leached by ground water, carried downward until it reaches a limestone bed, and then precipitated.

SALT AND GYPSUM

The composition of sea water is given on page 41. When sea water evaporates completely, the salts are precipitated out of solution and are deposited. The least soluble salts are deposited first. If calcium carbonate and iron oxide are present in the water, they are the first materials to be precipitated. Gypsum, $CaSO_4 . 2H_2O$, follows, and often with it some anhydrite, $CaSO_4$, is formed. After gypsum, common salt, $NaCl$, is deposited. The bitter salts consisting of sulfates and chlorides of potassium and magnesium are precipitated last. They are so soluble that they are not always deposited where salt and gypsum form, and even if they are deposited, commonly they are dissolved again. Great beds of salt and gypsum are interbedded with sedimentary rocks in Texas, Kansas, Michigan, Ontario, Ohio, and New York. Wherever soluble salts are formed, they are likely to be dissolved again unless they are protected to some extent against solution by water. In general, where they are found preserved, muds and clays, which keep out water, have been deposited above them.

At many places, red beds are associated with salt and gypsum. These beds, usually red sandstone and shale, are red because they contain small amounts of disseminated hematite, and we believe that they have formed in part under arid, or at least seasonally dry, conditions. Salt and gypsum are precipitated under arid conditions in bodies of water that have been cut off from the sea. They are also found in bays that extend landward from the sea, if water flows into the bay and is evaporated. This process is illustrated in the Gulf of Karabugaz on the east side of the Caspian Sea.

Karabugaz Gulf is only about 50 feet deep, and it covers about 7,500 square miles. It lies in a semi-desert region and is partly separated from the Caspian Sea by sandspits that form a barrier preventing free circulation between the sea and the gulf. The waters of the Caspian Sea contain about 1.3 per cent mineral matter. Evaporation removes the water from the surface as fast as it is brought in through the restricted connection with the sea. The water of the gulf becomes more highly concentrated than that of the Caspian Sea, and the less soluble salts are precipitated. Such marginal lagoons, or gulfs, are not uncommon, and in areas of great evaporation salt deposits may form in them.

Salt water and brine often are encountered in deep drilling, and crystals of salts may occur in shales or in other sediments below the surface. The brines of eastern Ohio and adjacent regions contain bromides in addition to common salt. These brines may be sea water trapped in the sediments at the time of their formation. However, some of them are more concentrated than sea water and probably have been changed greatly since they were a part of the sea.

BEDDED IRON ORE

Iron is found abundantly in various forms. On weathering under reducing conditions, it may be dissolved and carried in solution to fresh-water bogs or to the sea, where it is precipitated by chemical or biochemical reactions. In certain beds it has formed in large amounts. By surface enrichments under oxidizing conditions, these beds may become iron ore. Examples will be described under Sedimentary Rocks as Mineral Resources.

OTHER SEDIMENTARY ROCKS

The sedimentary rocks of major importance have been described in the preceding paragraphs. Several other types that deserve attention are summarized in Table 9.3.

TABLE 9.3   *Sedimentary Rocks of Lesser Importance*

Adobe	Argillaceous soil used for making sun-dried bricks
Bone bed	A rock, commonly limestone, containing numerous bones, usually fishbones
Buhrstone	Porous cherty or siliceous rock formerly used for millstones
Caliche	Soil cemented by calcareous, nitrogenous, or other salts that rose and were deposited by evaporation at the surface
Chalcedony	Cryptocrystalline silica (having very small crystals), probably a precipitate from a colloidal state
Catlinite	A red-clay "slate" containing abundant diaspore, an aluminum hydroxide mineral; carves easily and was used by Indians for making pipes; also called pipestone
Fire clay	A tough clay usually found underlying a coal seam; makes refractory bricks
Fuller's earth	Fine earthy clay with low plasticity
Guano	Phosphatic and nitrogenous materials formed from the excrement of animals
Gumbo	Clayey soils which become sticky mud when wet
Ironstone	A rock containing iron, commonly with clay or sand
Jasper	A siliceous red or variously colored rock resembling chalcedony

RECYCLING OF SEDIMENTARY ROCKS

Once formed, sedimentary rocks are, of course, not permanent; instead, they are subject to weathering and redistribution in the same way as other earth materials.

FIG. 9.12. *Sample cores of laminated (varved) clay, showing seasonal layers. The summer layer consists of light-colored coarse silt. The winter layer is darker and fine-grained. Varved layers are found in glacial lake deposits. These samples are from deposits at Haverstraw, New York, and New Haven, Connecticut. (American Museum of Natural History.)*

Conglomerates and sandstones may be broken into pieces ranging in size from boulders to dust. In addition, the original particles may be altered by chemical decomposition. Thus, feldspathic constituents may be converted to clay, iron-bearing silicates may become iron oxide or hydroxide, and calcium, magnesium, sodium, and potassium may be taken into solution. In time, only the minerals very resistant to weathering, such as quartz, may be left unaltered. When these weathered products are washed away, the resistant sand-sized grains may be sorted out from the fine clay particles so as to make a second-generation sandstone higher in quartz than the first. This type of recycling, when repeated several times, may result in a high-silica sandstone composed almost entirely of quartz grains. Quartz-pebble conglomerates presumably have had a similar development.

Shales, when weathered, break down into chips and tend to revert to mud. Silt particles in shale, incompletely weathered during the previous round, may then decompose further and increase the per-

centage of clay in the next deposit. Most shales weather readily.

Calcium carbonate removed from limestone by solution can be redeposited as another limestone under appropriate conditions elsewhere. Insoluble residues of clay, chert, iron oxide, and so on, upon release from the limestone, may be used in new clastic sediments.

Primary Structural Features

STRATIFICATION

The arrangement of sediments in layers, or strata, is their most distinctive structural feature. When the stratification is marked by a change in color, it it referred to as banding. Sediments can be called stratified when they readily separate into layers along bedding planes. Stratification can be due to different sizes and kinds of material or to some interruption in deposition that permitted changes to take place before more material was deposited. The difference in character of sediments may result from (1) variations in currents, (2) seasonal changes (Fig. 9.12), (3) climatic changes, (4) fluctuations of sea level, or (5) marked changes in the types or number of organisms. The individual layers range in thickness from a fraction of an inch in some clayey muds to many feet in coarser sediments. If the bedding planes are close together, the sediment is "thin-bedded"; and if they are far apart, it is "massive," or "heavy-bedded."

When the beds are laid down, they are generally nearly parallel to the surface over which they are deposited. As a rule they are approximately horizontal. At many places, however, the surfaces of deposition are undulating, and inclined stratification results. Sediments may be deposited in orderly sequence upon surfaces inclined as much as 30 degrees. The steepest slopes formed by deposition are found in small bodies of water and protected bays where there is slight agitation and very limited spreading of sediments.

CROSS-BEDDING

Cross-bedded sediments are those that show laminae inclined obliquely to the planes of general stratification (Fig. 9.13). Coarse sediments, such as pebbles and sand, are more likely to show cross-bedding, although some sandy shales and limestones are cross-bedded. Wherever steep slopes are produced by the rapid deposition of sediments, whether in rivers, lakes, or the sea, as at the front of a delta or on offshore bars, or barriers, inclined stratification occurs. Succeeding beds again may assume a horizontal position, and the cross-bedded layers thus may be interstratified with horizontal ones. Wind-laid deposits, such as sand dunes, characteristically are cross-bedded as the result of deposition on steep slopes at the front of the growing deposit (Fig. 9.13).

GRADED BEDDING

When a turbulent mixture of particles of different sizes, shapes, and densities is brought to the site of sedimentation, the coarser, heavier, and more nearly spherical grains tend to settle more rapidly than the others. As the smaller, lighter, and more angular ones follow in a more or less progressive series, the

FIG. 9.13. *Varieties of cross-bedding: (a) ordinary marine near-shore type; (b) common fluvial-current type; (c) torrential-stream type; (d) aeolian type, or dune structure.*

(c)

(d)

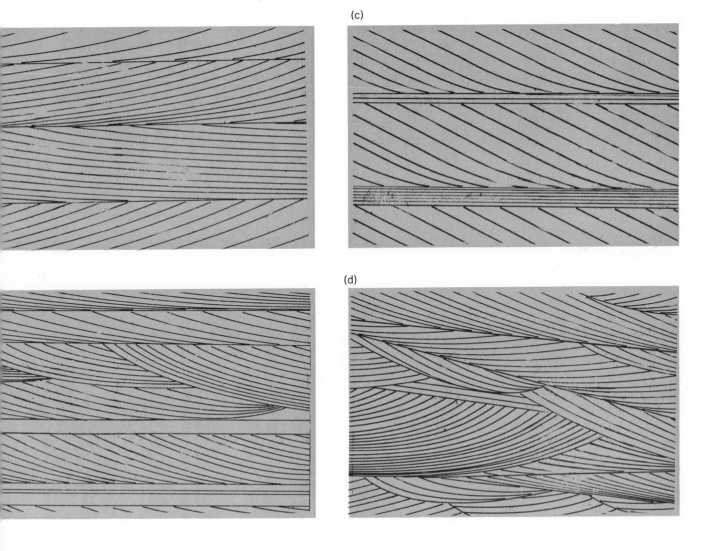

bed of sediment finally accumulated tends to show a segregation of the particles determined by their relative rates of settling. Thus the bottom portion of a bed may consist of coarse or heavy particles, whereas the upper portion is made up of relatively fine or light particles. Such an arrangement is called graded bedding (Fig. 9.14). Repetition of the process may develop graded bedding within each of the succeeding layers.

Where sedimentary rocks have been upended or, possibly, overturned by earth movements, graded bedding is useful to a geologist as a means of distinguishing the original tops and bottoms of the beds.

LENTICULAR BEDS

Massive beds, such as sandstones or limestones, at many places decrease rapidly in thickness and may be seen even to "pinch out" when traced along the face of a cliff. This is called lenticular bedding, and it is especially common in deposits

FIG. 9.14.   *Graded bedding.*

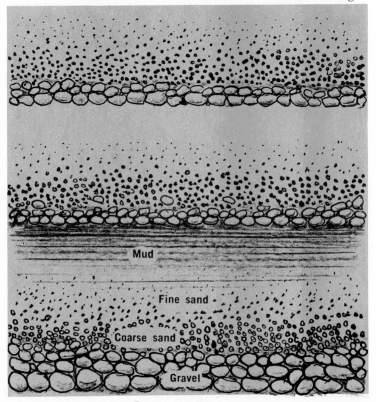

Mud

Fine sand

Coarse sand

Gravel

made at the outlets of rivers or in stream deposits generally. However, it is not limited to such localities. Where one kind of sediment grades into another kind, the change in thickness often takes place through an interbedded area, in which the ends of the beds are lenticular, or pinched out. Thus the bedding evidently is not parallel, although it is not to be classed as cross-bedding.

MUD CRACKS

Mud cracks are caused by shrinkage of mud on drying (Fig. 9.15). River flood plains and the floors of playa lakes (temporary desert lakes) are favorable sites. Some mud cracks are several inches wide and 10 times as deep. When the mud is thoroughly dried out, such cracks may remain open for months or even years. When water again covers them and sedimentation is renewed, they are filled by this later and perhaps different kind of sediment. In that event the sediment, when thoroughly indurated, preserves the mud cracks indefinitely in solid rock.

Where a mud-cracked area dries rapidly, under certain conditions the patches thus blocked out on the surface may peel and roll into cylinders. These *clay galls*, if preserved in the oncoming sediment, may resemble pebbles and produce a desiccation conglomerate.

RIPPLE MARKS

Ripple marks usually are formed by the drag of waves in relatively shallow water (Figs. 9.16, 9.17). They consist of a series of small, almost equally spaced ridges of sand or other fine sediment. They have rather sharp crests and may be symmetrical or asymmetrical, depending on the motion that formed them (Figs. 9.18, 9.19). Oscillatory or undulatory waves give rise to ripples with symmetrical sides, whereas currents at sea or in streams give rise to ripples with asymmetrical sides, the long slope being in the direction from which the current came.

As the undulation dies out in deeper water, the crests of the ripple marks are more closely spaced, although the coarseness or fineness of the sediment also affects the spacing.

Waves in shallow water may be too violent at the contact of water and sediment to produce ripple marks. Their action is destructive, and any ripple marks that may have been formed during a more quiet sea are obliterated. Modification of previous ripple marks may leave patterns that cross or interfere.

Sand waves, or giant ripple marks, may be formed by flooded streams or by tidal currents in narrow straits. Their crests may be 15 to 35 feet apart and 2 or 3 feet above the troughs.

The wind also makes ripple marks on sand dunes, and these resemble some of those formed in water.

RILL MARKS

As the tide retreats or storm waves die down, some water left in the sand of a beach finds its way back to the sea as rivulets that branch again and again, like the distributaries on a delta plain. These tiny channels are rill marks. They are observed on modern beach sands and are also found in consolidated sediments, where they may be mistaken for plant impressions.

WAVEMARKS

Wavemarks are formed on the sloping sands of a beach by the outer margins of spent waves. They show up as lines of fine sand grains, fragments of shells, bits of mica, bubbles, and flotsam. These wavemarks usually are festooned with loops extending landward, and the angles are marked by heaps of shells or other light sediments. Seaward from the outermost mark, the patterns produced by the sloshing water have an imbricated design like overlapping scales. Although they are abundant on beaches, not many wavemarks are known to be preserved in solid rock.

RAINDROP IMPRESSIONS

Raindrop impressions are made by drops of water falling onto the soft mud of a flood plain, playa, or mud flat along a shore. They may be produced by rain, the splash of waves, or by water dripping from vegetation. To preserve rain prints, the mud must be dried, hardened, and then covered quickly by another layer of sediment. Such marks are not

FIG. 9.15. *Mud cracks in clayey sediments on the floor of a dry stream bed, caused by shrinkage in drying. (U.S. Geological Survey.)*

FIG. 9.16. *Present-day ripple marks left by receding tide at Windsor, Nova Scotia. (E. M. Kindle, Canada Geological Survey.)*

FIG. 9.17. *Ripple marks preserved in the consolidated transitional beds at the base of the Beekmantown dolomite at Perth, Ontario. (M. E. Wilson, Canada Geological Survey.)*

FIG. 9.18. *Oscillation ripple marks. (After Shrock.)*

common, but excellent examples have been preserved.

Such features as mud cracks, ripple marks, rill marks, wavemarks, and raindrop impressions give lasting evidence of conditions of deposition.

FOSSILS

Many sedimentary rocks contain remains of ancient life known as fossils (Latin *fossilis*, dug up). As originally used, the word fossil referred to any curious object dug out of the earth. Today the term is applied to any organic remains or direct evidence of organisms preserved in the rocks of the earth's crust.

Fossils may be classified as follows:
1. Actual remains of organisms
   a. Soft parts only
   b. Hard and soft parts
   c. Hard parts only
2. Impressions or replacements of original substances, such as molds or casts
3. Tracks, trails, burrows, etc.

Since plants in general have fewer hard parts suitable for preservation than animals, plants are not so well represented by fossils as are animals. However, some very fine plant fossils do occur as carbonized remains or as impressions of leaves or stems in mud or sand deposits that later become shales or sandstones. Others have had their woody fibers gradually infiltrated with, and filled in by, silica, producing such fine specimens of silicified wood as may be found in the petrified forests of Arizona. Still other plants are preserved as coal, which is fossil vegetable matter. Cell structure may still be seen in thin sections of coal.

The bones, teeth, shells, and general skeletal matter of animals are more likely to be preserved (Fig. 9.20); but the tracks, trails, burrows, or impressions of animals also may form fossils. In some cases the entire animals have been preserved, constituting unique fossils of great value. The best-known of these are the fossil insects in Baltic amber and the woolly mammoths frozen in the gravels of Siberia.

Such fossils show the development of living things through the long ages of earth history. They provide a record not only of the more primitive forms of life characteristic of very early periods in earth history but also of the developmental changes to modern forms that occurred in succeeding times. The modern single-toed horse preserving the splint bones of two additional toes on each foot may be traced back to an earlier horse which had three functional toes, and that horse back to the still earlier *Eohippus*, which had four toes.

Since fossils show the development from the more primitive to the more complex forms of life,

FIG. 9.19. *Profiles of current and oscillation ripple marks. (After Shrock.)*

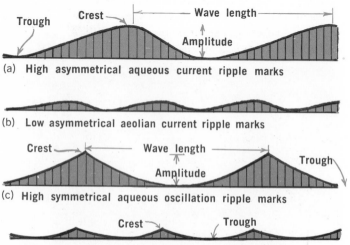

(a) **High asymmetrical aqueous current ripple marks**

(b) **Low asymmetrical aeolian current ripple marks**

(c) **High symmetrical aqueous oscillation ripple marks**

(d) **Low symmetrical aqueous oscillation ripple marks**

FIG. 9.20. *Densely crowded fossil shells imbedded in a silty sandstone. (W. T. Lee, U.S. Geological Survey.)*

a fossil-bearing rock may be dated by the character of the life existing during the deposition of the rock that contains it. Certain fossil forms have come to be known as guides to certain geologic units. Some of these are called horizon markers, because they are found only within certain horizons, or groups, of beds. Thus, if the fossils are alike in the sedimentary rocks of two widely separated areas, we infer that the sediments accumulated at approximately the same time.

Secondary Structural Features

Certain minor structural pecularities may develop after sediments have been consolidated.

CONCRETIONS

Concretions (Fig. 9.21) (Latin *concretus*, grown together) are variously shaped masses, or nodules, of seemingly foreign material that often occur in sedimentary rocks. They range in size from less than 1 inch to several feet in diameter, and certain loglike cylindrical ones are 10 feet or more in length. Concretions usually differ in composition

from the rocks in which they occur. Generally they are formed from one of the minor constituents of that rock. In limestone and chalk, concretions are usually of flint, chert, or pyrite; in shales, they are commonly of calcite, chert, pyrite, or siderite,

FIG. 9.21. *Calcareous concretions from clay beds. Concretions are formed when a minor constituent in the surrounding rock is dissolved by ground water and redeposited in concentric layers, displacing or partly enclosing the original rock.*

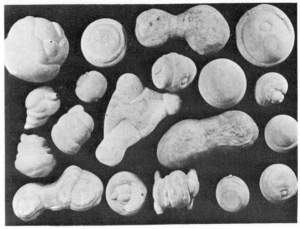

but barite and gypsum occur abundantly in certain localities. Concretions in sandstone generally are impure oxides of iron, pyrite, or calcite.

Concretions usually are spherical, lenticular, or discoidal in shape; more rarely, they are cylindrical or irregular. At many places the stratification of the beds in which they occur may be seen to thicken on entering the concretion; the upper beds are arched up, and those below are pressed down. Even cross-bedding may be found in concretions. At places fossils occur partly within the concretion and partly in the surrounding rock, or the center of the concretion may be one of the characteristic fossils of the formation in which it occurs. Sometimes concretions are very fossiliferous, although the surrounding rock may have very few fossils.

Concretions commonly show a concentric structure, with spherical layers one over the other. Concretions common in the black shales of Ohio are relatively smooth on the outside and separate easily from the enclosing shale. Many of them, in certain regions, are coated with a layer of pyrite, and rusty ones look like old cannon balls. At Kettle Point, Ontario, the large spherical concretions occurring in the Huron shale are composed of long, slender crystals of brown carbonate, which radiate from the center.

The concentric shells of some concretions differ in composition so much that weathering affects them differently. A shell inside the surface layer may disintegrate and leave the center loose. Such partly weathered concretions have been mistaken for fossil peaches or walnuts and are often referred to as rattle stones.

Concretions clearly were formed in place after the deposition of the beds enclosing them. They have grown up gradually from the center and have partly displaced and partly incorporated the rock which originally occupied their places. The material forming a concretion was probably once disseminated in the enclosing rock. Then it was dissolved by ground water, carried to the place where the concretion is now found, and, in most cases, precipitated around some nucleus, such as a fossil. Once started, precipitation continued, and the concretion increased in size.

Some concretions have been cracked or broken by jointing, and the cracks have been filled, vein-like, by material differing slightly in composition from that of the concretion. Such concretions are *septaria* (Fig. 9.22). Since septaria are usually disk-shaped and show an irregular pattern that slightly resembles the design on the back of a turtle, they have sometimes been mistaken for fossil turtles.

GEODES

Geodes (Greek *ge + eidos*, earthlike) are cavities partially filled with crystals (Fig. 5.11). The filling grows inward from the surface of the cavity, and the crystals in the hollow space commonly point toward the center. Most of them are composed of quartz or calcite, but some are composed of other material that was deposited from solution by ground water. They are common in all kinds of rock.

STYLOLITES

Stylolites (Greek *stylos*, column) are striated, or polished, columnar and variously shaped projections of rock that form an interlocking and interpenetrating series along partings in limestones (Fig. 9.23). The projections vary in length from a fraction of an inch to a foot or more and are equally variable in width. Such sutured contacts may bind the two parts together so firmly that the rock will break just as readily elsewhere as along the original parting plane. Stylolites result from different amounts of solution along a bedding plane or crevice, and their formation is promoted by the increased effectiveness of solution under different pressures at the points of contact on the two rock surfaces.

Environments of Deposition

Eventually the products of weathering find their way to the sea, although some are temporarily lodged in various continental environments, such as lakes or flood plains of rivers. Most areas of accumulation pass laterally into each other, as in the gradual transition between the waters of the deep and shallow sea, between a flood plain and a delta, or between a delta and the shallow-water marine realm. In addition, both flood plains and deltas have shallow lake basins in which sediments accumulate.

The basins and other places where sediments are deposited can be continental or marine. Since these two realms come into contact along the seacoast, an area adjacent to the shore line has some of the characteristics of both. Thus a third division of mixed continental and marine conditions may be included. The various places where sediments accumulate are shown in Table 9.4.

TABLE 9.4   *Locations of Sedimentary Deposits*

Continental	Mixed continental and marine	Marine
Terrestrial:	Littoral	Shallow sea
Desert	Lagoon	Intermediate sea
Glacial	Estuary	Deep sea
Fluvial:	Delta	
Piedmont		
Valley flat		
Lake		
Swamp (paludal)		
Cave (speleal)		

Continental Sediments

DESERT DEPOSITS

At the present time approximately 11 million square miles of arid desert regions exist on the surface of the earth. The sediments of these regions accumulate by wash from upland slopes, by intermittently torrential streams, by deposition from waters of playa and saline lakes, and by the deposition of wind-blown sediments. Most desert sediments are more or less etched, frosted, and polished. This is true especially of the coarser lag materials over the rocky desert platforms. The valley and gully deposits are composed of coarser detritus that extends up the valleys into the highlands and down the valleys to alluvial cones and fans. These coalesce laterally to form piedmont slopes, so that many desert mountains appear to rise out of gravel

FIG. 9.22.   *A septarian concretion.*

deposits. The fine sands and silts of the playa and salt lakes dovetail with the dune and piedmont deposits. Stratification is conspicuous in the laminated clays of the lakes and playas, whereas most of the gravels on the piedmont slopes are unstratified. The aeolian sediments are characterized by wedge-shaped, cross-bedded units. Wind-laid deposits will be described more fully in Chapter 15.

GLACIAL DEPOSITS

Glacial sediments, or those deposited by ice, are unstratified unsorted mixtures of both coarse and fine sediments. The fine-grained sediments of the glacial lakes may be varved (Fig. 9.12). A *varve*

FIG. 9.23.   *Stylolites (columns and corroded surfaces) developed by solution along bedding planes of limestone under vertical pressure.*

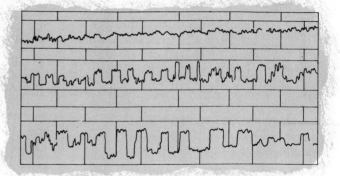

is a lamination representing seasonal changes in deposition.

Glacial sediments commonly rest with a sharp contact on striated and grooved rock surfaces, but they may be carried far beyond the outer ice margin and thus may be mingled with sediments resulting from the common rock-weathering processes and originating in distant regions. Such mixed sediments gradually lose their glacial peculiarities and take on the characteristics of ordinary river sediments, except that they may retain fragments of rocks belonging to drainage basins other than the one in which they find lodgment. Thus the upper Mississippi River has received glacially derived materials from Hudson Bay and the St. Lawrence drainage basins, transported them to the Gulf of Mexico, and built them into its own delta.

We shall discuss glacial sediments in greater detail in Chapter 12, Snow, Ice, and Glaciers.

FLUVIAL SEDIMENTS

Fluvial sediments are those deposited by streams. They represent the products of aggradation on piedmonts, valley flats, and the upper surfaces of deltas. Piedmont sediments accumulate about the bases of mountains as a result of soil creep, rainwash, rock streams, mudflows, and intermittent streams. It is estimated that the present extent of piedmont deposits in the Western states is equal in area to that of the mountains above them. In the Cucamonga district of California the deposits are more than 1,000 feet thick. They are composed of boulders, cobbles, gravel, sand, and silts. The sediments are poorly sorted and are indistinctly bedded, with the coarser fragments nearer the base of the mountains.

The sediments of the valley flats differ from those of the piedmonts in that they show better sorting and stratification, fewer large fragments, and more organic matter. Since most streams alternately aggrade and degrade, the sediments are only in place temporarily. Many flood plains contain lakes and swamps, both of which shift their positions as the streams change the location of their channels over the valley flats. There thus results a dovetailing of lake clays and silts with swamp mucks and peats, and these in turn alternate with sand and gravel transported by the streams. Many of the sedimentary rocks of the Great Plains were originally deposited as fluvial sediments.

LAKE SEDIMENTS

The origin and location of a lake basin greatly influence the type of sediment formed there. Lakes in mountain valleys receive more coarse material than those in the broad alluvial flats and delta regions of old-age streams; among the sediments of glacial lakes, much of the fine material may be still in the form of "rock flour" rather than clay resulting from mature weathering; and the sediments of saline and alkaline lakes include appreciable amounts of chemical precipitates. In general, lake sediments consist of gravels, sands, clays, marl, tufa, peat, iron and manganese oxides, iron carbonates, and such saline products of evaporation as salt and gypsum.

CAVE DEPOSITS

Cave deposits consist mostly of products of precipitation from underground water. However, much fine clastic sediment may descend through rock cracks and crevices and, together with the insoluble residue of the beds undergoing solution, may be distributed throughout the underlying caverns. In the silt-covered region of the Mississippi Basin, water dripping from the roofs of caves leaves much silt in the calcite that forms the cave deposits. During the active cave-forming stage, the walls of cracks and caverns may be coated with silt and clay. The caves that contain this fine silt lack the beauty of those with clear, unmuddied calcite.

Other clastic materials may fall from the ceiling or walls of the cave or may be brought in by wind or by rodents or other animals to make so-called "cave earth." Since artifacts, hearthstones, charcoal, bones, and other materials resulting from the occupation of caves by prehistoric man may be included, cave deposits are frequently important in archeology. In some caves the excrement of bats, rats, ground sloths, and other animals has accumulated to form guano, at places in sufficient volume to be used as a source of nitrate and phosphate fertilizers.

Mixed Continental and Marine Sediments

The sediments that accumulate where the continents meet the oceans are a mixture of materials derived from the land and from the sea. They accumulate along the littoral zone and in lagoons and estuaries. In addition, mixed continental and marine sediments are found in delta accumulations (page 243).

LITTORAL DEPOSITS

Conditions of deposition in the littoral zone (the section between low and high tides) are not always similar. Some shore zones consist of bare, rocky platforms; others are nearly vertical sea cliffs; and still others are composed of gravels, sands, muds, shells, and shell fragments. These sediments grade into each other alongshore and grade seaward by imperceptible stages into the offshore marine deposits. The sediments of the littoral zone are derived mainly from the shore by wave action. The waves are aided by frost, undercutting, and wind. The work of the wind is more important, however, in generating waves and currents that carry sediments to the beaches.

The materials of a beach vary with the source of supply and the vigor of the wave action. On a boisterous or surf-beaten coast, the material may be boulders or large cobblestones. However, where the supply of finer materials is extensive, the beach may consist of pebbles or sand, even on exposed coasts. On rocky coasts, boulders and cobblestones are common at the heads of indentations, although at places sand may occupy such positions. *Pocket beaches* are found along the coast of California at Carmel, at La Jolla, and at many other places. They are merely lodgment places in which the rock fragments are ground to fine particles and from which they are finally swept to sea by the returning water. The grinding process is caused by surf rolling up and down the beach and dragging the boulders, cobblestones, and pebbles back and forth over each other and over the rock-shod bottom. As agitation ceases and the sediments finally are de-posited, they are graded in order of size from the shore outward.

LAGOON DEPOSITS

In marginal lagoons the waters range from fresh water to water with a salinity greater than that of the adjacent sea. As in the shore zones, sediments that accumulate in lagoons exhibit a considerable variety. Land-derived sediments are brought by streams and wind; marine sediments are brought by ocean currents; and organic and chemical precipitates are produced from the salts in solution. Calcareous marls are precipitated by plants and invertebrate animals and to some extent by direct chemical action. In stagnant lagoons the bacterial activity leads to the formation of hydrogen sulfide, which causes the precipitation of black iron sulfide in the accumulating sediments. In such black muds carbonate shells dissolve and are replaced by iron sulfide. At places where there is extensive evaporation, the salinity may become so great that beds of salt and gypsum are deposited.

Marine Sediments

The realms of marine sedimentation include the shallow epicontinental seas; the continental, or intermediate, slopes; and the deep sea (Fig. 9.24). In addition to being deposited on the bottom of the present ocean, marine sediments cover a large portion of the land surface of the earth.

SHALLOW-SEA (NERITIC) DEPOSITS

The shallow sea is that portion of the ocean basin extending from the low-tide level to an average depth of about 400 feet (Shepard). It includes the major portion of the continental shelf, together with such epicontinental seas as the Baltic Sea and Hudson Bay. It covers about 11 million square miles, in tracts varying in width from a few miles to several hundred. The continental shelf is especially wide in the North Polar Sea along the coast of Siberia. Its average slope is only about 12 feet per mile; so the sediments deposited on it are practically flat-lying.

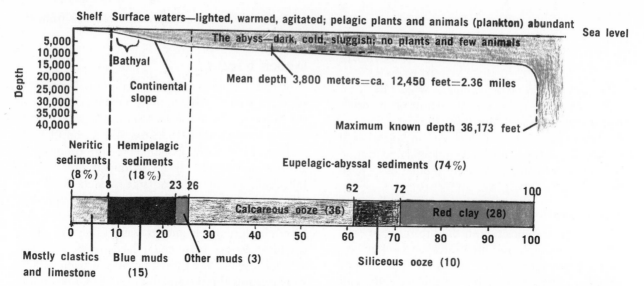

FIG. 9.24. *Distribution of marine sediments in relation to position in the sea. Relative areas of depth zones in per cent are shown above, and bottom sediments are shown below. (Data from Kuenen.)*

The distribution, expanse, and depths of the shallow sea have varied in geologic time with the nature and extent of diastrophic movements. Where the sea level rises, the deeper portions of the shallow sea are added to the intermediate slopes, and the lowlands along the coast are flooded, so that the former littoral zone is added to the area of the shallow sea. During the geologic past, when large areas were reduced by erosion to low, undulating plains (peneplains), a rise of sea level extended the shallow sea far into the interior of the continents and added many thousands of square miles to the areas in which shallow-water deposits accumulated. Most of the marine sedimentary rocks of the present-day continents accumulated in such basins.

The shoreward portion of the shallow-sea bottom lies within the range of wave and current action. Where currents are generated, the sediments are sorted so that the coarser materials usually are deposited near shore and grade into finer deposits seaward. However, there are many exceptions, for along low shores with few streams, fine muds and calcareous sediments may accumulate far up toward the beach. A study of the sediments from the con-

tinental shelf along the eastern coast of the United States shows that the distribution is extremely irregular.

In general, rock-bottom and coarse sediments occur off rocky points or rocky sea cliffs onshore, or wherever strong currents affect the ocean bottom, as between islands, in narrow straits, or on shoals (Shepard). Sand prevails on the continental shelf off sandy coasts or in areas of moderate currents. Mud is deposited off large river mouths, in sheltered areas near shore, and in depressions on the continental shelf.

The great bulk of shallow-sea sediments is made up of detritus derived from land by way of streams, glaciers, dust storms, sandstorms, shore erosion, and explosive volcanoes. Some sediment also is contributed by corals, calcareous algae, shellfish, and chemical precipitation.

Where the supply of land detritus is small, the sediments on the sea bottom may consist chiefly of organic remains and chemical precipitates. Some precipitates may be formed in the sea by reactions between constituents of different origin which produce insoluble compounds. Although some geologists believe that a certain amount of calcium carbonate is being precipitated by purely inorganic processes, we do not know to what extent this is true. It is doubtful that simple precipitation takes place to any great extent in the ocean under usual conditions, and probably most marine calcareous sediments are of organic origin. Such sediments form in comparatively shallow water, where lime-secreting organisms live in abundance but where there is relatively little sediment being carried in from the adjacent land. Partial disintegration of the shells, due to solution or to grinding by waves, may destroy their original structure before they have been transformed into solid rock, or recrystallization may destroy any remnants of forms. The resulting unfossiliferous rock might be mistaken for a direct chemical precipitate.

Many of the organisms that live in the sea have hard parts made of calcium carbonate or silica, and these are the materials which form some limestones and siliceous deposits. Organisms that precipitate calcium carbonate and amorphous silica also supply the cementing materials for other sediments. The rock-building life of the sea, therefore, is a geologic factor of great importance.

The common lime- and silica-secreting forms of life are chiefly the lower plants, such as the bacteria, diatoms, and algae, and the invertebrate animals. Bacterial remains seldom are preserved in recognizable condition in the deposits they make, but ancient limestones now wholly devoid of fossils may owe their origin to these organisms. Few of the marine plants, even of the algae, can be identified as fossils either, and yet in the modern seas the calcareous algae are active in rock building, locally even exceeding the animal life of the area in the rapidity of their work. Thus, on the typical "coral" island of Funafuti in the South Pacific two kinds of algae have formed more of the rock than all the corals combined.

The diatoms have siliceous tests, or capsulelike shells. These accumulate in abundance under favorable conditions and give rise to thick deposits of diatomaceous earth, or their siliceous material may be carried off in solution to contribute to the formation of flint or chert beds in adjacent limestones. The Radiolaria and certain of the sponges have siliceous skeletons which contribute to the formation of flint and chert.

The lime-contributing life of the sea includes almost every group from the Foraminifera to the highest division of the invertebrates. Their remains are found in abundance in the deposits they form. The most prolific limestone builders are foraminifera, stromatoporoids, corals, bryozoans, brachiopods, crinoids, and mollusks. Other animal groups also make contributions but are seldom of much importance. Certain areas of the shallow-sea bottom, especially those comparatively free from land detritus, are crowded with these groups, and their remains accumulate in abundance to form limestone (Fig. 9.25).

The calcium carbonate content of the offshore sediments is influenced by temperature, depth, salinity, degree of saturation of the water with calcium carbonate, and the activity of living organisms. It increases as the surface salinity rises. The rate of rise in carbonate is greatest between salinities of 34 and 36 parts per 1,000.

The structural features of offshore marine sediments are variable. Deposits near shore are usually lenticular beds, with much cross-bedding and a great range in particle size. Ripple and current marks have equally great variation in trend and extent of development. Where the sea floor has

FIG. 9.25. *The calcareous shells of foraminifera (one-celled organisms) in Cretaceous marl from New Jersey (greatly magnified).*

steep slopes, the sediments may slump and develop crumpled and irregular bedding planes. In deeper waters the strata are more nearly uniform, and the stratification is distinct. Some chemical sediments show well-defined seasonal laminations.

The rate at which sediments accumulate cannot be determined with a high degree of precision. Attempts have been made to arrive at average rates of deposition, but the most that can be expected is a mean for each basin of accumulation. The rate of erosion of a given region can be compared with the area of the basin receiving sediments, but figures obtained in this way are, at best, inaccurate. Another approach is to divide the total thickness of the column of sediments by the length of geologic time during which they have accumulated, as determined by the study of radioactive disintegration. This method may also have an extremely wide margin of error, for it does not take into account long periods when there was no deposition. The relative rates indicated in the accompanying table are reasonably accurate, but the total number of years listed for 1 foot of each type of sedimentary rock should be considered as little more than a rough estimate.

TABLE 9.5   *Estimated Rate of Sedimentation in the Epicontinental Seas of the Geologic Past*

Type of rock	Years required to deposit a thickness of 1 foot
Sandstone	450
Shale	900
Limestone	2,250

SOURCE: Charles Schuchert, *Nat. Research Council Bull.* 80, p. 13, 1931.

Umbgrove, in 1945, computed that nearly 30,000 feet of sediments accumulated in 4 geosynclines in Indonesia over a period of 60 million years at an average rate of 1 foot in about 1,800 years. Other areas yielded computed rates of as little as 1 foot in 9,000 to 20,000 or more years.

INTERMEDIATE DEPOSITS

Beyond the continental shelf the ocean bottom descends rather abruptly to the sea floor, which lies at an average depth of 2½ miles below the surface. This descent, called the continental slope, is the outer margin of the true continental mass. Since it begins at an average distance of about 40 miles from the coast, it is generally covered by fine sediments of land origin which remain in suspension for a long period. These collectively are called the blue muds, and they owe their color to the presence of organic matter and to the deoxidized condition of their iron content. Landward they grade into the shallower-water deposits, and seaward they pass into the oozes and red clay of the abysmal depths.

The blue muds probably cover 15 million square miles of the ocean basin. They have been encountered as far as 200 miles from land, and they extend a distance of 1,000 miles from the mouths of great rivers, such as the Amazon. Volcanic mud and pieces of pumice and scoria have been picked up by dredges more than 200 miles from the volcanic islands of Hawaii.

Land-derived vegetation has been discovered on the sea bottom even at a distance of several hundred miles from the land and in 200 fathoms of water. Such vegetation was found off the coast of Central America on both the Atlantic and the Pacific sides, where nearly every haul of the *Challenger* dredge brought up fruits, seeds, leaves, twigs, branches, and parts of the trunks of trees. This organic matter contributes to the deoxidizing agents of the blue-mud zone, but probably little is preserved in fossil form.

DEEP-SEA DEPOSITS

With increasing distance from shore the land-derived materials assume less and less importance. In the deep abyss many sediments are of volcanic; pelagic, glacial, and meteoritic origin. The temperature is approximately 35°F at all times; and since currents and waves of the near-shore type do not exist, there is no appreciable motion of the water. There is no light other than that emitted by the phosphorescence of deep-sea organisms. Fewer organisms exist than in shallower waters. The chief organic sediments consist of the hard parts of organisms which live in the upper, lighted waters. These surface-dwelling forms are chiefly

TABLE 9.6 *Areas and Depths below Sea Level of the Various Sediments on the Marginal Slopes of the Marine Environment*

Sediment	Area, square miles	Mean depth, fathoms	Depth limits, fathoms
Coral (and algal) muds }	2,236,800	740	1,820
Coral (and algal) sands }		176	
Volcanic muds }	600,000	1,033	260–2,800
Volcanic sands }		243	100–420
Green muds }	850,000	513	100–1,270
Green sands }		449	900
Red muds	400,000	623	120–1,200
Blue muds	14,500,000	1,421	125–2,800

SOURCE: Report of the *Challenger*.

simple types of plants and animals, collectively called the *plankton*. They consist of small mollusks, foraminifera, and algae, which secrete calcium carbonate, together with diatoms and radiolarians, which secrete siliceous skeletons. When these organisms die, their remains sink to the bottom, where the undissolved residue, together with volcanic, meteoric, and other dusts, forms oozes, or slimy deposits, that accumulate very slowly. These oozes are named according to the most abundant remains composing them. Thus there are the globigerina oozes, the pteropod oozes, the diatom oozes, and the radiolarian oozes, but they all grade into each other.

Globigerina ooze is by far the most extensive, and it is now forming over an area of 50 million square miles (Fig. 9.25). Diatom ooze is formed mainly in the cool waters of the North Pacific and in the waters of a belt surrounding Antarctica. The radiolarian ooze is found in some of the deepest parts of the sea.

We know that carbon dioxide and water form a weak acid which dissolves calcium carbonate. Therefore, since the carbon dioxide content of sea water increases with depth, the percentage of calcium carbonate in bottom deposits generally decreases with depth. The calcium carbonate content of oozes and muds of various origin on the sea bottom is shown in Table 9.7.

At great depths the ocean bottom is covered by a very fine red clay (most of it really chocolate brown), which is composed of terrigenous clay, insoluble portions of the plankton shells and other organic matter, volcanic ash, and meteoritic dust. This red clay occupies about 40 million square miles of the sea bottom, and most of the known area is in the Pacific Ocean. It indicates a cold-water condition of deposition. Moulton[2] states that more than 20 million visible meteors enter our atmosphere daily. However, most of them disintegrate in their passage through the air and settle as fine dust over land and sea. Although most of this dust is scattered over the ocean basin, the quantity is relatively trivial. Evidently sedimentation on the deep-sea floor is exceedingly slow.

The slow rate at which sedimentation is taking place is indicated by the skeletal remains that dredging brings up from the sea floor. The inner-ear bones of the whale are the most resistant parts of the whole skeleton and have thus accumulated on the sea bottom through many generations of whales; yet they are so thinly covered by red clay

TABLE 9.7 *Depth Variations of Calcium Carbonate in Bottom Deposits*

Fathoms	Per cent	Fathoms	Per cent
Under 500	86.04	2,000–2,500	46.73
500–1,000	66.86	2,500–3,000	17.36
1,000–1,500	70.87	3,000–3,500	0.88
1,500–2,000	69.55	3,500–4,000	None

SOURCE: F. W. Clarke, *U.S. Geol. Survey Bull.* 770, p. 133, 1924.

[2] Forest R. Moulton, *Astronomy*, The Macmillan Company, 1931, p. 305.

that they are often brought up by dredges, sometimes as many as 90 at a time. At Station 285, in the South Pacific, a single haul of the *Challenger* dredge brought to the surface 1,500 sharks' teeth, many of them representing extinct species, in addition to immense numbers of very small teeth and fragments. Evidently they had been accumulating for a very long time, but, although manganese-coated, they were practically without sedimentary covering.

Schott has estimated the rate of red-clay deposition in the Atlantic Ocean to be 1 centimeter in 1,200 years and that of globigerina ooze to be 1 centimeter in 265 to 1,700 years.

A core sample, 194 centimeters long, composed of alternating layers of red clay and globigerina ooze, obtained in the southeastern Pacific Ocean, was computed from radioactive materials to be at least 800,000 and possibly 990,000 years old at its bottom end. The bottom end of another core, 138 centimeters long, obtained farther south and hence composed entirely of red clay, was found to be possibly 1,231,000 years old or more. The alternations in such cores of globigerina ooze (attributed to warm-water conditions) and of red clay (corresponding to cold-water conditions) are thought to record a series of interglacial and glacial climates during a large part of the Pleistocene epoch. The indicated rates of sedimentation in the two cores are 1 centimeter in about 4,100 (or possibly 5,100) years and 1 centimeter in about 8,900 years, respectively. Comparable results have been obtained from similar cores obtained from the bottom of the Atlantic Ocean.

When one can capture a million years of accumulation of sediments in the deep sea in a core only a few feet long, the rate of deposition must be slow indeed. The study of deep-sea core samples is a very promising line of research.

Although the chalk beds of England and France are chiefly the remains of foraminifera and although a large part of the Monterey series at Lompoc, California, consists of the remains of diatoms, it is doubtful that these or any other beds found on the present continents correspond to the deep-sea oozes, or the red clays. Steinmann reports them in the Alps and the Apennines, and others consider some of the radiolarian cherts of the northern Appalachian region to be deep-sea deposits; but even if these should prove to be true abyssal deposits, the total known land area would be small.

Stratigraphic Relations of Sediments

CONFORMITY AND UNCONFORMITY

If a continuous series of beds has been deposited, one bed of rock is said to lie on another with conformity. If, however, there is an erosion surface between any two beds, there is evidently a dis-

TABLE 9.8 *Thickness and Rate of Sedimentation of Recent Marine Sediments in the Deep Sea in Equatorial Atlantic Ocean since End of Glacial Epoch*

	Blue mud	Glo-bigerina ooze	Red clay
Average thickness, centimeters	35.50	24.06	17.14
Greatest observed thickness, centimeters	66.00	42.50	26.50
Smallest observed thickness, centimeters	18.00	10.50	10.00
Average rate of sedimentation, centimeters per 1,000 years	1.78	1.20	0.86
Greatest observed rate of sedimentation, centimeters per 1,000 years	3.30	2.13	1.33
Smallest observed rate of sedimentation, centimeters per 1,000 years	0.90	0.53	0.50

SOURCE: W. Schott, in P. D. Trask et al., *Recent Marine Sediments*, Amer. Assn. Petrol Geologists, Tulsa, Okla., pp. 396–415, 1939.

FIG. 9.26. *Unconformity between the Laramie sandstone and the Wasatch conglomerate. Above, a photograph (Fisher, U.S. Geological Survey); below, a sketch of the same area.*

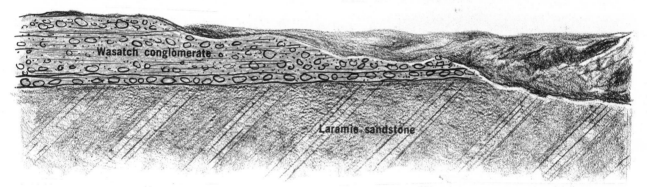

Wasatch conglomerate

Laramie sandstone

continuity in deposition. A region of deposition may be elevated, or uplifted, and thus converted into one of nondeposition or of erosion. After a time lapse the same region may be depressed, so that sediments again are deposited on the old surface. If the beds below the erosion surface are tilted so that they form an angle with the beds lying on top of it, the contact is called an angular unconformity (Fig. 9.26); but if the beds above and below the erosion surface are parallel, the contact is called a disconformity.

OVERLAP AND OFFLAP

In the normal course of such events as a rise in sea level or the sinking of a continent, the sea may gradually encroach upon the land. The deposition of the coarser sediments follows the retreating coast line and takes place progressively farther landward. This causes the newly deposited sediments to cover up the margin of the previously formed sediments. The bottom beds of the newly formed sediments rest in turn on an erosion surface of continually changing age. The result is an unconformable contact known as an overlap, or onlap (Fig. 9.27).

The reverse, however, takes place when the coast is rising; coarse sediments are laid down farther and farther seaward on top of the finer sediments. The sea is retreating, and each succeeding, or younger, division leaves a portion of the older one exposed to landward. This type of contact between differing sediments has been called offlap (Fig. 9.28). The conditions which form offlap may be followed by those of onlap, and the top sandstone of emergence in the offlap may be followed directly by the bottom sandstone of submergence in an onlap, thus producing a compound, or double, series, with the contact lying within the sandstone that represents both the emergence and the submergence.

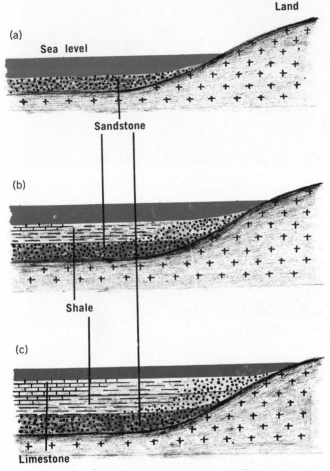

FIG. 9.27. *Diagram showing an overlap result-ing from progressive submergence of a land area or a progressive transgression of the sea: (a) beach sands are deposited on an old land surface; (b) muds that later form shale cover much of the sand as the shore line moves inland; (c) calcareous oozes that form limestone are deposited over the previous muds as the sites of deposition of sands and muds shift landward.*

LATERAL AND VERTICAL VARIATIONS

Sediments may grade laterally or vertically into other kinds of sediments, forming intermediate or mixed types. On the usually gently sloping coastal portion of the continental shelf, the coarse gravels are deposited near shore and are succeeded grad-ually by finer pebbles, sand, and mud, and then by calcareous mud and ooze. Wave action and shore currents, however, may disturb the regularity of this gradation seaward and hence interfere with the regular order of sediments that produce sedimen-tary rocks. But the calcareous muds formed from shell deposits and their fragments do not become limestones unless the quantity of land-derived sediment accumulating with them is small. Lime-stones usually are formed in shallow water where lime-secreting life is abundant and off coasts that are very low, so that the streams carry very little clastic sediment to the sea. A vertical section of the sediments forming off a coast may thus show gra-dations from conglomerate to sandstone to shale and finally to limestone, as the adjacent land is reduced by erosion to a lowland and clastic land-derived sediments fail.

The lateral variations of a sedimentary unit give rise to *facies*, that is different rocks in different geographic areas. Where these unlike subdivisions shift positions in the course of time, because of changes in location of shore lines, supply of sedi-ment, or other factors, the resulting stratigraphic column becomes complex horizontally as well as vertically. Repeated lateral shifting of the sites of deposition of sands, muds, and calcareous matter causes the edges of these deposits to dovetail, or interfinger, with one another. Detailed studies of such lateral changes of facies are especially impor-tant in the search for petroleum.

CONTROL OF SEDIMENTATION

As shown by cross-bedding, ripple marks, fossils, and other features, a large proportion of the sedi-mentary rocks on the continents are shallow-water marine sediments. In several mountain ranges these sediments are tens of thousands of feet thick. We can infer, then, that the accumulation of such great volumes of sediments in shallow water was made possible or was induced by progressive subsidence of the sites of deposition. The character of the sedi-ments depends in part on the degree of balance between the rate of subsidence and the rate of filling and in part on contemporaneous changes in the source areas. Notable uplift adjacent to the basin would supply a great bulk of coarse arkosic sediment, whereas long-continued erosion of a stable land would convert most of the sedimentary substances reaching the sea to fine muds and solutions. Hence sedimentary rocks, by their composition, texture, thickness, areal distribution, and other characteristics, reflect the complex interplay of a number of factors, of which diastrophic movements are perhaps the most influential.

INTERPRETATION OF SEDIMENTARY ROCKS

Since sedimentary rocks have many characteristics that reflect the environment of their origin, they tend to record the conditions of sedimentation existing at the time of their deposition. *Every rock tells a story.* Sandstones, for example, show ripple marks, wavemarks, cross-bedding, tracks, and burrows, just as do sands of the seashore today. Other kinds of sedimentary rocks, by their composition, structure, texture, fossils, and other features, also carry telltale signs of the past. Ancient sediments are interpreted in the light of our knowledge of what is taking place today. The present is the key to the past.

Ancient epicontinental shallow seas, former ice sheets, extinct lakes, and other features of the past are recorded by their sediments. Such sediments reveal not only the environments of their deposition but also something about their derivation, the relief of the land from which they came, the climate under which they were weathered, and other geographic conditions of the past.

Since sediments have been accumulating in an orderly succession throughout the ages, they constitute the main documents of geologic history.

Sedimentary Rocks
as Mineral Resources

Sedimentary rocks not only supply a record of geologic history but serve widely in industry. In order of their relative value, as measured by their production in the United States, the major nonmetallic sedimentary materials are petroleum and natural gas, coal, limestone and its products (in-

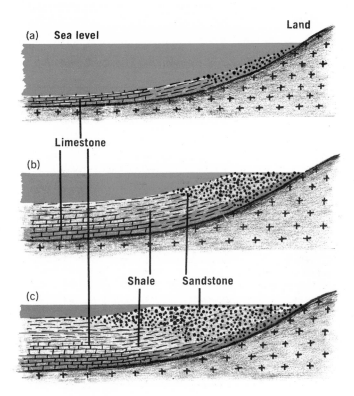

FIG. 9.28. *Diagram showing an offlap resulting from progressive emergence of a land area or a progressive recession of the sea: (a) near-shore sands give way laterally to muds and calcareous sediments; (b) and (c) as the sea recedes toward the left because of filling or of slow uplift of the land, sands are deposited over the offshore muds, and muds are deposited over calcareous oozes that later form limestone.*

cluding cement and lime), sand and gravel, clays, sulfur, salt, phosphate rock, potassium salts, bromine, boron minerals, gypsum, sodium carbonate and sulfate, and magnesium compounds. With the exception of barite, feldspar, fluorspar, and slate, most of the nonmetallic products listed in Table 9.9 are sedimentary in origin. In addition, most iron, aluminum, and manganese ores are sedimentary, as well as certain placer deposits of gold, tin, platinum, and diamonds.

PROCESSES OF CONCENTRATION

When rocks weather and are eroded, their materials are separated. Let us use as an example a granite composed of quartz, feldspar, and mica. It

TABLE 9.9 *Value of Nonmetallic Mineral Production in the United States in 1957*

Mineral	Millions of dollars
Petroleum	8,079
Natural gas	1,212
Coal	2,732
Cement	961
Stone	812
Sand and gravel	597
Clays	150
Salt	147
Lime	135
Sulfur	123
Phosphate rock	87
Potassium salts	84
Bromine	48
Boron minerals	41
Gypsum	30
Sodium carbonate and sulfate	24
Magnesium compounds from brines	16
Fluorspar	16
Barite	12
Slate	11
Feldspar	5
Others*	......
Total fuels	12,720
Total excluding fuels†	3,277
Grand total	15,997

  * Abrasives, talc and soapstone, pumice, mica, perlite, vermiculite, magnesite, garnet, graphite, etc.
  † Less duplication in stone and clays.
  SOURCE: *Minerals Yearbook*, 1957, U.S. Bureau of Mines.

breaks down and forms quartz sand and clay, which go to make up sandstones and shales. The iron in the dark mica may be carried by streams to the sea and may be deposited, along with iron from other sources, to form sedimentary beds. The quartz that is liberated as sand is valuable for making glass, the clay for making pottery, and the iron ore for making iron and steel. In the original granite these materials were not sufficiently concentrated to be of commercial value. Thus running water, together with the lakes and seas, may be regarded as a giant concentration mill.

By processes of gradation, deposits are formed of such valuable materials as petroliferous substances, gypsum, iron ores, manganese ores, gold, platinum, tin ore, salt, and phosphate rock. Some of these materials are carried along mechanically by water and are deposited along streams or along beaches of lakes and seas. Others, such as phosphate rock and some iron ores, are deposited by chemical precipitation from the waters. At many places gold, platinum, and tin ores are washed from the tops of their original deposits and concentrated by water as placers in ravines and creeks near their sources. Elsewhere materials eroded from the parent sources are carried to distant places. Residual deposits (those left behind) include ores of iron, manganese, and aluminum (bauxite).

PETROLEUM

Petroleum and natural gas are obviously not rocks, but because they are derived from sedimentary rocks, we shall discuss them here. In monetary value they lead the list of commercial mineral products.

Composition. Petroleum (rock oil) is a naturally occurring, complex mixture of liquid hydrocarbons, compounds consisting mostly of carbon and hydrogen, with minor quantities of nitrogen, oxygen, and sulfur. Most petroleum contains 82 to 87 per cent carbon and 11 to 15 per cent hydrogen. These elements are combined in several types of molecule, many of which have a very complex structure. Distilling off the light fractions of crude petroleum leaves a residue of light-colored paraffin wax, a dark tarry asphalt, or a mixture of the two. So crude oils sometimes are classified as paraffin-base, asphalt-base, or mixed-base oils. Asphalt-base and mixed-base crude oils are most abundant.

Origin. We do not know how or when petroleum is formed. Geologists agree, however, that petroleum is formed from plant and animal remains that accumulated on the sea floor along with the materials that formed sedimentary rocks. The evidence for organic origin seems conclusive.

1. Petroleum compounds have certain optical properties which are peculiar to organic substances.

2. The presence of pigments called porphyrins (compounds like the chlorophyll of plants and the hemoglobin of animal blood) is hardly explainable otherwise.

3. More than 99 per cent of all occurrences of crude oil are associated with marine sedimentary rocks. Oil is rarely found in igneous or metamorphic rocks or in fresh-water sediments, and then, with a few possible exceptions, only where these sources are associated with marine sedimentary beds. Oil found in such rocks has presumably migrated from marine rocks nearby.

4. Hydrocarbons resembling petroleum are reported to have been found at shallow depths in modern marine sediments.

The processes by which the parent organic matter is converted into petroleum are not understood. The contributing factors are thought to be bacterial action, shearing pressure during compaction, heat and natural distillation at depth, possible addition of hydrogen from deep-seated sources, presence of catalysts (substances which promote chemical reactions without loss of themselves), perhaps time, and, doubtfully, radioactivity. Anaerobic, or reducing, bacteria can liberate oxygen, nitrogen, phosphorus, and sulfur from organic matter and in this way increase the relative percentages of carbon and hydrogen remaining. Some bacteria produce the natural gas methane, CH_4, but methane's part, if any, in the development of petroleum is not known.

Whether the transformation of organic matter to petroleum takes place essentially at the time of deposition of the associated sediments, at some time after burial but before or during consolidation, or at a much later time is not known. However, many geologists favor an early origin.

Source beds. Source beds are the rocks in which the oil (or natural gas) originated. In many oil-bearing districts thick columns of dark-gray, chocolate-brown, blue, or black shale, darkened by organic matter, are thought to have served as sources. In other areas calcareous shales, siltstones, fine sandstones, or limestones apparently were sources. Recent marine sediments contain an average of 2.5 per cent by weight of organic matter. The organic content is closely related to texture. More organic matter is preserved in fine sediments than in coarse ones, because of differences in their depositional environments. So fine-textured dark shales and limestones seem to be especially favorable source beds for petroleum.

Reservoir rocks. Reservoir rocks are the permeable rocks in which the oil is stored underground. Even though petroleum may originate in shale, it cannot ordinarily accumulate in commercial quantities in such a sediment, because shale is not sufficiently permeable. Good reservoir rocks must have large and well-connected openings to provide both storage capacity and freedom of discharge; high porosity alone is not enough.

Oil generally accumulates in open-textured sandstone or in porous limestone or dolomite; in producing areas, these rocks, as a rule, have porosities of more than 10 per cent and are tens of feet thick. Some sandstone reservoirs are extensive sheets. Others are small lenses from former beaches or narrow stringers ("shoestring sands") from former offshore bars. Limestone reefs and solution cavities make excellent reservoirs. In some places highly fractured rocks of almost any type, including shale, basalt, chert, and schist, may yield oil.

Apparently, when a column of sedimentary rock is compacted by the weight of beds deposited later, petroleum, water, and natural gas are squeezed out of the soft source muds into the more permeable reservoir rocks, where these fluids then can migrate fairly freely. During compaction, the shaly source beds have their porosity reduced from as much as 90 per cent to 35 per cent or less, and they become almost impermeable because of the fineness of the openings.

Migration of petroleum. As soon as petroleum is expelled from the source rock into the reservoir rock, it rises to the top of the water-filled reservoir, because oil is lighter than water. If the reservoir rock is tilted, the oil held under the reservoir roof travels up the incline until it is caught and held in a trap. Oil accumulations found near the edges of certain structural basins may have moved laterally several tens of miles or more before being trapped.

Oil traps. An oil trap is a body of reservoir rock surrounded by impervious rock in such a way that the two form a closed-top container, in which the oil collects (Fig. 9.29). The oil is held beneath an

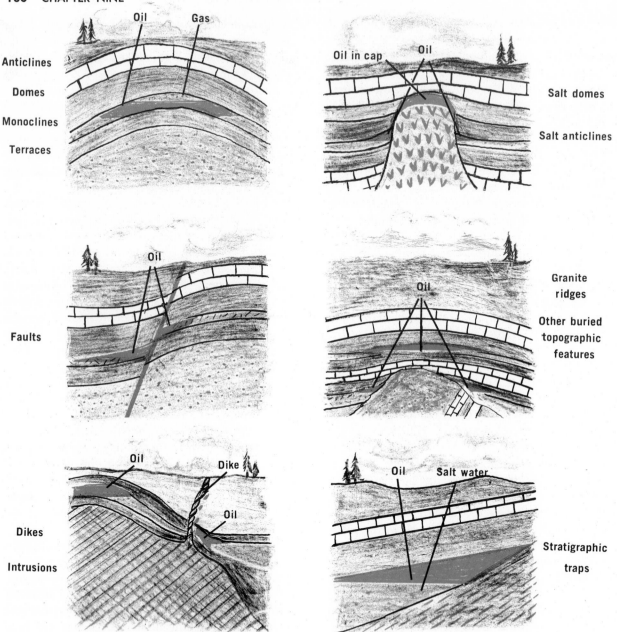

FIG. 9.29. *Diagrams showing some of the places of accumulation of oil and gas. (After Heiland.)*

impermeable *cap rock*, usually clay, shale, or dense limestone, or some other type of seal, such as a muddy or thoroughly cemented sandstone or tar. Some oil traps are formed by structural features, such as upfolded and domed strata (Fig. 9.30). Some are stratigraphic traps, resulting from such differences in permeability as those found in sandstone lenses and stringers, cementation variations, facies changes, and limestone reefs. Still other traps represent combinations of structural and stratigraphic conditions.

Associated gas and water. Natural gas and salt water are nearly always associated with petroleum. In the oil traps, the gas, oil, and water are separated into layers, since oil is insoluble in water and gas is only slightly soluble. The separation occurs in the order of increasing density, with gas (the lightest) on top, oil in the middle, and water (the heaviest) on the bottom. The gas may be present in small or large quantities. Under high pressures, much gas is dissolved in the oil, and its pressure assists in the recovery of oil. Free gas appears above the oil only when the oil is saturated with gas. The salt water is believed to be sea water which filled the openings in the sediments when they were laid down in the ocean. In many instances, however, the dissolved solids in the entrapped waters have been changed by reacting with the rocks or with petroleum, so the composition no longer matches that of sea water.

Oil pool and oil field. An oil pool is any accumulation of oil in reservoir rock that yields petroleum on drilling. Since the petroleum is distributed through rock, it is not a pool in the ordinary sense. An oil field (Fig. 9.31) is a geographic district containing underground accumulations of economic value. A single oil field may draw upon several different oil pools located in different stratigraphic and structural settings. Most oil fields occur near the edges of downwarped structural basins containing great thicknesses of marine sedimentary rocks.

Geographic distribution. The major oil fields of the world occur in the United States, Canada, Mexico, Venezuela, Trinidad, Argentina, Colombia, Peru, Kuwait, Saudi Arabia, Iraq, Iran, the U.S.S.R., Rumania, and Indonesia. In the United States, Texas, California, Oklahoma, Louisiana, Kansas, New Mexico, Pennsylvania, Wyoming, Michigan, and Arkansas are the leading producing areas.

Uses. Petroleum is tremendously important in modern civilization. It has two main uses—fuel and lubrication. It furnishes more than half our supply of energy. The principal refinery products, in order

FIG. 9.30. *Aerial photograph of an oil-producing anticline (up-folded strata) in Wyoming. This arched type of structure forms a trap for the oil and prevents its migration. (U.S. Geological Survey.)*

of bulk, are gasoline, residual fuel oil, distillate fuel oil, still gas, asphalt, jet fuel, and liquefied refinery gases. Minor products are lubricating oil, grease, road oil, kerosene, wax, and petroleum coke. In addition, petroleum yields thousands of chemical compounds, called petrochemicals, used in making such products as synthetic rubber, synthetic fiber, plastics, paints, solvents, dyes, detergents, resins, fertilizers, pesticides, and various drugs.

NATURAL GASES, FUEL GASES

Natural gas either accompanies oil, occupying the same reservoirs, or occurs separately. Even if separate, it is contained in the same types of trap, but where oil is absent, the gas lies directly above the water. Some gas comes from swamps (marsh gas) and coal beds. Most natural gas consists of colorless, odorless, and highly flammable methane (CH_4). In oil fields ethane (C_2H_6), propane (C_3H_8), butane (C_4H_{10}), pentane (C_5H_{12}), and vapors of gasoline may be present. The gasoline fraction can be recovered by compressing the gas,

FIG. 9.31. *Signal Hill Oil Field, Long Beach, California. This oil field represents an underground oil accumulation of much value, and so the wells are closely spaced. (Spence Air Photos.)*

condensing it at low temperatures, or passing it through a heavy oil. Butane and related gases can be liquefied under pressure and marketed in tanks, and they are widely used as bottled gas. Natural gas is a highly prized fuel, which is piped to nearly all parts of the country. Some if it is used to make carbon black. Texas, Louisiana, Oklahoma, California, Kansas, and New Mexico lead in natural-gas production.

OTHER GASES

Among the important noncombustible gases encountered in the earth are nitrogen, carbon dioxide, and helium. In some mixtures nitrogen and carbon dioxide exceed the quantity of flammable gases. Carbon dioxide, which is heavier than air, has been known to collect at low places in the topography and to cause the death of animals there by suffocation. Some oil wells in Colorado yield large quantities of carbon dioxide at such low temperatures that the oil comes out as partly frozen slush that is difficult to handle. Carbon dioxide, condensed into

dry ice, is a good commercial refrigerant. Helium is a light gas, and because it is not flammable, it is very desirable for inflating balloons. Nearly all the world's supply of helium comes from a few wells in Texas, New Mexico, and Kansas.

COAL

Distribution. Coal beds are widely distributed in the United States, China, Germany, Great Britain, France, Poland, U.S.S.R., Belgium, Canada, and Australia. The principal coal fields in the United States are (1) the anthracite field near Scranton, Pennsylvania; (2) the Allegheny-Appalachian field, extending from Pennsylvania to Alabama; (3) the Illinois field, reaching into western Indiana and western Kentucky; (4) the mid-continent field in parts of the states from Iowa to Texas; and (5) the Rocky Mountain–Great Plains field, extending southward from Montana and North Dakota to New Mexico (Figs. 9.32, 9.33, 9.34). Minor deposits occur in several other states.

Ranks. The Pennsylvania anthracite field is almost

the only American source of anthracite. Its area is less than 500 square miles, and much of it has already been worked out. The coal in the Allegheny-Appalachian, Illinois, and mid-continent fields is mostly bituminous. That in the Rocky Mountains–Great Plains field ranges from lignite in the Dakotas to generally subbituminous and bituminous grades nearer the mountains, depending on the former depth of burial and the degree of structural deformation. Some coal in Colorado and Arkansas ranks very high.

Fuel value. The fuel value of lignite is only 7000 to 8000 British thermal units (Btu) per pound (one unit will raise the temperature of one pound of water one degree Fahrenheit). High-grade bituminous and anthracite coals yield 13,000 to 15,000 Btu per pound. Impurities in the coal, of course, lower the fuel value.

Methods of mining. The methods of mining have to be adapted to the structure of the coal beds and their topographic setting. Since the Pennsylvania anthracite beds are steeply upturned, inclined and vertical shafts are used to reach the coal. It is then loosened by undercutting, loaded on skips, and elevated to the surface.

In the stream-dissected Allegheny Plateau, where many flat to gently warped bituminous coal beds are exposed on the sides of valleys, adits (single-opening entrances) are dug into the hillsides along the plane of the bedding. Where the overburden is thin, open-pit mining is practiced. Deeper beds require shafts. Nearly all the coal is machine-cut and machine-loaded. In the nearly flat-lying beds of the central interior of the United States, both shafts and open-pit mining are used extensively.

Preparation. Broken coal ordinarily is screened into several particle sizes to fit market requirements. Some coal is ground to a powder before being used. Rock particles and iron sulfide, which are undesirable in coal, may be removed by floating the coal on a heavy liquid medium or by washing it.

Uses. Coal is used primarily for fuel for domestic and various industrial purposes. Some is used directly, and some is first converted to coke by distillation in special ovens. Coke is valuable mainly

FIG. 9.32. *A bed of coal 8 feet thick with two clay partings, near Glendive, Montana. (U.S. Geological Survey.)*

as a fuel for smelting iron in blast furnaces. By-products driven off by the coking process are combustible gases and tars, from which a host of chemical products are obtainable—ammonia, dyes, perfumes, solvents, synthetic gasoline, and drugs.

Production. The world production of coal is closely tied to the heavy iron and steel industries. In the United States, the leading areas of production are Pennsylvania, West Virginia, Illinois, Kentucky, Indiana, Alabama, and Virginia. Altogether, coal is mined in about 30 states.

Reserves. Reserves are difficult to estimate because of changing technology and economic conditions, but by conservative standards the available supply of coal is ample to last many hundreds of years at the presently foreseeable rate of depletion.

IRON ORE

Most of the world's supply of iron ore comes from sedimentary beds of hematite, limonite, siderite, or other iron-rich minerals, as in the Lake states (Fig. 8.7) and Alabama. Some is derived from magnetite of contact-metamorphic origin, as in New York, Pennsylvania, Utah, and California.

The great iron-bearing deposits of the Lake Superior districts originally were chemical precipitates. The initial sediment was taconite, a cherty rock containing hematite, magnetite, siderite, and hydrous iron silicate (greenalite). The unaltered

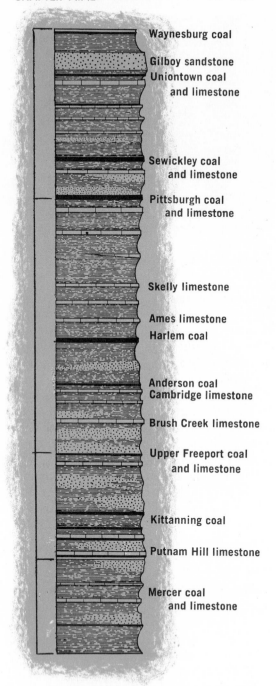

Waynesburg coal

Gilboy sandstone
Uniontown coal
and limestone

Sewickley coal
and limestone

Pittsburgh coal
and limestone

Skelly limestone

Ames limestone
Harlem coal

Anderson coal
Cambridge limestone

Brush Creek limestone

Upper Freeport coal
and limestone

Kittanning coal

Putnam Hill limestone

Mercer coal
and limestone

FIG. 9.33. *Diagram showing the repeated alternations of coal, sandstone, shale, and thin limestone in eastern Ohio. Total thickness of the strata is nearly 900 feet. (After Dunbar.)*

taconite contains only about 20 per cent iron. Where the taconite was altered by ground water, much of the silica was leached out and hematite was left behind. So the iron content was increased to 50 per cent or more, the usual shipping grade of commercial ore. In recent years methods have been devised to concentrate the iron minerals from only partially altered taconite, with great increase in ore reserves. In the Mesabi district of Minnesota, the ore is mined in enormous open pits along the outcrop of the gently tilted beds (Fig. 8.8). At Gogebic, Wisconsin, and Marquette, Michigan, where the beds are upturned more steeply, underground mines are used.

A newly developed iron-mining district lies in eastern Canada near the Quebec-Labrador boundary. Here too the ore is hematite, similarly enriched by weathering.

Beds of oölitic hematite of marine origin are worked for iron in Newfoundland, Alabama, France, and England. Near Birmingham, Alabama, one bed, the "Big Seam," has 15 to 20 feet of ore. The primary rock contains 30 to 40 per cent iron and a large quantity of calcium carbonate. The hematite is partly a replacement of oölitic limestone and calcareous shell fragments and partly a colloidal precipitate. The outcrops have been enriched by leaching. With iron ore, coking coal, limestone as a flux for smelting, and a substantial market all nearby, Birmingham has become a major steel-manufacturing center.

BUILDING STONE AND CRUSHED STONE

Limestones and dolomites are the sedimentary rocks used most extensively for building purposes (Fig. 9.35). Limestone necessarily has the same hardness as that of its chief constituent, calcite (hardness 3), and hence can be worked far more easily than igneous rocks, most of which are extremely hard. Limestone is quarried chiefly in the interior states, between the Rocky and Appalachian Mountains.

Some sandstones are used as building stones, but their adaptability to construction work depends largely on how well their grains are cemented. A

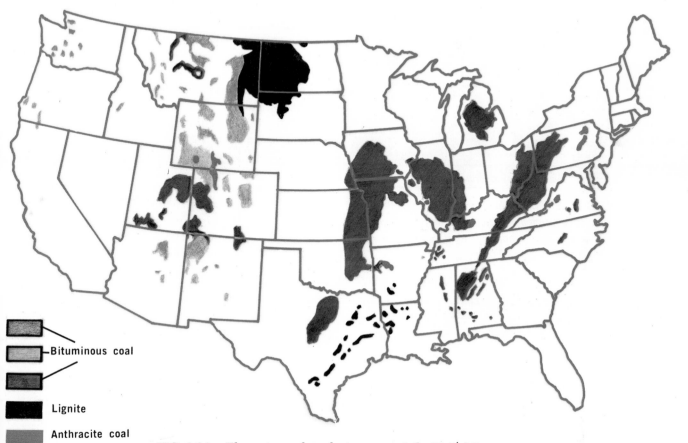

Bituminous coal

Lignite

Anthracite coal

FIG. 9.34. *The major coal-producing areas of the United States.*

thoroughly cemented sandstone makes a very durable building material.

Crushed stone is prepared in large tonnages from a variety of rocks, especially limestone, and is used as an aggregate in concrete for many types of structures. In several large areas the absence of natural aggregates, such as sand and gravel, makes the use of crushed stone a necessity.

SAND AND GRAVEL

The most extensive deposits of sand and gravel occur in the regions of recent continental glaciation. Deposited in outwash plains, valley trains (glacial outwash), eskers and kames (glacial ridges and hills), alluvial terraces, and deltas, they are distributed over a very large area. In nonglaciated regions well-sorted sand and gravel are more limited in distribution and tend to be confined to land forms produced by stream aggradation and wave action.

Sands may be classified in many different ways—for example, by mineralogical composition, by origin, by grain size, by use, or by a combination of two or more of these methods. Sand has many uses: some types are used in concrete blocks and concrete pavements; high-silica sands are used in making glass and Fiberglas; molding sands are used for foundry molds; and filter sands are used for filter beds in water-supply systems.

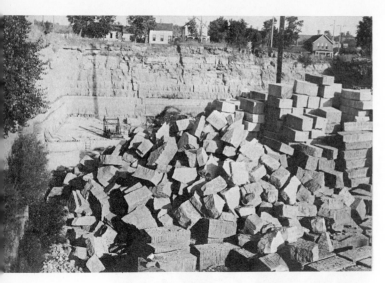

FIG. 9.35: *Limestone quarry in wall of Minnesota River Valley at Mankato. The quarried blocks are sawed into dimensions used as building stone.*

LIMESTONE

In addition to being one of the important building stones and a source of crushed stone for concrete, limestone is quarried and mined extensively for the manufacture of cement, as a flux for blast furnaces, and for the manufacture of quicklime, hydrated lime, soda ash, and other products that are used on a large scale in the chemical industry. Limestone constitutes more than two-thirds of all stone used.

Of limestone's many uses, the manufacture of cement is by far the most important, for cement accounts for about one-third of the total value of all nonmetallic mineral resources (other than fuels) produced annually in the United States. The raw materials most commonly used in making cement are mixtures of limestone and clay, which are heated to form a clinker. A small amount of gypsum is added, and the clinker is then finely ground for use in making concrete.

CLAY

Clay deposits are of two general types, residual and transported. In all cases the clay is of secondary origin; that is, it was formed by the alteration of some other rock. Clays have been classified in many different ways, but the behavior of a clay, and therefore its value and suitability for any specific use, depends on its chemical and physical properties. The most important physical properties of clays intended for ceramic use are plasticity, cohesion, tensile strength, texture, and drying shrinkage. Chemically, the clay minerals are complex hydrous silicates of aluminum. Some of them contain small amounts of potassium, sodium, magnesium, and iron. The chemical composition of a clay gives little indication of its physical properties or of its value in industry, but it may reveal the presence of impurities that would be harmful for certain uses.

The chief use of clay is in the making of brick, and clays suitable for this purpose are widespread (Fig. 9.36). A pure, fine-grained white clay is required for the manufacture of the better grades of pottery, chinaware, and porcelain. A type of clay that withstands high temperatures is called fire clay. It owes its refractory properties to the fact that it contains only very small quantities of elements which act as fluxes. Its principal uses are in making firebrick and other heat-resisting materials, such as the furnace linings required in the iron and steel industry and in making coke.

Certain clays possess the ability to decolorize, or bleach, oils, fats, and greases. Such absorbent clays —or fuller's earths, as they are commonly called— are characterized by exceedingly fine shreds and thin plates of a clay mineral, called montmorillonite, that contains small amounts of sodium and potassium. It is used extensively in the petroleum industry for decolorizing and stabilizing lubricants and in the fat and vegetable-oil industry.

Another absorbent clay, known as bentonite, has the ability to swell enormously when soaked with water. Some bentonites absorb up to 5 times their weight or 15 times their volume of water. Such clays are regarded as alteration products of volcanic ash. They are used most extensively in preparing oil-well drilling muds, in oil refining, and as a bonding material in molding sands.

BAUXITE

Aluminum is extracted from bauxite, an earthy mineral which occurs in a variety of forms and colors. It often shows a pisolitic or oölitic structure with rounded concretionary grains embedded in an amorphous or claylike mass. Some deposits are decomposition products of granites, syenites, and gneisses, but others are thought to be derived by solution of alumina from sediments, followed by its deposition as nodules and irregular pockets in limestone and dolomites.

More than 90 per cent of the production of bauxite in the United States comes from the central part of Arkansas, where the deposits were derived by the alteration of syenites and the replacement of silica by alumina. In tropical countries bauxite laterites are widespread, but high-grade bauxite deposits of large size are not common. British Guiana and Dutch Guiana have the largest known deposits in South America, and both France and Italy are large producers in Europe.

SULFUR

Sulfur has been obtained for many years from deposits associated with recent volcanic activity. Small amounts are still being mined from these sources in Japan, Spain, Italy, and Chile. The deposits formed at the craters of volcanoes or near the vents of hot springs are produced by the oxidation of hydrogen sulfide or by the interaction of sulfur dioxide fumes given off by the volcano.

FIG. 9.36. *Clay pit and plant near Joliet, Illinois. (Illinois Clay Products Co.)*

The most important commercial deposits, however, occur in sedimentary beds associated with gypsum, anhydrite, and other sulfates and carbonates. The sulfur may be formed by the reduction of sulfates, but at present the reducing process is not clearly understood. Undoubtedly bacteria play a part in the reduction, but chemical reduction by other means is possible.

The United States produces more than 80 per cent of the world's output of sulfur, and most of it is obtained from the "salt-dome" structures of the Gulf Coast region in Louisiana and Texas. There the sulfur is recovered by means of wells through which superheated water is pumped underground to the sulfur beds and molten sulfur is returned to the surface. Some sulfur (or sulfuric acid) is obtained from pyrite, smelter fumes, and petroleum refining.

SALT AND GYPSUM

Under arid conditions salt and gypsum are precipitated in bodies of water that have been cut off from the sea or in bays that extend landward from the sea, where the water flows into the bay and is evaporated. Great beds of salt and gypsum are interbedded with sedimentary rocks in Texas, Kansas, Michigan, Ohio, New York, southeastern Ontario, and many other places. Salt is obtained also from natural brines, such as brine springs, salt lakes, and sea water. For example, nearly all the salt produced in California is evaporated from sea water by the sun. Similar salt industries flourish at Great Salt Lake in Utah, Owens and Searles Lakes in California, and the Dead Sea in the Near East. In the United States, however, about 25 per cent of the production is now mined rock salt (Fig. 9.37).

Gypsum is more widely distributed than rock salt, for it is less soluble and therefore more readily precipitated. Gypsum has been precipitated in many basins of evaporation that failed to reach the concentration necessary for the precipitation of salt. In the United States gypsum is produced commercially in 17 states. At present Michigan is the leading producer, but California, Iowa, Texas, and New York have many active gypsum mines.

FIG. 9.37. *Salt mine 800 feet below ground at Winfield, Louisiana. This type of mined salt is called "rock salt," in contrast to salt obtained from the evaporation of naturally saline water. (Carey Salt Company.)*

Raw-gypsum rock is used primarily as a retarder in the manufacture of portland cement. Its second largest use is as agricultural gypsum, sometimes called land plaster, which acts chemically in the soil in a very complex way that is valuable to the growth of many plants. In addition, much gypsum is used in making lath and prefabricated wallboard, and it is also ground and used as a carrier of insecticides and as a filler in the manufacture of paper.

PHOSPHATE ROCK

The phosphate rock used as fertilizer is an earthy substance varying from a hard rock to a granular, loosely consolidated mass, consisting of more or less impure noncrystalline calcium fluorophosphate. It occurs as sedimentary beds, as concretionary nodules or irregular masses, and as a poorly cemented clastic sediment. All phosphate-rock deposits cannot possibly originate in the same manner, since we know they occur in a wide variety of forms and under very different conditions. We believe that the larger deposits are directly or indirectly traceable to animal remains. Some of the small deposits may represent phosphatic matter segregated from igneous rocks by atmospheric waters. The Russian deposits on the Kola Peninsula are in an intrusive mass in which apatite and nepheline (a sodium potassium aluminum silicate) are the most abundant constituents.

Phosphate rock is widely distributed on all continents, and its value in the manufacture of chemical fertilizers is so great that it forms a very important item in world commerce. In the United States it is produced in Florida, Tennessee, Idaho, and Montana.

POTASH SALTS

Potash salts is the commercial term for all the compounds of potassium used in the fertilizer and munitions industries. The naturally occurring compounds are mainly chlorides, sulfates, and carbonates. Some are double or triple salts of potassium with calcium and magnesium.

The large deposits of potash of inorganic origin are products of the evaporation of saline waters, such as sea water or the waters of some highly saline lakes or inland seas, such as Searles Lake in California and the Dead Sea. The largest and most important known deposits of this class are those of the Stassfurt district in Germany, where they are associated with beds of gypsum and anhydrite. These deposits cover an area of approximately 100 square miles and are estimated to occupy a volume of 10,790 million cubic meters, containing 20,000 million metric tons of potash salts, a quantity sufficient to supply the world's needs for 2,000 years at the present rate of consumption.

Potash can also have an organic origin, and the potash industry in the United States began with the production of potassium carbonate from wood ashes. Soon after the discovery of the Stassfurt deposits in Germany, however, the natural mineral potash was used almost exclusively. In 1915, Germany placed an embargo on the export of its potash, and the United States was obliged to find other sources. This resulted in systematic surveys and exploration projects which eventually resulted in discoveries of such magnitude that the United States has become permanently independent of foreign imports.

The largest deposits in the United States are in the salt basins of New Mexico, West Texas, and adjoining states, where the potash is associated with beds of salt and gypsum. The potash beds occur several thousand feet below the surface, where they are mined by modern mechanized methods. Brines of Michigan and California also yield potash.

OTHER USEFUL NONMETALS[3]

In addition to the major mineral resources described in the preceding sections, several other commercially valuable substances are derived from sedimentary rock. Some of these are summarized in Table 9.10.

TABLE 9.10 *Minor Nonmetallic Resources*[*]

Substance	Uses	Geologic sources	Geographic sources
Abrasives	Grinding wheels, powders	Sandstone, beds of volcanic ash, hard minerals	Ohio, Arkansas, Western United States
Asphalt	Paving, roofing, and waterproofing	In petroleum, in lakes (emulsified with water)	Texas, California, Trinidad
Boron minerals	Glass, porcelain, enamel, fluxes, alloys	Brines, evaporites, hot springs, fumeroles	Searles Lake and Kramer, California
Bromine	In making tetraethyl lead	Sea water and brines	Offshore Texas, Michigan, California, West Virginia, Dead Sea
Calcium chloride	Stabilizing dirt and gravel roads, refrigerating plants	Natural bitterns	Michigan, California, West Virginia, Ohio
Magnesium-bearing brines	Epsom salts and other chemicals	Natural bitterns, sea water	California, Michigan, New Jersey, Texas

[*] See also specific items discussed under Minerals in Chapter 5.

Summary

Sedimentary rocks come mainly from terrigenous, organic, and volcanic sources. Some are clastics, and others are chemical and organic precipitates or evaporites. Shales are especially abundant.

Loose sediments become solid rock by cementation, compaction, and recrystallization. The texture of sedimentary rock may be fragmental, crystalline, oölitic, pisolitic, spherulitic, or colloform. The color is white, gray, green, red, or black if the primary constituents are so colored; red, yellow, or brown if the rock is stained by iron oxide or hydroxide; or black if the rock is rich with organic matter or finely divided iron sulfide. Colors on weathered surfaces generally differ from those in the interior.

Common indurated clastic sediments include conglomerate, breccia, sandstone (including arkose, graywacke, and greensand), and shale. Nonclastics are limestone (including chalk, marl, coquina, oölite, tufa, and travertine), dolomite, diatomite, coal, phosphate rock, salt, gypsum, bedded iron ore, and others.

Primary structures in sedimentary rocks include stratification, cross-bedding, graded bedding, lenticular bedding, mud cracks, ripple marks, rill marks, wavemarks, rain prints, and fossils. Concretions, geodes, and stylolites are formed later.

The continental environments of deposition of sediments include deserts, glacial settings, piedmont alluvial plains, valley flats, lakes, swamps, and caves. Marine realms are neritic, bathyal, and abyssal. Littoral, lagoonal, estuarine, and deltaic deposits form along the shore. The deposits in each environment show distinctive characteristics.

In relation to associated rocks, sediments may be conformable, disconformable, or unconformable. They may display overlap or offlap, and they generally show facies changes laterally. Many features of sediments are determined by earth movements affecting the source areas and the basins of accumulation.

Sedimentary rocks are important sources of mineral fuels, construction materials, mineral fertilizers, sedimentary ore deposits, and other useful substances. Fuels are the most valuable of these resources, and next in order come limestone (and its products), iron ore, sand and gravel, clays, sulfur, and salt.

Sedimentary rocks record such paleogeographic features as environments of deposition, past distribution of land and sea, the relief of ancient lands, and former climates. The composition, texture, and arrangement of sediments tell us their source, and fossils, if any, tell us their age. Structures which we see on present-day beaches and flood plains, such as ripple marks, mud cracks, and animal tracks, can also be found in ancient rocks. Thus, the present is indeed a key to the past.

Suggestions for Further Reading

Dobrin, M. D.: *Introduction to Geophysical Prospecting*, McGraw-Hill Book Company, Inc., New York, 1952. How the search is conducted for petroleum and other mineral fuels.

Dunbar, C. O., and J. Rodgers: *Principles of Stratigraphy*, John Wiley & Sons, Inc., New York, 1957. A textbook of sedimentary rocks.

Hager, D.: *Practical Oil Geology*, McGraw-Hill Book Company, Inc., New York, 1951. A detailed study of petroleum.

Krumbein, W. C., and L. L. Sloss: *Stratigraphy and Sedimentation*, W. H. Freeman & Co., San Francisco, 1951.

Laliker, C. G.: *Principles of Petroleum Geology*, Appleton-Century-Crofts, Inc., New York, 1949. A not too technical textbook on petroleum.

Moore, E. S.: *Coal: Its Properties, Analysis, Classification, Geology, Extraction, Uses and Distribution,* John Wiley & Sons, Inc., New York, 1940. A textbook on coal and all its aspects.

Moore, R. C.: *Introduction to Historical Geology,* McGraw-Hill Book Company, Inc., New York, 1958.

Pettijohn, F. J.: *Sedimentary Rocks,* 2d ed., Harper & Brothers, New York, 1957.

Shimer, H. W., and R. R. Shrock: *Index Fossils of North America,* John Wiley & Sons, Inc., New York, 1944. A study of the fossils used to determine the ages of sedimentary rocks.

Shrock, R. R.: *Sequence in Layered Rocks,* McGraw-Hill Book Company, Inc., New York, 1948.

Shrock, R. R., and W. H. Twenhofel: *Principles of Invertebrate Paleontology,* McGraw-Hill Book Company, Inc., New York, 1953. A study of the fossils found in marine-deposited sediments.

Spock, L. E.: *Guide to the Study of Rocks,* Harper & Brothers, New York, 1953, pp. 144–190.

Trask, Parker D.: "Recent Sediments," Symposium of the American Association of Petroleum Geologists, 1939, *Soc. Econ. Paleon. Min. Spec. Pub. No. 4,* 1955.

Twenhofel, W. H.: *Principles of Sedimentation,* McGraw-Hill Book Company, Inc., New York, 1950. A basic textbook on sedimentation.

Chapter 10

GRADATION
BY GRAVITY

ONCE ROCK has been weathered and broken down by the physical and chemical means discussed in Chapter 8, certain physical agents operate to remove the debris and transport it to different locations, where it eventually forms the basis for new sedimentary rocks. In this and succeeding chapters we shall study the various forces responsible for this process. We turn our attention first to gravity.

Definition and Classification

The products of weathering, where accumulated over a mass of bedrock, form a protecting blanket which retards change in the underlying mass and, if thick enough, may prevent it entirely. The removal of weathered debris by running water, wind, and glaciation is readily recognized. But even in areas where these agents seem ineffective, the products of rock disintegration and decomposition may still be on the move; here the actuating force is gravity.

In conjunction with other factors, gravity may produce marked effects on the landscape (Figs. 10.0, 10.1). A familiar example is the landslide. Loose rock material ordinarily creeps downhill under the pull of gravity. However, on sloping surfaces where water is present, the shearing resistance is reduced, and extra weight is added to the rock material, so that the creeping suddenly becomes a fast, massive landslide. We shall discuss this later in the chapter.

The various types of mass movement (movement of surface materials by gravity) are difficult to classify, for the obvious reason that they tend to merge into each other. Some grade into other, quite different forms of movement of rock waste. Thus a mudflow, with a slight addition of water, may become a heavily loaded stream. Similarly, the action of frost is closely related to glaciation.

The rate of mass movement may be exceedingly slow or very rapid. In either event this movement accounts for a large and essential part of erosion.

C. F. S. Sharpe has divided mass movement of rock waste into three major categories:

1. Creep, or slow flowage—soil creep, rock creep, talus creep, rock-glacier creep, and solifluction

2. Rapid flowage—earth flows, mudflows, and debris avalanche

3. Sliding and falling (Fig. 10.2)—rock- and debris falls and slides, avalanches, and landslides and slumps

Rock movement also takes place below sea level, in the form of submarine slides.

Creep, or Slow Flowage

Creep is the slow but continuous downward migration of soil and mantle-rock under the force of gravity.

SOIL CREEP

Evidences of creep are to be found on almost every soil-covered slope. It expresses itself in such signs as tilted fence posts and telegraph poles, broken or displaced retaining walls, and curved trees, which are tilted down slope by creep but tend to return to a vertical position during growth. Even roadbeds and railroad grades may be moved out of alignment.

Degradation by creep down a slope may be going on even though a continuous covering of tough sod is present at the surface. In the headward portions of the drainage channels of western Kansas a slow creeping of the clays and soils takes place under the sod. Where boulders are present in the soil,

FIG. 10.0. *Gravity removal of loose rock material at Cathedral Mountain, Yoho National Park, British Columbia. Fragments are loosened from the cliff by frost, and blocks of assorted sizes fall to the slopes below. The detritus then rolls (as at lower left), slides, and creeps downhill. Various agents of gradation assist gravity to continue to move the loose material downward. Note the well-marked path swept by avalanches in the middle foreground. (Canadian Government.)*

FIG. 10.1. *Avalanche Lake, Glacier National Park, Montana. Rock waste is being moved down slope by such factors as ice, water, and mud. (National Park Service.)*

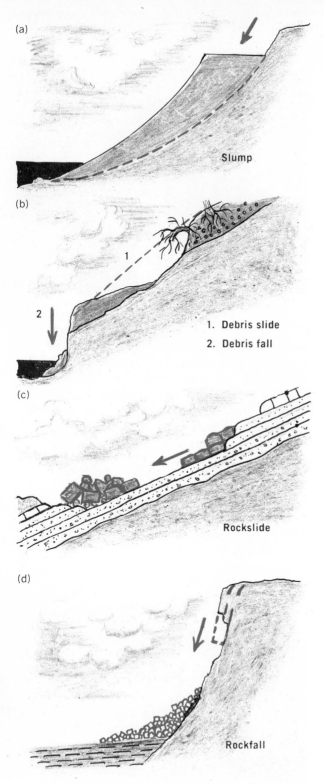

(a)

Slump

(b)

1. Debris slide
2. Debris fall

(c)

Rockslide

(d)

Rockfall

FIG. 10.2. *Types of landslide. (After Sharpe.)*

turf or sod rolls may be observed down slope from the creeping boulders. On some sodded slopes, there are crescentic scarps and cracks, a few to a 100 or more feet long, with the horns of the crescents pointing down slope. Such features are due to unequal rates of movement on the sloping surface.

The rate of creep, which is usually imperceptible except over a long period of time, depends on factors such as temperature changes, amount of rainfall, angle of slope, type of soil, and nature of parent material (Fig. 10.3). In aeolian soil, such as loess, which has a tendency to stand nearly vertical, creep is exceedingly slow, whereas in loosely consolidated, sandy soils with a high proportion of rounded grains the response to the force of gravity and creep is more pronounced. Rates of 5 to 10 feet in 50 years have been measured. On forested slopes the root mat tends to retard the movement, especially that of the coarser particles. However, clay and other fine soil minerals pass through the network of roots quite easily.

In areas where there is alternate freezing and thawing, the rate of creep is increased by the wedging and heaving action of ice. The power of frost heaving has been measured experimentally and found to reach pressures as high as 14 tons per square foot. The lifting action of frost acts at right angles to the slope of a hillside and may thrust surface materials upward as much as several feet. Subsequently, when the frost melts, the boulders and other rock particles settle back vertically under the influence of gravity, so that the new position of rest is down slope from the original. Under conditions of repeated freezing and thawing, therefore, rock materials move down a sloping surface far more rapidly than they would if the temperature never fell below the freezing point.

Other agents that assist creep are active in warmer climates. Clayey slopes may contract and crack during dry seasons, and when such desiccation fissures are closed or filled, there is a greater movement down slope than up. In hot, semiarid regions, where rocks and mineral grains crumble as a result of weathering processes, most of the products of weathering fall or roll down slope. Other things being equal, creep is more rapid in saturated

FIG. 10.3. *Soil formed from limestone on hillside slope near Trail Ridge, Utah. Much of this weathered material was formed higher up the mountain, but was transported to lower levels by creep and frost action. (U.S. Forest Service.)*

mantle-rock, but movement takes place even under the most arid conditions.

ROCK CREEP

Rock creep is the slow downhill slipping of large joint blocks wherever well-jointed massive formations crop out along a slope. By this process a joint block gradually widens the gap between itself and the parent outcrop and eventually tilts to the angle of slope of the surface. In bedded sedimentary strata or in slaty rocks, a downhill bending of the strata may be observed (Fig. 10.4). In some hillside outcrops the bedding planes not only sag but may even show a reversal of the true direction of dip.

TALUS CREEP AND ROCK-GLACIER CREEP

Talus creep is the slow down-slope movement of moderately coarse, irregular blocks of a talus or scree. Such blocks fall from receding cliffs where they are loosened by various agents of weathering (Fig. 10.5). This type of creep is found wherever a steep talus slope exists, and its rate of movement

is determined by the climatic conditions of the region. Where temperature differences are great, the rate is higher than where the daily temperature changes are slight, such as at low altitudes in the tropics. The most rapid movement occurs in cold regions, where the expansive force of the alternate freezing and thawing of ice in the spaces between or within fragments of rock waste tends to thrust the material down a sloping surface.

Rock glaciers (also very aptly called rock streams or stone rivers) occur in some parts of the mountainous states and in areas farther north (Fig. 10.6), where moving rock material often accumulates on steep slopes and in gullies, forming trains of debris suggestive in shape and action of glaciers or rivers. Frost action and an icy matrix play important parts in their movement, but gravity appears to be the basic factor. Their progress also is facilitated by the repeated freezing and thawing of water in the spaces between the rock fragments.

The growth of vegetation, especially tree roots forcing their way into cracks and other available spaces, may tip or wedge rock fragments into an

FIG. 10.4. *Rock creep. The edges of the steeply upturned sedimentary beds are bent downhill near the surface. Gravity will eventually bend the beds enough to follow the slope of the hillside. A shallow excavation here would give a false impression of the true slope (dip) of the beds. (Stose, U.S. Geological Survey.)*

FIG. 10.5. *Talus slope and rock slide materials at the Lake of Jade, Mount Revelstoke National Park, British Columbia. Note the relative coarseness of the loose material. Fragments on steep talus slopes tumble and slide readily. (Canadian National Parks Bureau.)*

unstable position, thus exposing them to such direct gravitative action that they move down the slope. Similarly, burrowing animals, or even the tread of passing animals, may throw rock fragments and particles into an unbalanced position. These may seem insignificant factors in the reduction of the land, but they contribute to the slow transfer of rock waste to lower levels, as do all the other gravity mass movements.

SOLIFLUCTION

Solifluction, or soil flowage, is the term applied to a type of creep that takes place in regions where the ground freezes to considerable depth. As the ground thaws during warm seasons, the upper thawed portion creeps downhill over the frozen material at greater depth. As thawing continues from the surface downward, the melt waters cannot drain downward, and eventually the upper, unfrozen layer of soil becomes saturated. In this condition it will move as a viscous liquid down slopes of as little as 2 or 3 degrees. Such slowly

moving masses of fine debris may carry in suspension blocks of rock of considerable size.

Solifluction is particularly effective above the timber line in mountain areas and in the subarctic and arctic regions, where permafrost, or perennially frozen ground, is present at depth and the superficial layers are softened by summer melting of their contained frost.

Rapid Flowage

The causes and influences responsible for slow flowage may also produce the more rapid movements, such as earth flows, mudflows, and debris avalanches, but in the latter case the conditions favorable to movement are accentuated. Hence we cannot draw a sharp line between slow and rapid flowage.

EARTH FLOWS

The simplest of the debris flows are the earth flows. Although they are the least obvious type of mass movement, they are continuous, and their results eventually may be striking. Earth flows are in the nature of landslides, but the movement is so slow that much time is necessary for the earth mass to attain stability at the new and lower position. The movement is usually on gentle slopes and may require months or years to be completed. Few slopes are free from earth flows.

MUDFLOWS

Mudflows resemble solifluction except that they move much faster and usually follow former stream channels. In steep mountain areas where large amounts of suitable rock material are available and where great quantities of water may be supplied by heavy cloudbursts of rain or by rapid melting of a heavy accumulation of winter snow, an impressive type of mudflow, the Alpine mudflow, occurs frequently.

An excellent example[1] is the Alpine mudflow that

[1] Robert P. Sharp and Laurence H. Nobles, "Mudflow of 1941 at Wrightwood, Southern California," *Geol. Soc. America Bull.*, vol. 64, pp. 547–560, 1953.

occurred in Southern California in May, 1941, when, during unseasonably warm days, the heavy accumulation of winter snow melted rapidly and supplied water to start the movement. The source of the rock material was largely the weathered micaceous schists in the shatter zone of the San Andreas fault high up on the north side of the San Gabriel Range. Here, at the head of Heath Canyon, the loosened debris started sliding down, then broke into a rushing and roaring mass, and left behind a steep, fan-shaped scarface rising 1,000 feet and a nearly vertical arcuate scarp 100 to 150 feet high at the top. Unable to funnel rapidly through a narrow, converging bottleneck into the narrow canyon below, the debris piled up to a thickness of 20 to 30 feet, and the more liquid portion cascaded over the retarded coarser material. The pent-up pressure, behind the temporary obstruction thus formed, caused the mud to break through at intervals, producing a periodic series of wavelike surges of liquid mud that plunged and raced down its course in a rumbling and grating flow, occasionally splashing mud 20 feet into the air and splattering trees, shrubs, buildings, and spectators alike. The supply of material continued about 1 week, rising to a maximum during midday, then decreasing gradually, and ceasing at night. In the more fluid portion the mud mass was about 25 to 30 per cent water (by weight), and the rock debris, making up the balance, consisted of a mixture of fine, medium, and coarse materials, including large boulders. Fragments 2 to 3 feet in diameter were common 1½ miles below the origin of the flow.

In the upper part of the course the flow was rapid, but the velocity decreased with distance because of the decreasing gradient of the path. Midway down, the surge fronts, the tops of which tended to outrun or move ahead of the base, maintained an average speed of about 9 to 10 feet per second, but near the lower end of the flow the velocity did not exceed 1 or 2 feet per second. The material in motion was rather thoroughly jumbled, resembling newly mixed concrete. Where the flow had sufficient force to move boulders, it bore them along as submerged masses, but where the mud became more viscous or the velocity decreased on

FIG. 10.6. *A rock glacier, Copper River region, Alaska. The rock fragments are imbedded in a matrix of ice, so the whole mass gradually flows downhill. The alternate freezing and thawing of the ice matrix helps to push the mass downward. (Moffitt, U.S. Geological Survey.)*

a lower slope, the heavier material was gradually nudged to the sides or shoved ahead at the front as a coarse aggregate. At some places the mud spilled over the edge of its channel, during a forward surge, and mud levees were built up by deposition of part of the load.

This mudflow was generally confined to a narrow strip 20 to 150 feet wide, although a width of 300 to 1,000 feet was attained in a few places. Its course is evident for a distance of 15 miles down the valley, some 5,000 feet below the source. Nearly 1¼ million cubic yards of debris was involved in the mass movement. In the lower reaches the movement of the mudflow was maintained on a slope of about 75 feet per mile.

Alpine mudflows have been reported not only in the United States and Canada but in the Andes, Alps, Himalayas, and elsewhere. They constitute one of the more spectacular types of mass movement occurring in the higher altitudes of the temperate zones.

Mudflows of the more common desert type are produced in arid or semiarid regions when water is suddenly supplied by heavy rainfall to an area in which there is much fine rock debris on moderately steep slopes. They are especially likely to occur in areas where deeply weathered material contains enough clay or silt to aid in lubrication of the mass. As a mudflow moves down a high-gradient valley, it acquires more and more load, and eventually the amount of debris in the frontal portion is so great that it acts as a temporary dam across the valley. The pressure of water, however, pushes the whole viscous frontal dam forward, including the assorted debris suspended in the muddy matrix.

In some parts of the United States mudflows are a common occurrence, and in several regions they have caused considerable damage. Most damage is done when the frontal dam bursts as the flow passes from the confining walls of a narrow valley onto the wide surface of an alluvial fan or cone. At that point the suspension of water and mud breaks through the frontal dam and rushes forward with tremendous force, carrying with it huge boulders and smaller rock debris. Along the Wasatch Range front from Salt Lake City northward, almost every canyon has a mudflow fan, and many of the flows have blocked highways, weakened or destroyed buildings, and ruined many acres of good farm land. Similar conditions exist in the rugged parts of Arizona, Nevada, and California, where immense quantities of rock waste have been transported from the mountainous areas and deposited on the piedmont slopes. See Fig. 10.7 for an illustration of a Nevada mudflow.

A third variety of mudflow is the *lahar*, or volcanic type. After a heavy rain, this type of flow commonly occurs on the steep slopes of active volcanoes newly strewn with thick accumulations of unstably poised dust and cinders.

DEBRIS AVALANCHE

In humid regions mudflows are rare, but a movement of rock debris somewhat similar to the rapidly moving snow avalanches in mountainous topography takes place on steep hillside slopes. Such a rapidly flowing slide is termed a debris avalanche. Debris avalanches occur along relatively narrow zones and follow heavy rains, which increase the weight of the loose surface material on the steep slopes. Slippage generally occurs on the smooth underlying rock surface.

Numerous debris avalanches have been reported from the Appalachian Mountains, the White and Green Mountains of New England, and the Pacific Northwest. They are common wherever there are steep slopes with easily detached rock material lying in unstable positions. Considerable snow and ice may be mingled with the rock waste, and debris avalanches may grade into avalanches of snow on snowy slopes. They leave a bare scarp where the debris originated and a disturbed path down to the place where the mass comes to rest.

Sliding and Falling

Free fall, rolling, sliding, gliding, slumping, and the like are common and characteristic movements of rock and rock waste wherever such materials are affected by an unbalanced factor of gravity (Fig. 10.2). Although movements of this type usually supplement other phases of mass movement, they themselves may determine the velocity of the mass. As the mass becomes free, it moves onward with as much speed as is possible against the resistance it meets. Thus in free fall the speed is the accelerating velocity of gravity. Masses falling in this manner are fractured and broken by impact when they strike the surface below, and from that point they may roll, slide, or glide forward until the energy of motion is spent.

ROCK- AND DEBRIS FALLS AND SLIDES

Free fall, or rockfall, is the chief factor supplying the talus material commonly found at the foot of cliffs in rugged regions. This rock waste may accumulate as a cone-shaped mass until the slope thus formed is at the angle of rest for such materials (with a maximum angle of about 30 degrees). When this angle is attained, there is little remaining obstruction to the movement of the fragments of later rockfalls. So when these strike the talus, they may set in motion other loose pieces of rock with which they come into contact. Parts or all of the disturbed rock debris then may tumble or slide on down the slope or over a cliff to a point where movement is temporarily checked.

Large blocks and boulders that have rolled or slid into mountain streams and that tend to block them may resume their journey downgrade after currents have slowly removed the gravel and rock fragments underneath them. This undermining process, repeated many times, brings mass movement into play again each time the boulders attain unbalanced positions, and thus transports them to ever-lower levels. By these mass-moving processes, larger quantities of fallen rock are subjected to weathering.

AVALANCHES

Avalanches are swift slides of snow. As they repeatedly follow the troughs of ravines tributary to major mountain valleys, they sweep the bottoms of the ravines clean of all loose material. Avalanches, therefore, leave bare, solid-rock "avalanche chutes" along their courses, which in forested areas are conspicuous because of the local lack of soil and timber. As a result of their momentum upon reaching the main valley floor, avalanches may even carry some material part way up the opposite side of the valley before making a turn down-valley.

LANDSLIDES AND SLUMPS

Where large masses of earth and rock slide bodily down steep slopes, breaking into discrete fragments, the movement is called a landslide. A large slump block (Fig. 10.8), however, more or less retains its identity and moves slowly down along a doubly curved plane.

Conditions especially favorable to landslides are (1) steep slopes (sea cliffs, riverbanks, road cuts,

FIG. 10.7. *Margin of a recent mudflow (now dry and sun-cracked) on an alluvial fan along the east side of the Stillwater Range, Churchill County, Nevada. Mudflows are produced in arid regions when a heavy rainfall washes clayey or silty rock debris off steep slopes as a soupy mixture. (Eliot Blackwelder.)*

canyons, fault scarps, and glaciated valleys); (2) weak, slippery, impermeable material (clay, shale, volcanic ash or tuff, serpentine, soapstone, or any deeply weathered rock); (3) jointed or much-broken rock on top; (4) an inclination (dip) of sedimentary beds toward the open side; and (5) heavy rains or melting snows.

The immediate causes of movement include (1) oversteepening of the slope by natural erosion or by man-made excavations, (2) overloading of the upper part of a slope, (3) earthquake vibrations, (4) increased water pressure in the rock pores, which reduces the cohesion of the material, (5) change in the water level, (6) solution of cementing substances, (7) spring sapping, and (8) "spontaneous liquefaction" occurring with the compaction of water-saturated materials. The role of water is especially important, for it adds weight, reduces the shearing resistance of the mass, and eliminates the holding effect of surface tension. Any loose weathered material, greatly weakened and overloaded by saturation with water, tends to collapse. To illustrate, a pile of dry sand will stand at a moderate angle of repose; a pile of wet, aerated

FIG. 10.8. *Landslide of the slump-block type at Point Firmin on the coast of California. In this type of landslide the mass retains its identity to some extent. (Spence Air Photos.)*

sand will stand at a high angle, because of the surface tension of the water; but saturated sand will collapse to a very low slope.

Methods of prevention or artificial control of landslides include (1) reduction of slope; (2) terracing; (3) interception or diversion of surface water; (4) underground drainage through tunnels, drainpipes, and wells; (5) a facing of asphalt, riprap, or concrete to keep out water; (6) artificial compaction; (7) freezing *in situ* (as at dam excavations); and (8) on small slides, the use of piling, concrete piers, or retaining walls to hold the material in place.

Landslides leave scars near their origin, tilt or jumble the component blocks, create slump-basin lakes, dam up valleys temporarily to make other lakes, and leave sites of ponds and lakes on the irregularly hummocky surfaces of the slides themselves. This assemblage of slide-formed topographic features is rather distinctive.

Many destructive landslides (including earth flows) have taken place during the past few centuries. In 1855, a mass of rock debris 3,500 feet

long, 1,000 feet wide, and 600 feet high descended in the valley of the Tiber River in Italy. It formed a dam across the valley so that the village of San Stefano was flooded to a depth of 50 feet. Many lives were lost, and buildings were destroyed.

In Canada, along the Lievre River, north of Buckingham, Quebec, an area of about 100 acres slid into the river. A clay terrace was resting on solid rock, and after several days of rain the clay had become saturated with water and slid under the additional weight. The momentum developed was so great that large masses of the clay were thrust up the opposite bank of the stream to a height of 25 feet.

Another destructive slide occurred in Canada in 1903, at Frank, Alberta, where the entire face of Turtle Mountain, estimated at 40 million cubic yards, broke loose and was dashed to the base of the mountain and hurled across a valley and 400 feet up the opposite side. The length of the slide was about 2½ miles. The entire landslide took place in less than 2 minutes.

In the Gros Ventre Valley, Wyoming, south of Yellowstone Park, a huge rockslide occurred in 1925 (Fig. 10.9). The slide mass, some 50 million cubic yards, descended about 2,000 feet, probably sliding down the inclination of the rock on a layer of saturated clay. The front of the mass plunged across the valley, rose 350 feet up the steep opposite side, and settled back. The dam thus formed across the valley was nearly 250 feet high and ½ mile long.

In Columbia River Gorge near Stevenson, Washington, numerous slides are continually creeping toward the valley.

Submarine Slides

Mass movement may take place even beneath the sea.[2] Studies of the ocean bottom suggest that sediments perched precariously—say near the top of the continental slope—may be dislodged by an earthquake or by any other trigger action and may

[2] Maurice Ewing, *Pacific Petroleum Geologist*, vol. 7, no. 3, p. 1, 1953.

FIG. 10.9. *The Lower Gros Ventre landslide in northwestern Wyoming. In 1925, the huge, light-colored mass slid out of the mountainside at the left and dammed the lake on the valley floor. The base of the slide is a half mile wide.*

therefore rush down the slope or through one of the submarine canyons in a manner very similar to that of an ordinary landslide or mudflow. As the slides travel down the canyons, they may change to mudflows and then to turbidity currents and thus carry rock materials long distances from the starting point of movement. Possibly submarine canyons, common along the continental slope, are maintained, or kept from filling up, largely by flows of mud and by density currents originating in the sudden movement of rock waste lodged temporarily at or near their upper ends. Submarine slides or mudflows, such as those which broke the Atlantic cable off the Grand Banks in 1929, may attain a very high velocity and produce results on the ocean bottom comparable with those that their counterparts produce on land.

Summary

Gravity can indeed be an awesome agent of mass movement. Like vulcanism, gradation by gravity is one of the few geological processes that have spectacular and rapidly produced results. The movements vary, however, from slow, barely perceptible creep, requiring or lasting years, to sudden rushes lasting only a few minutes. Slow types include soil creep, rock creep, talus creep, rock-glacier creep, and solifluction. The fast movements include rockfalls, rock slides, debris avalanches, snow avalanches, and some mudflows. Certain landslides start slowly, move fitfully for a while, then break loose in a tremendous surge, and later settle down to minor periodic advances for years afterward, before becoming stable.

Landslides are likely to occur where slopes are steep, the surface material is broken, the underlying material is clayey, the beds slant toward an opening, and water is abundant. Since water is the primary cause, the most effective way to prevent or stop slides is to improve both surface and underground drainage.

Landslides leave a distinctive topography of scars, jumbled blocks, hummocky surfaces, and lake basins.

Slides taking place beneath the sea are thought to generate mudflows and turbidity currents which continue the movement of sediments on the sea floor.

Suggestions for Further Reading

Anderson, J. A.: "Solifluction, a Component of Subaerial Denudation," *Jour. Geology*, vol. 14, pp. 91–114, 1906.

Blackwelder, Eliot: "Mudflow as a Geologic Agent in Semi-arid Mountains," *Geol. Soc. America Bull.*, vol. 39, pp. 465–480, 1928.

Boyd, Louise A.: "Weathering and Soil Flow in Mackenzie Valley," *Am. Geog. Soc. Spec. Pub.* 18, pp. 171–177, 1935.

Bryan, Kirk: "Cryopedology," *Am. Jour. Sci.*, 5th ser., vol. 244, pp. 622–642, 1946.

Howe, E.: "Landslides in the San Juan Mountains, Colorado," *U.S. Geol. Survey Prof. Paper* 67, 1909.

Krynine, D. P., and W. R. Judd: *Principles of Engineering Geology and Geotechnics*, McGraw-Hill Book Company, Inc., New York, 1957.

Legget, Robert F.: *Geology and Engineering*, McGraw-Hill Book Company, Inc., New York, 1939, pp. 211–246.

Sharpe, C. F. S.: *Landslides and Related Phenomena*, Columbia University Press, New York, 1938. Although not recent, this is still a very good textbook on the subject.

Woolley, Rolf R.: "Cloudburst Floods in Utah, 1850–1938," *U.S. Geol. Survey Water-Supply Paper* 994, 1946.

Chapter 11

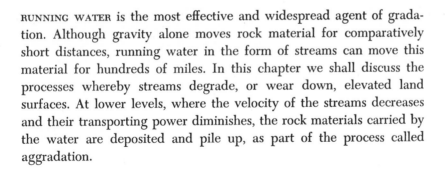

GRADATION
BY RUNNING WATER

RUNNING WATER is the most effective and widespread agent of gradation. Although gravity alone moves rock material for comparatively short distances, running water in the form of streams can move this material for hundreds of miles. In this chapter we shall discuss the processes whereby streams degrade, or wear down, elevated land surfaces. At lower levels, where the velocity of the streams decreases and their transporting power diminishes, the rock materials carried by the water are deposited and pile up, as part of the process called aggradation.

Degradation

RUNOFF

According to Rankama, about three-eighths of the total precipitation on land is carried seaward by streams as runoff. Runoff is the chief degrading agent on the land surface and, therefore, the most important factor in the process of erosion (Figs. 11.0, 11.1), or the reduction of land areas to lower levels. Since the average elevation of the continents is about ½ mile and the amount of water carried by streams is about 8,800 cubic miles per year, the energy available for eroding land is obviously very great.

Amount of runoff. The amount of runoff is not uniform in all areas, not even in areas with equal amounts of precipitation. In regions of

FIG. 11.0. *Rapids on a mountain stream. Running water is a most effective agent of gradation. (Frashers, Inc.)*

marked relief, the runoff exceeds that of the plains and prairies, and unconsolidated sediments or soils absorb more rain than indurated rocks. Porous formations, however, when saturated with water and frozen ground water, allow a high percentage of water to run off. The character and amount of vegetation also influence the amount of runoff. A heavy sod on a slope may shed water like a thatched roof. Most vegetation, however, holds water and delays the runoff. This is true especially of decaying plant tissue, for it acts like a sponge and absorbs large quantities of water. Weeds, brush, and logs also delay runoff by damming the surface water that otherwise would be free to flow away. The removal of forests, therefore, tends to increase both the variability of the streams' volume and the size and frequency of floods.

Dry, hot winds evaporate much of the water which remains on or near the surface. In arid regions, where the humidity is low, the winds are so dry that evaporation goes on rapidly. In the moist tropics, however, the humidity is high, and exposed surfaces remain damp. Under such conditions a smaller part of the rainfall is evaporated.

Ratio of runoff to rainfall. The percentage of rainfall discharged by rivers cannot be measured precisely, for no rule can be made to apply to all parts of a continent. In general, however, in areas with an annual rainfall of 50 inches, about 50 per cent is discharged by rivers, and in sections with a rainfall of 20 inches, only 15 per cent is discharged. The Ohio River discharges about 30 per cent of the rainfall of its basin, and the Missouri River carries away only about 15 per cent. In southwestern North America a number of the streams do not discharge more than 5 per cent of the rainfall. On some parched and porous soils the percentage of runoff may approach 0.

RAINWASH

Sheet flow and sheet erosion. On smooth slopes runoff takes the form of sheet flow, a thin film of water moving downhill more or less uniformly. Although the erosional effects of such a flow may appear negligible, careful studies of topsoil loss from cultivated fields have shown that sheet flow is responsible for the movement down slope of tremendous tonnages of soil materials. It usually carries off the finer ingredients and leaves behind the coarser, less effective materials, thus greatly decreasing the fertility of the land. Sheet erosion may be inconspicuous but is nonetheless real.

Gullying. On uneven slopes the runoff seeks out and follows the initial depressions and thus collects into rills. These rills then modify the original slopes by enlarging their runways into miniature valleys called gullies. Even where sheet flow prevails at the outset, in the absence of initial irregularities in a slope, a concentration of runoff may develop as a result of the differential erosion, for soft or weak materials will be worn down faster than the more resistant substances. Thus sheet erosion may give way to gullying.

Rainwash, whether by sheet erosion or by gullying, is an important, though somewhat neglected, phase of gradation by running water (see Fig. 11.2).

METHODS OF STREAM EROSION

Water which falls on the land and is not evaporated aids in transporting the products of weathering to the sea. The processes of weathering and erosion frequently act jointly and are so intimately

FIG. 11.1. *Grand Canyon of the Colorado River, looking west from the vicinity of Grand View Point. This great chasm, 12 to 15 miles wide and 1 mile deep, has been eroded by the river and its tributaries. (Spence Air Photos.)*

related that distinction is difficult. Certainly, if the agents of erosion did not remove the accumulated debris, the weathering processes would soon be much diminished or would even cease entirely. In most places running water is the agent chiefly responsible for this removal. The erosive work is accomplished by a number of subprocesses which act in cooperation with each other. These are:

1. Corrasion, or the mechanical wear of the stream bed due to the impact and friction of silt, sand, gravel, and boulders carried by the stream (Fig. 11.3). Attrition, the abrasive wearing of the rock fragments in transit by rubbing or grinding or by the impact of rock upon rock, commonly accompanies this process.

2. Corrosion, or the solvent action of water on the rock minerals.

3. Hydraulicking, or the quarrying effect of the impact of water thrown against loose debris, into concavities and recesses, or into joint cracks, as in the undercutting of stream banks. Much of the loose debris consists of the products of rock weathering.

Of course, all erosion, whether by corrasion, corrosion, or hydraulicking, implies removal or transportation.

Corrasion. The corrasive or abrasive action of clear water is slight, as is well illustrated by the Niagara River. The water supplying this stream is clear, since most of the sediment has settled in Lake

FIG. 11.2. *Sheet erosion and gullying by rainwash in a beanfield near Torrance, New Mexico. Although erosion by rainwash is sporadic, its effects are appreciable. Topsoil, as in this illustration, is washed away and the fertility of the field is decreased. (Soil Conservation Service.)*

Erie. Delicate plants, such as algae, grow at the very brink of the falls and form a green coating on the rocks. The current is very swift, but the force of the torrent is unable to tear the tiny plants from the rocky bed. But when running water transports sand grains or pebbles, it becomes a powerful agent of erosion, capable of excavating deep canyons and carving gorges in solid rock. The downcutting of a stream is accomplished chiefly by means of the "bottom load," the sand, pebbles, and silt which it sweeps along near its bed. With these as tools, it grinds and rasps the rocks of its bed in much the same way as sandpaper or a file abrades.

The corrasive power of river water varies as the square of the velocity of the stream. For example, if the speed of the current is doubled, it will hurl twice as many sand grains as before in the same period and will throw each grain against an exposed rock in the stream bed with twice as much force

as it had at its former speed. Thus the rock surface will be eroded four times as fast as it was before the speed was doubled. Other factors are also to be considered, such as the character and amount of the transported material and the character and structure of the rocks through which the channel is excavated.

Corrosion. Chemically pure water does not exist under natural conditions. Because of its solvent power, water is constantly charging itself with impurities, many of which greatly increase its efficiency as a solvent. The water of many streams, especially after flowing through bogs and marshes where decaying vegetation abounds, is charged with carbonic acid in solution. With the aid of this acid, together with atmospheric oxygen, stream water acts on the rock surfaces with which it comes in contact. The rate of dissolution of the rocks is almost imperceptible, except where calcareous sediments are corroded along joints and fissures. The amount taken in solution by any one stream may seem small, but the total amount of material thus dissolved from the land and carried into the sea is great. About 5 billion metric tons of solid material is estimated to go into solution on the continents annually, but the greater part of this is contributed by ground water.

FIG. 11.3. *Stream sediments on the bottom of a valley in Nevada. When carried by the stream, these rock fragments aid in abrading the valley. This type of stream erosion is called corrasion. (Erdmann, U.S. Geological Survey.)*

Hydraulicking. All mechanical methods of erosion by stream water itself, without the aid of tools, are included under the term hydraulicking. These methods are the scouring out of loose material by the stream current passing over it, the effect of the impact of flowing water against a stream bank, and the wedging loose and quarrying of joint blocks by hydraulic pressure.

Transportation

SOURCES OF MATERIALS

The materials carried by a stream are its load. This load is derived from a number of sources:

1. Most of the load is supplied by the weathering and removal of rock from the slopes of its tributaries by sheet flow and gullying. During a rain the immediate runoff is muddy with waste as it rushes along gullies or washes down the hillsides. In cultivated regions, where plowed fields lie on the slopes, numerous rills and minor tributaries carry the unconsolidated material to the larger streams.

2. Some of the load of a stream is obtained by wearing material from its banks or bed.

3. Some material may fall or slide into the river from steep banks where it has been dislodged by the pull of gravity or brought down by other methods of mass movement (Fig. 11.4).

4. In regions with sparse vegetation, earth particles are moved by the wind, and sand or dust may be dropped into the stream.

5. Great numbers of streams that owe their origin to the melting of glacial ice are turbid and loaded with silt. The ice and water from this melting carry "rock flour," produced by the grinding of the stones held in the ice.

6. In regions of volcanic activity, vast quantities of dust and ash are discharged into the atmosphere, and some of it falls into streams or is carried into them by rills during subsequent rainfall. During the Katmai eruption in Alaska in 1912, some streams were completely clogged with ash, and small boats were filled and buried under the debris.

7. Soluble materials are furnished in large quantities by ground water.

FIG. 11.4.   *Yellowstone River Canyon, Yellowstone National Park, Wyoming. Weathering loosens rock particles from the canyon wall. This material slides into the river, which acts as a continuous conveyor. (Northern Pacific Railway.)*

8. Streams are supplied with a small percentage of their load by the impact of driftwood or of floating blocks of ice on the walls of the stream channels and by disturbances resulting from the uprooting of trees and the work of animals and plants.

Along valleys with steep slopes where heavy rainfall soaks the loose products of rock waste that have accumulated on a clayey surface or on solid rock, landslides frequently take place, and these may form temporary dams across river channels. When the ponded water overflows or breaks through the dam, it carries everything before it. In this way, even small brooks become powerful erosive agents and displace hundreds of tons of material from the walls of their valleys in a few hours.

METHODS OF TRANSPORTATION

A body immersed in water loses weight equal to that of the water displaced. Most of the mineral and rock fragments carried by a stream weigh about

2½ times as much as water. Therefore, when immersed in water, they lose two-fifths of their weight. Water films, moreover, are attached to small particles, and this coating makes the fragments lighter and facilitates their transportation by running water.

Streams move their loads (1) by pushing and dragging angular pieces; (2) by rolling rounded and subangular pebbles along their floors; (3) by carrying in suspension fine grains of sand, clay, and silt; and (4) by dissolving and carrying in solution the more soluble compounds. Because of the irregularities of the stream bed, the velocity of the current varies at different places along the stream; and since there is greater energy where the velocity is increased, the movement of the sediment is not uniform. Particles fall to the bottom many times during their journey and remain lodged on the floor of the channel until deflection currents raise them to near the surface, where the velocity is greater. Most of the material carried a short distance above the floor of the stream proceeds by a series of short leaps or jumps. This type of progress is called *saltation,* a term also applied to the similar movement of sand grains transported by the wind. *Stream traction* is the process by which rock material is forced downstream by pushing, rolling, and saltation.

At very low velocities in a smooth channel the water of a stream flows along quietly, as if it were made up of a series of sheets, with the top ones sliding forward over those below; this type of movement is called *laminar flow.* Moderate to high velocities and irregularities in the channel, however, develop *turbulent flow,* in which the water molecules move in very irregular, twisting, winding, or eddying courses that tend to mix the water thoroughly. This turbulence has the effect of continually stirring up sediment from the bottom and of keeping it suspended in the water by preventing its settling. Nearly all streams are turbulent, floods especially so, and they are therefore readily able to pick up a load and to transport it down a valley.

Turbulence is especially marked at rapids, where the water plunges or "shoots" forward over each declivity and dashes against usually deeper, more slowly moving water below. The result is an ever-changing pattern of eddies, of smooth and looping water surfaces, of extremely turbulent "white water." Small wonder, then, that stream work is particularly effective at rapids.

VELOCITY AND TRANSPORTATION

The velocity of a stream is determined by (1) the slope, or gradient, of the stream bed, (2) the shape and configuration of the valley walls, (3) the volume of water in the stream, and (4) the amount of sediment the stream is carrying.

Since the flow of water is due to gravity, it is obvious that the greater the fall per mile, the faster the water will flow. The slope commonly decreases from headwaters toward the mouth of a stream, and consequently the velocity diminishes also. The average slope of the large rivers of all continents is approximately 2 feet per mile. On many of the navigable streams, however, it is less than 1 foot per mile. Irregularities of the channel walls and bottom cause the water to be checked by friction, and it follows that the smoother and narrower a channel is, the lower will be the loss of energy because of friction. A stream bed that is studded with boulders or that runs at right angles to rough, rocky ridges on its floor has obstacles that check the velocity of the flow.

An increase in volume accelerates the rate of flow of a stream by bringing about increased depth of water without greatly increasing the amount of friction. Thus the velocity of a stream varies from time to time as the source of supply of its water varies. In many regions this variation is a periodic one—for example, in rivers, like the Colorado, that have their headwaters in snow-covered mountains and that flow faster when their volume is increased by the melting of the snow in the spring.

The spectacular effects of floods in transporting both particles of large size and large total loads of debris prove that increases in velocity, though only moderate, greatly increase the transporting power of streams. In general, for coarse loads, the size of a particle transported by traction varies directly with the 2.6 power of the velocity.

Table 11.1 shows the velocities that river currents

must maintain in order to move materials of different sizes. Table 11.2 shows a similar relation between the progressive decrease in the velocity and the accompanying decrease in the grain size of the sediments on the beds of the Mississippi River between Cairo, Illinois, and the Gulf of Mexico. The figures are based on 600 samples taken from the river at low-water stage by the U.S. Waterways Experiment Station, Vicksburg, Mississippi. The bed load of gravel and sand near Cairo gradually gives way downstream to fine sand, silt, and clay.

TABLE 11.1   *Competency of Streams*

Material carried	Velocity of current, meters per second
Fine sand	0.2
Medium sand	0.3
Coarse sand	0.4
Granule gravel	0.6
Pebble gravel	1.6
Boulders	11.7

AMOUNT OF LOAD

The quantity of material transported by a river is not constant, owing to variations in the volume of water, the velocity of flow, and the amount of rock waste supplied by tributaries. In order to ascertain the total load, we must determine the average annual discharge of water, the average amount of solid sediments transported, and the average amount of salts carried in solution. We can find the amount of water discharged by multiplying the number of square feet in the average cross section of the stream by its velocity per second. This gives us the discharge per second in cubic feet. We can find the amount of silt to a cubic foot of water by filtering samples of the water taken from different parts of the stream during different seasons. The amount of salts in solution is determined by evaporating filtered samples, and the composition of the salts is found by chemical analysis.

The Mississippi River annually carries to the Gulf of Mexico about 22,000,000,000,000 cubic feet of water, containing a total load of 516,900,000 tons of rock waste; about 340,500,000 tons is transported in suspension, about 40,000,000 tons is rolled on the bottom, and approximately 136,400,000 tons is carried in solution. According to recent estimates, more than 800,000,000 tons of material in all is carried by the rivers of the United States each year. A train of ordinary freight cars long enough to carry this load would reach around the earth six times in the region of the equator. The total load carried in solution per year by all the rivers of the world is the equivalent of about 100 tons for every square mile of land surface on all the continents. The total detrital load is about six times as great.

ABRASION OF LOAD

Rock fragments dragged and rolled over one another and over the surface of the stream bed are

TABLE 11.2 *Mississippi River Sediments between Cairo and the Gulf of Mexico, Per Cent*

Material carried	Miles below Cairo					
	100	300	500	700	900	1,000
Large gravel	8	3	6	2	trace	
Medium gravel	10	2	6	2	trace	
Fine gravel	11	3	2	1	trace	
Coarse sand	30	22	9	8	1	
Medium sand	32	50	46	44	26	9
Fine sand	8	18	26	40	68	65
Very fine sand	trace	1	2	1	2	4
Silt	trace	trace	2	1	2	10
Clay	trace	trace	1	trace	1	10

SOURCE: Charles Nevin, *Geol. Soc. Amer. Bull.*, vol. 57, p. 672, 1946.

ultimately worn down. Such wearing is called *attrition*. Partly because of this action, the load is finer near the mouth of large rivers. Farther upstream, the size of rock fragments carried by streams is increased. A further reason for such distribution is that the velocity of the stream decreases toward the mouth, and hence the stream is unable to move coarse material. A high percentage of the fine silt in the lower courses of a stream, however, is derived from the attrition of the coarser material gathered by its headwaters. In many rivers the progressive increase in the degree of rounding of pebbles at increasing distances downstream eloquently emphasizes the wear such pebbles undergo en route.

RATE OF DENUDATION

A river system, with its numerous tributaries, covers the land with a network of watercourses, which carry their loads toward the trunk stream. With a uniform amount of rainfall the rate of denudation is greatest in the region of the headwaters of the stream, somewhat less over the more gentle slopes of the intermediate zone, and least in the level areas near the coast line. In a large drainage basin the rate of stream erosion is influenced by many factors, such as the velocity of the stream, its volume of water, the nature and amount of its load, and the character of the rocks or soils over which it flows.

In the headwaters the gradient of the stream bed is steeper, the velocity is greater, and the transporting power is higher than they are near the mouth. If the fragments collected by the headwaters are composed mainly of resistant minerals, such as quartz, and the floors and walls of the valley farther down the river's course are composed of softer rocks, the valley will be eroded much more rapidly than if the load is mostly clay or silt. To cut rapidly, the stream must carry some resistant sediment as tools, but not so much as to decrease its velocity, for then the force of its tools is diminished. Sedimentary rocks, especially those cemented with calcium carbonate, are much more easily eroded than massive igneous rocks. Thin bedding of sediments and the presence of joints and fissures also favor rapid erosion.

Estimates of the rate at which certain rivers are eroding the areas they drain have been made by various groups of investigators. The Mississippi River and its tributaries, draining an area of approximately 1,265,000 square miles, are now lowering the basin of that river at the average rate of about 1 foot in 9,000 years.

Valleys

A large part of the water that falls as rain runs off the surface of the region where it falls. If the surface has a smooth, uniform slope, like a gently pitching roof, it flows off as a sheet, and no channels are developed. Such smooth surfaces, however, are rare. Slight irregularities lead to the formation of rills, which erode small furrows. The rills unite to form rivulets, and the uniting rivulets form torrents, which cut deep gorges and canyons. Eventually, these canyons are transformed into wide valleys with gentle slopes. We shall now discuss some of the details of this transformation.

GROWTH

The lengthening of a valley is accomplished for the most part by head erosion. Many streams start at or near the places of their outlets and grow in length by cutting backward into the slopes, thus increasing the area that they drain (Fig. 11.5). This process continues until the gulley reaches an obstacle, such as a resistant rock formation, or until it reaches a point where lack of slope or the tributaries from the opposite side of a slope stop its progress. This interstream area, or line of separation, constitutes the *divide*, or *interfluve*. If the erosion on the two sides of the divide is about equal, a *fixed divide* is established, for even though continued rainfall may tend to lower it, its geographic position remains unchanged. Where erosion on one side is more rapid than on the other, however, the divide shifts slowly toward the side of less rapid denudation.

If, in its migration headward, a stream reaches a lake, the lake basin becomes a part of the stream system, and the streams flowing into the lake become tributaries of the same system. The retreat of

GRADATION BY RUNNING WATER 211

the stream is retarded at the lake until the stream cuts downward to the level of the lake basin and drains it.

DEEPENING

A valley deepens as it grows in length, for a stream, in cutting backward, also wears its bed downward. During each successive downpour the gully acquires more surface water and is washed out deeper. Side gullies develop and grow into tributaries, the tributaries also acquire side gullies, and the surface water of a large area is directed through the one main channel. Thus, the erosion of the main channel is increased, for increased volume means increased velocity, and hence greater eroding power. As long as the valley is shallow, its supply of water is limited to the immediate runoff at the time of rainfall. Streams that flow only during a rainy season or during a downpour of rain are *intermittent* streams. As a valley is deepened, the floor of its channel approaches the level below which the pore spaces of the rocks are filled with water, that is, the ground-water table; and after the bottom of a valley penetrates this level, its reserve of water is sufficiently increased so that it supports a stream even during the dry seasons. Streams that have their valleys cut below the ground-water level are *permanent* streams.

In regions where the gradients are steep, downcutting by the streams proceeds much more rapidly than where the slopes are low and the streams are sluggish. In fact, many slow streams make their valleys shallower, for they deposit more than they take away. Where the gradient is such that the amount a stream erodes balances the amount it aggrades, the stream is said to be *at grade,* or is referred to as a *graded* stream. In a long valley, like the Mississippi, deepening may be in progress toward the upper end, even though the valley may be becoming shallower at the other end, because of deposition in the lower course of the river. Where the rate of deepening exceeds that of the erosion of the banks, deep canyons with clifflike walls are developed (Fig. 11.6). The depth to which a valley may lower its bed depends on the elevation of the land in which it has been cut. High plateaus, such as the Colorado Plateau, or high

FIG. 11.5. *Headward erosion of a young valley of the canyon type invading the forest slope on the south side of Mount Pinos in Kern County, California, at an elevation of a little more than 8,000 feet. Lengthening and deepening of a valley is accomplished by this type of backward erosion. (Spence Air Photos.)*

mountains, such as the Himalayan Range, commonly have valleys of great depth.

The depth limit of a valley is determined by the level of the body of water into which its river flows. Near its mouth, the channel of a large river, such as the Mississippi, may be cut somewhat lower than sea level, but in general the level of the lake or ocean is approximately the depth limit of the valley of the river that discharges into it. Only the lower end of a valley ever attains this limit, for the stream bed must have a gradient, or the river will not flow. The lowest possible level to which a stream can erode its drainage basin by mechanical wear is called the *base level* of stream erosion.

WIDENING

The widening of a valley, or lateral erosion, goes on in conjunction with its deepening. Otherwise, all valleys would be canyons with steep walls. In some regions, conditions for downcutting are more favorable than for lateral erosion, as along the

FIG. 11.6. *Canyon carved by the Little Colorado River and its tributaries near Cape Solitude, Arizona. This type of canyon is found in areas with steep gradients. Streams downcut rapidly. Where the rate of deepening exceeds the rate of erosion of the banks, deep canyons are formed. (Fairchild Aerial Surveys, Inc.)*

Gunnison River in Colorado and along the upper portions of Zion Canyon, Utah, where nearly vertical walls over 2,000 feet high are only a few hundred feet apart at the brink of the canyon. Most valleys are much wider than their streams, however, although the character of the rock over which the stream flows may produce local variations in the width, so that narrow portions alternate with wider ones. If a stream crosses a tilted bed of hard, resistant rock lying between softer materials, the valley widens faster both above and below the hard bed than it does where the stream crosses it. A *narrows* is formed where the stream cuts across the resistant rock.

Valley widening is accomplished in many ways, the most important of which are (1) by creeping or slumping, (2) by rainwash, (3) by the activities of animals and plants, (4) by glacial abrasion, (5) by undercutting, and (6) by tributaries.

1. While the slopes are steep, the loose products of rock weathering creep slowly downward under the action of gravity. If clayey material becomes thoroughly saturated with water during a rainy season, large masses of it may slide or slump toward the valley floor and carry debris with it. This process is in progress on a large scale along parts of the valley of the Columbia River, where huge landslides are moving toward the valley, transporting forests and buildings with them. The presence of water not only increases the weight of the precariously perched rock waste but also, by exerting pressure in the pores, decreases its shearing strength, thus helping to cascade the debris into the lowland, where it lodges.

2. Rain falling on the slopes of a valley washes away loose material; and where the valley is in unconsolidated sediments, furrows and gullies are excavated in its walls. The debris is carried toward the stream channel, and the valley is widened.

3. Many land animals visit streams to obtain water or to graze along the banks; and as they walk along the valley slopes, they dislodge loose debris. Burrowing animals bring to the surface sand and clay, which are readily washed down the slopes. Roots of trees aid in the disruption of the rocks along the valley; and when the trees are overturned, more material is loosened and eventually carried downward.

4. In high-altitude valleys partially filled with glaciers, the bottom is widened by ice as rapidly as the walls are eroded back, and so wide, flat-bottomed valleys result.

5. A stream rarely has a straight course, and at each curve it usually cuts more on one bank than on the other (Figs. 11.7, 11.8). The water tends to pile up on the bend, and the outside of the curve receives a greater volume of water; thus the velocity is locally increased, and the bank is undermined and moved back.

As a valley approaches base level, its gradient decreases, and the flow of its stream becomes more gentle. In such a slow stream the currents easily are deflected (1) by some obstacle on the floor of the channel, (2) by a projection of more resistant rock along the bank, or (3) by the entrance of swifter currents from a tributary stream. The deflected current strikes the opposite bank and, as it moves downstream, tends to be thrown back again to the side from which it first issued. Thus the stream

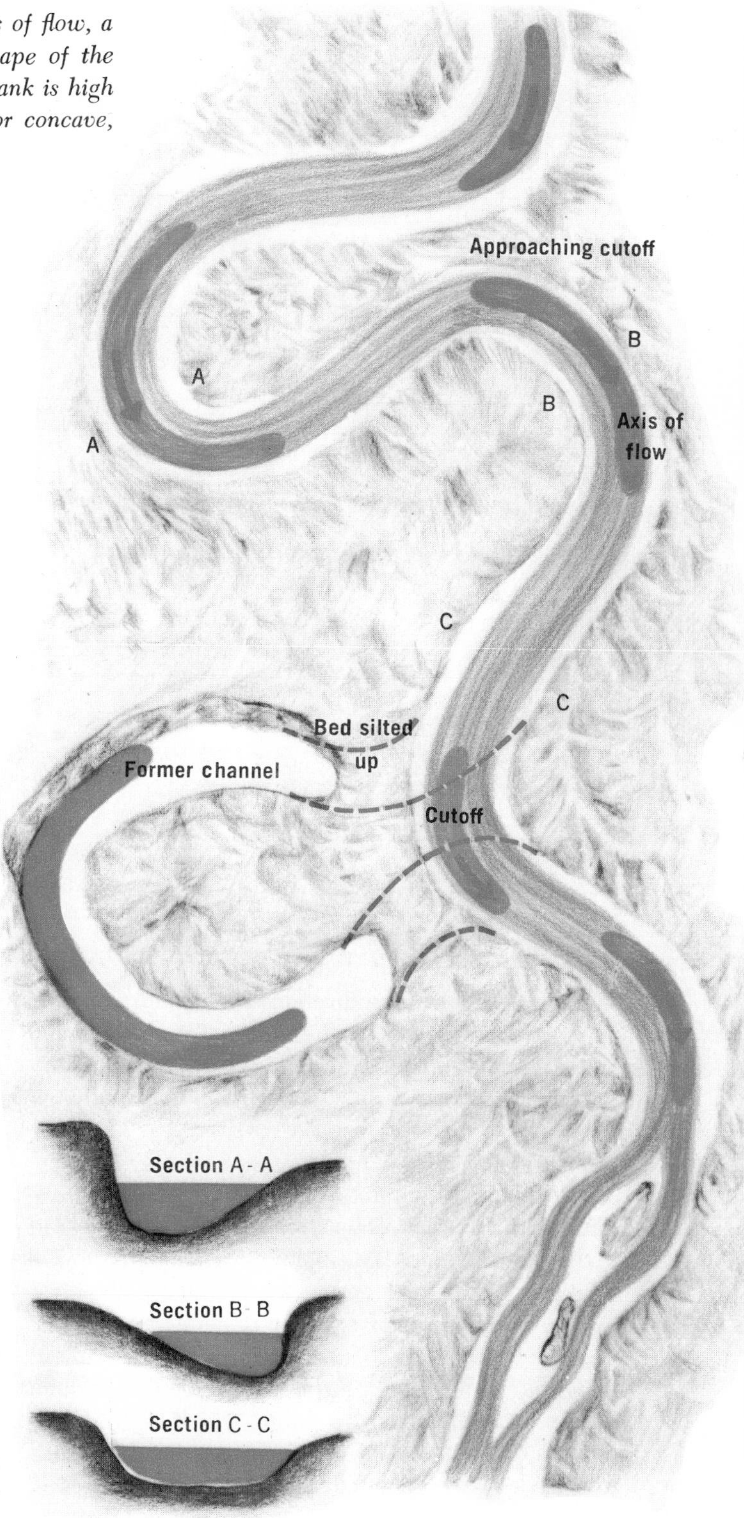

FIG. 11.7. *Diagram of a meandering stream showing axis of flow, a cutoff, and in the sections on the left, the changes of shape of the channel. On the outer, or convex, side of each bend the bank is high and steep owing to undercutting, whereas on the inner, or concave, side it slopes at a gentle angle. (After Thomas and White.)*

develops a series of winding curves, or meanders (Fig. 11.9). In a sluggish stream the successive meanders tend to be of about the same size; the strip within which these are confined is called the *meander belt.* According to M. S. W. Jefferson[1] this belt is about 18 times the width of the stream; but on flood plains of very low relief, the meander belt itself meanders, thus complicating any attempt to define it, although the general concept seems to hold true.

Once started, the meanders become more and more pronounced, and finally a series of loops separated by narrow necks of land are developed. Eventually the stream cuts through the narrowed neck of land between two loops and leaves the meander as a long, curved *oxbow lake* (Fig. 11.7). Where this happens, the river shortens its course, and the current is modified, so that a new meander is likely to be formed because of the shifting of the currents. The old, deserted loops with their shallow lakes are converted gradually into stagnant pools and bogs, which are characteristic of flood plains in the later stages of their development.

Level or flattened areas commonly accompany the widening of a valley, especially where the stream has cut its channel down to a low gradient. Such flats are temporary base levels established by the local conditions that govern the stream's gradient. Later, when conditions of velocity, volume, and load are altered, the stream may cut deeper into the flats and leave them as terraces along the valley. The Mississippi River has developed flats along its upper course where the floor of the valley is more than 600 feet above sea level. A short distance south of St. Paul a flat more than 1 mile wide has been cut about 250 feet below the general level of the region. In the neighborhood of St. Louis the flats are about 400 feet above

[1] *Natl. Geog. Mag.,* vol. 13, pp. 373–384, 1902.

Approaching cutoff

Axis of flow

Bed silted up

Former channel

Cutoff

Section A - A

Section B - B

Section C - C

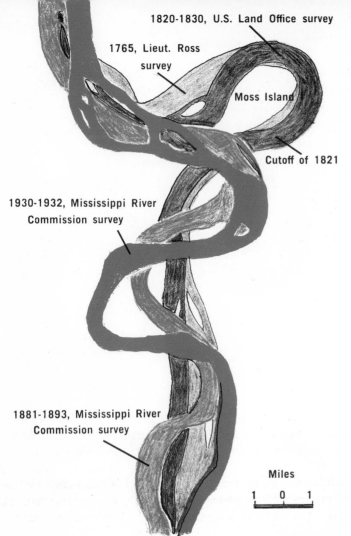

FIG. 11.8. *Progressive changes in the channel of the Mississippi River above Memphis, during a period of more than 150 years. The sketch shows meanders and the meander belt of a major stream on its flood plain. (United States Army Engineers.)*

sea level and about 150 feet below the regional upland. Still farther downstream in Tennessee and Arkansas the flats are 35 miles wide and lie 220 feet above the sea.

The width limit of a valley depends on the distance between neighboring streams. Parallel valleys may be widened until the divide between them becomes a sharp, narrow ridge, which is gradually lowered as the regions appoach base level, or until the divide is eliminated and the valleys coalesce.

Cycle of Erosion

A newly uplifted land area marks the starting point of the history of a river drainage system. Naturally, as such an area is drained, the progress of erosion produces a series of changes in the topography. These changes are determined in part by the altitude of the uplifted area and the character and structural relations of its subsurface rock formations. Erosion first roughens the surface of the area by excavating gullies and valleys and by leaving ridges and hills as divides. Eventually, the divides are lowered, and the result is a comparatively level surface. Hence, erosion tends eventually to produce a plain. A cycle of erosion is the time required for a region to pass through the various stages of topographic expression that transform it ultimately into a featureless plain.

For purposes of the comparison and study of land surfaces, the cycle of erosion is divided into three stages—youthful, mature, and old. The topography of a valley is youthful when most of the work of the stream is not yet done; it is mature when the erosive agents have accomplished so much work that most of the area consists of slopes; and it is old when erosion has nearly finished its work. Mature topography is the most rugged, but the cycle is a continuous one, and obviously there is no clear line of demarcation between any two stages. The amount of time required for each stage varies with the particular area; one valley may reach maturity in a much shorter time than an adjoining one, especially if the former is cut in relatively soft rocks and the latter in a region of more resistant material. A distinction should be made also between the age of the stream in the cycle of erosion and the stage in the erosion cycle to which the area it drains has progressed, for certain streams with youthful characteristics may traverse regions that are typically mature.

YOUTHFUL STAGE

Most youthful streams are rapid streams that flow in V-shaped canyons or gorgelike valleys with steep sides. The slopes are steep because sufficient time has not yet elapsed to widen the valleys. If the area has been recently uplifted, the streams are not numerous, and they have few tributaries. Since they have not had time to erode extensively, they still may have rapids and waterfalls along their courses. The divides are wide and poorly drained, as shown by the presence of upland lakes and swamps. This condition is illustrated in the valley of the Red River of the North and in portions of the coastal-plain areas of the Southeastern United States. The gorge of the Niagara River, the canyon of the Yellowstone, and the valley of the Rhine are all youthful valleys. The Grand Canyon of the Colorado, which also is a young valley, is the most spectacular of all examples.

MATURE STAGE

As erosion continues, the topography changes until the features characteristic of youth are chiseled into different forms, and valleys with flaring sides and gently rounded upper slopes take the place of the sharp, straight lines of the youthful landscape. Because the headwater tributaries have been cut backward, the divides are narrowed, and the region becomes thoroughly dissected by a complex network of valleys. This type of topography is very rugged (Fig. 11.10). The number of tributaries is to some extent determined by the amount of rainfall. Since the southeastern section of the United States has a heavy annual precipitation, tributaries and streams are more numerous in this area than in the semiarid or arid plains of the Southwest. As the tributaries are deepened, the lakes and swamps are drained or filled, and the escarpments that produced waterfalls and rapids are lowered, so that the rivers attain approximately the lowest gradients over which their loads of sediment can be transported. Toward the close of this stage the lower courses of the streams become graded, and then they swing from side to side, thus widening their valleys and developing flood plains.

From the standpoint of human activity, rugged mature topography offers many obstacles, and is the least desirable for many enterprises. Because

FIG. 11.9. *Meanders and oxbow lakes along Mudjatik River in northern Saskatchewan, Canada. The scrolls of former channels on the flood plain are conspicuous. Meanders are characteristic of a sluggish stream, and are caused by deflections in the stream's current. (Royal Canadian Air Force.)*

FIG. 11.10. *Mature topography, Kern County, California. Streams are numerous, the land is all in slope, and the divides are narrow. (Spence Air Photos.)*

of the network of deep valleys, roads cannot follow straight lines, but must follow the crests of the main divides or the winding valleys of the major streams. Railroad grades cross areas of mature topography by using high trestles over the valleys and by penetrating the hills with long tunnels. Typical mature topography now exists in the region of the Allegheny and Cumberland Plateaus to the west of the Appalachian Mountains.

OLD STAGE

By continued erosion the rugged relief of the mature stage of topography gradually is reduced, and the deep channels are transformed into broad valleys with gentle slopes and low divides. The gradient is lowered until the streams lose their vigor and deposit rather than erode. The valleys become shallower, owing to deposition, and the sluggish streams swing from side to side in long, looplike meanders over the deposits of their own flood plains. A land area thus worn down to a plain, with the gentle slopes of extreme old-age topography, is called a *peneplain*. Frequently, isolated hills or

mountains of more resistant rocks rise above the general level of the peneplain. These are called *monadnocks*, after the example of Mount Monadnock in New Hampshire.

BASE LEVEL

Theoretically, the base level of all stream valleys is sea level. Since the flow of a stream is influenced by gravity, however, it is evident that erosion can proceed only as long as a stream retains sufficient gradient to transport its load. As a land surface approaches a peneplain, it also approaches base level (Fig. 11.11). In regions remote from the sea, a peneplain condition is produced while the region is still several hundred feet above the level of the sea.

DISTURBED EROSION CYCLES

As the drainage basin of a river system passes through the successive stages of a normal cycle of erosion, it may be interrupted at any stage by various geological processes. Among them the following are perhaps the most important: (1) glaciation and

TABLE 11.3   *Summary of Changes during a Cycle of Stream Development*

Characteristics	Youthful stage	Mature stage	Old stage
Trends of channels	Straight	Meanders common	Meanders numerous
Gradient and velocity	High	Moderate	Low
Waterfalls and rapids	Many	Few	None
Nature of erosion	Downcutting predominates	Lateral planation prominent	Lateral planation predominant
Width of valleys	Narrow, V-shaped	Broad and well-defined	Very broad with low boundaries
Depths of valleys	Moderately deep	Deepest	Shallow
Number of tributaries	Few, small	Maximum number	Few, large
Nature of divides	Wide, low to high	High and narrow	Low and narrow
Relief	Maximum for entire drainage system	Maximum for region of headwaters	Low
Number of lakes	Many on uplands	Few, if any	Many on lowlands
Adjustment to structure	Not adjusted	Well-adjusted	Little affected by structural control
Material transported	Coarse and fine	Sands and silts prominent	Silts and solutions predominant
Deposition by streams	Minimum deposition	Deposition at insides of curves	Deposition in channels and on levees
General drainage	Poorly developed	Well-drained, most efficient	Drainage sluggish

other interferences by gradational agents; (2) volcanic action; (3) diastrophism.

Glaciation and gradation. A glacier may fill a stream valley with ice or cover its basin with a snow field that protects the surface from weathering and stream erosion. During the Great Ice Age, when most of northeastern North America was subjected to continental glaciation, many areas within that region were in the mature stage of topography. As the glacier receded, however, enormous amounts of glacial debris were deposited irregularly, forming hills, ridges, knobs, and depressions over the preglacial topography, with the result that youthful features again were developed and superimposed on large areas which had been eroded far beyond this stage. This is true especially of the region to the south and east of the Great Lakes in the United States.

The encroachment of sand dunes, the deposition of sheets of loess, the escape of the surface runoff into limestone sinks and caverns, and the blocking and lateral shifting of the mouth of a stream by waves and shore currents along a seacoast also delay the progress of a stream's work.

Volcanic action. Lava may flow down the slopes of a valley and completely fill its stream channel; if the volume of lava is great enough, it may even bury the entire region and profoundly modify the drainage system. In such areas the erosion cycle is interrupted, and a new cycle is initiated on the surface of the lava field. The Columbia Plateau, covering an area of over 200,000 square miles in Washington and Oregon, is a lava field which, at many places, completely buried the streams and valleys of the old erosion surface.

Diastrophism. Diastrophism, or movements of the earth's crust, may bring about interruptions that vary both in character and in the results produced. It may modify the cycle of erosion only locally and temporarily, or it may cause the streams to start their work anew. Changes in level may be produced by elevation or by depression.

DROWNING

Depression of the land or rise of sea level hastens the development of old age by bringing the de-

FIG. 11.11. *The even skyline of the Laurentian peneplain, looking eastward at Long Lake, the upper portion of Manigotagan River in southeastern Manitoba near the Ontario border. Peneplains are characteristic of extreme old-age topography. At that stage erosion has beveled the rocks, regardless of their internal structure, until base level is approached. (Geological Survey of Canada.)*

pressed area nearer base level and by decreasing the amount of material the streams must remove before a featureless plain is developed. When such a rise in sea level occurs along a coast line, the sea occupies the lower ends of the valleys and converts them into bays and estuaries. The valleys then are "drowned." Thus the Hudson River is drowned as far north as Albany, and the St. Lawrence River appears as an arm of the sea as far as Montreal. Narragansett, Delaware, Chesapeake, and other bays along the coast of the United States are drowned valleys resulting from a sinking of seaboard areas or a rise of sea level.

Before submergence took place, many of the streams which now flow into Chesapeake Bay discharged their waters into the lower course of the Susquehanna River, to which they were tributaries (Fig. 11.12). Such tributaries, isolated from their trunk streams by drowning, are called *dismembered* streams. With subsequent emergence they would extend their courses and again become parts of the major stream system.

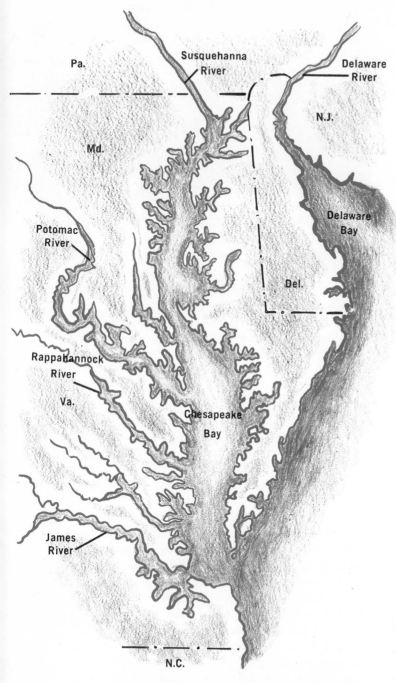

FIG. 11.12. *Drowned valleys of Chesapeake and Delaware Bays. The tributaries on the left, which formerly emptied into the Susquehanna River, are dismembered and end in estuaries.*

REJUVENATION

If a peneplained area is elevated, the gradients of the streams are increased, and they set to work cutting gorges and canyons in the bottoms of their old valleys, with the result that the region again takes on the characteristics of youth. Such a region is said to be rejuvenated; the infusion of new vigor through an increased gradient quickens the velocity of the streams, and they become rejuvenated streams.

After such an uplift a river sinks its valley within the new upland; and if the old streams had meandering courses before rejuvenation, the winding channel is deepened and the old meanders become entrenched (Fig. 11.13). Eventually, during renewed maturity, the wide lobes of the individual meanders become separated by mountains formed by the dissection of a slowly elevated plain.

Rejuvenated streams with entrenched meanders are common in the Appalachian region. The Susquehanna River of southern New York and northern Pennsylvania and the New River of the Cumberland Plateau are examples. The Yakima River of central Washington and the San Juan River of southeastern Utah are both deeply entrenched. Some of the natural bridges of Utah owe their origin to the perforation of necks between entrenched meanders. The famous Rainbow Bridge, carved out of sandstone, has a height of 305 feet and a span of 270 feet across the neck between old meanders (Fig. 11.14).

Uniform slow emergence, or elevation, affecting extensive areas may revive the streams without greatly altering the major features of the topography. In this way an old peneplain may be lifted up to an altitude of several thousand feet above sea level without greatly warping the old erosion surface.

Faulting (movement along fractures in the earth's crust) may produce tilting. Where the movement is upward, the streams are revived, and the cycle of erosion is interrupted. If the movement is downward, the gradient is decreased, and the velocity of the stream is checked. Notable depression or elevation along a fault line across a valley may so

FIG. 11.13. *Entrenched meanders ("goose necks") in San Juan Canyon, Utah. The meandering course of the stream was developed during a previous erosion cycle, when the river was flowing over a graded plain. The meanders became entrenched when the stream was rejuvenated by an uplift of the area. (Spence Air Photos.)*

impede the flowing streams that the waters become *ponded* and the rate of erosion is changed.

Differential Stream Erosion

The shapes into which the land is sculptured by stream erosion are determined to a great extent by the composition and subsurface structures of the rocks of the region. Land forms commonly reflect the structure of the component rocks. Hence, wherever the rocks are not homogeneous, stream erosion produces topographic effects that are very different from those found where a valley develops in uniform rocks.

CONTROLLING STRUCTURES

The principal structures which affect the way erosion proceeds are (1) igneous bodies, (2) folds, (3) joints, (4) faults, and (5) cleavage.

1. Igneous bodies, such as volcanoes, dikes, sills, stocks, and batholiths, as shown in Fig. 6.28, interrupt the erosion of an area by providing particularly resistant rocks.

2. Folds in sedimentary rocks, such as homoclines, anticlines, synclines, basins, and domes, also expose more or less resistant strata when eroded. Homoclines consist of uniformly tilted beds; anticlines are elongate arch-shaped folds; synclines are troughlike folds; structural basins are roundish dishlike structures resembling nested saucers; and domes are rounded arches.

3. Joints are merely cracks in the rocks, generally arranged in a certain pattern or system, which contribute to erosional weakness.

4. Faults are fractures along which displacements have occurred by differential movement of the adjoining blocks (Fig. 17.24). Faults may directly create such topographic features as scarps, basins, and ridges. Since they bring into juxtaposition blocks of rock of dissimilar resistances to erosion, they also provide the setting for various erosional scarps. Along the planes of movement they commonly have broken or ground-up rock that is easily eroded along narrow slots.

FIG. 11.14. *Rainbow Natural Bridge, southern Utah. The bridge, 305 feet high, was formed by the stream undercutting the narrow neck of one of its entrenched meanders and leaving a resistant layer of sandstone spanning the 270-foot gap. (National Park Service.)*

5. Cleavage, like jointing, contributes to erosional weakness (Fig. 18.9).

STREAM COURSES

The course followed by a stream in its journey to the sea may owe its position and its trend to one or more of the following factors: (1) the original slope and natural irregularities of the surface, (2) differential erosion, (3) jointing, (4) faulting, (5) folding.

1. A river whose course has been determined by the original slope and the irregularities of that slope is called a *consequent* stream (Fig. 11.15). Such streams are characteristic of coastal-plain areas, where the surface is comparatively uniform and regular, with a gentle slope to the sea. Many of the streams along the Atlantic and Gulf Coasts of the United States are of this type. Other consequent streams flow off volcanic cones, across lava fields, or over irregular rolling plains of glacial deposits. The overflow of a lake also takes a consequent course.

FIG. 11.15. *A radial stream pattern developed on the surface of the domelike uplift of the Black Hills in South Dakota.*

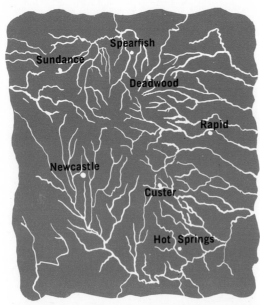

2. As erosion proceeds, new channels develop, independent of the original topography. In the absence of any directional control, as in areas of flat-lying sediments or of massive crystalline rocks, the headward growth and multiplication of tributaries produce a dendritic drainage pattern (Figs. 11.16, 11.17). At many places, on the other hand, the stream courses are directed by differences in the structure and character of the bedrock formations. The streams tend to follow the softer, or weaker, beds. Such variations lead to differential erosion, so that eventually a stream may undergo marked changes in position and direction and alter its original consequent course. Rivers formed in this way are called *subsequent* streams (Fig. 11.18) because they have been developed by subsequent erosion determined by structure. Topographic features produced by differential erosion are described on the following pages.

3. The position of a valley often is controlled by the direction of the joints or fissures in the bedrock of the area which it drains. Guided by such joints during headward erosion, the streams—especially, small tributary streams—develop angular drainage patterns (Fig. 11.19). Such patterns are particularly evident in the Colorado Plateau, Connecticut, and Ontario, where large areas of strongly jointed rocks are exposed at the surface.

4. In regions where faulting has taken place on a large scale, many valleys follow the fault zones for great distances, since the fractured rock there is relatively nonresistant to erosion. At some places, long, narrow blocks of the earth's crust have been depressed to form valleylike basins, which later become stream channels. The Dead Sea Basin and the Jordan Valley are typical examples. In California, Owens Valley has a similar history; and, in Germany, a large portion of the valley of the Rhine is a structural trough flanked by the Vosges and the Black Forest mountains, in which many of the steep slopes facing the valley are escarpments produced by the displacement of the rocks along fractures.

5. Long, parallel mountain folds influence the trends of valleys by governing the directions of the major consequent streams which follow the troughs

of the folds. Small streams flow from the crests of the folds into the troughs, where they unite to form the larger ones. At such places the walls of the valley are the limbs of the folds; and since the courses and profiles of the valleys are determined by the structure of the rocks through which they pass, they are called *structural valleys*. Certain tributaries of the Columbia River in central Washington follow such valleys. Subsequent valleys, carved from folded rocks, also are influenced by the trend of the folds (Fig. 11.20).

STREAM PIRACY

In the process of valley development, each stream continues to extend or to modify its drainage basin until all its divides become stationary. During this process, it frequently happens that one stream finds more favorable conditions for growth and extension than does another, on the opposite side of the divide, and, by the extension of tributaries, cuts back until it steals some of the headwaters of the less favorably situated stream and diverts them to its own channel. Such invasion is called stream piracy, and the stream whose territory has been invaded is said to have been "beheaded" by the pirate stream (Fig. 11.21).

The conditions which may give a stream an advantage over an adjoining one are (1) a greater volume of water, (2) softer rocks in which to excavate its channel, and (3) a higher gradient due to a shorter course to the sea. If the amount of precipitation is greater on one side of a mountain range than on the opposite slope, the streams receiving the greater volume of rainfall have a higher velocity and therefore erode more rapidly; they are thus able to extend their headwater tributaries farther than streams on the opposite side of the divide.

If streams drain regions in which different types of sedimentary rock alternate as a result of tilted strata, the larger streams tend to follow the outcrops of the less resistant beds, and their smaller tributaries join them nearly at right angles. Where such conditions prevail, the larger streams flowing in the softer rocks are able to behead the streams that cut across the hard strata. During high water, the higher stream overflows into the valley of the

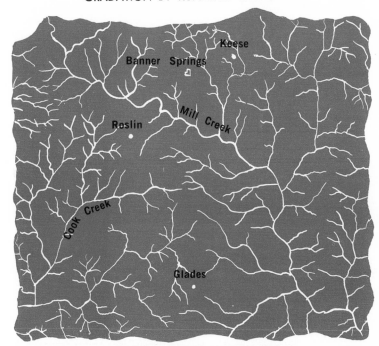

FIG. 11.16. *A dendritic drainage pattern characteristic of an area underlain by horizontal strata or by massive crystalline rock of uniform hardness.*

FIG. 11.17. *Dendritic drainage pattern in central Africa. This type of drainage is found where directional control of erosion is lacking. (United States Air Force.)*

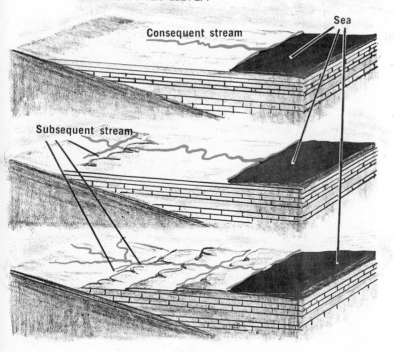

Consequent stream

Sea

Subsequent stream

FIG. 11.18. *The development of subsequent streams, tributaries to an initial consequent, by easy headward erosion along the strike in belts of nonresistant sediments.*

deeper stream and establishes a channel which later becomes permanent.

If a stream flows across tilted strata, a *narrows*, or a *water gap* (Fig. 11.22), is developed where the valley crosses the harder beds. If a stream is diverted from the water gap by piracy, the narrow portion of the beheaded valley is called a *wind gap.* Wind gaps are common in the Appalachian region, and at many places they served as passes through the mountains for the early pioneers traveling by wagon to settle in Kentucky and Tennessee. About 300,000 people passed through the Cumberland Gap in their migration westward during the last quarter of the eighteenth century. Some of the gaps of the Blue Ridge became strategic points during the campaigns of the Civil War.

ANTECEDENT STREAMS

Some well-developed streams continue to follow their long-established courses regardless of later

warping of the surface on which they have formed. These streams antedate the local transverse uplift and have been able to deepen or adjust their channels as fast as the change in altitude has taken place. They are called antecedent streams, and the Columbia River is regarded as a classic example.

FLAT-LYING STRATA

Where the strata are horizontal or only slightly inclined, the valley form is determined by the nature of the rock formations. If excavated in strata of uniform resistance, the valley slopes show few irregularities, and the angle of the slope is determined by the ratio of lateral erosion to the deepening of the channel. As erosion continues, successive layers are exposed, and in an area of maturely dissected topography the outcropping beds swing out around the spurs between tributaries and up into the tributary valleys. If followed upstream on one side, a given stratum at the level of the stream crosses the stream and turns back on the other side.

FIG. 11.19. *A rectangular stream-drainage pattern near Elizabethtown, New York. The pattern is characterized by right-angled bends in both the main stream and its tributaries. It is controlled by right-angled jointing and faulting of the rocks.*

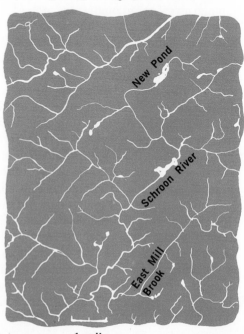

New Pond

Schroon River

East Mill Brook

1 mile

ROCK TERRACES

Where rock formations are not uniform, the resistant layers are etched into relief by differential weathering and erosion, and the slopes of the valley become terraced. Such structures are called rock terraces, since they are cut in solid rocks rather than in alluvium.

The downward slope of a rock terrace is the exposed edge of a hard stratum and is usually steep and clifflike, whereas the slope rising above the terrace is formed by the eroded edge of the softer stratum above and is normally a gentle slope covered with weathered rock waste. If the resistant beds are thick, extensive escarpments may develop, as is shown on a magnificent scale in the Grand Canyon of the Colorado River (Fig. 11.1).

As the topography becomes more mature, the terraces are cut back farther from the channel, and broad, flat areas, many miles in width and parallel to the stream, may be developed on both sides of its valley.

MESAS AND BUTTES

In regions where there are horizontal sedimentary strata or where sheets of lava cover soft clays or partially indurated sediments, flat-topped areas are isolated by the headward cutting of tributary streams as the region passes from youthful to mature topography. Such plateaulike areas are called mesas, from the Spanish word meaning table. The level top of a mesa consists of a resistant horizontal bed that tends to protect the less resistant strata below it. Where erosion reduces a mesa to a hill, it becomes a butte (Figs. 11.23, 11.24). Many of the striking mesas and buttes in the semiarid plains of New Mexico and Arizona are remnants of former plateaus dissected by erosion (Fig. 11.25). Other buttes are erosional remnants of volcanic necks, dikes, or other steep-standing resistant rock structures.

BADLANDS

Under special conditions, the differential erosion of flat-lying beds produces peculiar and striking types of topography (Fig. 11.26). Among these are

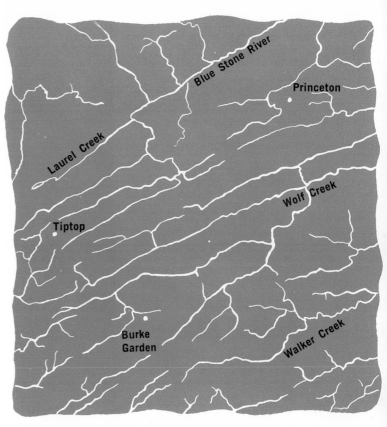

FIG. 11.20. *An adjusted stream pattern characteristic of the mature stage of an erosion cycle in a region of folded or tilted strata of different degrees of resistance to erosion. The arrangement resembles a trellis.*

the badlands, which are well developed in the northwestern Great Plains region of the United States and Canada, especially in the Dakotas, Wyoming, and Montana. Badlands are flat-topped, or buttelike, hills with rugged, barren slopes. The ruggedness is due chiefly to numerous gullies cut in the slopes of slightly consolidated sediments, in which certain layers are sufficiently resistant to erosion to arrest denudation, at least temporarily. A semiarid climate, in which rainfall is concentrated in a few heavy showers, is favorable to the development of such features. The prevailing dryness is largely responsible for the lack of vegetation on the slopes, and this lack results in the exposure of the loosely consolidated material to the torrents of water precipitated during the rare but violent rainstorms.

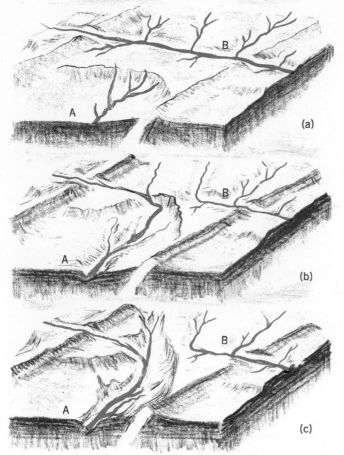

FIG. 11.21. *Diagrams illustrating stream piracy: (a) the tributaries at A are advancing by headward erosion toward the valley of the stream B; (b) the stream B has been beheaded or captured, and its headwaters are diverted to the pirate stream A; (c) the valley of A is extended and deepened. (After Davis.)*

TILTED STRATA

Where a region underlain by tilted strata (Fig. 11.27) is eroded toward maturity, the inclined beds are exposed, and some of the alternating layers are more easily eroded by running water than others, with the result that the streams tend to travel over the less resistant beds and to cut across the resistant ones, thus flowing as short a distance as possible on resistant beds. The less resistant strata,

therefore, become the sites of valleys, and the resistant strata stand up as ridges or mountains. Such changes in the course of a stream, which enable it to develop a definite and stable relation to the subsurface rock structures, are called *structural adjustment*. The Hoosic Valley of Massachusetts, the Shenandoah Valley of Virginia, and the Lehigh Valley of Pennsylvania are all examples of valleys that are eroded in relatively soft rocks.

The adjusted streams, flowing parallel to the strike (compass bearing of the tilted strata), frequently cut vertically through the weaker strata until they encounter a hard or resistant bed and then shift down the dip (the angle at which the strata are inclined from the horizontal). This develops a valley with a dip slope on one side and a steep escarpment on the other (Fig. 11.28). Such lateral shifting down the dip is called *monoclinal shifting*, and the resulting valley is asymmetrical because of the difference in profile of the two slopes. When parallel streams flow at right angles to the strike of slightly inclined beds, the strata crop out in parallel belts with sharp bends.

CUESTAS

Where warping has tilted the rock strata to low angles, as along the Atlantic Coastal Plain, whose beds dip seaward from 5 to 12 degrees, the ridges developed on the more resistant layers have steep slopes facing landward and gentle descents toward the coast. Ridges of this sort, with steep erosional escarpments on one side and dip slopes on the other, are cuestas (Fig. 11.29). Where there are alternating beds of hard and soft formations, alternating zones of lowlands and highlands are formed in roughly parallel bands. For example, the Black Prairie of ‾Alabama, bordering the Appalachian Mountains, consists of a belt of lowland formed over easily eroded sediments. A cuesta at the margin of the prairie faces the lowland and rises abruptly about 200 feet above its surface.

HOGBACKS

Where strata are inclined at high angles (Fig. 11.30), the ridges formed on the more resistant layers have slopes that are more nearly equal. The

FIG. 11.22.   *The Delaware Water Gap where the river cuts across the level-topped ridge known as Kittatinny Mountain, on the Pennsylvania–New Jersey border. This type of narrows is found where a stream flows across a resistant ridge of tilted rock. (Aero Service Corporation.)*

side corresponding to the cuesta escarpment develops a moderate slope, and the dip slope on the opposite side is steep. Ridges with such profiles are hogbacks. They are commonly developed on the flanks of folded mountains, such as those of the Rocky Mountain system, where they are especially conspicuous along the east margin of the Front Range, in Colorado and Wyoming. Eastward toward the plains there are all gradations—from hogbacks with steep slopes formed in highly tilted beds, through cuestas formed where the inclination is low, to mesas and buttes in the horizontal strata of the plains—and all are simply remnants of erosion that assume different profiles as a result of the different attitudes of the rock formations.

FOLDED STRATA

On symmetrical folds, such as a series of parallel anticlines and synclines, the initial consequent streams flow in small gullies on either side of the crests of the anticlines and drain away from their axes. These small streams discharge into the synclinal troughs. As tributaries cut back into the flanks of the anticlines, they develop gorges that soon become sufficiently deep to develop lateral gullies of their own. Working in rocks that were fractured during folding, these tributary gullies rapidly cut deep into the axial portion of an anticline, where there are frequently numerous fractures and joints to hasten the process of denudation. In time, the divides between the tributaries that flow on the crests of the folds are narrowed and lowered, and lateral erosion widens their valleys until the valleys include the flanks of the anticlines. Stream conquest, or piracy, between adjoining folds follows, and eventually the streams along the crests of the anticlines become the master streams, and the major valleys become anticlinal valleys (Fig.

FIG. 11.23. *A sketch showing the development of mesas and canyons by the erosional dissection of a high, semiarid plateau in Mesa Verde, Colorado. (After W. H. Holmes.)*

11.31). The synclinal divides stand in high relief, forming broad ridges and, at places, mountains. Lookout Mountain is an example of a synclinal divide which terminates at the north in a steep

FIG. 11.24. *A lone erosional remnant at Red Butte, Wyoming. This type of hill is called a butte. The resistant layer of rock capping the hill protects the softer sediments underneath from erosion. (U.S. Geological Survey.)*

escarpment 1,500 feet high at Chattanooga, Tennessee, and extends southwest over 50 miles into Alabama. A deep anticlinal valley 4 to 5 miles wide flanks Lookout Mountain on the west, and still farther westward, beyond this valley, is another broad synclinal plateau.

CURVED VALLEYS AND ZIGZAG RIDGES

Where symmetrical folds pass through a cycle of erosion, the resistant layers form parallel ridges that are paired on the two limbs of a fold. If, however, the axis of a fold is not horizontal but is tilted so that it plunges into the earth, the erosional ridges present a different topographic pattern. If the folds plunge steeply, some of the pairs of ridges end after the layers producing them plunge below the regional base level. If the plunge is less steep, the pairs converge and eventually join to form a continuous ridge with a sharp, elbowlike flexure within which there is a valley shaped like one end of a canoe. If several resistant layers are present, each forms an encircling ridge, and the ridges are separated by curved valleys. A series of alternating plunging anticlines and synclines, therefore, produces zigzag ridges (Fig. 11.32), like those characteristically developed on the Appalachian peneplain in Pennsylvania and Virginia.

DOMES AND BASINS

On a newly uplifted domelike structure the initial streams form a series of radial valleys extending in all directions from the crest of the dome. These consequent streams may unite to form one or more trunk streams at the lower margin, or base, of the structure. As erosion cuts through the strata on the summit of the uplift, the formations begin to crop out in a series of narrow belts around the crest of the dome (Fig. 9.32). If beds of varying hardness are present in a series of sedimentary strata, the harder sandstones and limestones form ridges, and the flowing tributary streams adjust themselves to the softer, shaly layers. In this way the subsequent valleys are converted into concentric, or *ring*, valleys, separated by hogbacklike ring ridges. The scarps face the center of the dome. Examples are found in Montana and South Dakota.

FIG. 11.26. *Badlands carved by rainwash and gullying near Scotts Bluff, Nebraska. In semiarid climates, badlands are formed when a maze of gullies is cut into loose sediments of varying resistance. (Darton, U.S. Geological Survey.)*

FIG. 11.25. *Erosional remnants in Monument Valley, Utah. The talus slopes indicate that the hills are still being reduced. (Spence Air Photos.)*

FIG. 11.27. *Erosion of inclined strata exposing dip slopes in a rather mature topography at Creation Rock, Red Rocks Park, near Denver, Colorado. Streams in areas underlain by tilted strata tend to cut across the harder rocks and flow along the softer beds. (Denver Tourist Bureau.)*

As structural basins pass through a cycle of erosion, they tend to show concentric features similar to those of ring valleys, but with escarpments facing outward. The structural relations resemble those observed in a low nest of shallow plates, in which the largest is placed at the bottom and the smallest at the top. In such a nest the outer edges of the plates correspond to the encircling ridges of harder rock that rim the basin as the region is base-leveled. The Lower Peninsula of Michigan and the Paris Basin in France show such structural relations.

SUPERIMPOSED STREAMS

Although streams tend to adjust their valleys to the structure of the rocks they encounter, the courses of certain streams do not conform to the structure. These obviously are out of adjustment and require explanation. Where tilted beds, for example, have been peneplained and covered by later flat-lying beds, the new drainage system may be wholly independent of the hidden structure of

the underlying tilted beds. As such a system, by continued erosion, is let down onto the surface of the tilted beds, the streams cutting downward in valleys begun in the horizontal beds may be compelled to cut across the tilted beds. Such streams are superimposed (Figs. 11.33–11.36).

In the Appalachian region the Hudson, Delaware, Susquehanna, and Potomac Rivers are considered to be superimposed from a former cover of sediments subsequently removed. In the Rocky Mountain region many rivers, including the Bighorn, Madison, Platte, Arkansas, Green, Snake, and others, are superimposed very impressively in spectacular canyons across mountain ranges. In the Grand Canyon the Colorado River is superimposed on ancient crystalline rocks that underlie the nearly horizontal rocks of the Colorado Plateau.

FIG. 11.28. *Diagram showing monoclinal shifting of valleys. As the earth's surface was lowered by erosion from the upper profile shown on the dotted line to the profile shown by the continuous line, valleys A and B moved down the dip of the strata of A' and B'.*

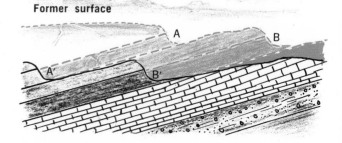

Former surface

Special Features

MAJOR WATERFALLS AND RAPIDS

The geologic significance of waterfalls may be slight, but from a scenic point of view they form a fascinating part of a river system. There is no sharp distinction between a rapid and a fall. Steep rapids are commonly called falls, and, when small, both are referred to as cascades. Where an enormous volume of water falls over a precipice, the term cataract is used.

Falls and rapids occur at many places and are formed under various conditions. Wherever the bedrock is made up of layers that have different degrees of resistance to erosion, the resistant layers hold back the streams in their trenching processes. Since erosion of the less resistant beds farther downstream proceeds without any such delay, a change in gradient develops between the part of the stream that lies above the outcrop of the resistant layers and the part that lies below. The result is a series of rapids which get steeper and steeper with continued erosion down-valley until they finally become a waterfall.

The structural conditions that favor the formation of falls include (1) harder sedimentary rocks overlying softer ones in a nearly horizontal series, (2) igneous sills or flows interbedded with flat-lying sedimentary strata, (3) successive igneous flows of varying resistance, (4) dikes of igneous rock, or any hard layer, in other formations, and (5) vertical joint planes in massive rocks. Falls may be developed in tributary streams as a result of a rapid deepening of the main valley. In this way a series of waterfalls may develop on the tributaries, with each one downstream receding a little farther from the gorge of the main stream. A similar condition may develop through glaciation. The ice may erode the trunk valley below the bottom of the side valleys, and when the glacier later recedes or disappears, the side valleys are left hanging with falls at their junction with the major stream, which succeeds the glacier in the main valley.

FIG. 11.29. *Cuesta upheld by resistant sandstone, Comb Ridge, Utah. The gently tilted strata forming this ridge are dipping to the right in this photograph. (Spence Air Photos.)*

Niagara Falls (Fig. 11.37) offers a magnificent example of an escarpment formed in nearly horizontal beds where a resistant rock caps notably weaker strata. This cataract plunges about 160 feet over a brink-making limestone, about 80 feet thick, that overlies a very soft shale formation. The falls are divided into two parts by an island in the stream channel. The American Falls has a frontage of about 1,060 feet, and the Horseshoe, or Canadian, Falls has a curved frontage of nearly 2,800

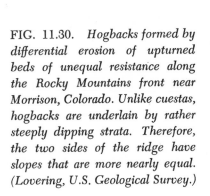

FIG. 11.30. *Hogbacks formed by differential erosion of upturned beds of unequal resistance along the Rocky Mountains front near Morrison, Colorado. Unlike cuestas, hogbacks are underlain by rather steeply dipping strata. Therefore, the two sides of the ridge have slopes that are more nearly equal. (Lovering, U.S. Geological Survey.)*

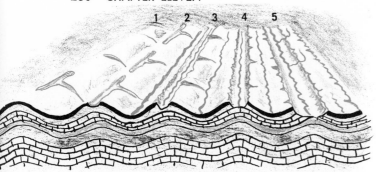

FIG. 11.31. *Diagram of a series of eroded folds, showing the development of anticlinal valleys and synclinal ridges, progressively from left to right. The maximum fracturing is along anticlines. Fold 1 shows three tributaries that flow into the consequent synclinal valley between folds 1 and 2. In fold 2 the tributaries have developed valleys along the axis of the anticline. In fold 3 the tributary in the foreground has captured the headwaters of the second tributary, and in fold 4 all the tributaries have been captured by one downstream beyond the diagram. In fold 5 the stream has cut through the resistant sandstone on the crest of the anticline, and therefore it can erode downward more rapidly than the stream in the syncline between 4 and 5. Eventually it diverts the water of the stream in the syncline as shown by the tributaries to the right of 5. Thus the syncline becomes a divide. (After Lobeck.)*

FIG. 11.32. *Zigzag ridge produced by the erosion of plunging folds.*

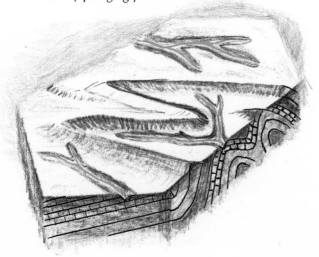

feet. Approximately 500,000 tons of water per minute, or nearly 94 per cent of the water of the river, passes over the Canadian Falls. This great body of water has carved out a gorge 200 feet deep beneath the level of the water below the falls, so that the total depth of the gorge from the rim to the bottom of the water is about 360 feet (Fig. 11.38). As the swirling water behind the falls loosens the soft, shaly formation, it removes it piecemeal and undermines the capping limestone, until finally the limestone cap remains as an inadequately supported, overhanging ledge from which large masses of rock plunge into the pool at the bottom of the falls. This process of undercutting is termed *sapping*. Thus, foot by foot, the escarpment has receded up the river, leaving the deep gorge that marks its course from Lewiston at the edge of the cuesta forming the Niagara escarpment, 8 miles south of Lake Ontario, to its present position about 7 miles farther south (Figs. 11.38, 11.39).

The rate of recession of Niagara for an extended period is difficult to determine. A series of factors of unknown value enter into the problem, such as the variation of the river volume and the increase in thickness, toward the south, of the capping limestone rock. Measurements have been made from time to time, and a comparison of records indicates that the average rate of recession since 1875 was approximately 3 feet a year (Fig. 11.39). At this rate, 12,320 years would have been required for it to recede 7 miles. The Canadian Falls is now receding much more rapidly than the American Falls, because of its greater volume of water. Since the American Falls receives scarcely 6 per cent of the stream's water, it is receding only a few inches per year.

OTHER WATERFALLS

Along the north shore of Lake Superior, many high-gradient streams have cut steep gorges into the Keweenawan lava flows and exposed conglomerate beds separating the successive layers of basaltic rock. At many places the conglomerates or softer amygdaloidal flows are more easily eroded than the overlying massive basalts, and numerous waterfalls result.

At Yellowstone Falls, a steep-standing mass of resistant igneous rock crosses the weaker rocks in which the deep canyon of the Yellowstone River is excavated (Fig. 11.40). Falls of this sort will not recede a very great distance, for the resistant mass must be cut away from above. As it is worn down, the softer formations upstream will be eroded to the gradient of the river, the crest of the falls will sink, and the falls eventually will disappear or become rapids.

In mountains that have been glaciated, the trunk-stream valley commonly is eroded deeper than tributary valleys, because the glacier of the trunk stream was much thicker than the glaciers of the tributary streams. After the ice melted away, these glacial valleys again became watercourses, and the waters of tributary streams fall into the main stream over steep precipices. Many of the highest waterfalls of the world were formed in this way. Yosemite Falls in California (Fig. 11.41) plunges over a granite cliff into the Merced River Valley with an initial drop of 1,430 feet. It then cascades for about 800 feet over a jagged surface with a steep slope and finally plunges 320 feet more over a vertical cliff to the flood plain of the river. Prior to glaciation, the Merced Valley possessed a typical V-shaped profile, but during the Great Ice Age, a glacier slowly ground its way through the valley, deepened it greatly, and shaped its sides into vertical cliffs over which the tributaries now discharge as falls.

Vertical joints in massive rocks influence stream erosion in much the same way as bedding planes in inclined strata (Fig. 11.42). Such joint planes are widened by erosion, and large blocks of rock may be removed from the stream bed. As the blocks are removed, a vertical cliff may be developed, over which a falls is initiated. Near Ithaca and Trenton, New York, falls are developed in jointed limestone.

In mountain ranges where zones of hard rocks cross stream beds, these rocks are eroded more slowly than the softer material below them. Vertical escarpments may not be developed, but under such conditions, the water leaps from ledge to ledge in a series of sparkling cascades, which may grade imperceptibly into rapids.

FIG. 11.33. *Diagram showing dendritic valley development in a flat-lying stratum that rests on the eroded edges of tilted strata. Compare with Fig. 11.34.*

FIG. 11.34. *Diagram of the region shown in Fig. 11.33 after erosion has removed the horizontal bed. The streams, let down from above, are not in structural adjustment because the old drainage pattern is superimposed upon the tilted strata.*

FIG. 11.35. *A superimposed stream flowing over truncated folds; the Susquehanna River, near Harrisburg, Pennsylvania. (After D. W. Johnson.)*

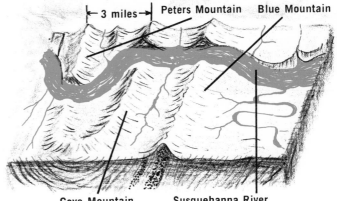

←3 miles→ Peters Mountain Blue Mountain

Cove Mountain Susquehanna River

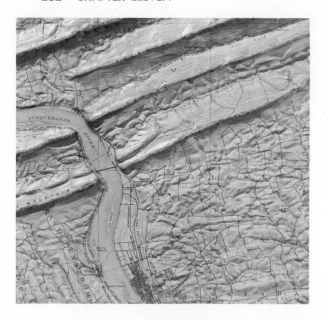

FIG. 11.36. *Photograph of part of a relief map showing the water gaps of the Susquehanna River where it crosses Second Mountain and Blue Mountain near Harrisburg, Pennsylvania. The Susquehanna River is a superimposed stream. When horizontal sediments are deposited over tilted strata, the new drainage pattern will follow the pattern for flat-lying beds. With continued erosion, the river will cut across the now-exposed tilted rocks because the already established drainage system is still in effect. (Aero Service Corporation.)*

Along the east margin of the Appalachian Mountains, roughly paralleling the Atlantic coast, the Piedmont Plateau area is bordered by a coastal plain composed of sands and clays not yet indurated into solid rock strata. Streams, flowing from the Appalachian highlands toward the Atlantic, pass from the hard crystalline rocks to the soft unconsolidated sediments nearer the coast, where they cut more rapidly and develop rapids and falls along the line of contact of the two different types of rocks. Because of the great number of cascades along a relatively narrow zone, the region is referred to as the "fall zone."

Under exceptional conditions, falls may originate by damming due to the deposition of material in the stream bed by processes other than stream erosion. Landslides, glacial deposits, or lava flows may form temporary rapids.

PLUNGE POOLS

At the base of a waterfall, the falling mass of water commonly excavates a basin called a plunge pool. Such a pool below the 400-foot abandoned waterfall at Dry Falls, downstream from Grand Coulee, Washington, forms the basin of Fall Lake, about 80 feet deep and a half a mile wide. The progressive recession of a waterfall tends to lengthen a plunge pool headward and thus to form an elongate basin on the valley floor.

POTHOLES

Where rapidly flowing streams produce eddying currents, the energy of the stream tends to concentrate at certain places along the channel. If water that is carrying sediment is given rotary motion by the eddies at such points, it tends to grind out round or kettle-shaped excavations in the bedrock of the valley floor (Fig. 11.43). These are potholes, or "giant's cauldrons." Once a rounded depression is started, the swirling currents in the excavation have their velocities increased during periods of high water, so that the rate of deepening is accelerated. Certain potholes are spiral-shaped and have a larger diameter near the bottom than at the top. They may be formed in massive igneous rocks, such as basalt, or in granite, or in softer sedimentary strata, such as limestone or shale. The currents below a waterfall or along walls of a high-gradient stream with rapids favor their development. They range in size from a few inches to 10 or 20 feet in diameter, and they also vary in depth. Some of the larger potholes in Interstate Park at Taylor's Falls, Minnesota, are 20 feet in diameter and are sunk 50 feet or more in solid basalt. Pothole formation can assume a very important role in the cutting of steep, gorgelike valleys, such as the valley of the inner portion along the Colorado River above Hoover Dam or the canyon of the ancient outlet of Owens Valley, near Little Lake, California.

FIG. 11.37. *Niagara Falls from the air. The river begins to cascade near the upper end of Goat Island (center) and finally plunges over the limestone brink, most of the water going over the Canadian Falls (right). Resistant limestone caps softer shale. The falls are receding because of sapping underneath the limestone capping. Note the fallen blocks. (The Photographic Survey Corporation, Ltd.)*

CANYONS AND GORGES

Where extensive areas stand at high altitudes, swiftly flowing streams tend to develop deep valleys; and if the conditions that promote widening are lacking, precipitous-walled valleys—canyons or gorges—are developed (Fig. 11.44). Arid regions, traversed by streams that have their headwaters in snow-capped mountains or in regions of more abundant rainfall, are usually favorable to the development of canyons, especially if the valley is cut in firm rock capable of standing as steep cliffs. Lateral cutting, due to the eddies deflected toward the side of the stream, and weathering of the steep rock slopes exposed to the atmosphere broaden the canyon, so that the lofty walls gradually are cut back and the distance from rim to rim becomes wider. The canyon walls in arid areas remain comparatively steep, however, because there is little side wash.

The greatest canyons known are the trenches which the Colorado River and its tributaries have cut into the plateaus of the Southwestern United States. Their total length is over 500 miles, and their depths are measured in thousands of feet. Here the great size and extraordinary beauty of the canyons are the result of the following conditions: (1) a large volume of water, (2) high velocity, (3) an abundance of sediment with which to corrade, (4) great thickness of firm rocks to penetrate before reaching grade, (5) an arid climate with little weathering and side wash on the walls of the canyon.

The Colorado River has a total length of about

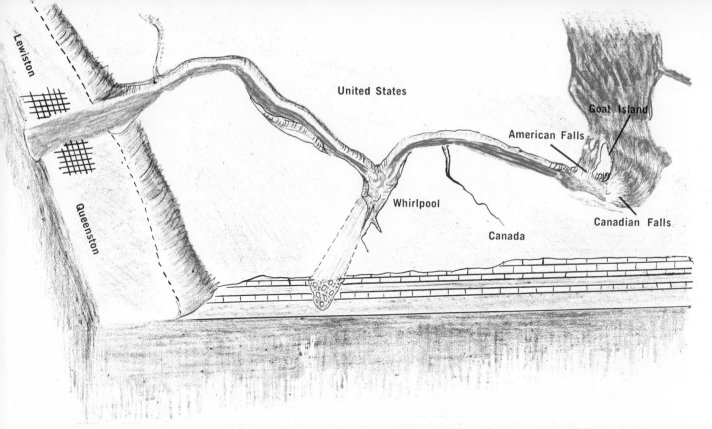

FIG. 11.38. *General setting of Niagara Falls and Gorge. The falls began at the cuesta scarp at the left (north) and have receded about 7 miles. An earlier gorge is buried near the whirlpool. Goat Island separates the American from the Canadian Falls. (After Gilbert.)*

2,000 miles and drains an area of about 225,000 square miles, most of which is a high plateau 6,000 to 8,000 feet above sea level. It trenches the high plateau of northern Arizona with the colossal Grand Canyon, 220 miles long and more than a mile deep. Where it reaches this great depth, the total width from rim to rim is 8 to 12 miles, but its width at the bottom is only slightly greater than that of the stream. If the slopes of the canyon were uniform, it would have an angle of less than 15 degrees, but the variations in hardness of the sedimentary strata have produced gigantic steplike slopes, or rock terraces; the steep faces of some of these terraces drop vertically for more than 1,000 feet. The upper series of rocks in which the canyon is cut is composed of flat-lying beds of limestones, sandstones, and shales (Fig. 11.1). Beneath this the stream has disclosed ancient crystalline schists and massive igneous formations.

NATURAL BRIDGES

An arch of rock across a valley, an exceptional and striking feature of the topography, may be formed in numerous ways:

1. Where a surface stream disappears into the joints of the bedrock of a valley, it may flow underground for some distance and then reappear at the surface. As erosion continues, a "valley" is excavated beneath the surface, and if the surface does not cave in, the rocks span the valley as a bridge.

2. If the rock of a stream bed is jointed above a waterfall, some of the water may descend through a joint and then follow a bedding plane until it issues into the main channel below the falls or behind the curtain of water forming the falls (Fig. 11.45). The joint is slowly enlarged until the channel can accommodate all the water; thereafter, the mass of rock from the escarpment that produced

Canadian Falls

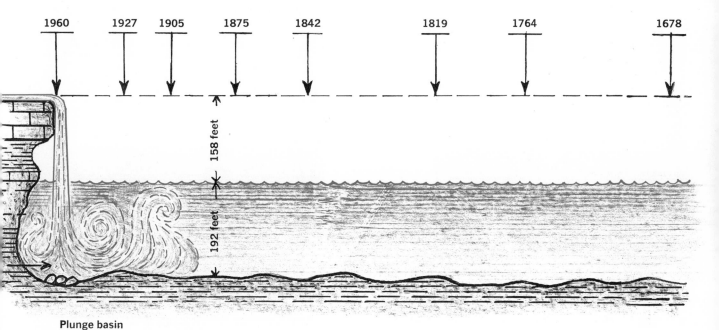

FIG. 11.39. *Canadian Falls, showing its known retreat in about 280 years by sapping of relatively weak rocks beneath a resistant cap rock of limestone. (After Gilbert.)*

the former waterfalls, upstream from the vertical joint, remains as a natural bridge (Fig. 11.46). In Two Medicine River, in Glacier National Park, this process is now in progress, and a natural bridge is partially developed.

3. Where ancient peneplains have been rejuvenated, many of the meandering streams become deeply entrenched, and the lateral swinging of a stream against the clifflike walls undercuts the neck of a meander at the level of the water. This process continues from both sides until a hole is cut through and the stream flows through the perforation, leaving an arch of rock as a bridge over the stream. The famous Rainbow Natural Bridge in San Juan County, Utah, was formed in this way.

4. Where the tributary streams are extended into steeply sloping divides by headward erosion, the watershed may be reduced to a very narrow ridge. If the divide is capped by a resistant formation overlying soft sand or shale, the divide may be perforated under the more massive cap rock.

5. In the petrified forest of Adamana, Arizona, a silicified log that has been undermined by stream erosion forms a very unusual natural bridge. The trunk of the petrified log, which is about 3 feet in diameter, lies diagonally across a canyon about 30 feet wide and 200 feet deep. The rock in which the log was embedded is poorly cemented and therefore easily eroded.

6. In the volcanic areas of the West many natural bridges have been formed by the incomplete collapse of the roofs of lava tunnels.

7. Other natural bridges are the products of wave erosion, sandblasting by the wind; and differential weathering.

Aggradation

Stream transportation is attended by stream deposition. Anything that decreases the transporting power of a stream promotes deposition. Along the

FIG. 11.40. *Lower Falls and Grand Canyon of the Yellowstone River, Yellowstone National Park, Wyoming. The waterfall is held up by a vertical mass of fresh hard rock, whereas the river has been able to entrench itself downstream in comparatively weak rock that has been altered and softened in the past by hot water and steam. This type of waterfall will not recede greatly because it cannot be undercut, but must be cut down from above. (Northern Pacific Railway.)*

FIG. 11.41. *Yosemite Falls, Yosemite National Park, California. This tributary to the Merced River is suspended on resistant rock and discharges from a hanging valley. Hanging valleys are formed where the principal stream or a glacier has deepened the main valley far below the level of the tributaries, so that the tributaries are left suspended. Both river and ice lowered the main valley here. (Southern Pacific Railroad.)*

course of every river the current frequently is checked, and at such places sediments are deposited. Even a stream with a relatively high velocity will have part of its bed covered with rock fragments, which it was forced to drop because of decreases in the transporting power of its currents. Since conditions favoring transportation vary from time to time and from place to place, sediments derived from the land generally are not all carried directly to the sea; some may be deposited to form definite features in the topography as a region passes through a cycle of erosion.

CAUSES OF DEPOSITION

Diminished velocity. A slight diminution in the rate of flow of a loaded stream will initiate deposition. A loss of velocity may be brought about by (1) a decrease of the slope, or gradient, of the stream bed; (2) a decrease in the volume of the stream; (3) a change in the configuration of the valley; (4) obstructions, such as heaps of residual boulders formed from more resistant dikes or beds that cross the valley, or temporary dams formed by floating trees or rafts of logs; (5) freezing of the water; (6) the flowing of the stream into a body of quiet water, such as a lake, estuary, or bay.

Diminished volume. Since the volume of water directly affects the carrying power of a stream, variations in volume cause streams alternately to aggrade and degrade their beds. Many streams have seasonal high-water stages, during which more and coarser sediments are carried; later, when the amount of rainfall decreases, these are deposited. Diminished volume may also result from other causes. Some of the water of the stream may sink into the earth where the stream flows through a dry region. In arid lands the bottom of the valley does not reach the ground-water level, and some of the water of the stream is absorbed by the soil and rocks over which it flows. Such absorption is common in areas underlain by permeable gravel and sand. Further loss of volume may be caused by evaporation in arid regions and by diversion of the water for irrigation or for other purposes. Over

FIG. 11.42. *Giant Stairway Falls at Paradise Creek, Alberta. The fall escarpment consists of a series of low, steplike falls. Both vertical and horizontal joints have contributed to these steps. (Geological Survey of Canada.)*

FIG. 11.43. *Potholes on the bed of the Susquehanna River at Conewago Falls, Pennsylvania, as exposed during unusually low water stage in 1947. These remarkable pits have been abraded by swirling waters of the rapids at high-water stages, with the aid of stones. (Lancaster Intelligencer Journal.)*

long periods of time, a progressive drying of the climate of an area may change the regimen of the streams and leave only dry washes in a region that was formerly moist. Conversely, an increase in precipitation may increase both volume and transportation. Such variations may be seasonal and periodic, or the shift to dry may be permanent.

Increase of cross section. Where a stream breaks up into a number of distributaries, the volume of each branch is less than that of the original stream, but the total cross-sectional area of the stream becomes greater. Any such division, or even the mere widening or flattening of a stream channel, increases the bottom friction, slows the velocity, and reduces the efficiency of the stream as an agent of transportation. If, as a result of division, a stream drops much of its load in its own channel, it then flows as small distributary streamlets through and over its own sediments.

FIG. 11.44. *Big Thompson Canyon, north of Denver, Colorado. The steeply dipping sedimentary and metamorphic rocks have prevented widening of the stream channel. (Denver Tourist Bureau.)*

PLACES OF DEPOSITION

Stream deposits, or alluvium, may accumulate in a number of different places, such as (1) at the foot of steep slopes, (2) in stream channels, (3) on flood plains, and (4) at débouchures (river mouths).

FORMS OF STREAM DEPOSITS

The principal forms of stream deposits include (1) alluvial fans and cones, (2) piedmont alluvial plains, (3) bars and channel fill, (4) flood plains, (5) alluvial terraces, and (6) deltas.

ALLUVIAL FANS AND CONES

Where a stream descending a steep slope issues from the mountains on a plain or in a wide valley, its velocity suddenly is diminished, and a large part of its load is deposited and spread out in the

form of a fan-shaped heap at the opening of the ravine or gully through which the stream flows (Fig. 11.47). As the deposit piles up, its thickness becomes greatest at the mouth of the steep valley, and a cone-shaped structure is developed. The slope of the cone's surface varies with the size and velocity of the stream and the character of the transported sediment. In general, coarse materials tend to pile up as cones and finer ones to flatten out as fans, but there are many gradations in between.

Conditions favorable to the formation of fans or cones are not entirely topographic. Climatic changes may also be a factor. An abrupt change of slope was the chief factor in the formation of the fans at the western base of the Sierra Nevada in California and at the eastern base of the Front Range of the Rocky Mountains. Huge fans have been built up also at the base of the Himalaya in India, at the

FIG. 11.45. *Trick Falls, Glacier National Park, shows an early stage in the making of a natural bridge. When the strata underlying the waterfall are jointed, some of the water flows through the unseen joints and emerges near the foot of the falls to rejoin the part of the stream that flows over the falls. (Ethel M. Rodgers.)*

base of the Andes in Argentina, and at many other places.

PIEDMONT ALLUVIAL PLAINS

Where streams discharge near each other on the same plain, their fans may coalesce and form a continuous sheet of aggraded sediments along the base of the mountain range. Eventually these sediments may build up a piedmont alluvial plain (Fig. 11.48), sometimes called a compound alluvial fan, a bajada, or an alluvial apron.

BARS AND CHANNEL FILL

Deposits that are made in a stream's channel generally show great diversity of form, but as a group they are called bars or simply channel fill. Some bars are mounds of gravel and sand that form submerged shoals in the stream, some are islands (at least at low-water stages), some are accumulations before or behind obstructions, and others are deposits left at the edges of the channel. A very

FIG. 11.46. *Natural Bridge, Virginia. Lace Falls, which probably formed the bridge during its recession, cascades into the gorge several hundred yards farther upstream. (C. D. Walcott.)*

FIG. 11.47. *Alluvial fan (foreground) at the lower end of Hanaupah Canyon on the west side of Death Valley, California. When a stream descends from the mountains onto a plain, it loses velocity and deposits much of its sediment in this shape. The channels on the surface of the fan show that it has been partly dissected since it was deposited, either because of an increase in water supply or because of a decrease in available load upstream. (Spence Air Photos.)*

characteristic type forms at the inner side of each sharp bend of a stream's course. The main current makes a rapid sweep along the outer bank, and undercurrents pass across to the inner side of the curve and deposit parts of their loads. Deposits so formed, when exposed during the low-water stage of a stream, are the familiar sandbanks or pebble beaches of streams. At high-water stages, bars are subject to a shift in position or an alteration in form; some may be destroyed entirely, and new ones may appear elsewhere.

BRAIDED STREAMS

A heavily loaded stream (Fig. 11.49), especially one that is subject to loss of volume in semiarid regions, deposits sediment continually, and the bed rises steadily until, eventually, numerous sand bars deflect the currents. Then the river does not flow in a single channel, but in many interconnecting streamlets, which, together with the sand bars that

FIG. 11.48. *A dissected piedmont alluvial plain at Huntington Palisades, near Santa Monica, California. This type of plain is formed by the coalescence of a line of alluvial fans. In the foreground we can see that the streams have lowered their courses through the alluvium. Wave erosion (at the lower left) has truncated the edge of the deposit. (Spence Air Photos.)*

separate them, are continually shifting. A river which, owing to deposition, is split into many branching and reuniting channels is called a braided stream. One example is the Platte River in Nebraska, which flows in a broad alluvial valley nearly 1 mile wide. During most of the year a small volume of water finds its way in a tortuous course through a series of interlacing streamlets whose positions shift at every flood.

SCOUR AND FILL

When the volume and velocity of an aggrading stream are suddenly increased, as in time of flood, the stream digs new channels in the sediments on its floor. When the flood subsides, these channels are again filled. Such alternate filling and excavating are referred to as scour and fill. One of the most striking examples of a stream that transports its sediment in this manner is the lower portion of

the Missouri River. During periods of high velocity, scouring reaches a depth of almost 80 feet in the vicinity of Nebraska City, and 25 miles upstream from Omaha a fill of about 40 feet is cut to bedrock during seasons of flood. The products of such excavation are moved downstream and eventually, after many periods of rest, reach the sea.

FLOOD PLAINS

In times of flood, when the volume of a stream is high, fine silt, mud, and sand are laid down on the level tract, or flood plain, over which the river spreads. During each high-water stage, the bed of alluvium becomes thicker, and the height of the flood plain is increased until with the deepening of the main channel by erosion, the flood plain is so high above the normal stream that it is no longer overspread by the river, except during very high floods. The part of the flood plain of the Mississippi River that extends from Cairo, Illinois, at the junction of the Ohio River, to the Gulf of Mexico varies from 30 to 60 miles in width and is approximately 600 miles long. Most flood plains are bounded on either side by relatively steep slopes. These slopes may be sufficiently steep to form bluffs, especially if the valley has been widened by lateral cutting in resistant rocks. At some places where the rocks bordering a valley are weak and easily eroded, the slopes are so gentle that it is difficult to detect where the flood plain ends and the valley sides begin.

Wide flood plains commonly are sheet plains interrupted by sloughs, whereas narrow flood plains on steeper slopes have a characteristic channel-and-bar topography. The surfaces of other flood plains exhibit a combination of broad, shallow pans and low mounds.

During floods, the whole flood plain may be covered with waters flowing seaward. In this wide expanse of water, the current is most rapid along the axis of the river channel, where the water is the deepest. Along the margin of the channel, where the rapid currents come in contact with the slowly moving water of the flood plain, the velocity suddenly is checked, and the currents drop all but the fine sediments carried in suspension. In this way the flood-plain deposits are built up highest on the immediate border of the channel and slope gradually toward the valley sides. These embankments of aggraded material resemble the man-made· levees constructed to confine a stream to a narrow channel, and they are known as *natural levees* (Fig. 11.50).

The levees are low ridges, seldom more than a few feet higher than the backland, toward which they descend with a slope so slight that the region appears flat. Some levees, however, are so high that during flood-time they stand out as long, low islands with the main channel of the river on one side and the floodwaters of the backland and uplands on the other side. During moderately high water, natural levees serve as protection to the river flats, as they retain the waters in a definite channel. However, during unusually high floods, a river may break through its embankments and flood the lowlands beyond with numerous streams.

Along many rivers, the levees are so high that tributaries flow parallel to the main stream for considerable distances before they find a place to join the main stream. The Yazoo River, which parallels the main channel of the Mississippi River for about 200 miles, serves as the typical example of this *Yazoo effect.*

Many cities are built on flood plains, which offer the advantages of flat ground for buildings and ready access to water transportation. Such cities, however, are almost certain to be inundated during high water. Disastrous floods occur nearly every year along the Mississippi River and its tributaries, and cities built along their flood plains must expect frequent inundation.

ALLUVIAL TERRACES

A stream that has aggraded its valley to a considerable depth may excavate part of the deposits previously laid down. The alluvial sediments are then carved into one or more terraces, or narrow plains and flats, that fringe the sides of the valley. Such flat-topped stream terraces are the remnants of former flood plains, below which the streams that made them have cut their channels to develop new flood plains at lower levels (Fig. 11.51).

FIG. 11.49. *A braided stream, Rakaia River, South Island, New Zealand, at low-water stage. The belt of braided channels and intervening bars is more than a mile wide. Braided streams are usually formed when heavily loaded streams break into a network of channels through their own deposits. (V. C. Browne, Christchurch.)*

The chief factors that aid the development of stream terraces are (1) uplift, or rejuvenation, of the stream; (2) partial loss of load and renewed ability to erode farther downstream; (3) failure of the supply of sediment in the upper stream course; (4) exchange of a small amount of coarse sediment

FIG. 11.50. *Diagram of the flood plain and natural levees of a large river. Note the oxbow lake and the Yazoo effect on the marginal tributaries.*

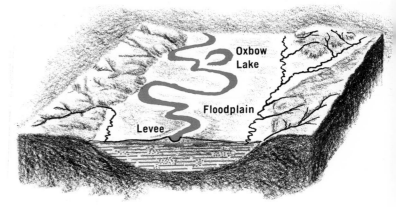

FIG. 11.51. *Alluvial terraces along the Esk Valley, Canterbury, New Zealand. Former flood plains have been converted to discontinuous benches by subsequent downcutting by the streams. (V. C. Browne, Christchurch.)*

for a large amount of finer material; (5) elimination of meanders and consequent increase of velocity; and (6) increase in the volume of the stream, due to piracy or to other causes.

Terraces are a normal feature of the history of any stream. They appear first in the lower, or older, part of the valley and are gradually extended upstream. Where traced upstream or downstream, they are found to pass into the flood plain. It is rare that terraces of the same age are equally developed along both sides of a stream at the same time, for the new, or lowered, channel is likely to lie near one side of the old flood plain. Even if terraces are formed on both sides, erosion is constantly attacking them and may destroy them; the older the terrace, the smaller the remnants become, until finally the terrace disappears. Alluvial terraces protected by spurs of hard rock underneath them or on the upstream side are said to be *rock-perched* or *rock-defended* terraces.

DELTAS

Where rivers laden with sediments flow into a body of quiet water, such as a lake or a bay, or into the sea, the velocity suddenly is checked, and rapid deposition of sediments follows. Where the shore currents are not strong enough to transport the load brought in by the river or where coastal configuration protects the mouth of the stream from rapid tidal currents, the debris which the river brings settles near its mouth and builds up a delta, named from the Greek letter Δ, the shape of which it somewhat resembles. Where a river discharges into a sea, the silty fresh water tends to float on the heavier salt water until the fresh and the saline waters mix. Where fresh water, with fine silt in suspension, mixes with the sea water, the salts of sea water cause the silt to be deposited.

Since waves, tides, and currents are weaker in lakes than in the sea, deltas are more common in lakes. However, the larger deltas are built in the sea, for there the largest rivers discharge. Some streams build no deltas, because of the lack of sediments. The Niagara River as it flows into Lake Ontario is so free from silt that no sediments are being deposited.

Growth. A delta consists of successive layers of debris brought down from the land and spread out over a fan-shaped area on the bottom of the basin at the mouth of the river. Where the stream current reaches quiet water, the bulk of its coarser load is dropped, and the finer material is carried farther out. Since accumulating sediments tend to reduce the gradient of the stream, the stream aggrades rapidly and soon begins to break up into distributaries which wind to and fro over the newly formed alluvial land (Fig. 11.52). Deposition continues in these currents until many of the channels are completely choked and new ones are opened; later, these also are choked and abandoned. In this way, many partially filled areas remain as lakes in the delta, and coalescing distributaries enclose islands. The main channels build their accumulations of coarse debris farther and farther out into the sea, and the minor distributaries assist by adding their products of aggradation until the deposits are built up to and above sea level.

The *rate of growth* of deltas varies with the size and velocity of the rivers and the geologic nature of the drainage basins. The Mississippi River is pushing the embankments of its chief distributaries into the Gulf at a rate of about 1 mile in 16 years. The northern portion of the Adriatic Sea is being filled so rapidly by the Po and other streams that cities originally built on the coast line are now far from the sea. Adria, formerly a port, is now 14 miles inland; on other parts of the coast line, zones 20 miles wide have been built up within the past 1,800 years. The Tiber River, yellow in color because of the abundance of sediment which it carries, is adding to the coast line around its mouth at the rate of about 1 mile a century. At the mouth of the Danube, a great delta is growing into the Black Sea. At the major outlets, the water is shallowing so fast that the lines of soundings of 6 and 36 feet deep are advancing into the sea nearly 400 feet per year.

The Ganges-Brahmaputra Delta has an area of approximately 60,000 square miles, with an apex 200 miles inland. The Mississippi Delta began to form north of Cairo, Illinois, and deltalike deposits are found southward for 600 miles. Its width varies from 30 to 60 miles. The total area, including its northerly extension, is over 30,000 square miles. Only about one-third of this area has been formed during recent geologic time. Most of Holland represents the combined deltas of the Rhine, the Maas, and the Scheldt Rivers.

Structure. The structure of a delta is essentially the same at the mouth of every large river. A vertical cross section of the delta shows nearly horizontal beds of fine silt or clay at the bottom. Because of their basal position, these beds, laid down in the area beyond the delta proper, are termed the *bottomset* beds. Above them is found a series of more steeply inclined strata of silt and sand, or less often, gravel, which constitute the heavier load dropped by the river currents as they encountered the quiet waters of the sea. The slopes of these beds, called the *foreset* beds, approach the angle of repose of the material of which they are composed, but on large deltas these slopes are usually only a few hundred feet per mile. The foreset beds, in turn, are capped by nearly horizontal strata, the *topset* beds, which represent the last deposits of variable texture left by the river as the distribu-

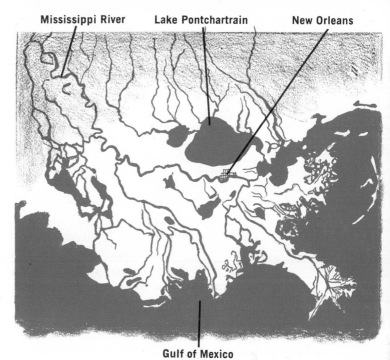

FIG. 11.52. *A map of part of the delta of the Mississippi River. (Drawn from maps and aerial photographs.)*

taries aggrade the alluvial flats of the growing delta (Fig. 11.53).

A delta consists of two parts: (1) a seaward margin, or submerged part, resting upon the marine continental shelf and (2) a landward part, which is not submerged but which is covered with fresh-water sediments. The land portion gradually is built out over the submerged part, which, in turn, is steadily built out into deeper water. Because of these relations, oceanic deltas have marine beds that grade upward and landward into fresh-water sediments. Fluctuating shore lines cause these marine and fresh-water sediments to dovetail, or interfinger.

Subsidence. Subsidence of large deltas has been noted at the mouths of many rivers. In general, aggradation has kept pace with the sinking, but in some delta deposits marine limestones and shales are interbedded with fresh-water sediments and old soils. From the structural relations of the sediments, it is evident that at times subsidence gained on upbuilding and that the delta surface again was covered by the sea. Deep borings in various deltas

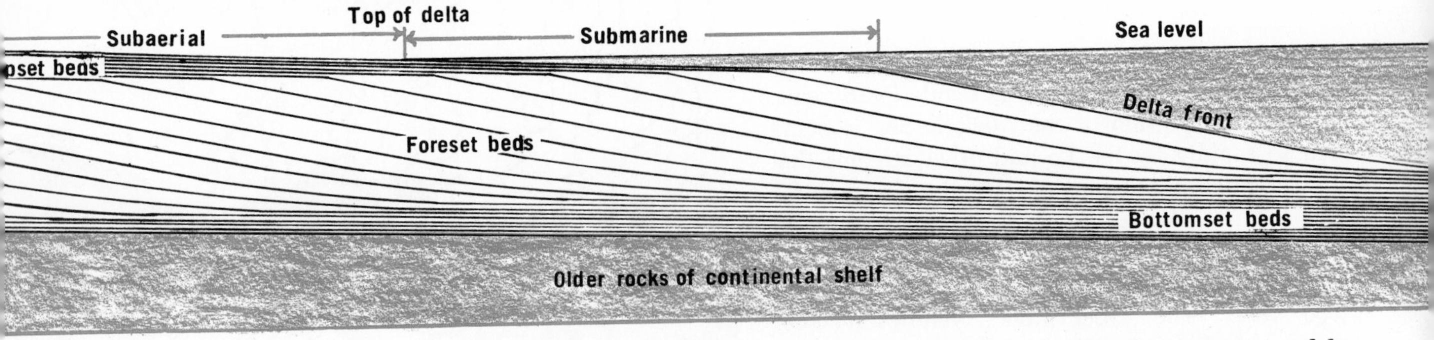

Subaerial — Top of delta — Submarine — Sea level

set beds

Foreset beds

Delta front

Bottomset beds

Older rocks of continental shelf

FIG. 11.53. *Diagram illustrating the form, growth, and internal structure of a delta. Materials are added mainly as a gentle embankment on the frontal slope as foreset beds, subordinately on the beyond as bottomset beds, and across the top as topset beds. Each of the continuous lines represents a previous surface during the growth of the delta. In subsiding areas the topset beds may attain considerable thickness, whereas in rising areas they may be reduced or removed.*

reveal similar successions. At New Orleans, driftwood was penetrated at 1,042 feet. Depths of 500 to 800 feet are not uncommon in many deltas now being formed. During earlier geologic times some deltas subsided to depths of more than 10,000 feet as the river-borne sediments accumulated on the surface. In the region that is now the northern Appalachian Mountains area an ancient delta was once deposited, and the Susquehanna River has since excavated its channel through the delta beds, which show a thickness of 13,000 feet.

CHEMICAL PRECIPITATION

In arid regions the solids dissolved in a stream may become concentrated enough to be precipitated as a coating on pebbles at low-water stages. In humid regions a stream fed by cold springs highly charged with dissolved calcium bicarbonate may deposit calcium carbonate along its course, as carbon dioxide is released by warming, by agitation over rapids, or by organisms. Most stream waters, however, are too dilute to make chemical deposits en route to the sea.

Stream Work in Dry-land Areas

Unlikely as it may seem, stream work is not lacking in deserts, and in semiarid regions it is easily the dominant gradational process, even though long periods go by with little or no precipitation. Some deserts may have no rainfall for several years and then be subjected to a veritable deluge of water that dashes down slopes in sheet floods and valley torrents. Such flows sweep with them everything loose and rip off whatever is not strongly attached or anchored.

Most of the deserts and semideserts of the United States are internal, or closed, drainage basins separated by mountain ranges from regions with outlets to the sea. This is also the condition in some other desert regions, such as the Sahara, the Libyan, and the Kara Kum. In the Great Basin, these basins and mountains are of fault-block origin. Some desert basins extend below sea level, and sediment can escape from them only by solution or by wind activity. Such basins, however, are eventually built up to reach the common base level toward which the general erosion of the land is tending.

PEDIMENTATION

Desert regions in areas of soft or slightly consolidated bedrock may show only a slowing-up of the base-leveling processes, but where the bedrock varies in its degree of resistance to erosion, cliffs and ridges of the more durable material soon develop over the surface, especially if the beds are folded or faulted. These features tend to perpetuate themselves throughout the greater part of the ero-

FIG. 11.54.   *Receding cliffs and detached remnants rising above a pediment in Monu-ment Valley, Arizona-Utah. Runoff from the cliffs has planed off the bedrock at their bases. (Santa Fe Railway.)*

sion cycle. Although the same features may occur in a humid area, they are much more conspicuous in a dry region (Fig. 11.54).

Such rains as may fall on the higher lands above the scarps at the margins of the desert basins form the usual pattern of rills and minor streams that join and produce a few canyonlike gullies, or wadies. Since the amount of rock debris swept down these steep gullies by an occasional torrent is moderate, the streams are often still capable of eroding when they arrive at the abrupt end of the canyonlike parts of their courses. This results in the beveling of the solid rock below the flaring gullies, the undercutting of the cliffs bordering the higher ground, their collapse and gradual recession or retreat, and the formation of a gradually sloping surface where the cliffs formerly stood. This truncated rock surface is called a *rock fan,* or *pedi-ment.* It is essentially a surface of bare rock, but it bears scattered rock fragments fallen from the crumbling cliffs or even a thin mantle of rock waste brought down the wadies from the higher areas.

Weathering and erosion, although slowed down by the scarcity of water, continue. When the joint-ed and disintegrated masses topple from the face of a cliff, they fall into innumerable fragments, which are still further broken as they strike the hard rock surface of the pediment below. Over this surface the shattered materials move down-ward under any impetus, however slight. The near absence of vegetation and the lack of the binding effect of roots in these loose surface materials favor movement of the rock debris. Bare cliffs (Fig. 11.55) rising sharply above the pediment show a conspicuous lack of talus slope or other accumula-tion of loose rock at their bases.

The pediment surface passes gradually down slope into the piedmont alluvial plain (bajada), which, in turn, may give place basinward to a salt or playa lake or its desiccated remnants. The usual sequence, then, is cliff, pediment, bajada, and playa (Fig. 11.55).

Adjacent pediments may grow laterally so that they ultimately unite to form a compound pedi-ment resembling a piedmont alluvial plain. One pediment may be invaded and regraded by an

FIG. 11.55. *Retreating cliffs and growing pediment at their foot, Painted Desert near Cameron, Arizona. (Spence Air Photos.)*

adjacent lower one, or the whole area may be captured and converted into the usual valley form by the tributaries of a stream flowing to the sea.

Many geologists are inclined to regard the high-level erosion surfaces of the Rocky Mountains as remnants of former pediments rather than of pene-

FIG. 11.56. *Alluvial deposits in Death Valley, California. The alluvial fans deposited by tributaries of the main streams coalesce as sloping alluvial plains on each margin of the lowland. (Spence Air Photos.)*

plains, since their upper reaches slope as much as 200 to 400 feet per mile.

DEPOSITION

In arid regions, the rainfall is so slight that the runoff is not able to transport all the sediments brought into the larger valleys and closed basins by the rainwash. For this reason, a large part of the material derived from the erosion of the bordering hills or mountains, where the rainfall may be considerable, is deposited in the valleys, where the rainfall is much less, with the result that sediments accumulate to a depth of many hundred feet.

Desert-valley filling is characteristic of the intermontane valleys of Arizona and California (Figs. 11.56, 11.57). Many of the valley walls are angular mountain slopes with narrow, gorgelike tributary valleys leading back into the mountains. Each stream forms a huge alluvial fan or cone at its mouth. Where the gradients are high, the fans are composed of boulders and large stones, transported by the torrents that sweep over such areas at rare intervals as a result of occasional short but violent cloudbursts. A new lot of rock waste is added to the lowland with each such storm period.

The several fans unite laterally to form a compound alluvial fan, or piedmont alluvial plain, that continues basinward and gradually buries any hills or other irregularities that it encounters. The turbulent water ends its journey in the temporary or playa lakes at the foot of the slopes, where desiccation takes place.

In wide basins, the outer margins of the fans are composed of fine sand and silt, and here wind work becomes active, and sand dunes develop. In some of the valley bottoms, the wind is a more effective agent of transportation than running water.

ARID CYCLE OF EROSION

The arid cycle of erosion differs from that in humid regions not only in rate and, to some extent, in method but also in the base-leveling process. Gradation of enclosed desert basins and bordering mountains includes leveling up as well as leveling down, for as filling of the basins progresses, the base level rises accordingly.

The stage in an arid cycle is said to be young when the individual basins are discrete and at greatly different levels, mature when the alluvial floors of the separate basins become confluent at nearly a common level by overflow of waste from the higher ones, and old when the highlands are reduced to monadnocklike inselbergs (island mountains) standing above broad pediments and when the valley floors are greatly widened and raised by the associated deposits (Fig. 11.58).

Stream Erosion and Man

Certain aspects of stream work affect man quite intimately, even disastrously. Degradation probably poses more serious problems than aggradation. Heavy rains and the resulting floodwaters from streams not only carry away the soil from cultivated fields but also ruin buildings, dams, and power installations; flood highways; wash out railway embankments and bridges; and cover valuable agricultural bottom lands with heavy deposits of sand, gravel, and boulders, thus rendering them useless for farming.

SOIL EROSION

One of the principal problems arising from the gradational work of running water is that of soil erosion. Soil is the superficial layer of disintegrated mantle-rock that normally shows a profile of weathering and is capable of supporting plant growth. Generally, it is colored dark by decaying organic matter, and it contains the many substances that promote plant growth, these being derived from the rocks, from the air, and from water. Each year, parts of the soil are washed away, and each year, additions are made by weathering. If the additions are less than the losses, the land deteriorates.

Of about 600 million acres of agricultural land in the United States, about 100 million acres of once-productive land already have been essentially ruined for practical crop use, and about twice as much more has lost a large part of its topsoil or is in serious danger of doing so. About 100,000 acres are being lost each year. The total loss in value of

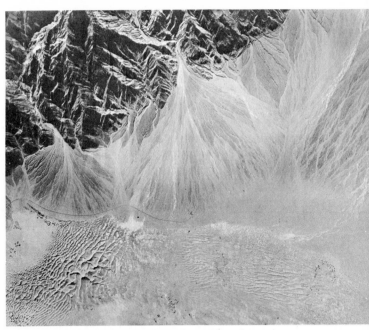

FIG. 11.57. *Vertical photograph of alluvial fans and associated sand dunes near Stove Pipe Wells, Death Valley, California. Note the lobate outlines of the fans and the multiple stream channels that cross them. (Fairchild Aerial Surveys, Inc.)*

the land and in its productivity is estimated to be about 400 million dollars a year.

Causes. The most severe erosion takes place on slopes, particularly on slopes where cleanly tilled crops, such as cotton, corn, and tobacco, are grown. Soil erosion is much less severe where grasses, alfalfa, and small grains are grown. Forests protect the soil from erosion, and where these are cut down, particularly where the slash and undergrowth are removed or burned, erosion is greatly increased (Figs. 11.59 to 11.61).

At Bethany, Missouri, which has a mean precipitation of 33.5 inches, experiments on an 8 per cent slope that was cropped continuously to corn showed a loss of 67.4 tons of soil per year per acre. Where corn was rotated with wheat and clover, less than half that was lost; and where alfalfa was grown, the loss under the same conditions was only 0.2 ton of soil per acre. The water lost by runoff was greatly increased as soil loss increased; it was

FIG. 11.58. *Late stage of pedimentation in Castle and French Buttes area in northeastern Arizona. An earlier surface (center right) is being regraded to a lower level. (Spence Air Photos.)*

FIG. 11.59. *Aerial photograph of soil erosion near Lumpkin, Georgia. The headward growth of gullies is encroaching upon the cultivated land on the upland. (United States Air Force.)*

26 per cent where corn was grown and only 3.4 per cent where alfalfa was grown. Grass crops are almost as effective as alfalfa in conserving soil and decreasing runoff.

Other factors contributing to soil erosion include single cropping, overcropping, destruction of soil structure by improper tillage, breaking of the prairie sod, careless logging, burning of grass and stubble, dry farming of submarginal lands, exposure of fallow land, overgrazing, concentrated rainfall, and up- and down-slope plowing and cultivation.

Prevention and control. Various methods are in use to decrease soil erosion and land destruction. Dams of earth, rock, or logs are built in gullies to check their growth, and vegetation is planted on the bare surfaces to hold the soils (Figs. 11.62, 11.63). Where slopes are farmed, strips of tilled crops are planted along contours to alternate with strips of small grain, grass, or other nontilled crops, which catch the rain water flowing down the slopes, spread it out, and protect the tilled ground from erosion. They greatly increase the water absorbed by the ground and decrease the runoff.

FIG. 11.60. *Soil profile with thick humus layer in the A horizon (topsoil), on flat topography in eastern Texas. (Soil Conservation Service.)*

At places terracing, trenching, ridging, and furrowing along contours can also be effective. These are preventive measures. Where lands already are deeply trenched with many gullies, the problems are those of reclamation. Small dams and terraces

FIG. 11.61. *Soil profile on gently sloping surface near area shown in Fig. 11.60. Soil erosion has removed the humus layer of the A horizon. (Soil Conservation Service.)*

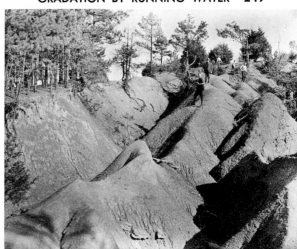

FIG. 11.62. *Gullies on an upper Tennessee Valley farm, photographed Dec. 5, 1933, just before treatment. (Tennessee Valley Authority.)*

are built to catch the soil in transit, and small, rich garden and orchard plots are thus provided. Certain areas have been reforested and others put to grass. Notwithstanding all these methods of conservation, land destruction by erosion steadily gains in the United States in regions where rain-

FIG. 11.63. *The gullies shown in Fig. 11.62 after treatment, photographed July 24, 1935. The treatment consisted chiefly in planting black locust seedlings. Some stone check dams were built, one of which can be seen in the foreground. (Tennessee Valley Authority.)*

storms are violent and tilled crops are cultivated over vast areas.

Other desirable practices in soil management include the selective use of the land, use of cover crops, crop rotation, contour plowing and cultivation, proper tillage, use of fertilizers, use of trashy fallow, protection of stream banks, prevention and control of floods, and return of submarginal lands to forest or permanent pasture.

OTHER PROBLEMS

Streams affect man's activities in several other ways. The shifting of stream channels complicates political boundaries. Rivers in flood undermine bridge footings, destroy property, devastate lowlands, and do other damage. Hence, the prevention and control of floods and the protection of riverbanks and levees deeply concern man. Man is interested also in the maintenance of steady flow for maximum power development, in the silting of reservoirs, in the recovery of gold and other valuable materials from stream gravels, and in the use of streams for water supply, navigation, fishing, recreation, and the disposal of sewage and industrial wastes.

Summary

Rainwash and streams continually erode the land. Streams erode by corrasion, solution, and hydraulicking. They obtain their loads by direct erosion, rainwash, mass movement, tributaries, wind, melting glaciers, ground water, and volcanic eruptions. They transport their loads by traction, in suspension in turbulent waters, and in solution. Their capacity and competency are markedly enhanced by increase in velocity, as during floods. During transit, sand and gravel undergo attrition, rounding, and selective sorting.

Valleys grow in length, depth, and width as they approach base level. Stages of youth, maturity, and old age, ending in a peneplain, are recognized in a cycle of erosion. Cycles may be interrupted by glaciation, volcanic activity, uplift (rejuvenation), or drowning.

Stream erosion tends to be selective, so it etches various rocks into relief according to their structures. The results include rock terraces, mesas, buttes, badlands, cuestas, hogbacks, zigzag ridges, canoe-shaped valleys, ring ridges, and ring valleys.

Stream courses may be consequent, subsequent, antecedent, or superimposed. They show dendritic, trellis, braided, and other patterns. Special conditions give rise to waterfalls, rapids, canyons, and natural bridges.

Streams lose velocity and make deposits when their gradient decreases, when the volume of water decreases, when there is an increase in cross section, when they encounter obstructions, or when they enter still water. They deposit alluvial fans, alluvial cones, piedmont alluvial plains, channel fill, bars, flood plains, and deltas. Alluvial terraces develop from former flood-plain deposits.

In dry-land areas, the runoff develops a spatial sequence of cliffs, pediments, bajadas, playas, and general valley fill. The arid cycle of erosion in enclosed basins is distinguished by a rise of base level as filling proceeds.

In our study of gradation by running water, we have acquired an understanding of many of the earth's physiographic features. In addition, we have seen that although some of the effects of stream work, such as soil erosion and floods, are destructive, other effects benefit us by supplying water, sand and gravel, routes of commerce, rich flood-plain soils, scenic landscapes, and recreational opportunities.

Suggestions for Further Reading

Atwood, Wallace W.: *The Physiographic Provinces of North America*, Ginn & Company, Boston, 1940. A good basic work, helpful on stream erosion.

Bryan, Kirk: "The Retreat of Slopes," *Assoc. Am. Geographers Annals*, vol. 30, pp. 254–268, 1940.

Cotton, C. A.: "Classification and Correlation of River Terraces," *Jour. Geomorphology*, vol. 3, pp. 27–37, 1940.

Cotton, C. A.: *Geomorphology*, John Wiley & Sons, Inc., New York, 1952. A good basic text on landscapes developed by erosion.

Johnson, Douglas: *Stream Sculpture on the Atlantic Slope*, Columbia University Press, New York, 1931. One of the classic studies on stream erosion.

King, Lester C.: "Canons of Landscape Evolution," *Geol. Soc. America Bull.*, vol. 64, pp. 721–751, 1953.

King, Lester C.: *South African Scenery: A Textbook of Geomorphology*, 2d ed., Edinburgh House Press, Edinburgh, 1951.

Leopold, Luna B., and Thomas Maddock: "The Hydraulic Geometry of Stream Channels and Some Physiographic Implications," *U.S. Geol. Survey Prof. Paper* 252, 1953.

Lobeck, A. K.: *Geomorphology*, McGraw-Hill Book Company, Inc., New York, 1939.

Russell, I. C.: *Rivers of North America*, G. P. Putnam's Sons, New York, 1907. Although out of date, this book was one of the classics in its field.

Russell, R. J.: "Lower Mississippi Delta," *Louisiana Dept. Conserv. Geol. Bull.* 8, 1936.

Thornbury, W. D.: *Principles of Geomorphology*, John Wiley & Sons, Inc., New York, 1954.

Chapter 12

SNOW, ICE, AND GLACIERS

GLACIATION IS still another process of gradation. As a matter of fact, glaciation can interrupt other processes of gradation, such as stream erosion, and superimpose its own erosional and depositional patterns.

As late as 10,000 years ago, during Pleistocene times, the continents were covered extensively with glaciers. Although these glaciers have since receded, they have greatly influenced our topography. In addition to studying this widespread continental glaciation, we shall examine present-day alpine and piedmont glaciation.

Occurrences of Ice

Ice forms wherever water freezes—in streams, lakes, the sea, the atmosphere, and the ground. It is most familiar in the form of snow, which is composed of skeletal, hexagonal crystals of great delicacy and beauty (Fig. 12.1), but it also occurs in various other forms, among them frost crystals and needlelike, dendritic, and plumelike forms, such as aggregates on windowpanes. On bodies of water it forms either irregular aggregates of large acicular (needlelike) crystals or solid masses of long hexagonal crystals, the long axes of which stand at right angles to the surface of the water.

LAKE ICE

A body of quiet water, such as a lake or inland sea, does not commonly freeze at the surface until all the water from top to bottom is near the freezing temperature. Fresh water is densest at 39°F, and when the surface water reaches this temperature, it sinks and is replaced by warmer water from below; this vertical circulation continues until the whole body of water reaches its greatest density (Fig. 12.2). As the temperature of the lake surface continues to approach the freezing point (32°F), this colder water remains afloat and finally forms a crust of ice. Thus lakes of average depth freeze over at the surface completely when the temperature is below the freezing point for an extended period. Deep lakes, such as the Great Lakes, freeze near shore lines but do not completely freeze over, even in the coldest winters.

If a lake is shallow for some distance from shore, the ice anchors itself to the bottom, and by freezing the water in the sediments on the floor of the basin, the ice covering of the basin becomes continuous with the frozen land at the level of the lake. With fluctuations of temperature, the ice expands and contracts. When it contracts during a period of low temperature, it forms cracks which are filled with water that congeals to cement the fractures. In this way, a continuous sheet of ice is formed again to fit the outlines of the basin. If the temperature is later raised, the ice expands, so that the ice cover becomes too large to fit the basin and crowds the shore line, exerting an enormous horizontal thrust in all directions. In this way, much loose material is pushed ashore, and, after melting of the ice, it forms walls of sand and gravel and larger boulders that parallel the shore lines. They differ from beaches or bars in that the material is often unsorted, and it slopes steeply toward the basin. Hundreds of glacial lakes in the upper Mississippi Valley region have conspicuous *ice ramparts* (Fig. 12.3) formed in this way.

On many lakes underlying the vegetation of a floating bog, ice is continuous laterally with the ice of the surrounding soil. At such places the expanding ice arches up the soil in a series of ridges parallel to the shore. Many small lakes in the glaciated region of the northern part of the United States are entirely surrounded by wire-grass bogs underlain by thick beds of peat that are saturated with water. The shove of shore ice on such lakes

FIG. 12.0.   *Athabaska Glacier, Alberta, as it appears in summer. This vast expanse of ice shows many fractures caused by movement downhill over an uneven base. (Canadian Pacific Railway.)*

pushes the ice of surrounding bogs into domes and ridges.

Should strong winds arise when the ice on a lake is breaking, large cakes of ice with enclosed pebbles and boulders are driven ashore and pushed out on the beach. If the drift of ice rafts parallels the shore line, the banks are eroded by the ice, which tears away the beach materials or smooths them into terracelike structures.

SEA ICE

Sea water does not freeze until it reaches a temperature of 26 to 28°F. The freezing temperature is not nearly so uniform as that of fresh water because of the varying salinity of the sea. In high latitudes, all the sea water is near the freezing point, but after the ice attains a thickness of 6 to 10 feet it protects the water below from the intense cold of the polar winters. Where ice forms along the shore in the high latitudes, it is frequently over 50 feet thick. Such masses are the result, not of the direct freezing of the ocean water, but of the con-

FIG. 12.1. *Snowflakes, showing some of the skeletal hexagonal crystal patterns assumed by water vapor as it solidifies from the atmosphere. (U. Nakaya, Hokkaido University.)*

version of snow into ice by the spray from waves and of the heaping up of ice alongshore by storms. Such ice, commonly referred to as the "ice foot of the shore," is an important factor in shore-line erosion. It protects the shore from wave action and serves as a raft on which debris, broken from the cliffs by frost during the winter, may gather and be carried out to sea when the ice breaks.

Broken sea ice floats in large cakes, called *floes*. This floe ice frequently is jammed together into ice packs that have very irregular surfaces and stand high above the water, because of the crowding of the ice cakes. Along the coast of Labrador, and in many arctic bays, ice forms on the sea bottom, and this is spoken of as *ground ice*, or *anchor ice*.

RIVER ICE

When river water freezes, it exerts a disruptive effect at the sides and bottom of its channel similar to the effect caused by the freezing of ground water. Mud, gravel, and boulders that become incased in the ice are pushed downstream, floated by thick cakes of ice to the banks of the stream, or halted by an ice jam across the valley. If a large amount of ice accumulates at a narrow place in the valley, the water is ponded, and deposition of the stream's sediment follows. When the jam eventually breaks, the volume of the stream is greatly increased, and the accompanying acceleration of velocity raises the transporting power of the stream immensely. Many of the Canadian rivers flowing into Hudson Bay are dammed at their rapids in this manner. As the ice breaks in early summer, many of the incased boulders are stranded on the shores, where they remain until they are pushed or floated farther along during the next high-water season.

FROZEN GROUND WATER

All soils are porous, and nearly all solid rocks near the surface have innumerable joints and fissures that contain water. The expansion of such water as it freezes is an important factor in rock disintegration. The processes involved include frost wedging (Fig. 12.4), frost heaving, and some types of mass wasting, such as solifluction. The results include a wide range of surface features, such as talus, patterned ground of various kinds, and some types of rock glaciers.

In northwestern Canada frost wedging has lifted large blocks, as much as 25 feet in diameter, from flat exposures of crystalline rocks through vertical distances of more than 12 feet. In high mountainous districts and in the arctic or subarctic regions, where there is a marked daily fluctuation of temperature, small angular fragments are wedged from the surface of exposed cliffs and accumulate as heaps of talus at the base of steep slopes and crags. Along the coast of Greenland and in Alpine regions the amount of rock disruption caused by frost is enormous. There some of the snow of the long winters is melted during the summer months, and water fills the joints and fissures of the rocks. The summer nights are sufficiently cold to freeze water, and the resulting ice splits off large blocks from the cliffs. In mountain valleys with high gradients talus material creeps under its own weight and fre-

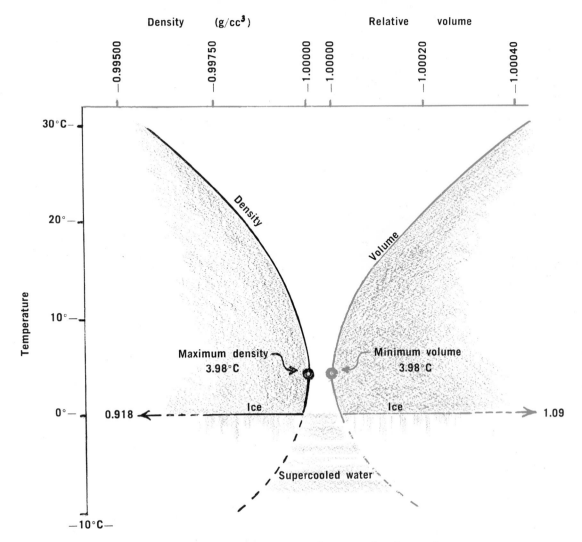

FIG. 12.2. *Curves showing the reciprocal changes in density and volume of water caused by differences in temperature. The maximum density of pure water is reached at 3.98°C. Surface waters made dense by cooling, therefore, sink until the whole mass attains that maximum density. Further cooling thereafter causes the surface waters to expand and hence to float on top, where at 0°C they may freeze. Ice expands upon crystallization about 1/11 in volume (far beyond the range of this diagram). Like other solids, ice once formed also expands and contracts as its temperature (below freezing) is raised or lowered.*

quently forms "rock streams," or "rock glaciers," that move slowly down the valley. Such mass movement of surface materials by gravity has been discussed previously; but we wish to point out here that the freezing of water in the talus accelerates the down-slope movement and may even initiate it.

Water frozen in soils forms an icy cement which binds together the fragments of the mantle-rock, fills the pore spaces, and hinders the downward penetration of water as the snow melts in the spring. On hillsides and mountain slopes such a frozen surface may become a gliding plane in the rock waste, and huge masses of water-soaked rock debris may collapse toward the valley in the form

FIG. 12.3. *An ice rampart, 8 to 10 feet high, along the shore of Lake Mendota at Picnic Point, Madison, Wisconsin. This wall of bouldery drift was carried by ice pushed from the lake during the ice-expansion stage brought about by warmer temperatures in February. (Wisconsin Geological and Natural History Survey.)*

of landslides. In agricultural districts where the soil is composed of bouldery clay, each season's frost carries boulders nearer the surface. The boulders are moved by the expansive force of freezing water-soaked clay, which yields in the direction of least resistance. In general, such frost heaving is toward the surface of the earth. When the frost leaves in the spring, the particles of soil sink back to their original positions, but the boulders are prevented from settling by clay or pebbles which fall into the cavities that the boulders had occupied. In time much of the bouldery material of the mantle-rock may come to lie at or near the surface. In some regions farmers have cleared these boulders from their fields and have used them to build stone fences.

PERMAFROST

In regions adjacent to existing icecaps or continental glaciers and in some high mountainous areas, the rocks are filled with perennial frost. This is called permafrost, because of its persistence. Permafrost is very extensive in northern Eurasia and North America. Antarctica and the lower end of South America also have areas where the ground remains permanently frozen, but only a relatively small amount of land in the Southern Hemisphere is properly situated in the high latitudes where permafrost can develop. Permafrost is a reservoir of cold which may accumulate or waste with climatic variation. It probably precedes and lingers on after every glacial period, or it may occur independently. A mean annual air temperature of 30 to 24°F is generally necessary to produce permafrost, but other factors may also be of assistance. These are given by Robert F. Black as follows:

1. Long, cold winters and short cool, summers
2. Low precipitation the year round and especially low snowfall
3. Clear winters and cloudy summers
4. Rapid evaporation the year round
5. Strong, cold winds in summer and winter
6. Low degree of solar radiation

Permafrost includes more than frozen ground water. In addition to cementing rock fragments and thus completely sealing the pore spaces in mantle-rock, the ice crystals increase in size and add to their number to form films, veins, wedges, irregular bodies, and continuous lenslike layers of relatively clear ice that may be of large size. Poorly drained areas underlain by clay, very fine silt, or peat offer especially favorable conditions for the development of these extensive masses of clear ice. Not only does frost form a subsurface mass impervious to the downward movement of water, but this cementing material is easily activated by temperature changes. Freezing increases the volume of soil partly because of the expansion of water changing to ice and partly, in the regions of permafrost, because of the formation of masses of clear ice within the soil. Since water will move readily toward growing crystals of ice, the additional moisture necessary to produce the volume increase is drawn by capillarity from any adjacent source. In silts this volume increase may more than double the size of the bed affected.

Many mountaintops undergo active mass movement of rock waste by frost even though permafrost does not exist. Thus, in such regions, fields (felsenmeer) of rock fragments, many of them angular blocks, may be produced from bedrock by frost action. These loose masses move down slope, becoming subangular to rounded as they travel.

Peat rings. Frost thoroughly stirs or kneads soil materials in the process of alternate melting and freezing. Although areas of bare soil are more intensely affected, the heave and thrust also tear the tough mat of peat commonly covering the soil of sodded areas and thus form peat rings or polygons, and leave bare scars of naked soil where parting takes place. These rings, or chunks of sod, creep down slope or move under a viscous flow to a lower level. Wherever the frost is unduly confined, pressure increases, and the upward expansion may become explosive and toss aside the surface materials and fragments of rock as the strain is relieved. Freezing and thawing may cause the surface to move laterally and may produce tension on slopes and buckling on flats. The removal of much of the ice or water from boggy soil or inflated silts and peat may cause the surface to cave in.

Stone rings. In regions above or beyond the timber line, where frost action is a major factor in breaking up rock and displacing the fragments, there are unique arrangements of the rock waste. Large areas are covered by loose rocks, many of them angular, that have been torn from outcrops or from large boulders. Terracelike accumulations of the outward-moving angular blocks may result. However, where angular fragments are split from large boulders and fall, frequently on edge, around the parent mass, or core, a somewhat circular or polygonal arrangement is formed, called a stone ring or stone polygon. Where there is strong frost action, such an arrangement may be caused by heave from centers even below the surface, and the rings may be composed of frost-ejected fragments. Such rings or polygons are found on nearly level ground and on slightly sloping surfaces.

If the source boulders that undergo frost splitting are somewhat evenly spaced, the resultant stone rings may give rise to a rather uniform pattern, with each unit enclosed by a ridge or wall of rock

FIG. 12.4.   *Effects of frost heaving, Glacier National Park, Montana. The joint blocks have been pushed apart and toppled downhill by the freezing of water in the joints.*

material fragmented by the process. The diameter of such rings or polygons, in regions of permafrost, may range from 6 to 30 feet, but miniature polygons composed of smaller fragmental material have been reported in less rigorous climatic areas.

Garland tongues. On sidehills or mountain slopes, where gravity becomes the major motive force, the developing rings creep down the hillsides and elongate into ellipses and loops to form a mesh or net of garlandlike stony borders or walls that are the margins and ends of long tongues of finer material on the move. These garland tongues range from 2 to 6 or more feet across and have a flattened convex surface. The stony border may be several feet wide and contain rock fragments 2 feet or more in diameter.

Stone stripes. If garland loops and tongues reach steeper slopes or if their mobility is otherwise increased, they may continue to elongate; in this way they pass into stone stripes, which may be traced as nearly parallel stony ridges (Fig. 12.5) for several hundred feet down slope before they lose their identity. On still greater slopes garland loops and tongues may not be able to form, and the stone stripes develop directly from frost heave. Even the stone stripes fail to form on even steeper slopes, and the frost-heaved rock fragments merely slide or roll down to a lodgment area below. Many of these features of frost action are excellently developed, and are still being formed, from British Columbia northward through the Mackenzie District, the Yukon, and Alaska.

Present-day land surfaces show relics of ancient stone rings and stone stripes beyond the borders of permafrost, even as far distant as Nova Scotia, New England, and Pennsylvania; and other features characteristic of permafrost are general about the borders of the Wisconsin drift-covered area and even far down along the Appalachian Mountains. All such formations may have developed during the time when a subarctic climate extended far south of its present limit and when frost action controlled the physiographic processes beyond the edge of the ice front as it then existed.

FIG. 12.5. *Stone stripes, St. Elias Range, Alaska. Frost splitting from boulders forms rings of stones. On mountain slopes these rings gradually creep downhill, elongating as they go, until they form stripes for a distance of several hundred feet before losing their identity. (Robert P. Sharp.)*

DEPTH OF PERMAFROST

The depth of permafrost varies from place to place. In Alaska, on the Seward Peninsula, it ranges from zero near lakes, large streams, and warm springs, to 300 feet or more; south of Barrow, it is 1,000 feet. On the Kezhevinkov Bay, in northern Siberia, it is 1,700 feet, and at Nordvik permanently frozen ground occurs to a depth of 2,000 feet.

In the Northern Hemisphere the outer, or southern, border of perennially frozen ground is fringed by a wide area where permafrost is discontinuous and sporadic for a distance of 500 miles or more. Permafrost underlies the tundra region of the north and continues out under the conifer forests. Conifer trees spread their roots horizontally into the loose soil over the frozen ground. To them the frost is an asset, since it supplies plenty of moisture even where the annual rainfall is limited. In Canada permafrost extends as far south as the southern shores of Hudson Bay. In Siberia it reaches as far south as the Amur Valley. Some of the northern Siberian rivers flow on a bed of ice the year round.

Seasonal thaw in the frost zone penetrates from 1 to 10 feet, depending on insolation (solar radiation), insulation, drainage, and type of soil or rock material. Drilling has indicated that the permafrost is deepest beneath hills and shallowest in valleys. It is known to thin rapidly to the north under the Arctic Ocean and to thin gradually to the south.

Permafrost is thin or absent under some glaciers and in certain areas from which glaciers have recently receded. The Pleistocene continental glaciers, now largely melted, were very thick, so that the ground or rock surface beneath them may not have been frozen. However, permanently frozen ground, or permafrost, must have been present at the outer margin of the ice sheet and must have extended as far outward as conditions favored its development.

Cumulative data in Europe show that during the height of Pleistocene glaciation, permafrost occurred in southern England, northern France, Germany, and Poland. The remnants of surface features similar to those developed over areas now affected by permafrost have been recognized at various places in the glacial drift of the upper

Mississippi Valley and from Maine through New York, Pennsylvania, and farther south. Even the sweeping slopes and gently rounded forms characteristic of much of the drift topography in North America suggest that gradation due to freezing and lingering permafrost must have occurred before the present vegetation took over.

SNOW

When water vapor condenses directly into the solid state, crystals of snow are produced. When several of these crystals adhere to one another, they fall to the earth's surface as snowflakes. Symmetrical crystals of snow form only when the air is still and the temperature very cold. Most crystals are packed together in such a manner as to reflect light in great abundance, thus producing a visual sensation of whiteness. The presence of air in snow renders it opaque; otherwise it would be transparent like massive ice and many other crystalline substances.

In winter, snow commonly occurs on many portions of the earth's surface, and it may occur even at the equator on elevated plateaus and mountains. At any time of the year, high-flying aircraft can encounter snow, and icing is an aviation problem that requires special attention. When the atmosphere becomes saturated with moisture, a slight drop in temperature produces condensation. If the temperature is above freezing, this excess moisture is eliminated in the form of rain; but when the temperature is less than 32°F, the moisture commonly takes the form of snowflakes (Fig. 12.1). A large portion of the moisture that is precipitated as rain runs off as surface water, but snow generally accumulates in the region where it falls and tends to remain as long as the temperature of the air in contact with it is below the freezing point.

Newly fallen, dry snow has very low density and therefore high porosity. These properties, together with the very irregular shapes of the flakes, give it an enormous internal surface area. This allows it to exchange moisture readily by evaporation and by sublimation. Such molecular exchange between the solid phase and the vapor phase is greatest at the points of the lacy snowflakes, and so clusters of

these flakes gradually change their shape and become nearly spherical grains. Such granular snow is called *firn* (German) or *névé* (French) (Fig. 12.6).

SNOW FIELDS

In regions where the mean annual temperature is near the freezing point of water, much of the snow remains unmelted from one year to the next and consequently accumulates to great depths. The elevation of the lower limit of this accumulating snow is called the *snow line*, but usually it is a very irregular line. The regions where such low temperatures commonly prevail are chiefly in high latitudes or at high elevations. The location of the snow line is also influenced by the regional topography, the wind, the variation in minimum temperature from year to year, and similar local conditions. Apart from the temperature, the amount of snowfall is perhaps the most important factor.

Where the amount of snow that accumulates during the cold season is greater than the amount removed by melting during the warmer season, a snow field is formed. Snow fields are widely distributed. They may occur in any latitude at high

FIG. 12.6. *Crevasses and coarsely granular snow, or névé, on the surface of the Columbia ice field, Jasper National Park, Alberta, Canada. (Government Travel Bureau, Ottawa, Canada.)*

altitudes and at all altitudes in high latitudes. Snow fields are common in the high mountains of South America and Mexico and in the Rocky Mountain system of the United States, Canada, and Alaska (Fig. 12.7). They become progressively more widespread toward the north. In Eurasia snow fields exist in the Himalaya, the Caucasus, the Pyrenees, and the Alps, in the ranges of the Scandinavian Peninsula, and on various northern islands, including Iceland, Spitzbergen, Nova Zembla, and others along the arctic borders of Siberia and North America. In Africa snow fields and valley glaciers occur on Kilimanjaro and Ruwenzori, which are near the equator. Certain of the high mountains of New Zealand also have snow fields.

The snow grades downward into solid ice and thus becomes an *ice field,* but there is no very marked distinction to be made between an ice field and the snow field from which it originates. As accumulation continues, the mass of ice may begin to move down slope or to be squeezed out from

FIG. 12.7. *Unstable snow masses above ice fields in Alaska. The melting and freezing, sliding, and avalanching of such masses of snow are partly the cause of the steep, blunt upper ends of cirques. Snow fields are formed where the rate of snowfall during winter exceeds the rate of melting during summer. (United States Air Force.)*

the area of greatest thickness, with very little definite indication of the point where motion begins.

The two largest areas of snow and ice on the surface of the earth are those of Greenland (Fig. 12.8) and Antarctica, and of these Antarctica is by far the larger and contains more ice and snow than all the glaciers and snowfields of the rest of the world combined. These two regions alone have more than 5,700,000 square miles of ice-covered territory. Sonic, or echo, soundings in Greenland show the ice to be as much as 8,000 feet thick, and sounding in Antarctica indicates even greater depths. It has been estimated that, if these two great icecaps were completely melted, the level of the sea might be raised as much as 200 feet.

CONVERSION OF SNOW INTO ICE

The transformation from snow to névé and from névé to ice is very slow and is brought about by the interaction of a number of factors that result in the larger granules growing at the expense of the smaller ones. Although granular, the névé is in reality a haphazard heap of ice crystals, each of which has its edges and faces obliterated because of the ease with which ice changes to liquid and back to solid again. The face of the crystal and the thin edge between faces are most exposed to this change. Deeper down in the névé, the granules are continually changing, assuming new forms, moving into closer contact, filling in vacant spaces, and reorienting themselves with reference to adjacent granules (Fig. 12.9). This process is referred to as the growth of crystal granules. Not only does it produce a solid mass of ice with interlocking crystals, but it is a powerful factor in glacial motion. Accumulated masses of compacted snow, perched high in the mountains, may be released by changing weather conditions and may slide down the slope in the form of avalanches (Fig. 12.7). In the snow fields the weight of the upper layers of snow, aided by successive storms and drifts or by avalanches from neighboring peaks, squeezes the lower layers, which are thus recrystallized into solid ice.

During the summer months the surface of a snow field frequently reaches a temperature sufficiently warm to melt most of the flaky snow above the névé bed, and a thin crust of ice is formed when the temperature is again lowered. This crust separates the névé below from the snow of the next winter and remains in the névé field as a thin layer of ice; such layers give the whole deposit a stratified structure. Stratification is still more marked where wind-blown dust and coarser debris accumulate on the surface and are covered by subsequent snowfalls. In some Himalayan snow fields the separate strata of névé between successive layers, or crusts, of ice indicate an enormous amount of annual precipitation. In others, such as the firn fields of the Alps, each yearly deposit forms a thin layer 2 to 5 feet thick. In some Alpine snow fields the total thickness of the névé beds is over 1,500 feet.

The time required for the conversion of névé into ice ranges from 1 year to several decades, or even to several centuries, depending on the temperature and the rate of accumulation of snow. This rate varies greatly from place to place. It is high in a maritime climate, such as that of Iceland, whereas in a continental climate it is low. The Vatna Glacier in Iceland, at an elevation of approximately 4,000 feet, receives a mean annual precipitation of about 150 inches of water, whereas the Antarctic ice sheet receives no more than 5 inches annually.

GLACIERS

When granular snow or the massive ice resulting from its recrystallization accumulates to a great thickness, it begins to move, or flow, outward under its own weight and thus forms a glacier. These ice masses in mountain ranges vary in size from short but wide tongues of ice or snow on the narrow benches of a cliff, such as the snowbank glaciers of the Big Horn Mountains of Wyoming, to the long tongues of ice extending tens of miles down the valleys from the mountains of Alaska or from the Himalaya in Asia.

The Seward Glacier in Alaska is 50 miles long and 3 to 5 miles wide. The Hubbard Glacier of Alaska is somewhat longer, but not so wide. The Asiatic glaciers, in the vicinity of Mount Everest, are more than 30 miles long. Those in the Alps are

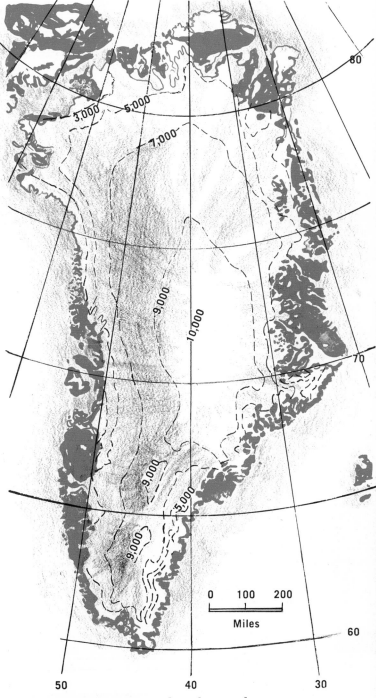

FIG. 12.8. *The continental ice sheet on the surface of Greenland. The main part of the island is covered by glacial ice, and only a narrow fringe of land (color) protrudes along the coast.*

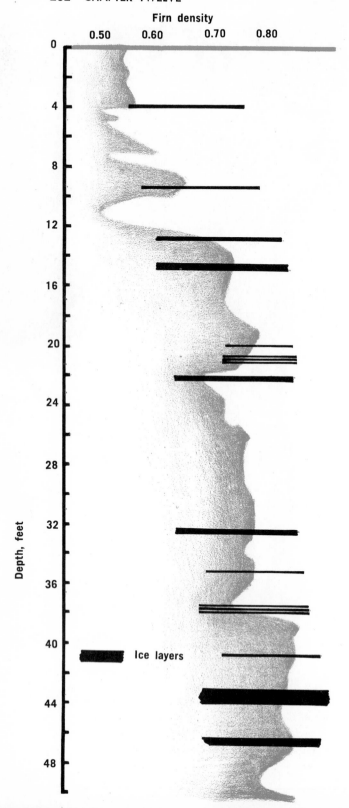

FIG. 12.9. *Bulk density of névé in deep pit on Upper Seward Glacier, Alaska. The névé is much more compact at depth. (After Robert Sharp.)*

numerous, but usually not more than a few miles in length. The thickness of the ice in mountain glaciers is difficult to determine, but in many of them it does not exceed 2,000 feet. Still greater glaciers are found in the arctic and antarctic regions, where extensive névé and ice fields have accumulated and spread out in all directions.

TYPES OF GLACIERS

As glacial ice spreads or flows from the place where it was formed, it assumes various shapes that are molded to a considerable extent by the surface over which the ice flows. On the basis of their mode of occurrence, all glaciers may be classified as follows: (1) mountain, or valley, glaciers, which descend from high peaks and occur along the flanks of mountain ranges; (2) confluent, or piedmont, glaciers, which are the joined extrusions of several alpine glaciers; and (3) continental, or ice-sheet, glaciers (also called icecaps), which cover vast areas (Figs. 12.10, 12.11).

Although all glaciers may be included conveniently within these types, several subtypes are often recognized. Some of these, which are probably special cases of the alpine, or valley, type, have certain peculiarities that have suggested their names. Thus a *reconstructed* glacier is one that cascades down a steep slope or projects from a hanging valley, breaks off, and falls in the form of blocks, or chunks, which pressure and freezing reunite at the base of the plunge. Perched on the upper part of a cliff, often at the head of a steep, blunt-ended valley, there may be a broad, snow-capped mass of clear ice, often crescent-shaped; this is called a *cliff* glacier, or *hanging* glacier (Fig. 12.12). The *polar*, or *high-latitude*, glacier of northern Greenland is a steep-sided, blunt-ended tongue of ice extending down a valley from the plateau on which the ice sheet is located. The *tidewater*, or *tidal*, glacier though basically a valley type, extends out into the sea, where its outer end, usually rising and falling with the tide, periodically breaks off in great chunks, or blocks, which float away as *icebergs*.

The term icecap may be regarded as synonymous with continental glacier, or ice sheet, but the term has been used also in a more limited way to designate the smaller patches or remnants of ice that spread or move out from a center. Those still present on Iceland (Fig. 12.11) are excellent examples.

Mountain, Valley, or Alpine Glaciers

Mountain, or valley, glaciers are streams of ice that descend from high peaks (Fig. 12.13) and occur along the flanks of mountain ranges in nearly all latitudes. They are fed by snowfields on slopes and in catchment basins above the snow line, and they represent the discharge or solid drainage of ice through valleys that were originally formed by streams. Since they merge into each other, it is frequently difficult to draw a definite distinction between a true glacier and its contributing snow field. One mountain glacier may be formed by the union of a number of smaller tributary ice tongues, each of which in turn is fed by the snow field. Obviously, there is some motion in the snow or ice field, since it discharges its excess into the glacier.

DISTRIBUTION

Valley glaciers occur in most of the high mountain ranges of the world. The Alps alone have approximately 2,000 in the depressions on the sides of their lofty peaks. In northern Scandinavia several large plateaus have glaciers moving into their marginal valleys. The Himalaya in Asia are famous for their wonderful valley glaciers, some of which extend far down from their sources. In the United States, the valley glaciers are confined to isolated mountain peaks, but in the Selkirks of British Columbia and farther north in Alaska, hundreds of glaciers of this type fill mountain valleys.

The form of alpine glaciers is, in general, similar to the shape of the valley, and their size is dependent upon the extent of the snow field, the amount of precipitation, and the temperature. Mountain glaciers are not present in all mountains which rise above the snow line, for on many isolated peaks the topography is unfavorable to the accumulation of snow. Extinct or dormant vol-

FIG. 12.10. *Penny Ice Cap on Baffin Island, Canada. Two outlet glaciers join to form Coronation Glacier, in the foreground. The dark lines on the glaciers are lateral and medial moraines. (Royal Canadian Air Force.)*

canoes may have great masses of snow and ice within their craters but few, if any, alpine glaciers on their slopes. However, many ancient volcanic cones that were deeply dissected by streams before the last glacial epoch now harbor hundreds of ice streams in their steeply sloping valleys. Such lofty peaks as Mount Shasta, Mount Rainier, and Mount Hood send down large glaciers in all directions. On Mount Shasta, some are 2 miles long, and on Mount Rainier several glaciers are nearly 7 miles long.

LIMITS OF GLACIERS

The position of the upper end, or head, of a valley glacier is generally the place where the more rapidly moving ice breaks away from the incoherent or sluggish snow or ice field. It is commonly marked by one or more arcuate, gaping cracks, or crevasses, known as the *bergschrund*. As the glacial ice moves away from the snow field, it carries with

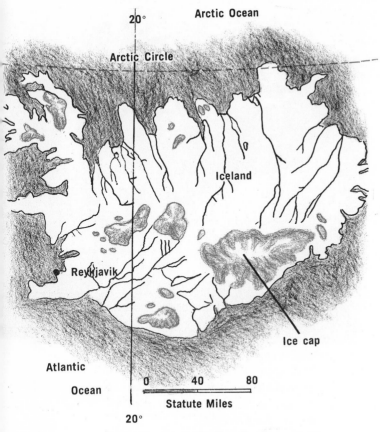

FIG. 12.11. *Iceland, showing small icecaps which are the remnants of a former, more extensive glaciation covering the whole island.*

it large masses of rock plucked from the mountainside.

Experimental tests have shown that the strength of adhesion of ice frozen to rock is as great as the cohesive strength of the ice itself. Obviously, therefore, an enormous quarrying force must be exerted on the rock wall from which the ice breaks off. As this process is repeated, it develops a broad depression and gives rise to a steep, blunt-ended valley. Such an amphitheaterlike valley head is called a *cirque*. It may have precipitous walls hundreds of feet high.

Once started, the basin of a cirque serves as a collecting ground for the snow of successive storms and for that swept into it by winds or carried into it by avalanches from the snow fields above. The cirque wall, therefore, becomes the upper limit of the glacier, and the basin serves as the feeding ground for the glacial ice.

Not all valley glaciers, however, begin with a cirque. In fact, at many places, particularly in the Alps, it is exceedingly difficult to distinguish the glacier from the ice field. If a limiting line is drawn, it must be more or less arbitrary. The bergschrund, even though only slightly developed, may still serve as the most satisfactory mark of separation.

The lower limit, or terminus, of an alpine glacier is generally in the mountain valley, where the amount of ice waste, or melting, is about equal to the forward movement, or flow, of the ice. In most latitudes, this position is some distance below the general snow line of the area; but in higher latitudes, glaciers extend progressively to lower and lower altitudes, until near the polar regions they push downward to the sea, where large blocks break off and float away as icebergs. This process is commonly known as *calving*.

FLUCTUATIONS OF LOWER LIMIT

The end of a glacier is rarely stationary. When the temperature becomes such that melting exceeds the forward movement, the edge of the glacier retreats; and when more ice moves down than is melted, the edge of the glacier advances. The ice moves forward at all times, but the position of the edge depends on the degree of balance between the rate of advance and the rate of melting. The amount of advance or retreat is dependent upon temperature and snowfall; and since both usually show annual variations, the lower ends of glaciers fluctuate. The most marked variations seem to appear with climatic cycles.

The Swiss glaciers showed a steady advance during the Middle Ages and reached a maximum about 1820. This advance was followed by a progressive retreat until about 1840, when they again began to advance, but since 1860, many have shown a marked retreat. During the past few years, however, the glaciers of the French Alps have been advancing from 70 to 150 feet per year. Monthly observations on the Bossons Glacier on Mont Blanc show that it is advancing with an oscillating movement—first on one side, then on the other, then in the middle. A recession of the edges of glaciers in Glacier Bay, Alaska, is now in progress on a large scale, and it has been estimated that the edges of the Muir Glacier have retreated 7 miles in the past 20 years (Fig. 12.14).

On Mount Rainier in Washington, Nisqually Glacier, which is about 4 miles long, retreated 4,131 feet between 1857 and 1944. Paradise Glacier, on the same mountain, has shrunk to such an extent that its terminal portion has become stagnant. The ice is so thin that it no longer flows under its own weight.

Some Alaskan glaciers are known to have advanced at an abnormal rate. During a period of 5 months in the winter of 1936–1937 the terminus of the Black Rapids Glacier advanced 3 miles. This represents a daily average of 115 feet, possibly the highest rate on record for any glacier. Very heavy precipitation of snow occurred in this area for several years prior to this rapid ice advance.

MOVEMENT OF GLACIERS

The nature of glacial motion is still not well understood, but the fact of movement was established as early as 1705. The first estimates of the amount of movement were made by noting the changes that took place in the surface debris. Conspicuous boulders on the surface of the ice were seen to change their positions slowly from year to year. Later such crude observations led to careful measurements of the rate of change, which was found to vary considerably, not only in different glaciers but in different parts of the same glacier.

The rapidity of glacial flowage is influenced by several factors, mainly the gradient of the valley, the thickness of the ice, and the temperature. To these may be added the smoothness of the surface over which the ice moves, the amount of water in the ice—both that which falls on it and that produced by melting—and finally the amount of debris in the ice. If a glacier is loaded with boulders, sand, and finely ground rock waste, it moves more slowly than clean ice.

Alpine glaciers move 1 to 3 feet per day. The Bossons Glacier carried the bodies of three guides,

FIG. 12.12. *Cirque lakes, Lake Ellen Wilson and Lake Lincoln, with Mount Jackson in the background, at Glacier National Park, Montana. Several cliff glaciers are shown on the mountainside, with an excellent one above the lake in the lower right. (Great Northern Railway.)*

FIG. 12.13. *Sharp, jagged peaks above effective glaciation in the Alps. Here the snow blows and slides off into the basins of glacial accumulation, leaving the tops of the mountains bare in summer.*

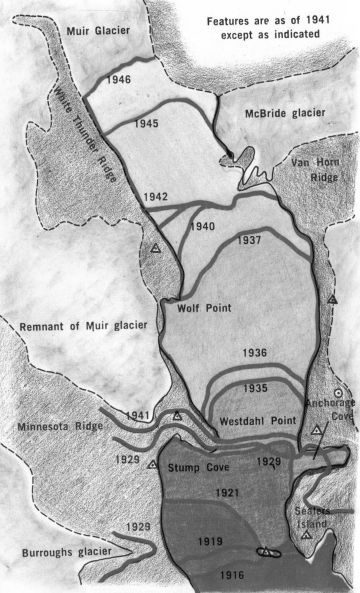

Features are as of 1941
except as indicated

Muir Glacier

1946

White Thunder Ridge

1945

McBride glacier

Van Horn Ridge

1942

1940

1937

Wolf Point

Remnant of Muir glacier

1936

1935

Anchorage Cove

Minnesota Ridge

1941

Westdahl Point

1929

Stump Cove

1929

1921

Sealers Island

1929

1919

Burroughs glacier

1916

FIG. 12.14. *Map showing the recession of Muir Glacier, Alaska, from 1916 to 1946. (After W. O. Field, Jr.)*

who perished in a fissure, a distance of nearly 8,000 feet in 41 years, or an average of about 1 foot in 2 days. It has been calculated that a particle of ice would require approximately 500 years to move from the summit of the Jungfrau to the end of the

Aletsch Glacier, an ice stream about 10 miles long. Many of the large Alaskan glaciers flow more rapidly. The Muir Glacier commonly moves as much as 7 feet a day, and the Child Glacier flows nearly 30 feet per day during the summer months. Extraordinary velocities have been recorded for the ice tongues which descend to the fiords along the coast of Greenland, where rates of nearly 100 feet a day have been observed, but in the same region, the inland ice at some distance back from the narrow fiords moves only a fraction of an inch per day.

The movement of a glacier resembles that of a river in many ways; the center moves more rapidly than the margins, where it meets resistance along the walls of the valley, and the surface moves more rapidly than the deeper portions of the ice, where its load of debris is greater and irregularities are encountered on the valley floor. At curves the convex portion of the glacier moves more rapidly than the concave, in much the same way that the velocity of a stream is accelerated on a long limb of a curve and checked on the opposite side.

Since some parts of the ice flow faster than other parts, the movement of a glacier is spoken of as "differential movement" (Fig. 12.15). The amount of differential movement has been determined in many glaciers by placing stakes in a straight line over the surface of the ice in alignment with fixed points on the walls of the valley. After a few days, the line of pegs curves downstream, which indicates that the central part moves more rapidly than the sides. At many places near the center of a glacier, the ice moves four times as fast as it does near the sides. Similarly, by driving a vertical line of pegs where a wall of ice is exposed at the side of a glacier, it is found that the top moves faster than does the bottom.

METHODS OF MOVEMENT

No universally acceptable theory of glacial movement has been formulated. Experts agree, however, that the method of movement at and near the surface of a glacier differs from that at depth. In terms of movement, a glacier can be divided into a near-surface zone of fracture and a deeper zone of flowage. The top zone is between 100 and 200 feet thick. Here the ice is brittle, and when force is applied, it breaks rather than changes its shape by flowage. At greater depth, deformation takes place because of the pressure of the overlying ice. Therefore, the ice moves at different speeds in different parts of the glacier.

Experimental and microscopic data on glacial ice show that the main causes of glacial motion are the reactions of the ice itself to the changing conditions under which it exists. The ice particles cannot have the freedom of movement accredited to those in a liquid, not even a viscous liquid. Any flowage observed must be solid flowage.

We believe that the movement is caused partly by innumerable, minute slippages along planes parallel to the base of the hexagonal ice crystals. Such slipping in ice crystals has been demonstrated in the laboratory. The millions of crystal grains in glacial ice do not have uniform orientations as they do in lake or river ice. However, the transfer of water which results from melting at points of compression between grains may permit the reorientation of the grains of ice within the glacier. In névé, or firn, the individual ice grains are known to rotate with respect to one another, and this rotation tends to develop a parallelism of ice crystals in the glacier.

Another method of movement, observed in the terminal parts of glaciers, is the shearing of thin, tabular masses of ice over each other, along distinct planes. The movement tends to be forward along closely spaced, upward-directed surfaces of thrusting, similar to thrust faulting in deep-seated rocks. Where the lower portion of a glacier carries the most debris, it is greatly retarded by its load, and the clean ice above moves so much faster that it is sheared over the part near the bottom. Such shearing planes are conspicuous in the glaciers of high latitudes, where vertical or overhanging ice cliffs, hundreds of feet high, show us the structure of the ice.

As its temperature rises, ice expands and thrusts the glacier forward. When cooling takes place, the whole body of ice does not contract correspondingly; instead, cracks, or crevasses, form. These

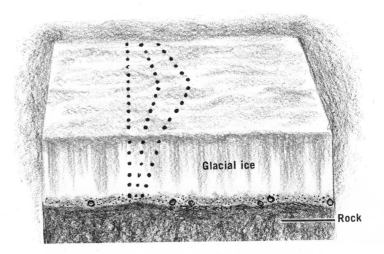

FIG. 12.15. *Diagram illustrating the differential movement of a valley glacier. Stakes driven in a straight row across the top of a glacier in a short time show a curve downstream. Pegs placed on the side of a glacier demonstrate that the top moves faster than the bottom.*

may later be healed or closed in various ways and thus obliterated, but always by added snow, ice, or debris. The expansion, contraction, and filling-in of the cracks contribute to the forward movement.

All glaciers move down slope under the influence of gravity. On steep slopes, as in high-gradient mountain valleys, a large fraction of the total glacial movement may be due to the slipping of the ice over bedrock. This has been measured directly at the margins of some glaciers, but it plays a very minor role in continental ice sheets.

Glacial motion is the sum of all the factors mentioned—crystal gliding, shearing, fracture filling, and sliding.

FISSURES FROM MOVEMENT

Bergschrund. At the upper end of a mountain glacier where the ice breaks away from the névé fields, there is a great crevasse or a series of open fissures known as the bergschrund. The névé and ice forming the upper margin of the bergschrund stand higher than the portion that has moved away. The displaced block has been subjected to both a downward and a horizontal movement, so that a huge crack is formed in the ice. Such movement is greatest during the summer months. During the winter the process is halted, and the bergschrund fills with snow and ice that enter the irregularities and joints of the rock wall. The following spring, when it opens again, large blocks of rocks are again torn away. In this way huge amphitheaters are formed at the upper ends of glacial valleys.

Crevasses. Where glacial ice passes over irregularities in the bottom of the valley, a change from a lesser to a greater gradient is encountered, and tension is produced in the upper surface, so that the rigid ice cracks. The resulting fissures are called *crevasses* (Fig. 12.16). Their direction on the surface of the glacier generally is roughly transverse to the long axis of the ice stream. When first formed, they extend downward nearly vertically; but since the upper surface of the glacier moves more rapidly than the lower portion, they assume an inclination which dips up the valley. They also curve downstream because of the more rapid movement of the ice in the center of the valley. Such fissures are widest in the central portion of the glacier and taper gradually to narrow cracks at their extremities. They vary in depth from a few to several hundred feet and in width from minute cracks, measuring only a fraction of an inch, to great chasms. It is safe to descend to the bottom

FIG. 12.16. *Diagrams illustrating the origin of crevasses: (a) crevasses produced by cracking due to a change in the gradient of the bed of the glacier; (b) marginal oblique crevasses produced by the more rapid movement of the central part of the glacier, which tends to pull the ice apart from the more slowly moving marginal parts.*

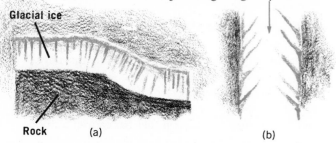

Glacial ice

Rock   (a)   (b)

of some crevasses, and in those near the upper end of the glacier, where englacial debris is not abundant, the wall ice is perfectly clear, with a greenish-blue transparency. The sides of the crevasses are frequently hung with icicles and embossed with wreaths of snow.

Most glaciers have marginal fissures as well as transverse crevasses. The marginal crevasses (Figs. 12.17, 12.18) do not extend in the direction of the long axis of the glacier but point up the valley about 45 degrees. They are due to the more rapid movement of the central portion of the glacier. Longitudinal crevasses occur also, especially where a glacier issues from a narrow portion of a valley into a wider one. There it has room to spread and, in so doing, tends to fall apart, forming longitudinal fissures. Similar structures are also common on terminal lobes.

NOURISHMENT OF GLACIERS

Valley glaciers are nourished by snowfalls, by wind-drifted snow, and by great avalanches of snow that plunge from the snow fields above them. The position of the terminus depends upon the relation of the amount of nourishment to the amount of wastage. When nourishment balances wastage, the terminus is stationary, and it is said to be in equilibrium. Any imbalance causes the advance or retreat of the terminus.

WASTAGE IRREGULARITIES

The surface of a glacier is exposed to the heat of the sun and to dry winds, both of which produce irregularities by melting and evaporation. This process is known as *ablation* (Figs. 12.19, 12.20), and the jagged ice surfaces so produced are called *seracs.*

Morainic material on the glacier protects the ice from the sun's rays, so that at places the moraines, or belts of debris, lie on ice walls that project upward 100 feet above the general surface of the ice. Such ridges are especially conspicuous on the Aar Glacier in Switzerland, and in Greenland some are nearly 400 feet high. In the same way, flat blocks of rock shelter the ice beneath and thus remain on pillars or pedestals as the surrounding

FIG. 12.17. *Crevasses on the surface of the Athabaska Glacier in the Canadian Rockies, Alberta. (Canadian Film Board.)*

surface is lowered. Such structures are spoken of as *ice tables* or *glacier tables* (Fig. 12.21). The tables are rarely horizontal but are generally inclined to the side that is most exposed to the rays of the sun. As melting continues, the blocks of stone perched on the columns of ice are dislodged, and the pinnacles that formerly supported them remain on the surface of the glacier as irregularities called *ice pyramids*.

Small heaps of dust and thin slabs of rock absorb the sun's heat and so become sufficiently warm to melt the underlying ice. They sink below its surface, forming depressions, or *dust wells*. For the same reason thin, bouldery moraines sometimes are found sunk below the surface of the glacier, and scattered pebbles are found at the bottom of water-filled pits. Leaves are blown on the surface of some

mountain glaciers, and during the summer months they are warmed by the sun and sink below the surface.

Ablation may reduce the thickness of a glacier several inches per day and thus produce marked effects in the course of a few weeks (Fig. 12.19) during the melting season.

On warm days the surface of a glacier has innumerable rills and pools of water, which unite to form small streams that rush and tumble as waterfalls into the crevasses and are lost in the depths of the ice. The water carries with it mud, sand, and boulders from the surface moraines. These erode the crevasses and produce vertical shafts that are referred to as *glacier mills* or *moulins*. Once formed, a moulin moves down the valley with the glacier, but since the irregularity in the floor of

FIG. 12.18. *Tumbling Glacier as it enters Berg Lake. This crevassed surface is the outer end of one of the glaciers that discharge surplus ice from Mount Robson, British Columbia. (Canadian National Railways.)*

the valley that produced the crevasse in which the moulin formed remains stationary, the process is repeated many times near the same place, and a long row of deep shafts is developed in the ice. Some of these streams erode subglacial channels that form large tunnels in the basal part of the ice.

GLACIATED VALLEYS

Most valley glaciers do not excavate valleys of their own. Instead, they usually move down valleys formed by the erosion of running water prior to the appearance of the ice. But a glacier immediately begins to modify the region it occupies. The results of erosion by valley glaciers are so charac-

teristic and differ so widely from those produced by other gradational agents that a glaciated valley is readily recognized even though the glacier itself has entirely disappeared. The erosion may be accomplished (1) by cleaning off the residual, loose debris; (2) by breaking or wearing off the surface of the bedrock over which the glacier passes; and (3) by *plucking*, whereby joint blocks are pulled out and carried along with the ice. Such erosion is accomplished not merely by the pressure of the ice but by the sharp sand, angular pebbles, boulders, and other rock debris that serve as the abrasives with which the glacier grinds and polishes. We can appreciate more fully the intensity of this action by considering the force exerted when a thick mass of ice passes over a rock surface. Since 1 cubic foot of ice weighs about 57 pounds, a glacier 1,000 feet thick would exert a pressure of approximately 28 tons per square foot.

The boulders and pebbles left in a glaciated valley are polished and striated in a manner which indicates that the ice was sufficiently rigid to hold the debris firmly. The embedded rocks act like the teeth on a gigantic file, or rasp. Many glaciated valleys look as if such a tool had been pressed down heavily and dragged along the valley. The irregularities on the floor and walls of the valley are gouged, scraped, and smoothed on the upstream side and show sharp, angular projections on the leeward side, where plucking, rather than abrasion, was more active. Much of the waste of such glacial abrasion is carried away in suspension as finely ground "rock flour," which gives a milky appearance to the streams that issue from the end of a glacier.

LANDSCAPE CHANGES

U-shaped valleys. Valleys that have been occupied by glaciers for an extended period of time develop ice-sculptured topographic features that replace those made by ordinary atmospheric weathering and stream erosion. A youthful river valley is usually V-shaped in cross section; but when such a valley is glaciated, its sides are eroded as well as the bottom, and a broad, flat-bottomed, U-shaped valley results (Figs. 12.22, 12.23).

FIG. 12.19. *Ablation, or surface melting, in 12 days, midsummer 1950, on Emmons Glacier, northeast side of Mount Rainier, Washington. The amount of ablation is shown by the difference in level between the point the man indicates on the rod and the ice surface on which he stands. The vertical rods had been set in holes drilled 6 feet into the ice and were further supported by sand piled around them. (George P. Rigsby.)*

Facets and canals. Since ice is rigid and far less mobile than water, it cannot swing around the sharp curves and bends developed by running water in a valley that was eroded by a mountain stream. As a result, it rubs and grinds against the projecting and overlapping spurs and eventually snubs or truncates them into facets. In this way the valley walls are made smooth and straight. In Alaska many such valleys are referred to as canals.

Cirques. Glaciated mountain valleys have steep, clifflike heads at their upper ends in the mountainsides, where amphitheaterlike depressions are developed by the quarrying action of the ice. These cirques are very striking features in the mountain topography of such regions as the Selkirks in Canada, the Rocky Mountains of the United States (Figs. 12.24, 12.25), and the Alps of Switzerland. Their precipitous walls are produced by the plucking and sapping action of the ice, which adheres to the rocks by filling the joints and fractures near the base of the cliffs. During the warmer season, as the ice moves down the valley, it tears away from the walls of the cirque but pulls part of the

walls with it, plucking out the loose blocks of rock and carrying them along. When winter comes, the process is halted, and the large crevasses, or bergschrund, between the moving ice and the rock wall fill with snow and ice; but the following spring they open again, and more rock is quarried from the cirque wall.

Arêtes. As cirques are progressively enlarged, deepened, and extended headward, those on one side of a mountain range eventually recede into the area of others growing in the same way on the opposite side of the divide. The space between them is narrowed, leaving sharp, serrated, comblike ridges (Fig. 12.22), or arêtes, and horns, such as the lofty Matterhorn of the Swiss Alps. Saddle-shaped passes across the divide between opposing cirques are known as cols. Most of the deep, clear lakes (tarns) that lend beauty to the mountains rest in rock basins that are part of glacial cirques.

Roches moutonnées. The floor of a glaciated valley is often characterized by dome-shaped bosses that are sloping and smooth on the side from which the glacier moved but rough and jagged on the leeward side, because of glacial plucking. Such rock structures are known as roches moutonnées (sheep-shaped rocks).

Hanging valleys. In a normal river system the

FIG. 12.20. *Vegetation growing on the debris-covered surface of Variegated Glacier, Yakutat Bay, Alaska. (E. S. Moore.)*

FIG. 12.21. *A glacier table, or rock-capped ice pillar, on the surface of Gornergrat Glacier, Switzerland. The column of ice is protected from melting by the shadow of the slab of rock. (E. S. Moore.)*

tributary streams enter the main valley at the level of the main stream. If such a system is glaciated, the main valley, because of its greater volume of ice, is deepened more rapidly than the valley of the smaller tributary, and when the ice disappears, the elevation of the tributary at the junction is higher than that of the main channel. In many mountain streams the difference amounts to hundreds of feet, and in some to more than 2,000 feet. Valleys that discharge high above the floor of the main stream are called hanging valleys (Figs. 12.23, 12.26), and their streams leap in a series of cascades into the major channel or discharge as waterfalls, such as the famous Yosemite Falls.

GLACIAL DEBRIS

Since mountain glaciers are surrounded by large areas of exposed rock that are constantly being subjected to denudation, they collect a great deal of rock waste that is carried by the ice toward the terminus of the glacier. This debris, called moraine, is supplied chiefly by the mechanically weathered material which falls from the walls of the valley and by rock abraded from the bed; it is classified as superglacial, englacial (Fig. 12.27), or subglacial debris, depending on whether it is located on, in, or under the ice. When the ice eventually is melted, both ice and water play a part in the deposition of the sediments. The heaps of debris dropped directly by the ice are called *glacial deposits*, and those made by glacial streams are called *glaciofluviatile deposits*. The term *glacial drift* is commonly applied to all the material transported and deposited by glacial ice. *Till* is unstratified glacial drift.

Ground moraine. Moraine can be classified as ground moraine, terminal moraine, lateral moraine, and medial moraine. The basal portion of a valley glacier may become so filled with debris that the ice cannot transport it all; in that case part of the debris remains upon the bottom and is overridden as the ice moves onward. A glacier is most likely to be overloaded for some distance beyond a place where an irregularity at the lower surface of the ice favors the gathering of debris or near the end, where the ice mass is thinner.

All the material deposited beneath the advancing ice, together with that deposited from the base as an irregular sheet during melting, constitutes the ground moraine. It consists of a heterogeneous, unassorted, and unstratified mass of fine clay or sand, striated pebbles, and boulders. Such material is sometimes called boulder clay, because it is made up of fine to coarse sandy clay interspersed with boulders of all sizes, weighing up to many tons.

FIG. 12.22. *Diagram showing the relations of landforms made by mountain glaciation.*

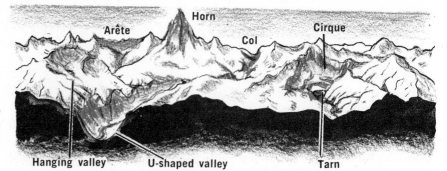

Horn

Arête

Col

Cirque

Hanging valley

U-shaped valley

Tarn

FIG. 12.23. *Citadel Mountain in Glacier National Park, Montana. This mountain is an arête, or knife-edge ridge, separating the U-shaped, hanging valley of Virginia Creek from the next valley to the right. In the foreground is St. Mary Lake.*

Terminal moraine. At the terminus of a glacier, where the amount of ice waste due to melting equals or nearly equals the advance due to glacial movement, debris is dropped in a crescent-shaped ridge known as a terminal moraine. The end of the glacier, and hence the position of the terminal moraine, advances or retreats whenever the factors determining its location are thrown out of balance.

In many regions where the glaciers at one time pushed out upon the piedmont areas and halted there for a number of years, the moraines are still present as well-defined topographic features. They are usually crescent- or horseshoe-shaped in outline, with their concave sides toward the head of the valley.

The height of such a moraine is dependent to a considerable extent on the length of time that the front of the glacier remained stationary, for it is obvious that a rapid retreat would not allow much material to be piled up at the same place. If a glacier receded 1,000 feet a year, even though its ice moved forward at the rate of 500 feet a year, very little debris would be piled up at any spot, and consequently no pronounced morainic ridge would be formed. The rock debris of the whole 1,500 feet melted would be distributed over the 1,000 feet of recession as part of the ground moraine.

Lateral moraine. The debris that accumulates on the borders of a valley glacier forms the lateral moraines of the moving ice stream. When the glacier melts, the lateral moraines are left as ridges or terracelike structures bordering the steep-sided mountain valleys. In most glaciated valleys they are more conspicuous than either the ground moraines or the terminal moraines.

Where the gradient of the mountain valley is not too great, the glacial streams leave most of the material of the terminal moraine where ice deposited it, and at such places the lateral and terminal moraines unite as a continuous ridge, or dam, across the valley, and the enclosed basin becomes occupied by a lake, swamp, or meadow.

Medial moraine. When two tributary glaciers meet, a medial moraine (Figs. 12.28, 12.29, 12.30), is formed by the union of the lateral moraines. As

FIG. 12.24. *Glaciated mountain valleys, now free of ice. This aerial photograph was taken looking southward from the northern border of the Canyon Ranges, Mackenzie Mountains, Northwest Territories. The glacial sculpturing increases toward the interior, where excellent cirques appear. (Royal Canadian Air Force.)*

FIG. 12.25. *Cirques enclosing small, crescentlike glaciers in the high Sierra Nevada near Mount Sill, California. (Spence Air Photos.)*

FIG. 12.26. *Mount Athabaska and glacier-filled hanging valleys. Athabaska Glacier in the foreground is a tongue of ice extending down from the Columbia Ice Field, Jasper National Park in the Canadian Rockies, Alberta. (British Photo Laboratories.)*

a rule, the medial moraine loses its identity toward the terminus of the glacier. Often, however, the moraines remain distinct and may be seen for miles, stretching up the glacier side by side.

GLACIAL RIVER DEBRIS

In the region where the melting of glacial ice is in progress, innumerable streams are formed on the surface, margins, and bottom of the glacier. During the summer months great torrents issue from ice caves or tunnels and carry boulders, pebbles, sand, and fine rock flour; but as the streams emerge from the restricted channels on or in the ice, they spread out over a greater area or divide into many distributaries. Consequently they become overloaded and drop a large part of their sediments. Since the streams issue from the ice in the region where the terminal moraine is being deposited, most of the glaciofluviatile sediments are carried beyond the terminal moraine.

The shape of the water-laid deposit where the glacier ends on a plain area is similar to that of an elongated alluvial fan. Where the end of the glacier is confined by the walls of the valley, the fluviatile deposits are confined to the width of the valley and build a *valley train*. Its sediments are sorted and stratified, grading horizontally from coarse gravel and boulders near the glacier through fine sand to silt and rock flour at a distance of a few miles below the terminus.

Piedmont Glaciers

Piedmont glaciers derive their name from their position at the foot of mountains. They are formed on the gently sloping lands at the base of the mountains, where descending valley glaciers escape the confines of valley walls and so flow laterally as well as forward, forming a broad, flat lobe, or ice apron. Where several of these lobes coalesce, a piedmont glacier is formed. This type is found only in subpolar regions having mountains of strong relief and valleys extending to plains of low altitude, where several adjacent mountain glaciers spread out or deploy and become confluent. The sloping ice surface formed in this way is like a piedmont alluvial plain. Because of the marked change in gradient of the valleys as they reach the piedmont area, the movement of the ice is greatly retarded, and in many piedmont glaciers it becomes almost imperceptible.

The Malaspina Glacier on the western side of Yakutat Bay in Alaska is the original and classic example of this type of glacier (Fig. 12.31). It consists of three principal lobes, and each lobe represents the expanded bulblike lower portion of one or more large valley glaciers that move down the slopes of Mount St. Elias. These lobes are fed by the Seward, Agassiz, Tyndall, and Guyot Glaciers. The piedmont glacier formed by their coalescence is a vast, nearly horizontal plateau of ice that is 70 miles wide along the Alaskan coast. Another example is the Frederikshaab Glacier on the west coast of Greenland.

Where the individual valley glaciers emerge from their mountain valleys, differential movement is initiated in the ice plateau, and its surface becomes broken by thousands of crevasses. Toward the margins, where ice movement decreases and melting and refreezing increase, these crevasses are gradually healed, and the surface shows only minor

FIG. 12.27. *The terminus of Windermere Glacier, British Columbia, where it discharges into a lake. Note the crumpled structure as outlined by the glacial debris. (Canada Department of the Interior.)*

FIG. 12.28. *Unteraar, an Alpine glacier in Switzerland, showing well-developed lateral and medial moraines.*

FIG. 12.29. *An Alaskan glacier with numerous tributaries forming a series of cirques, or blunt, steepheaded valleys. (United States Air Force.)*

irregularities. The outer margin, for a width of 5 miles or more, is covered with moraine. At certain places this marginal ice has become so stagnant that forests grow upon the moraine, even though ice hundreds of feet thick is still present below the morainic soil.

Continental Glaciers

The great sheets of ice that cover large land areas are known as continental glaciers. They combine snow field, ice field, and glacier all in one. Continental glaciers are very thick. They spread outward in all directions, over highland and lowland alike, with little regard to the topography of the surface over which they move. They differ from valley glaciers in that they are not confined within valley walls. They differ from small icecaps, such as those on Iceland (Fig. 12.11), only in size. Continental glaciers are in fact large caps.

The surface of continental glaciers is relatively featureless and gently sloping, except where an occasional bare hill, or peak, known as *nunatak*, protrudes above the ice surface. The continental ice sheets are not fed by small tributaries with marginal belts of ice and rock and they have no

medial moraines to correspond to the medial moraines of valley glaciers. Above the zone of melting the ice is clear and white.

Two large areas are now covered by continental glaciers. These are Greenland and Antarctica.

GREENLAND

Greenland is an island with an area of somewhat more than 800,000 square miles. Its central, domelike plateau reaches an elevation of approximately 10,000 feet. The coastal areas are very irregular (Fig. 12.8) and fringed with rugged mountains.

About 80 per cent of the island is covered by a vast continental glacier; only the mountainous margin is comparatively bare. Even in this rugged border most of the valleys are filled by tongues of ice that extend down to the sea from the great ice mass in the interior.

The adjacent large islands of Canada, such as Ellsmere, have icecaps that are related to the Greenland glacier, although they are no longer continuous with it.

ANTARCTICA

The Antarctic Continent comprises about 6 million square miles, an area larger than that of the United States and Mexico, and nearly all of it is

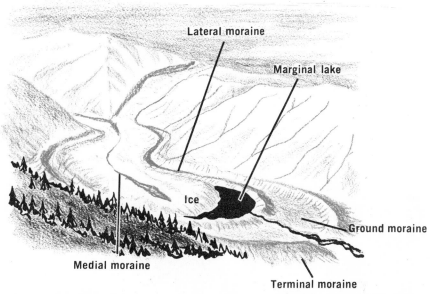

FIG. 12.30. *Generalized diagram of a mountain glacier showing the position of the various moraines. (Modified after Matthes.)*

covered by the Antarctic ice sheet. This glacier is more than seven times larger than that of Greenland, and its surface is less regular, for it is interrupted in many places by ranges and groups of mountains and seems to be broadly related to the topography of the bedrock on which the ice rests. The glacier varies in depth, but thicknesses of as much as 14,000 feet have been reported.

At many places the glacier joins the *ice shelf,* or frozen sea water, that extends out into the ocean from the coast line. Through the passes in the mountains that border parts of the Antarctic Continent, great tongues of ice, such as the Beardmore Glacier, descend to the coast and push out into the sea beyond. In many coastal areas the ice pushes out into the deep water and eventually is buoyed afloat.

The Ross Ice Shelf, on which Little America is situated, half fills the Ross Sea (Figs. 12.32, 12.33). Its seaward face is a cliff of ice that stands nearly 200 feet high. Here great blocks of ice break off and float away as gigantic icebergs, some of which are as much as 100 miles in diameter.

ICE-SHEET EROSION

The efficiency of a continental ice sheet as an instrument of erosion is particularly well shown by the effects of the vast icecap that covered north-

eastern North America during the late Pleistocene ice age. A study of the features developed at that time shows that corrasion is by far the most important erosion process. Corrasion, it will be remembered, is accomplished primarily by the scouring and grinding action of rock fragments, either frozen into the bottom of the glacier or pushed along beneath it. The glacier thus becomes a gigantic cutting and polishing tool. It acts much like an enormous rasp, gouging into and scraping off irregularities on its bed and smoothing and grooving the bedrock beneath it. Glacial plucking occurs only in areas of steeply dipping or highly jointed rock formations or on overridden hills.

A feature peculiar to extensive lowlands that have been glaciated by ice sheets is the almost total absence of residual soils or mantle-rock waste. Such loose soils and rotten rock are scoured off and dragged along by the passage of the ice, and bare, rounded, and striated surfaces of fresh rock remain (Figs. 12.34, 12.35). Similar features are formed by mountain glaciation. In some regions, such as the plains of the upper Mississippi Basin, glaciers moved over large areas of residual soils without greatly disturbing them, but these soils are now covered with a thick bed of glacial drift or till.

The effect of a continental ice sheet on the regional topography and relief is less obvious than

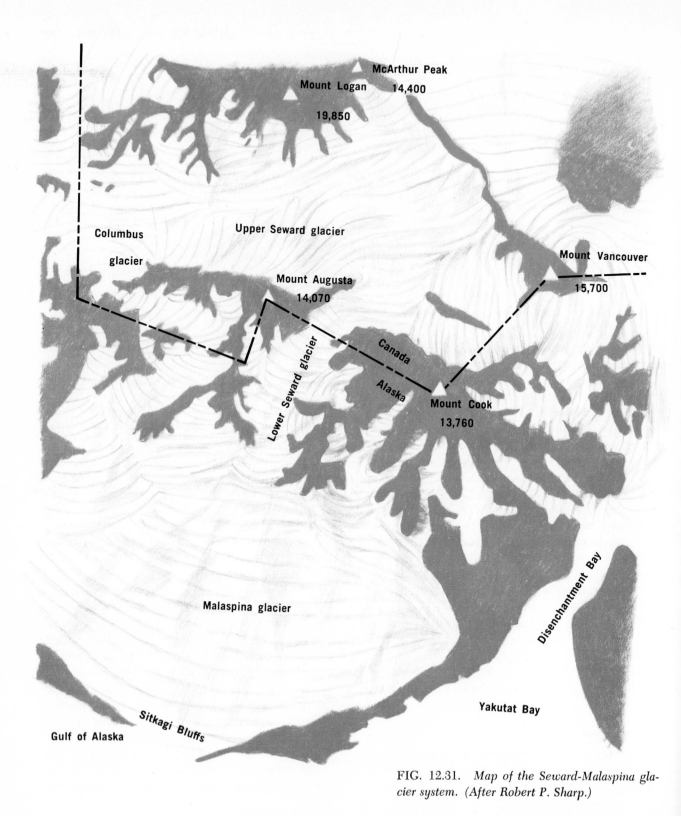

FIG. 12.31. *Map of the Seward-Malaspina glacier system. (After Robert P. Sharp.)*

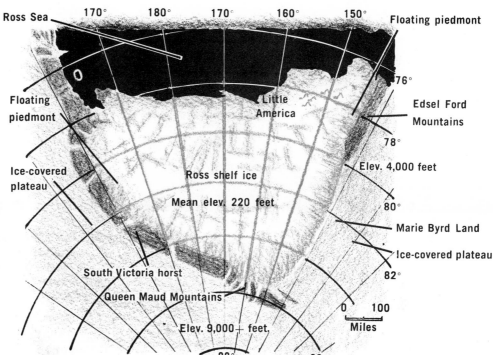

FIG. 12.32. *Map of the Ross shelf ice, Antarctica. A floating mass of ice about 1,000 feet thick covers more than ¼ million square miles. (Redrawn from a map by L. M. Gould.)*

that of a mountain or valley glacier, for an ice sheet erodes the region between the valleys nearly as intensely as it does the stream channels. Where the direction of movement of the glacier parallels that of the major streams of the region, however, some of the valleys are gouged and deepened, and the regional relief is markedly increased. Conversely, where the ice moves across the valleys and partially or completely fills them with glacial drift, the relief is decreased.

DEBRIS IN ICE SHEETS

The ice at the margins of the Greenland ice sheet and other large icecaps is heavily charged with rock debris. Part of this debris represents the mantle-rock that was pushed along or scraped off by the ice; some was obtained by scouring and some by plucking from the bedrock under the ice. This material is carried upward and becomes incorporated throughout the ice by differential movement within the mass. Some debris is redistributed near the margins by the shearing of slices of ice over each other.

DRIFT

The most characteristic feature of the drift deposited by a continental glacier is its heterogeneity. In a small area both stratified drift and unstratified till may be found, with variations in size from fine clay and sand through coarse gravel (Fig. 12.36) to huge boulders. The size and shape of the particles depend considerably on the resistance of the rock to abrasion (Fig. 12.37). Rocks such as schists, clayey limestones, and shales are readily broken by the ice and easily converted into glacial clay, silt, or small pebbles. However, massive igneous rock, hard limestone, and quartzites are more resistant, and these constitute most of the larger boulders. Glacial drift generally contains rocks of many different kinds, depending on those present in the areas over which the ice moved.

The thickness of the drift varies greatly, according to (1) the irregularities of the surface upon which it was deposited, (2) the amount of debris carried by the ice, (3) the rate of advance or retreat of the glacier, and (4) the amount of

FIG. 12.33. *Folds in the Ross shelf ice over the Bay of Whales near Little America, Antarctica. (L. M. Gould, Byrd Antarctic Expedition.)*

erosion subsequent to its deposition. As a general rule, high, rugged regions have very thin coats of drift, and extensive low, smooth areas, like those of central Iowa and south central Minnesota, have 100 to 600 feet of drift and very few rock outcrops.

UNSTRATIFIED DRIFT (TILL)

Erratics. Erratics are large glacial boulders that are foreign to the underlying rock (Figs. 12.38, 12.39). Some immense masses of rock have traveled

FIG. 12.34. *Glacial grooves in bedrock, Kelleys Island, Ohio. The former glacier scoured off all the loose rock material, leaving a clear surface.*

hundreds of miles from their sources. One of the largest erratics known in the United States is a mass of granite at Madison, New Hampshire, which measures 90 by 40 by 30 feet. Other notable examples are found on Mount Tom, near Northampton, Massachusetts, where large, angular granite boulders are perched on the top of a high ridge of basic igneous rock. Such boulders are located in positions where no agent of transportation other than ice could have placed them.

Terminal moraines. The terminal moraines of a continental glacier are more conspicuous and more complex than those developed by a valley glacier. This is due in part to the absence of streams of high gradient, such as those which issue from mountain glaciers and transport much of the debris to the valley trains. Where the terminus of a continental glacier is in a partially peneplained area, most of the morainic material remains where it was dropped at the margin of the melting ice. If the ice front is nearly stationary or if it fluctuates for an extended period in a zone not more than a few miles wide, series of morainal ridges are developed coinciding with the outline of the marginal lobes of the glacier. These constitute the terminal moraines. Such moraines are characterized by many small, rounded hills of drift and adjacent depressions distributed in a disorderly fashion in a relatively long, narrow zone that paralleled the ice front at the time of deposition (Fig. 12.40). In many regions one side of the system of hills has a steeper slope than the opposite side, and the steep slopes lie in the direction from which the ice came. Many of the larger ridges have superimposed upon them smaller hills and conical mounds, which make the depressions seem still deeper. Because of its irregularity, such topography is commonly referred to as "knob-and-kettle," or "hummocky," topography.

Where a receding glacier halts in its retreat and its edge remains in a nearly constant position for a considerable period of time, a moraine may develop. Such a deposit is called a *recessional* moraine (Fig. 12.41).

Ground moraines. The ground moraine is the most important and the most widespread depositional feature of a continental ice sheet. It is the drift that was deposited below the ice during the advance or recession. Instead of being concentrated in high knobs and ridges, as is the terminal moraine, it is scattered over the surface where the ice melted. Youthful ground-moraine topography commonly is characterized by numerous large depressions occupied by bogs, swamps, and lakes with no apparent relation between major streams and higher land. Such areas are usually poorly drained because of the damming of the preglacial streams and the unequal distribution of glacial till (Fig. 12.42). Their surfaces undulate haphazardly in "swell-and-swale" forms.

Drumlins. Certain areas of the ground moraine have small, smooth, oval hills of till that are lenticular in horizontal section, with their longer axes parallel to the movement of the ice which formerly covered them. Such hills are called drumlins (Figs. 12.43, 12.44). They are commonly 25 to 150 feet high, and many of them are 1,000 to 3,000 feet long and about 500 feet wide. In some regions they show many variations in size and shape, from mammillary, or dome-shaped, hills to slender, or linear, ridges. They are conspicuously developed in Nova Scotia, the Boston area of Massachusetts, western New York, the northern part of the Lower Peninsula of Michigan, eastern Wisconsin, north central Minnesota, parts of Saskatchewan, Alberta, British Columbia, and the Northwest Territories of Canada. They also occur in various parts of Europe. Most drumlins are composed of unsorted till that exhibits very little lamination due to water action. The gentle slope of many drumlins lies in the direction toward which the ice moved. This is the opposite of the formation that results where the ice erodes.

The mechanics of drumlin formation have not been fully explained; but the wide distribution of these streamlined hills indicates that conditions suitable to their formation were commonly met during the depositional stage of the glacier. Their composition of mixed glacial debris, often of the clayey rather than the gravelly type, their location on the glacier side behind a terminal or recessional moraine, their parallel orientation and streamlined

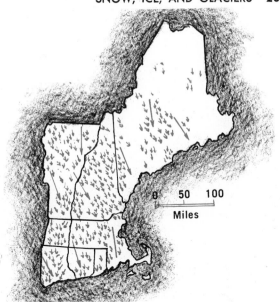

FIG. 12.35. *Outline map of New England, showing the direction of movement of glacial ice as indicated by striae on the bedrock surface. (After Goldthwait.)*

FIG. 12.36. *Interbedded sorted and unsorted glacial drift.*

shape, and their usual grouping adjacent to an abundant supply of the suitable materials have suggested that drumlins may have been formed either by overloading of the basal portion of the glacier from locally abundant loose material near

FIG. 12.38.   *A glacial erratic. This huge granite boulder is about 15 feet high and weighs more than 100 tons. It is wholly unlike the underlying rock and is far from its source. No natural agent other than a glacier could have transported it to its present location.*

its outer edge or by the overriding of an end moraine by a slight advance of the ice. In any case the shape probably was created by the forward movement of the ice sheet. This is indicated near Carp Lake, in northern British Columbia, where the stoss ends of the drumloids, or "rock drumlins," that is, the ends facing the direction from which the glacier came, are rock outcrops followed by a crag-and-tail effect.

STRATIFIED DRIFT

Outwash plains. The water from the melting ice at the edge of an ice sheet flows through the terminal-moraine debris as a great number of streams rather than as a continuous sheet of water. Each of these streams builds a low alluvial fan, and the fans coalesce into a plain that slopes gently away from the terminal-moraine area. Since this plain is composed of material washed out beyond the terminal moraine, it is called an outwash plain. The heaviest load is deposited near the terminal moraine, in the form of gravel and coarse sand. Farther away, the slopes are more gentle, and the deposits are fine sands and silt. Many of the outwash plains of the northeastern part of the

United States are so nearly flat that often they are referred to as prairies.

Small, kettlelike depressions with no outlets are formed in outwash plains by the melting of great masses of ice left during the recession of the ice front. Where such depressions are numerous, the outwash areas are called *pitted plains.*

Eskers. Eskers are winding ridges (serpent ridges) (Fig. 12.45) of irregularly stratified sand and gravel that are found within the area of the ground moraine. Many of them are several miles long, and they are rarely more than 15 or 20 yards wide. Their courses are roughly parallel to the direction of the movement of the glacier. Some are so nearly symmetrical in outline that they resemble railroad grades. The ridges are evidently the beds of streams which flowed in tunnels or ice-walled gorges in or beneath the ice and aggraded their beds before the streams issued from the ice

FIG. 12.40.   *Terminal moraine topography south of Saint Paul, Minnesota. The low area in the middle is a typical ice-block kettle. It is entirely surrounded by high morainic knobs and hummocky ridges like that in the background. (Kenneth M. Wright.)*

FIG. 12.39.   *Maps showing glacial boulder trains in New England. The black, iron-bearing rock of Iron Hill was distributed over a progressively wider area southward toward Newport. The rocks from Red Hill and Mount Ascutney were spread in a similar manner.*

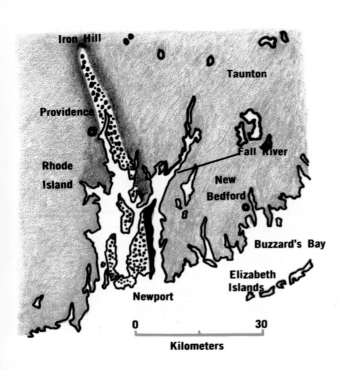

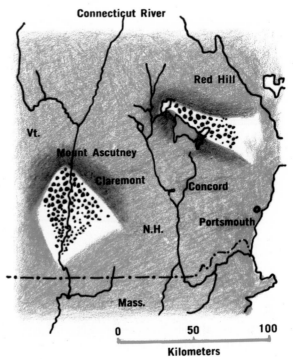

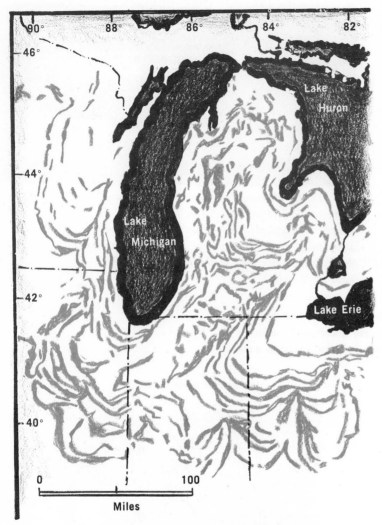

FIG. 12.41. *Map of terminal and recessional moraines of the north central United States. The festooned pattern outlines the former ice lobes. (After Glacial Map of North America, Geological Society of America.)*

front. Some undoubtedly are crevasse fillings. They are seldom continuous for long distances, and some of them serve as ridges, or divides, between shallow lakes and bogs in the ground moraine.

Kames. Kames are conical hills of gravel deposited by heavily laden glacial streams flowing in

and on the ice near the terminus (Fig. 12.46). Some of them may be short ridges formed in the reentrant angles of the ice front, where subglacial water under pressure escapes and deposits its overload. Kames are likely to be associated with the terminal-moraine belt and with the numerous kettle lakes common to that environment. The eskers and kames that are preserved as part of the characteristic drift topography were formed during the recessional or stagnant stage of the last ice sheet, for any later active advance of the ice sheet would have destroyed all such surface features.

TEMPORARY GLACIAL LAKES

Since a continental glacier covers all the land, it follows that divides between drainage basins also are buried under the ice. If a land surface in front of the glacier slopes toward the ice edge, water derived from the melting of the glacier will accumulate against the high land, or divide, and the margin of the ice will serve as a dam and prevent the water from following its former course. In this way large areas of land may be flooded and turned into marginal glacial lakes. Such lakes will rise until they are at a high enough level to escape across the lowest point in the divide. Numerous lakes were so formed along the margins of the continental ice sheets that covered parts of Europe and North America during the recent ice age. The outlets of many of these lakes cut broad and deep channels through the divides of drainage systems and, at a number of places, excavated valleys across continental divides where no streams exist at the present time. Most of these lakes were small and were soon filled with sediments derived from the glacier. Some, however, covered hundreds of square miles and existed for sufficiently long periods to form important depositional features.

The former presence of temporary glacial lakes is shown by shore-line features such as beaches, beach ridges, bars, deltas, and the finer sediments deposited over the lake bottom. At many places a series of shore lines are found at different elevations, because of the fluctuating levels of the water.

Lake Agassiz. The receding ice sheet southwest of Hudson Bay formed the largest temporary gla-

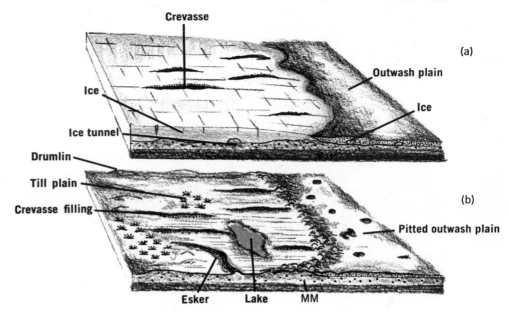

FIG. 12.42. *Diagrams to illustrate the field relations of various types of glacial deposit and their relation to the part of the glacier by which they were formed: (a) the margin of a retreating continental ice sheet, (b) the same area after the ice has melted. Note the pitted outwash plain, the hummocky topography of the terminal moraine (MM), the swamps and lakes of the poorly drained till plain, the drumlins, crevasse fillings, and the esker that was deposited in an ice tunnel. (After Trewartha.)*

cial lake on the North American continent (Fig. 12.47). Its development was due to the northward slope of the valley of the Red River of the North. After the glacier receded over the divide between the Minnesota River and the Red River, the water accumulated along the south and west margins of the ice, and as the ice continued to retreat, the lake increased in size and depth until eventually the water stood at a sufficiently high level to flow over the crest of the continental divide and into the Minnesota River at Browns Valley, Minnesota. At its maximum extent, Lake Agassiz was about 700 miles long and 250 miles wide. It covered over 100,000 square miles, more than the combined area of all the present Great Lakes. Lake Winnipeg in Canada and Lake of the Woods on the international boundary occupy depressions in the bed of this ancient lake.

While the glacier continued to block the northward drainage, so that Lake Agassiz received the melt water, the overflow into the Minnesota River produced a broad, turbulent stream, sometimes referred to as Glacial River Warren, that cut its channel 50 to 90 feet below the present level of the Minnesota River and discharged into the Mississippi at Fort Snelling. Later, when a northward

escape for this melt water was uncovered, Lake Agassiz disappeared, River Warren dwindled, and its valley became clogged with the sediments over which the present river finds its way.

Ancestral Great Lakes. The Great Lakes owe much of their size and importance to the erosional and depositional effects of glaciation on the middle

FIG. 12.43. *Drumlin (small, oval hill of unstratified till) near Gleasondale, Mass. The long axis of a drumlin parallels the ice movement, and in many instances its gentler slope lies in the direction toward which the ice moved. (W. C. Alden, U.S. Geological Survey.)*

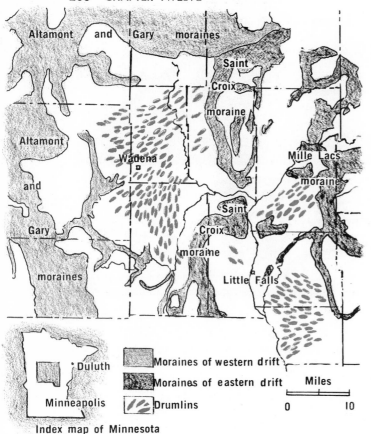

FIG. 12.44. *Map of drumlin fields in central Minnesota. (After Allan Schneider.)*

FIG. 12.45. *An esker, or "serpent ridge," near Fort Ripley, Minnesota, as seen from the air. Eskers are believed to represent former streams which flowed beneath the glacial ice or in crevasses. (W. S. Cooper.)*

and upper portions of the St. Lawrence system. Glaciation scooped out their present basins, and the rock materials thus obtained were added to the glacial load and then deposited as part of the drift farther to the south and west.

During the recessional stages of the continental glacier, while the St. Lawrence outlet to the Atlantic was still blocked by ice, marginal lakes, formed in the uncovered southwestern extremities of these basins, spilled over the divides and discharged the melt water through streams draining southward (Fig. 12.48). These outlets, especially to the St. Croix from Duluth and to the Illinois from Chicago, are conspicuous features of the present-day topography.

Adjacent to the lakes, particularly Lake Superior in Minnesota and Lake Erie in Ohio, the old shore lines, beaches, and lake-shore cliffs of these marginal lakes can still be seen plainly. The early pioneers of Ohio used the old lake beaches as roads, and parts of them still serve that purpose. These beaches indicate the various levels assumed by the lakes as melting of the ice sheet uncovered successively lower outlets, which gradually dropped the water level until the channel and mouth of the St. Lawrence itself were finally freed from ice and the drainage was established in its present course. The intricate history of these changes has been worked out in detail and forms a remarkable chapter in the glacial history of the region.

GLACIAL-LAKE SEDIMENTS

The cold waters of the marginal glacial lakes had a higher density than water at moderate temperatures. For this reason the settling of silts and clays was retarded, and the fine sediments in suspension became diffused throughout the lake waters and were deposited over the floor of the entire basin. The fine-grained sediments were laid down in plainly separated annual layers called *varves* (Swedish, the deposits of a season, whether of winter or summer or of a wet or dry season) (Fig. 16.14). Glacial-lake varves commonly consist of two laminae, one of which was laid down during the summer and the other during the

FIG. 12.46. *Kames in Ninemile Valley, New York. Kames are gravel hills deposited at the edge of a glacier by former glacial streams emerging with a heavy load. (Gilbert, U.S. Geological Survey.)*

winter. The summer band consists of a light-colored, coarse silt, whereas the winter band is darker in color, finer-grained, and thinner. The winter band is sharply separated from the summer band above but grades into the summer band below. Thus each varve represents a year.

Since the varves vary in thickness and in other characteristics, it is possible to match, or correlate, the top sets in one lake with the bottom sets in the next lake, in the direction of recession of the ice, and thus to count the years consecutively. In this way the rate of recession of the last ice sheet has been calculated. It has been shown, for example, that 4,300 years elapsed while the ice was retreating 185 miles up the Connecticut River Valley from Hartford, Connecticut, to St. Johnsbury, Vermont. Varved clays are well exposed along Mink Brook at Hanover, New Hampshire.

STAGNANT-ICE DEBRIS

During the retreat of the last continental ice sheet, large areas of ice stopped moving forward and became great masses of stagnant ice. This may have been due to climate changes or to the nature of the topography over which they spread. As the stagnant ice melted, no recessional or mar-

ginal moraines were formed, since such moraines can develop only where there is forward movement of the ice accompanied by melting at the ice front.

Where wastage took place without movement, stratified drift is more abundant than glacial till. The preponderance of stratified drift is due to the fact that melting occurred over a large area instead of being confined, for the most part, to the marginal zone of the glacier. Under such conditions, the channel of the melt-water streams on and under the ice were not disturbed by the movement of the ice. Consequently the water flowing through crevasses and tunnels in the stagnant ice built up long, narrow strings, or trains, of sand and gravel, which were left as ridges of stratified drift after the ice wasted away. Many eskers were built in this way.

Where the ice had an intersecting network of cracks and crevasses that became partially filled with sediments, the crevasse fillings formed ridges, or hummocks, that enclosed depressions, or "kettles," when the blocks of ice between the crevasses melted away. Many of the kettles now contain ponds, lakes, or swamps. Where lakes fed by melt water existed at the margin or on the surface of the stagnant ice, streams deposited deltas and lake

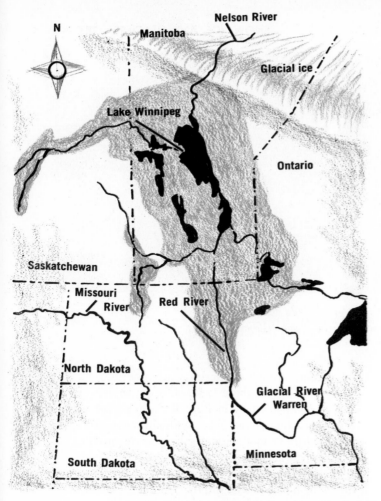

FIG. 12.47. *Map showing the extent of glacial Lake Agassiz during its highest water stage. (After Upham, U.S. Geological Survey.)*

sediments on the floors of the lakes. When the ice was melted and the water level lowered, such lake sediments remained as flat-topped terraces along the channels through which the waters drained. Such deposits along valley walls are *kame terraces*.

STREAM DIVERSION

The unequal deposition of glacial drift had a profound effect upon the topography of the areas affected. Numerous valleys were completely filled with glacial till, and as the ice receded, many old channels were so obstructed that new surface-drainage courses were established. Even such major streams as the St. Lawrence, the Mississippi,

the Ohio, and the Missouri Rivers were locally turned from their preexisting channels by the work of the glaciers. In regions of rugged and mountainous topography the channels were not so greatly diverted, but in a number of regions drift accumulations in a valley buried projecting spurs of bedrock, and postglacial streams eroding new channels through such deposits have become superimposed on the old buried ledges that formerly were parts of valley walls.

PREHISTORIC GLACIATION

Our present-day glaciers are regarded as either the dwindling stage or a renewal of the last ice age, the Pleistocene. Ice still covers one-third or more of the area over which continental glaciers spread during their last major advance some 9,000 or 10,000 years ago (as determined by radiocarbon dating).

Present-day glacial conditions are indicated by the fact that in northern Ontario, just south and west of Hudson and James Bays, snowbanks linger long into the spring, many of the small lakes are slow to thaw out completely, and perpetual frost

TABLE 12.1 *Summary of Features Produced by Glaciation* (X = common, r = rare, — = absent)

Feature	Valley glacier	Continental glacier
Cirques	X	—
Striations	X	X
Polished surfaces	X	X
Matterhorns	X	—
Hanging valleys	X	r
U-shaped valleys	X	r
Fiords	X	—
Lateral moraine	X	—
Medial moraine	X	—
Ground moraine	X	X
Terminal moraine	X	X
Recessional moraine	X	X
Unstratified drift (till)	X	X
Stratified drift	X	X
Kames	X	X
Kame terraces	X	r
Eskers	r	X
Drumlins	r	X

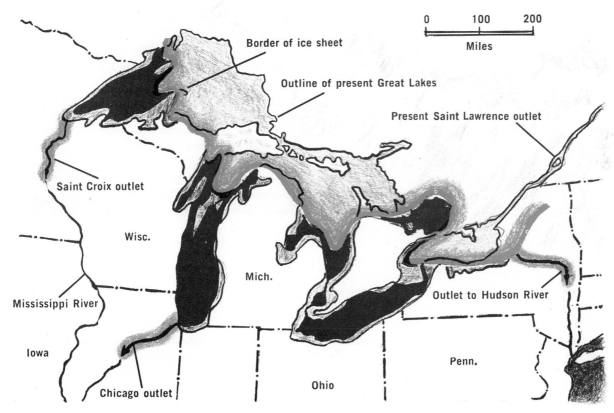

FIG. 12.48. *Map showing overflow drainage outlets of the Great Lakes prior to the melting of the ice that blocked the St. Lawrence outlet. (After Taylor.)*

occurs within the soil only a few feet below the surface. Even in some of the valleys of the New England mountains the last snowbank is melted scarcely more than a month before the first fall of winter snow, and occasionally, in some favored ravines, snow lingers through the year. The water well drilled on top of Mount Washington, in the White Mountains, penetrated cold rock and froze at 260 feet. It would appear that the White Mountain region of New Hampshire is just emerging from the chilling effects of the glacial invasion that so recently covered a large portion of North America. A drop of only a few degrees in the average annual temperature or an increase in the amount of winter snowfall might restore continental glaciation over a vast area.

The Pleistocene ice sheet on North America originated in the north and northeastern part of the continent and spread out in all directions. It extended northwest into the Arctic Sea and southward to the valleys of the Missouri and Ohio Rivers. A smaller ice field formed in the mountains of the Northwestern states and the adjoining mountains of western Canada. It consisted of scores of valley and piedmont glaciers that coalesced at many places into a nearly continuous ice sheet. The great Columbian snow and ice field that now exists in British Columbia (Fig. 12.26) is either a remnant or a successor of that great ice mass.

Geological field evidence indicates that there were ice ages many millions of years before the Pleistocene epoch. The record is fragmentary, for erosion tends to destroy the effects of glaciation, but good evidence has been preserved in consolidated till and other glacial sediments. *Tillites,* rocks formed from cemented or lithified glacial till, have been found associated with late Paleozoic rock formations in New England and in Australia. These formations are more than 200 million years old.

Near Kimberley, South Africa, a bed of hard tillite occurs over glaciated bedrock surfaces that are striated and polished. In Australia thick tillite beds occur at several geological horizons. Similar and even more ancient deposits have been reported from central Canada and from northern Norway. In eastern Massachusetts a Permian conglomerate is regarded as a tillite. The formation is exposed at many places in the Boston Basin, where it contains striated and faceted pebbles and other indications of its glacial origin.

There is evidence that there were several advances of the ice and prolonged intervening warm periods during some of these ancient ice ages, as in the recent glaciation. These fluctuations in climatic conditions, from warm to cold and back again, appear to be characteristic of an ice age. So widespread glaciation on a continental scale is not a phenomenon of recent development but one that has affected the earth's surface at intervals over a very long span of time and may be expected to occur again.

CAUSES OF GLACIATION

The causes of glaciation are for the most part climatic, and many hypotheses have been offered to account for the climate that resulted in such widespread continental glaciation, but none is generally accepted. Undoubtedly two entirely unrelated factors are involved, namely, topography and solar heat.

We long have recognized that the high, broad, uplifted land areas of the geologic past produced more climatic contrasts than did the expansive low-lying areas with widespread epicontinental seas. However, we have no conclusive evidence that the altitude of northern and northeastern North America fluctuated sufficiently prior to and during the Pleistocene glaciation to have caused high-altitude glaciation that could have spread out from that region.

One possible contributing cause for climatic variations is a fluctuation in the total solar energy (heat) received from the sun. We now know that the sun's radiation does fluctuate as much as 3 per cent, and it may have varied more during the geologic past. One computation suggests that variations of 6 per cent or more would lead to glaciation at relatively low altitudes in middle latitudes. If, however, the fluctuations of solar heat are cyclic, there should have been numerous glacial ages throughout the geologic past, characterized by rhythmic advances of ice similar to those of the Pleistocene epoch. Yet there is no geologic evidence to support so many regularly recurring ice ages.

Another hypothesis is based upon possible variations in the amount of carbon dioxide and water vapor in the atmosphere. Experimental evidence indicates that both carbon dioxide and water vapor prevent the radiation of much of the heat derived from the sun. Presumably, then, when these substances are less abundant, the amount of radiation from the earth increases, and a colder climate ensues. The enlarging of the land areas may have decreased the amount of water vapor in the atmosphere and thereby decreased its ability to retain the heat derived from the sun.

The most recent explanation, the solar-topographic theory proposed by Dr. Richard Flint of Yale University, postulates a combination of minimum solar heat and high topography. If a period of lower than average solar heat is joined with the low temperatures of high and extensive continents, then perennial snow may accumulate to form glacial ice sheets. This theory assumes that the fluctuations of solar radiation, now minor, were much greater in the past.

It is interesting to note that we still are unable to determine whether we are in the last stages of one glacial epoch or in an early stage of a new one.

Certainly, there is relatively little present-day glaciation, but it remains to be seen whether the ice will dwindle to the point of making Antarctica and Greenland habitable or whether it will increase. In any event, the process of change is very slow, and its direction will not become apparent for a long time.

Summary

Ice on lakes pushes up debris ramparts along their margins. Shore ice and ice floes at sea serve as debris rafts. River ice plucks and rafts debris, forms ice jams, and causes floods. Ice in the ground causes rock disintegration by frost wedging and frost heaving and assists in mass wasting. Solifluction, rock glaciers, stone polygons, garland loops, and stone stripes result.

Perennial accumulations of snow form snow fields, recrystallize to granular névé, and spread downhill by their own weight as valley, piedmont, or continental glaciers. Valley or alpine glaciers are very numerous. Associated features include berg-schrund, cirque wall, crevasses, surface moraines, seracs, ice tables, ice pyramids, dust wells, and moulins.

Alpine glaciers rasp and pluck the valleys they traverse, thus developing U-shaped valleys, faceted spurs, cirques, arêtes, horns, glacial cols, tarns, roches moutonnées, and hanging valleys. They deposit ground moraines, terminal moraines, and lateral moraines. Their melt waters deposit stratified valley trains.

Piedmont glaciers, such as the Malaspina, are coalescent extensions of valley glaciers. They make extensive deposits along mountain fronts.

Continental glaciers, like the ice sheets on Greenland and Antarctica, also erode by plucking, rasping, and gouging. They deposit heterogeneous, unsorted, unstratified till as terminal moraines, recessional moraines, and ground moraines (locally including drumlins). These moraines contain numerous erratics. Outflowing waters deposit stratified outwash plains, eskers, and kames, all made of sand and gravel.

Temporary ice-margin lakes, such as the glacial Lake Agassiz and the forerunners of the Great Lakes, received varved deposits on their floors and left a telltale assemblage of wave-cut cliffs, beach ridges, deltas, and overflow channels in their wake.

Stagnant ice masses in places gave rise to eskers, crevasse fillings, kettles, and kame terraces.

During Pleistocene time continental glaciers occupied much of Canada and the northeastern and north central parts of the United States. Similar glaciers appeared in North America and other continents at several geologically ancient times. The causes are not certain, but a complex combination of fluctuations of solar radiation, variations in the earth's atmosphere, and changes in the elevation of the lands may be involved.

In this chapter we have seen some of the far-reaching effects of glaciation, such as widespread, rolling morainal topography, an abundance of lakes, barren ice-scoured hills, stony soils, and picturesque mountain scenery. Let us turn our attention next to the effects of waves and currents along our shores.

Suggestions for Further Reading

Black, R. F.: "Permafrost," *Smithsonian Inst. Ann. Rept. for 1950*, pp. 273–301, 1951.

Coleman, A. P.: *Ice Ages, Recent and Ancient*, The Macmillan Company, New York, 1926. A thorough study on glaciation.

Coleman, A. P.: *The Last Million Years: A History of the Pleistocene in North America*, University of Toronto Press, Toronto, 1941. A nontechnical account of glaciation.

Cotton, C. A.: *Climatic Accidents in Landscape-making*, John Wiley & Sons, Inc., New York, 1948. A discussion of the effect of glaciation on geomorphology.

Crohn, P. W.: "A Contribution to the Geology and

Glaciology of the Western Part of Australian Antarctic Territory," *Australia Dept. of National Development, Bureau of Natural Resources, Geol. and Geophys., Bull.* 52, 103 pp., 1959. A well-illustrated report on recent work in Antarctica.

Flint, R. F.: *Glacial and Pleistocene Geology,* John Wiley & Sons, Inc., New York, 1957. An excellent study of continental glaciation.

Gresswell, R. K.: *The Physical Geography of Glaciers and Glaciation,* Hulton Educational Publications, London, 1958. Part of an illustrated nontechnical series on geography.

Lewis, G. N.: "Thermodynamics of an Ice Age," *Science,* 1946. This article discusses the causes of continental glaciation.

Muller, S. W.: "Permafrost or Permanently Frozen Ground and Related Engineering Problems," *U.S. Geol. Survey Spec. Rept., Strategic Eng. Study* 62, 2d ed., 1945.

Opik, E.: *A Climatological and Astronomical Interpretation of the Ice Ages,* Armagh Observatory, Ireland, 1953. A technical publication.

Sharp, R. P.: "Glacier Flow," *Geol. Soc. America Bull.,* vol. 65, pp. 821–838, 1954.

Vial, A.: *Alpine Glaciers,* Batchworth Press, London, 1952. A study of Alpine glacial effects.

Chapter 13

SEA MOVEMENTS

AND THEIR EFFECTS

WATER IS constantly in motion in the "restless" sea. The motion is ceaseless because disturbances in any part of the ocean are transmitted for thousands of miles. Ocean waves and currents are still another means of gradation. We shall begin our study of these forces by examining the various types and causes of sea motion, which continuously alters, and eventually smooths, our coast lines.

Sea Movements

Sea movements include waves, undertow, rip currents, longshore currents, tides, surface ocean currents, subsurface oceanic creep and other density movements, piling up by storms, the spreading of river waters and heavy rains, waterspouts, and giant sea waves (tsunamis) caused by earthquakes.

CAUSES OF MOTION

Wind friction. One of the common causes of movement is the drag, or friction, of the wind as it passes over the surface of the water. Such movements are strongly influenced by the weather and vary greatly according to the strength and direction of the wind. During heavy storms these movements are awe-inspiring, and their destructive power is very great. The pressure exerted by storm waves may exceed 1 ton per square foot, and they may cause damage even at considerable heights above sea level. In the lighthouse at Dunnet Head, on the

FIG. 13.0. *The fury of the Pacific Ocean attacking a rocky shore, Boiler Bay State Park, Lincoln County, Oregon. (Oregon State Highway Commission.)*

north coast of Scotland, windows 300 feet above sea level have been broken by stones hurled up by the waves.

Severe storms. Very severe storms may cause the sea to rise and move forward. Thus, on Oct. 5, 1864, a violent storm at Calicut, on the Malabar Coast of India, raised the level of the sea about 24 feet and inundated a large area. Similar results were reported for the Galveston storm of Sept. 8, 1900, and for the Puerto Rican storm of Sept. 13, 1928. Such storms are of the typhoon or hurricane type and may cause marked destruction along coasts. In a 1935 hurricane that struck the Keys, off the south coast of Florida, the ocean swept between islands where railroad embankments had been built, and the twisted rails with their ties attached were left 100 yards from their former locations. Much of the archway of the interisland viaduct was ruined, and both railroad and highway were washed out for miles. Waves rolled over part of the land and added to the destruction. Buildings and steel towers fell before their attack, and in a well-populated section, where the storm was most severe, one lone house remained after the hurricane had subsided.

Evaporation. Evaporation removes great quanti-

ties of water from the ocean, increasing the salinity of the surface waters and therefore the density of the sea. These effects are most pronounced in the tropics. Along the coast of India it has been found that evaporation from the free surface of the sea amounts to about 23 feet per year. The cold, dense waters from the polar regions, which fill the deep sea as they creep equatorward, rise in the warm latitudes and take the place of the vast quantities removed by evaporation or by surface currents. Changes in the density of sea water, whether due to evaporation, to the removal of calcium carbonate from sea water by lime-secreting life, or to other causes, produce motion, and all such changes contribute to the circulation of sea water.

Rivers. Rivers entering the ocean discharge a great quantity of water at the coast line, where it tends to pile up. This comparatively warm, fresh water is lighter than salt water, and so it floats for a time as it spreads out and mingles with the sea water. The Mississippi and other rivers entering the Gulf of Mexico contribute largely to the Gulf Stream as it passes out into the Atlantic Ocean. Excessive rainfall on any part of the sea also causes the water temporarily to pile up, and during its distribution, motion is inevitable.

Earthquakes. Earthquakes may cause waves of destructive violence, which have been known to sweep inland 7 or 8 miles. Waves of this sort are technically called *tsunamis*, but they are frequently referred to as tidal waves, although they have no connection with the tides caused by the attraction of the sun and moon.

WAVE MOTION

The winds and other agents produce water waves. Wave motion is oscillatory, with each particle of water describing a nearly circular orbit and returning approximately to the point of origin of the motion (Fig. 13.1). Actually, a small amount of water is driven forward or blown over the crest of the wave. The diameter of the orbit at the surface of the water is equal to the height of the wave, that is, the vertical distance between crest and trough.

The form of the wave approximates a trochoid,

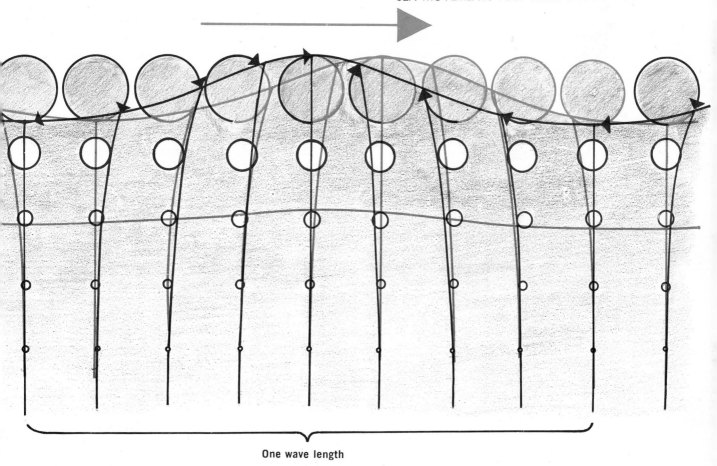

One wave length

FIG. 13.1. *Sketch of a wave to show the relative movements of the water particles at different parts of the wave form and at different depths. The orbits are drawn to scale. The colored lines show the progression of the wave a short time later. (After Kuenen.)*

the line described by a dot on the spoke of a wheel rolled along on the undersurface of a table. The shape of a trochoid can vary from nearly a straight line (as described by a dot on the axis of the wheel) to nearly a cycloid (as described by a dot on the rim), but most water waves are many times longer than they are high, and their troughs are wider and flatter than their crests. The length of the wave is the distance from crest to crest.

Most waves are 20 to 30 times as long as they are high, but exceptional ones may have a length only 12 to 15 times greater than their height. The ratio of the length to the height determines the amount of motion that is transmitted downward.

For example, in a wave 100 feet long and 5 feet high, with a period of 4.4 seconds, the orbital diameter at the surface is 60 inches, whereas at a depth of 50 feet it is only about 2.5 inches, and at a depth of 100 feet it is scarcely $\frac{1}{8}$ inch. In a storm wave 500 feet long and 20 feet high, with a period of 10 seconds, the amplitude of the movement at a depth of 500 feet (equal to the wave length) is still about $\frac{1}{2}$ inch. It has been found that the motion decreases rapidly with depth. Hence very little movement takes place at a depth of $\frac{1}{2}$ wave length. In ordinary seas motion is scarcely perceptible below 20 to 30 feet, although long, high storm waves reach to depths of 300 to 500 feet or more with sufficient vigor to move fine sand. Thus most waves are relatively superficial. The level at which wave motion becomes negligible changes from day to day and from season to season in keeping with the state of the sea.

The period of the waves is usually a few seconds and only rarely longer than 10 or 12 seconds, although periods of 20 seconds or more have been observed.

A train of waves is not perfectly rhythmic; rather, it is somewhat irregular. Great storms at sea are especially likely to produce irregular or choppy patterns of simultaneous waves of different dimensions and orientations; so the surface of the sea is more like crumpled crepe paper than corrugated iron. As storm waves travel from the region of disturbed conditions into an area of relative calm, they preserve or increase their lengths and velocities but diminish in height, passing into the common ground swells, or broad undulations, of the sea.

Wave heights and the velocities of the swell have been found to be governed by the velocity and duration of the wind and by the time and distance of travel of the waves during their growth and their decline. With the aid of weather maps of oceanic areas and with knowledge of the laws of waves and swell, it is possible to predict the arrival time and the height of the swell.

BREAKERS

As waves approach a shelving coast line, they begin to drag bottom when the depth of the water is about half the wave length. Hence the lower part of the wave is retarded by interference from the sea bottom, whereas the surface portion, because of its inertia, tends to maintain the wave motion. The wave length and velocity are reduced, and so, to compensate, the crest of the wave rapidly becomes higher and the trough deeper, until finally the crest moves ahead of its supporting column of water, curls over, and "breaks," or plunges, over the side of the wave into the trough in a turbulent, foaming mass called *surf*. The forward motion of the water then carries it bodily onshore as *swash* until its energy is released in

turbulence, friction, and work. The excess of water sloshed forward runs down the face of the beach as *backwash*, only to be caught in the next wave and hurled toward shore again (Fig. 13.2).

Since waves of the same height break at about the same distance from shore, a line of breakers, or *plunge line*, is formed. However, the position of the line of breakers shifts back and forth with changes in the height and length of the waves. The plunge line develops in shallow water where the depth of the water is about equal to the previous height of the wave in deep water offshore. This depth is usually less than 10 feet and rarely more than 50 or 60 feet.

The terminology of the environs of the shore is illustrated in Fig. 13.3.

WAVE INTERFERENCE

Wave gauges which record automatically, such as the one at La Jolla, California, show that many waves are compound, that is, that several waves of different lengths and heights are superimposed upon one another. When their crests coincide, they reinforce each other and rise to exceptional height. When the crest of one meets the trough of another, the waves are out of phase and nullify each other. Interference can generally be seen readily when two sets of waves of comparable size approach the shore from somewhat different directions. Such interference is the basis, no doubt, for the popular notion that every seventh wave (or some other number) is unusually large.

WAVE REFRACTION

When a wave obliquely approaches a uniformly shelving shore, one end of the wave begins to drag bottom in shallow water while the remainder of it goes forward unhindered. The wave, therefore, tends to become bent, or refracted, in such a way as to strike the shore nearly head on, regardless of the original direction of approach.

A similar refraction of a series of waves, setting up crossing wave-train patterns, takes place over any shoal, against a rocky island or an artificial obstruction, from submarine canyons, or against a peninsula or headland protruding seaward. This

FIG. 13.2.   *Beach at Ecola State Park, Oregon. Waves break on a gently sloping bottom, water sloshes forward onto a sandy beach, and the excess water returns to the sea as backwash. Lobate marks left by the waves can be seen upon the sand. The sea shown is relatively quiet and near low tide. (Oregon State Highway Commission.)*

FIG. 13.3.   *Terminology of shore features. (After Shepard.)*

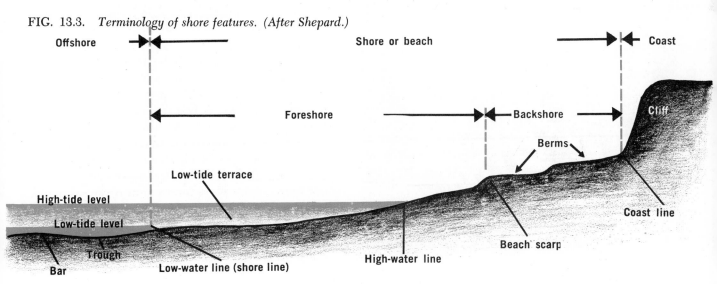

refraction tends to concentrate the energy of wave attack by convergence against the three sides of the headland and to disperse the wave energy in a bay (Fig. 13.4). On the other hand, deep water near shore may transmit the waves with undiminished energy against the adjacent shore. Refraction patterns appear on many photographs of irregular, rocky shore lines (Fig. 13.5).

UNDERTOW

The water from the backwash of waves on the beach has commonly been thought to return to sea beneath the breakers as a sheetlike current along the bottom, called an *undertow*. This undertow has even been considered a hazard to surf swim-

FIG. 13.4. *Wave refraction near La Jolla, California. A southwest swell in the open sea at the upper left with a period of 16 seconds turned, locally more than 90 degrees, to strike the shore nearly head on. The two bulges are less refracted as they forge ahead over deeper water in the branching head of a submarine canyon. (After Munk and Traylor.)*

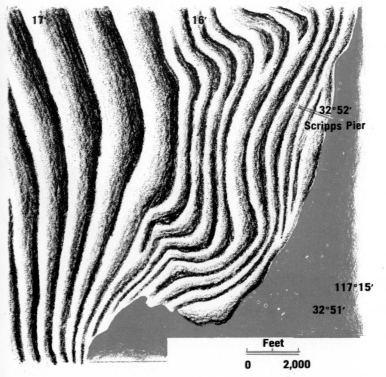

17′ 16′

32°52′
Scripps Pier

117°15′

32°51′

Feet

0   2,000

ming. Measurements with a current meter, however, though difficult at best, fail to prove the existence of any undertow. Inside the line of breakers turbulent mixing is the rule. Since the only water that needs to be returned beyond the breakers is that blown along by the wind on the surface of the waves, the quantity of water involved ordinarily is small and its speed very low. Nevertheless, if there is any undertow, its pulsating movements may help to shift mud and fine sand down slope seaward. The question of undertow is open to debate.

RIP CURRENTS

Rip currents[1] are strong currents of surface waters that flow seaward through the breakers wherever large breakers are found. "Feeder" currents come together in the surf, turn seaward (as rip currents) in a narrow "neck" through the breakers, and then spread out in a "head" with swirling eddies (Fig. 13.6). These currents attain speeds of as much as 2 miles an hour, and it is likely that they have been mistaken for undertow by swimmers. They make channels in sandy bottoms and are presumably important factors in moving large quantities of sediment away from the beach.

LONGSHORE CURRENTS

When waves strike the shore line obliquely, a longshore current is generated parallel to the coast line. This current is capable of transporting sediment along the submerged part of the shore as *shore drift*. The movement in shallow water probably shifts complexly. Tests with floats indicate velocities inside the breaker zone as high as 3 knots. Deep water at the mouth of a bay may tend to interrupt the transport until a bar has been built across it, and a point of land may divert the current seaward so as to shift the deposit of sediment out to sea, although in places sand is carried round rocky headlands. Various modifications result from other local conditions.

[1] F. P. Shepard et al., "Rip Currents: A Process of Geological Importance," *Jour. Geology*, vol. 49, pp. 337–369, 1941.

Oblique waves, somewhat refracted, also shift gravel and sand along the beach. The combined effect of the oblique swash of the waves and of the gravity return of the water almost directly down slope causes particles of rock to oscillate up and down the beach in saw-tooth paths (Fig. 13.7). Naturally, the trajectories, modified in form by gravity, are more pronounced for sand than for pebbles. These alternations shift the materials along the beach, hence the term *beach drift*. Tests with marked stones or bricks have shown that this movement may carry pebbles many miles from their sources, sometimes at very rapid rates, and may transport sand tens of miles or more. The quartz sand of the beaches of the east coast of Florida has been shifted southward from Georgia and the Carolinas.

TIDES

The periodic rise and fall of the sea (which rises twice in 24 hours and 52 minutes) constitute the *tide* (Fig. 2.7). It is produced by the differential attraction of the sun and moon on the earth, as discussed in Chapter 2, Earth as a Planet. This attraction is effective on both land and sea, but the sea is more mobile and therefore yields more readily to the pull.

In the open ocean the tidal variation of sea level probably does not exceed 2½ or 3 feet, but along the continental borders the differences between high and low tide are much greater. In narrow bays with broad seaward openings, such as the Bay of Fundy, it may exceed 20 or even 50 feet. This is partly due to resonance.

The tide usually comes in as a series of waves, each reaching higher and higher until the crest of the rise is attained, after which recession sets in, and this continues until low tide. At certain places, however, the tide rises suddenly, coming in as a wall-like wave of water, known as a *bore*, which may be as much as 25 feet high. The bore is especially well developed on the coasts of China and India. Wherever the tide runs through restricted passages, such as narrow straits or bays or between islands, currents are developed which scour the bottom and shift about the loose materials.

FIG. 13.5.   *Curved wave fronts resulting from refraction, Curry Couny, Oregon. Obstructions in the irregular shore line cause the arcuate wave fronts. A small bay at the left is cut off by a bay bar (behind tree), and sand also has accumulated in the lee of the small stacks (resistant rock isolated by erosion). (Oregon State Highway Commission.)*

The tide is not a very important agent of erosion. However, there are broad belts of the earth's surface adjacent to the sea, usually referred to as tidal flats, which are covered by water part of the time but exposed to the ordinary weathering processes during the remainder of the day or night.

OCEAN CURRENTS

In regions where the winds have more or less constant direction, such as in the trade-wind belts, the surface waters are dragged along in the same direction with a velocity less than that of the wind itself (Fig. 13.8). Since these winds blow from the northeast north of the equator and from the southeast south of the equator, the water is being urged toward the equator from both sides; there it drifts

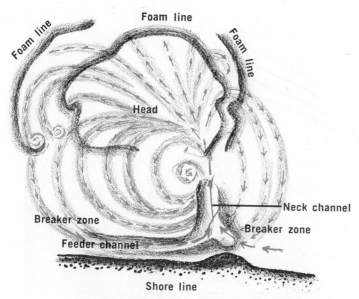

Foam line

Foam line

Foam line

Head

Neck channel

Breaker zone

Breaker zone

Feeder channel

Shore line

FIG. 13.6. *Sketch of a rip current, showing a feeder channel, neck, head, and foam lines in relation to the breaker zone and shore line. The lengths of the arrows indicate relative velocities. (After Shepard.)*

westward as one current, which would encircle the earth if the ocean covered the entire earth. This *equatorial drift*, contributed to and modified by numerous other factors, is the origin of the currents in equatorial oceans. Thus in the North Atlantic the westward-drifting equatorial waters strike the eastward-projecting portion of Brazil, and part is deflected up along the north coast of South America, striking the eastern terminus of the Greater and Lesser Antilles, where it is again divided, part of it crossing the Caribbean Sea and entering the Gulf of Mexico. Augmented by the great quantity of water being poured into the Gulf by rain and rivers, it emerges through the Straits of Florida as the Gulf Stream. Similar currents are formed in the South Atlantic and in the Pacific Ocean, where the equatorial drift is more pronounced.

These ocean currents are not due to wind alone. The surface heating of the equatorial waters and their consequent expansion, together with their cooling in the polar regions, are in themselves sufficient to produce circulation. Far out at sea the

Gulf Stream can be recognized by its color, due in part to the excess of fresh water which has poured into it. The shape of the continental shelf, the configuration of the coast line, and the rotation of the earth modify these currents and control their movements to some extent; but as long as the generating forces act, they keep moving. Since these currents carry little sediment, their chief effect is climatic.

SUBSURFACE OCEAN CURRENTS

Cold polar surface water sinks in the North Atlantic off the coast of Greenland and creeps southward as a "depth current" as far as Lat. 60°S (Fig. 13.9). Beyond that position cold antarctic winter water dives below it as a "bottom current." Another current, the "intermediate current," flows northward from Lat. 50 to 60°S to about Lat. 30°N at a depth of about 1,000 meters. Other near-surface currents sink at about Lat. 30°N and 30°S and flow at a depth of about 600 meters toward the equator, where they well up and begin to return along the surface. Thus a complicated circulatory system prevails in the Atlantic, delicately balanced in dynamic equilibrium among heating, cooling, dilution by fresh water, and concentration by evaporation. This circulatory system is modified by such factors as the shape of the basin, configuration of the bottom, and the earth's rotation.

Cold antarctic water also flows northward into the Indian and Pacific Oceans, which likewise have complicated circulatory currents below the surface.

Radiocarbon measurements by J. L. Kulp indicate that this deep oceanic circulation requires thousands of years to complete its cycle.

In partially enclosed basins special considerations apply. In the Mediterranean Sea, for example, evaporation greatly exceeds precipitation and runoff. Hence a strong current of 2.5 miles an hour flows from the Atlantic Ocean through the Strait of Gibraltar to make up the difference. Through long-continued evaporation all the water in the Mediterranean has become extra saline (3.8 per cent), so that its increased density causes a current to flow out into the Atlantic over a "sill," or submerged ridge, separating two basins in the Strait of Gibraltar beneath the inflowing current. There it flows along the bottom until its density, due to its high salinity (offset somewhat by its high temperature), is balanced by that of the deep Atlantic water. Then it fans out as a great subsurface tongue of warm extra-saline water that spreads as far west as the Azores and from the equator to Ireland before it loses its identity by mixing.

If the sill in such a basin were very shallow, so that only an incoming current could flow, the continued concentration of salts within the basin in a dry climate would ultimately produce such a high salinity that deposition of some of the salts would result. Some of the deposits of gypsum and rock salt of the geologic past may have been formed under these conditions.

In a partially enclosed basin in a humid climate, on the other hand, the excess of water, being lighter, flows out to sea along the surface. If the sill is shallow, as in many Norwegian fiords, the subsurface water in the basin becomes stagnant, its oxygen is used up, most organisms die, and hydrogen sulfide forms. The lack of ventilation by subsurface currents affects the life and sediments in such a basin.

Other subsurface currents in the ocean have been discovered in recent years. One is a countercurrent underneath the Gulf Stream in the North Atlantic. Another is a remarkable undercurrent moving eastward in the equatorial Pacific beneath the west-flowing South Equatorial Current. This current is 250 miles wide and flows for a distance of at least 3,500 miles, ending up west of the Galapagos Islands. Its core lies at a depth of about 300 feet and has a velocity of 3 knots. The mechanics of these and possibly other, yet unknown undercurrents remain to be worked out.

Gradation by Waves and Shore Currents

METHODS OF WAVE EROSION

Movements in sea water produce mechanical effects of vast importance because of the mass and velocity of the moving water. Thus the waves beat-

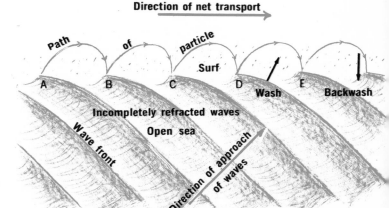

FIG. 13.7. *Beach drift caused by oblique approach of waves. The inclined uprush of each wave carries particles of sediment diagonally up the beach, and the backwash returns them nearly directly downslope. In the meantime the next succeeding wave will have moved forward. So the particles are caught by the next swash and hurled up beach again. The net movement is from A to B, B to C, and so on, but many trips from many waves are required to move more than a wave length, instead of the single trips shown.*

ing upon a coast gradually wear it away. In loose materials the *impact* of the waves alone is sufficient. In solid rocks the water takes advantage of joints, pries blocks loose by hydraulic pressure, and eventually *quarries* away, block by block, great masses of rock. Erosion by impact and by quarrying is covered by the term *hydraulicking*.

Waves also erode by *abrasion*, as the rock fragments quarried out by the waves or rolled down into the water are hurled back by the waves against the shore. Rock fragments are thus effective tools in cutting the shore line or undercutting promontories. The overhanging rock then topples into the sea, and more tools are supplied to continue the attack. The tools themselves, of course, are worn by *corrasion* and undergo reduction in size, or *attrition*, as they are carried back and forth, as if on a washboard. Shells and rocky materials are reduced by grinding between coarser pieces. They

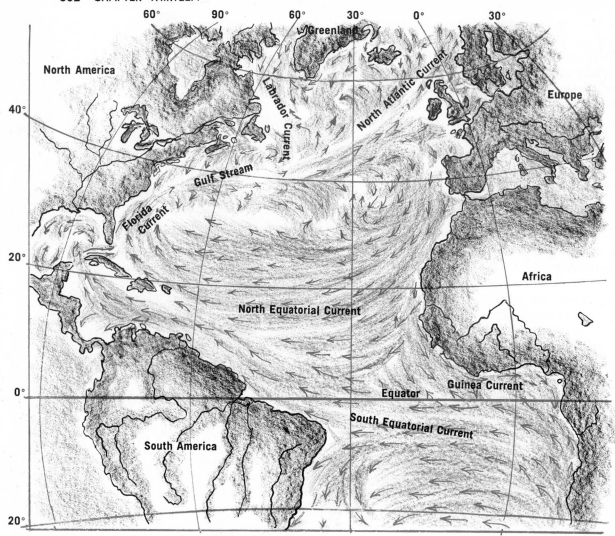

FIG. 13.8. *Surface ocean currents in the Atlantic Ocean. The westward equatorial currents, the Gulf Stream, and the large gyral in the North Atlantic are outstanding features. (After Schott.)*

are worn finer and finer as they are dragged or rolled to and fro on the beach by the moving water.

The compression and decompression of air, despite the cushioning effect, enable the waves to reach and to quarry beyond the water itself. Currents *scour* the bottom in shallow water and thereby assist in shore erosion. Sea water also *dissolves* mineral matter from the rocks, especially from coral or other limestones.

RESULTS OF WAVE EROSION

The cliff developed by undercutting of waves is known as a *sea cliff* (Fig. 13.10). Such cliffs, on the south shore of Nantucket Island, have been cut back by the waves as much as 6 feet per year. Many cliffs show a horizontal *notch*, or *nip*, at the base, as a result of the chopping or sawing action of the waves (Fig. 13.11).

On rocky coasts the continued advance of the

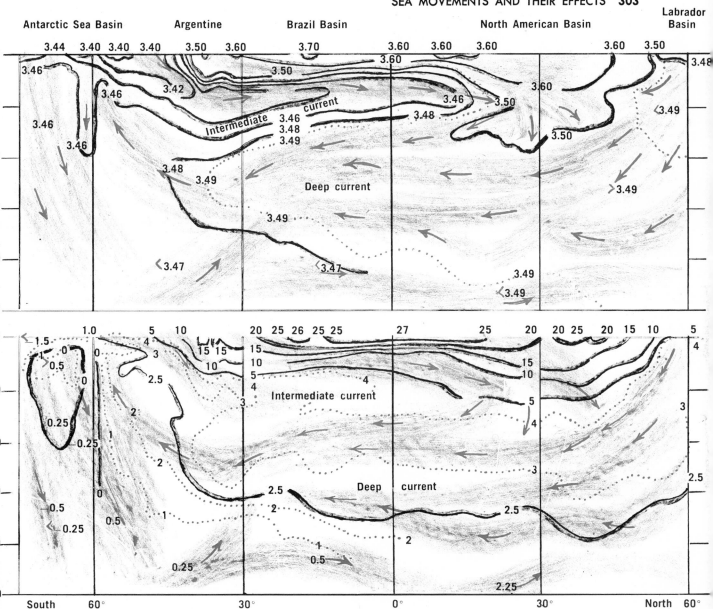

FIG. 13.9. *North-south profile of subsurface density currents in the Atlantic Ocean, based on (a) differences in salinity and (b) differences in temperature. (After Wüst via Schott.)*

sea due to the erosion and retreat of the sea cliff produces a beveled rock bench, called a *wave-cut terrace, strand flat,* or *wave-cut platform,* which is partly exposed at low tide (Fig. 13.12). A multitude of *flutings, grooves, furrows, scour pits,* and other small-scale features on its surface testify to abrasion of its surface in the turbulent surf. Unusually resistant materials may be left standing as *rock reefs.* In places the returning water from the spray and splash of storm waves rotates

FIG. 13.10. *Sea cliff and caves at La Jolla, California. This type of cliff is produced by the undercutting of waves. (Arnold, U.S. Geological Survey.)*

FIG. 13.11. *The wave-notched base of a sea cliff near Nanaimo, British Columbia. (Canada Department of Interior.)*

the water and sediments caught in small rock basins, grinding the holes deeper and producing the familiar *tidal pools* ("crabholes"). Jug-shaped holes of this origin are known on the north shore of Lake Superior, but they are more common on seacoasts.

In rocks which are highly jointed or broken by faults, wave erosion may quarry out *sea caves*. If erosion breaks through the roof or top of the cave, it forms a *spouting horn,* or *blowhole* (called *gloup* in England). Because most rocks are close-jointed, at least locally, caves may be expected along any rocky shore line subjected to vigorous attack by waves, as along the New England and Pacific coasts. Occasionally caves formed on opposite sides of a narrow promontory may break through to form a pierced rock, or natural bridge (Fig. 13.13). When the bridge, or arch, falls, the seaward mass becomes an island, or *sea stack* (also called *chimney rock,* or *skerry*). Most stacks, however, develop as a result of the isolation of resistant masses of rock by the removal of the less resistant rocks surrounding them (Fig. 13.14), without the formation of any intermediate natural bridges. Indentations without roofs quarried out by the waves are *joint chasms* (Fig. 13.15).

Waves easily discover differences in the resistance of rocks on shore, and so they erode differentially. Rocks which are weak because of joints or because of a lack of induration are eroded back to form *coves,* whereas more resistant rocks stand out to form *headlands*. In detail, a shore line of coves and headlands becomes minutely irregular, or *crenulate*. In unconsolidated rocks, however, such as gravel, sand, clay, or glacial till, a cliffed shore line may remain straight.

When the maximum irregularity has been developed and erosion is balanced on coves and headlands alike by differences in exposure, the shore line is said to be *mature*. Thereafter the shore line advances upon the land without significant change in form.

TRANSPORTATION OF MATERIAL

It is also the job of waves and longshore currents to remove the products of erosion. During this removal the materials are subjected (1) to further wear in transit (with resulting attrition and rounding) (Fig. 13.16) and (2) to sorting, according to size, shape, and specific gravity, in the perpetual milling action of the sea. The fine particles stay in suspension and eventually settle offshore.

DEPOSITION OF MATERIAL

Storm waves commonly toss coarse materials far up on shore out of reach of the ordinary waves, and of course the slackening of any of the waves or longshore currents also leads to deposition. Materials carried by traction on the bottom are deposited as a result of a reduction in velocity of a current across deep water, where a part of its energy is used to move a thicker, slower-flowing sheet of water.

BEACH DEPOSITS

The oversize, the overload, or the rejects from the surf "mill" accumulate along the shore as a beach embankment, or beach ridge. The term beach is used broadly for the entire area along the sea extending from the line reached by high tide and the highest storm waves to the low-tide mark. However, along a rocky cliffed coast much of the beach as thus defined may be nearly barren of deposits, whereas along a sandy coast a sandy beach may be almost continuous. Local accumulations of gravel or sand in bays are *bayhead beaches* (Fig. 13.17), and those at the heads of smaller indentations are *pocket beaches.*

The materials of beach deposits vary greatly in grain size, from sands through pebbles and cobbles to boulders. In the sequence of seasonal changes a beach characterized by gravel in winter may be converted to a wide belt of sand in summer. Where most of the beach pebbles are flattened, disk-shaped ones produced from rocks having this type of fracture pattern, such as thin-bedded limestones, they may overlap so as to form a *shingle beach* (Fig. 13.18).

Certain beaches are composed of shell fragments or coral sand, as in the "pink beach" of Bermuda, or olivine sand, as in the Bay of Naples, but by far the greater number are mainly quartz sand. Local

FIG. 13.12. *Elevated sea terrace, sea cliff, and wave-cut terrace exposed at low tide, near Devils Punch Bowl State Park, Oregon. Both terraces bevel the tilted layers of sandstone and mudstone. The continued advances of the sea by erosion formed both terraces, the upper one before uplift of the coast and the lower one afterward. (Oregon State Highway Commission.)*

concentrations of native gold, magnetite ("black sand"), zircon, rutile, cassiterite (tin ore), and other useful minerals in some deposits form the basis of certain beach placer mines.

Where an excess of sand is present, as at the mouth of a river, a wide series of beach ridges may be added to the shore so as to extend the land

FIG. 13.13. *Marine arch left standing by the collapse of most of the roof of a sea cave in the sandstones at Laguna Beach, California.*

FIG. 13.14. *Group of sea stacks, Bandon, Oregon. Wave erosion has removed the less resistant rock which formerly surrounded them. (Oregon State Highway Commission.)*

seaward as a *prograded shore*. A good example is Clatsop Plains, just south of the mouth of the Columbia River.

Wind-blown sands derived from beaches commonly pile up on shore as coastal dunes.

BARRIER BEACHES

On a number of gently sloping sandy shores the waves and currents have built up ridges of sand to form strips of land some distance offshore (Fig. 13.19). Such ridges are known as *barrier beaches* (*offshore islands*, or *island bars*). The area behind the barrier beach is more or less shut off from the open ocean as a lagoon.

The origin of these barrier beaches is in doubt. Johnson[2] thought that they were formed just landward of the line of breakers, mainly by the throwing of sand thereto from the seaward side until a chain of islands and finally a ridge were built near sea level. The sand could be thrown somewhat above sea level by storm waves and then whipped

[2] D. W. Johnson, *Shore Processes and Shoreline Development*, John Wiley & Sons, Inc., 1919, pp. 365–367.

up still higher into dunes by the wind. Recent observations show, however, that the line of breakers is a place of maximum turbulence rather than of sedimentation and that it is characterized by a furrow, or trough, instead of a ridge, although a low sandbank (or a series of bars and intervening troughs, sometimes called balls-and-lows) may lie beside the trough. The trough and bar change with the state of the sea, but none has ever been seen to form a barrier beach.

Another possible explanation is that the barrier beaches were begun as relatively simple beaches on a nearly flat sea bottom during the ice age, when sea level was lower than it is now. As sea level slowly was restored, the waves gradually may have driven the beach ridges landward and upward to their present positions. It is noteworthy that the valleys behind the lagoons are drowned by the postglacial rise of sea level.

Barrier beaches line the coast of Texas and the Atlantic coast from New Jersey southward. They are in different stages of development and modification. Some of them are single ridges, and some are multiple; some are islands, and some are connected to the mainland at one or both ends. Many of them have subsidiary deposits along their edges and in the vicinity of tidal inlets. A modified lagoon with associated deposits is shown in Fig. 13.20.

BARS AND SPITS

A longshore current shifts sediments parallel to the coast line, but, owing to the tendency of a current to continue in a straight line, it fails to follow any indentation that may have been produced by a drowned river valley or by a bay of any origin. Where the longshore current passes from shallow to deeper water at the entrance of such indentations, or bays, deposition is almost certain to take place. A ridge, which becomes a land projection, or *spit*, is thus built up. When a spit is built almost or entirely across the entrance to the bay,

FIG. 13.16.   *Three building bricks showing successive stages of rounding by wave erosion. (F. H. Lahee, Field Geology.)*

it becomes a *bay-mouth bar* (Fig. 13.21). Bars cut off the indentations and tend to simplify the form of the coast line. Islands become connected with the mainland or with each other in a similar manner. Such islands are said to be *tied*, and the bars acting as the lines of connection are called *tombolos* (Fig. 13.22). They are numerous along the New England coast, where several islands in succession may be tied together, and the string thus formed may be connected with the mainland. Nahant, Massachusetts, is a land-tied island. The Rock of Gibraltar is similarly united to the coast of Spain.

If the free end of a spit is beaten by violent

FIG. 13.15.   *Joint chasm being eroded along a fracture in basaltic lava. Note the "tools" in the lower right.*

FIG. 13.17.   *Bayhead beach, Emerald Bay, Laguna Beach, California. The highway is on a sea terrace. (Spence Air Photos.)*

FIG. 13.18. *A shingle beach at Thrum Cap, Nova Scotia. A shingle beach consists of disk-shaped, flattened beach pebbles which overlap one another. (Geological Survey of Canada.)*

FIG. 13.19. *Model of the New Jersey coast at Barnegat Bay, showing the long barrier beach. Barrier beaches are offshore sand ridges built up by waves and currents. (Aero Service Corporation.)*

storm waves or by those of seasonal storms, it may be deflected, or cut back, and the terminal materials thus turned back may be deposited as a *recurved spit*, or *hook* (Fig. 13.23). By prolonged deposition the curved end of the hook may be extended until it reaches the mainland and forms a *loop*.

Cuspate forms. Where sediment-laden longshore currents are deflected seaward on both sides of a point of land, a projecting spit with cusped or curved sides is built out as a *cuspate spit* (Fig. 13.24), or, on a larger scale, a *cuspate foreland*.

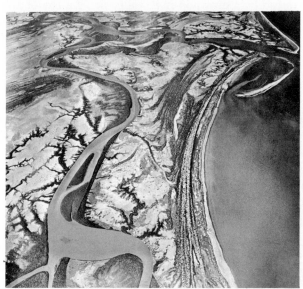

FIG. 13.20. *Aerial photograph of coastal zone of northeastern Australia. Former tidal flats are channeled by streams. These deposits constitute a form of barrier beach. (United States Air Force.)*

Cape Fear, North Carolina, and Cape Canaveral, Florida, are outstanding cuspate forelands.

Submerged bars. Besides the shore deposits, which are obvious because they stand above sea level, underwater bars are built up by waves and longshore currents (Fig. 13.21). These, according to local conditions, take the shape of variously oriented ridges, sandy shoals, and anomalous forms that are not readily classified.

In addition, a mantle of sediments is distributed over the sea bottom below the level of wave and current activity. This has been called a *wave-built* terrace or shore-face terrace by some authorities, who have thought it to be continuous with the surface of the wave-cut terrace. However, such a constructional terracelike embankment is said not to be found in the present sea. Instead, the sediments seem to be spread unevenly. The Pleistocene changes of sea level may be partly responsible for this irregularity.

FIG. 13.22. *Land-tied islands, Spruce Head Island, Maine. The sand bar tying the island to the shore is called a tombolo. (Bastin, U.S. Geological Survey.)*

FIG. 13.21. *Bay-mouth bars and coastal lagoons near Eureka, California. The lagoon in the center is cut off from the Pacific Ocean by a sand bar. A similar lagoon occurs above (south). This type of sand bar has been formed from a spit which has been elongated to cut off the bay. Bay-mouth and other sand bars have the effect of simplifying a shore line. (Fairchild Aerial Surveys, Inc.)*

All the various constructional features formed by waves and currents are subject to change from season to season and from year to year; and so a beach, spit, barrier beach, bay-mouth bar, or submarine bar may show very different outlines within a decade.

ARTIFICIAL SHORE CONTROLS

To protect harbor works and other water-front property, man builds such structures as sea walls, bulkheads, revetments, and breakwaters, but these prove difficult to maintain against the fury of the sea unleashed in storms. Jetties commonly are used to protect navigation inlets, but they also interrupt the longshore transport of sand. Accretion of sand then normally occurs on the upcurrent side, as at Lake Worth Inlet, Florida, where jetties interfered with the southward sand drift. In certain situations artificial changes may result in starvation of the beaches farther down the coast on the lee side, as at Palm Beach, where erosion of the beach followed the construction of the Lake Worth Inlet jetties. Construction of a breakwater in 1929 to protect the harbor at Santa Barbara, California, caused about 300,000 cubic yards of sand per year to collect in front of the breakwater. By 1934, the capacity was reached, and sand began to go round the end of the breakwater and to fill in the harbor;

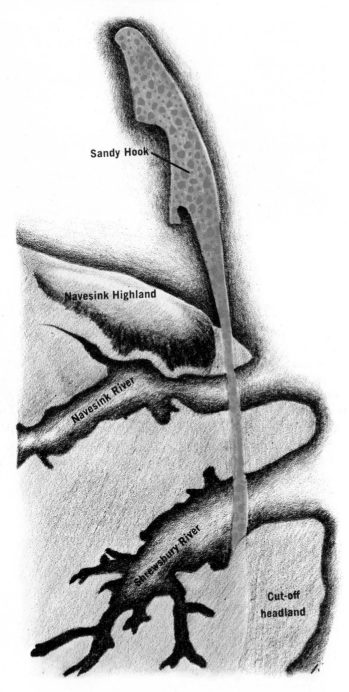

Sandy Hook

Navesink Highland

Navesink River

Shrewsbury River

Cut-off headland

FIG. 13.23. *Diagram showing the erosion of headlands and the deposition of the eroded material as a bar and hook at Sandy Hook, New Jersey, at the entrance to New York harbor. (After Loomis.)*

by 1952, more than 5 million cubic yards of sand had accumulated in the harbor behind the breakwater. Part of the fill has been used to stock-pile the beach down drift, where beach erosion had become serious.

To stabilize beaches or to induce prograding, a series of groins may be built perpendicular to the shore athwart the shore drift. The interference with the natural balance by such forced deposition may lead, however, to erosion elsewhere. Considerable success has been had at moderate cost on the coasts of New Jersey, Florida, California, and Lake Michigan with artificial nourishment of beaches by sand dredged or pumped from nearby sources, as at Atlantic City, Palm Beach, Santa Monica, and Chicago.

Long breakwaters placed offshore parallel to the coast line provide shelter for small ships, but they also create a wave shadow, where the effects of wave refraction, wave diffraction, and modification of the shore currents cause deposition on the beach front. Thus a 2,000-foot breakwater built about 2,000 feet offshore at Santa Monica, California, led to a somewhat cuspate accumulation of sand onshore, which in 30 years grew to be several hundred feet wide. Sea stacks and islands offshore have a similar effect in their lee.

By anticipating the effects of various engineering structures on the work of waves and longshore currents, it is possible to select a design appropriate to a particular setting with reasonable success and to take steps to counteract undesirable changes which might result.

Shore Lines

JOHNSON'S CLASSIFICATION

A once widely accepted classification of shore lines, proposed by Johnson, grouped them in four main categories:

1. *Shore lines of emergence,* generally characterized by a nearly flat coastal plain covered with unconsolidated marine sediments; terraces onshore and barrier beaches offshore are also typical

2. *Shore lines of submergence,* characterized by

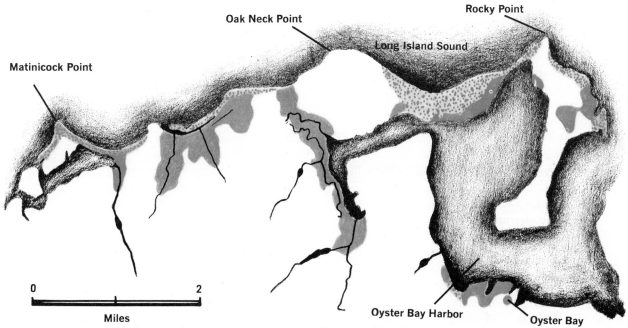

FIG. 13.24. *A youthful shore line of submergence undergoing simplification, near Oyster Bay, Long Island, New York. Matinicock Point has the form of a cuspate spit. Oak Neck Point is a cliffed headland flanked by bay-mouth bars. (After Oyster Bay Topographic Map, U.S. Geological Survey.)*

drowned valleys, deep bays, bold headlands, and islands

3. *Neutral shore lines,* which do not show the effects of either emergence of a former sea floor or submergence of former land, include:
   a. Delta
   b. Alluvial plain
   c. Outwash plain
   d. Volcanic
   e. Coral reef
   f. Faulted

4. *Compound shore lines,* which show features that are a combination of at least two of the preceding classes

This classification met with some objections. Because of sea-level changes during the ice age the supposedly stable "neutral" shore lines actually have undergone both emergence and submergence. Moreover, for the same reason, nearly all shore lines are compound. Thus shore terraces and drowned valleys occur together in many places.

SHEPARD'S CLASSIFICATION

To avoid the shortcomings of Johnson's classification, Shepard has proposed another classification, which may be summarized as follows:

A. Primary, or youthful, coasts and shore lines, shaped primarily by nonmarine agencies
   1. Shaped by terrestrial erosion and drowned by deglaciation or downwarping
      a. Drowned river-valley coasts (ria coasts)
      b. Drowned glacial-erosion coasts (with deep estuaries, fiords, or glacial troughs and basin depressions)
   2. Shaped by terrestrial depositional agencies
      a. River-deposition coasts (deltaic coasts, drowned alluvial plains)
      b. Glacial-deposition coasts (partially sub-

merged moraines, partially submerged drumlins)

    c. Wind-deposition coasts (prograding sand dunes)

    d. Vegetation-extended coasts (mangrove)

  3. Shaped by volcanic activity

    a. Coasts with recent lava flows

    b. Shore lines due to volcanic collapse or explosion (breached calderas)

  4. Shaped by diastrophism

    a. Fault-scarp coasts

    b. Coasts due to folding

B. Secondary, or mature, coasts and shore lines, shaped primarily by marine agencies

  1. Shaped by marine erosion

    a. Sea cliffs straightened by wave erosion

    b. Sea cliffs made irregular (crenulate) by wave erosion

  2. Shaped by marine deposition

    a. Shore lines straightened by building of bars across estuaries

    b. Coasts prograded by wave and current deposits

    c. Shore lines with offshore bars and long-shore spits

    d. Coral-reef coasts

FIG. 13.25. *Diagram illustrating the landforms developed along a coast line of submergence. (After D. W. Johnson.)*

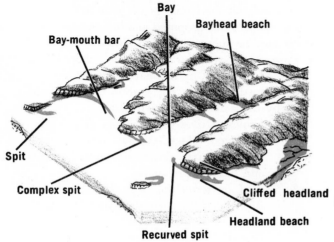

Shepard's subdivisions of coastal regions are (1) coasts with young mountains, (2) coasts with old mountains, (3) coasts with broad coastal plains, and (4) glaciated coasts.

GUILCHER'S CLASSIFICATION

A third classification, by the French oceanographer André Guilcher, is partly genetic and partly descriptive:

1. Ria coasts
2. Fiord coasts
3. Glacial lowland coasts
4. Unglaciated lowland coasts
5. Coasts dominated by structure

    a. Coasts with longitudinal structure—Pacific or Dalmatian type

    b. Transverse coasts—Atlantic type

    c. Coasts of oblique structure

    d. Coasts of arcuate structure

    e. Coasts of rectangular structure

    f. Coasts of discordant structure, or contraposed coasts

    g. Volcanic coasts—circular or lobate coasts and caldera coasts

6. Coasts chiefly connected with marine action

    a. Cliffs and rock platforms

    b. Beaches and dunes

    c. Estuaries, marshes, and deltas

    d. Coral formations

A comparison of the three classifications given above illustrates the difficulty of classifying complex phenomena into any simple set of neat categories. Let us keep in mind that, regardless of how coast lines may begin, they undergo sequential development under the influence of the shore agents, mainly waves and longshore currents. Indeed, one of the problems in classification is the fact that many of the present shore lines have had long and complicated histories.

DEVELOPMENT

To illustrate the progressive development of shore lines, let us consider the changes wrought with time on two different types of coasts, representative of Shepard's two main divisions. One is a nonmarine, youthful, drowned river-valley coast (ria). The other is a more mature marine coast, with a wide coastal plain.

Youthful coast. The ria coast can begin with long estuaries, bold headlands, and islands. At first, sea cliffs are cut on the exposed headlands and on the seaward shores of the islands. The resulting sediments are deposited as spits to make "winged headlands," and bay-mouth bars are extended across the deeper waters of the bays (Fig. 13.25). The dismembered tributaries of the drowned valleys build deltas in the sheltered portions of the bays. As these processes continue, the islands are cut away and the headlands recede (Fig. 13.23). Spits and bay-mouth bars simplify the outline of the shore line, which now approaches maturity. The mature stage is characterized by high sea cliffs (crenulate or straight, according to the resistance of the material) and by wide, wave-cut terraces. The terraces extend seaward as far as the original headlands that were removed by wave erosion. The shortened bays are filled with delta sediments, and the shore line is shortened and simplified to the greatest extent. It is then mature. After this stage is reached, the shore line retreats slowly, and the wave-cut terraces are widened until the force of the wave action is lost as the waves have to cross the wide, rocky platforms.

Mature coast. The second, more mature type of coast may be considered a nearly flat coastal plain underlain by newly exposed, unconsolidated marine sediments (Fig. 13.26). Most of the irregularities of

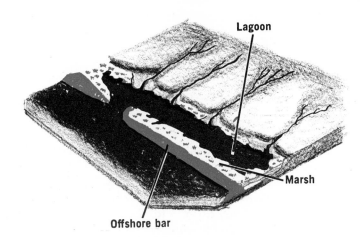

FIG. 13.26. *Diagram illustrating a coast line of emergence. (After D. W. Johnson.)*

the sea bottom have been obliterated by the deposition of sediments. Erosion, however, begins immediately, with the early stages characterized by the development of barrier beaches or offshore bars. Shallow-water lagoons lie between the offshore bars and the shore line (Fig. 13.19). The lagoons are gradually filled by sediments from the land, by the growth of vegetation, and by other, less evident agencies. Later on, the waves continue to beat on the barrier beaches and drive them landward. The lagoons are changed into tidal marshes (Fig. 13.26), and the marshes may be completely filled. As wave action continues, the barrier beaches are forced back onshore and eliminated, and the shore line is made straight and simple. During the succeeding stage a wide, wave-cut terrace is developed as the shore moves landward.

Summary

Waves and shore currents erode the shores by hydraulicking (impact and quarrying), corrasion, scouring, and solution. They form wave-cut cliffs, notches, wave-cut terraces, flutings, grooves, pits, sea caves, sea stacks, spouting horns, joint chasms, rock reefs, coves, and crenulate headlands, in a fascinating array.

They deposit beach ridges, barrier beaches, spits, bay-mouth bars, tombolos, hooks, loops, cuspate spits, cuspate forelands, submerged bars, and wave-built terraces.

To control shore lines, we use sea walls, bulkheads, revetments, jetties, groins, and breakwaters, which stop beach erosion, induce deposition, or otherwise modify the natural regimen.

Shore lines are shaped not only by waves and shore currents but also by glaciation, volcanic activity, changes of sea level, growth of deltas, and earth movements. Regardless of their origin, however, shore lines undergo progressive development in an orderly sequence of forms.

Suggestions for Further Reading

Gresswell, R. K.: *The Physical Geography of Beaches and Coastlines,* Hulton Educational Publications, London, 1957. Part of an illustrated nontechnical series on geography.

Guilcher, André: Coastal and Submarine Morphology, Methuen & Co., Ltd., London, 1958. A very good book on the subject.

Johnson, D. W.: *Shore Processes and Shoreline Development,* John Wiley & Sons, Inc., New York, 1919. One of the early books on shore lines.

Kuenen, Ph. H.: Marine Geology, John Wiley & Sons, Inc., New York, 1950. A very well known textbook.

Shepard, F. P.: *Submarine Geology,* Harper & Brothers, New York, 1948. A very good text by one of the foremost submarine geologists.

Shepard, F. P.: "Submarine Topography of the Gulf of California," *Geol. Soc. America Mem.* 43, part III, 1950.

Sverdrup, H. V., M. W. Johnson, and R. J. Fleming: *The Oceans: Their Physics, Chemistry, and General Biology,* Prentice-Hall, Inc., Englewood Cliffs, N.J., 1942. A very useful standard text on oceanography.

Chapter 14

GROUND WATER

THE WATER that saturates the pores and cracks of the soil and rocks beneath the surface of the earth is called underground water, or simply ground water. Although it is an agent of gradation, its results are generally not seen aboveground. In this chapter we shall discuss not only the corrosive effects of ground water but also the mineral deposits it leaves. In addition, we shall study the geologic conditions which are likely to provide us with this important resource. Ground water, which is removed from the ground by digging, boring, or drilling wells, supplies much—and, in some areas, all—of the water needed for domestic and industrial uses.

Occurrence and Movements

Along with the waters of the oceans, lakes, rivers, and the air, underground water completes the sphere of the earth known as the hydrosphere. It is that portion of the hydrosphere which fills voids in the lithosphere.

SOURCES

Of the three sources of ground water, the most important is *meteoric* water, which falls from the atmosphere as rain or snow (Fig. 4.20).

A second source of ground water is the water that occupied the spaces between sediments as they were being laid down on the floors of oceans or lakes. Such trapped water, called *connate* water, is com-

FIG. 14.0. *Ground water flowing through a cave in Endless Caverns, near New Market, Virginia. Mineral-bearing waters seeping into the cave from above have coated the rock shelf with a sheet of travertine (calcium carbonate) that continues over the edge in pendant form. (Endless Caverns Corporation.)*

monly found along with oil in the productive beds of many oil fields. Connate water usually differs in composition from present sea water, for during the long periods of geologic time that it has been in the rocks, it has dissolved additional mineral matter, has lost some to the rocks, or has been diluted. Some connate water is found as a strong brine.

A third possible source of ground water is the steam derived from deep-seated magmas. Such *magmatic*, or juvenile, water is added to the regional ground water wherever large masses of magma are thrust upward into the outer crust of the earth. The waters of certain hot springs are probably, in part, of magmatic origin, especially in such areas as Yellowstone Park and the region of the active geysers in New Zealand. Magmatic waters are thought to be the sources of certain ores and of unusual mineral deposits.

DESCENT OF GROUND WATER

The amount of rain water that penetrates the earth is determined by several main factors, as follows:

Amount and type of precipitation. Within cer-

tain limits the amount of water that soaks into the ground is determined by the amount and type of precipitation. In desert areas ground water generally lies deep, and little water occurs near the surface, because there is little rain.

Rate of precipitation. The more rapidly rain falls, the less water sinks into the ground, for the surface soon becomes saturated. The same is true of the melting of snow—the more rapid the rate of melting, the less water sinks into the ground, especially into frozen ground.

Surface slope. The steeper the slope of the ground, the greater the amount of runoff. The flatter the ground, the greater the percentage of water that sinks below the surface, because the runoff is retarded and the water has a longer time to soak into the ground.

Rock and soil porosity. Weathered and stratified rocks are usually more favorable for the entrance

FIG. 14.1. *Spherical particles in circumscribed cubes, showing the method of packing of mineral grains of uniform size that would produce maximum porosity in a rock. The spheres occupy only slightly more than half the volume of the cubes.*

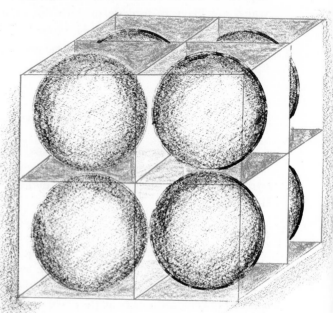

FIG. 14.2. *Photographs of sand and gravel, illustrating the effect of grain size and degree of sorting on the pore size. This, in turn, influences the permeability. Upper right, all coarse with large pores and high permeability. Lower right, all fine with very small pores and low permeability. Upper left, all intermediate. Lower left, mixture of the other three; here the fine grains fill the pores between the larger grains and thus decrease the permeability.*

of water than massive, igneous rock. The porosity of a rock is determined by the voids it contains (Fig. 14.1). Thus if 1 gallon of sand will hold

0.3 gallon of water when saturated, the porosity is said to be 30 per cent, for three-tenths of its volume is made up of pores between the grains. The porosity of different types of rock varies from less than 1 per cent in massive granite to more than 40 per cent in poorly cemented sandstones. The granite selected for Grant's Tomb was considered the strongest granite in the United States. Porosity tests showed that it possessed about ¼ of 1 per cent pore space. Thus, even the strongest and most massive of rocks contain measurable pores.

The porosity of sedimentary materials depends on the following factors:

1. The shape and arrangement of the constituent particles

2. The degree of sorting of the particles (Fig. 14.2)

3. The degree of compaction and cementation

4. The amount of mineral matter removed through solution by percolating waters

Rock and soil permeability. Permeability, or the ability of a rock formation to transmit water or other fluids, is a measure of the velocity of percolation and may be said to be the rate at which a rock will allow water to pass through it under a given amount of pressure.

A rock with high porosity is not necessarily highly permeable. The permeability varies with the degree of sorting and with the arrangement of grains of coarse and fine material. Coarse-grained sand and clean gravel, without fine-grained particles in the spaces between grains, are the most permeable rock substances, and water moves through

FIG. 14.3. *Diagram showing the relation of the water table to hills and valleys, intermittent and permanent streams, and lakes and swamps. The arrows show the trend of the water movement underground as gravity attempts to level out the water table.*

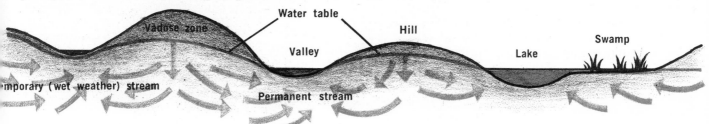

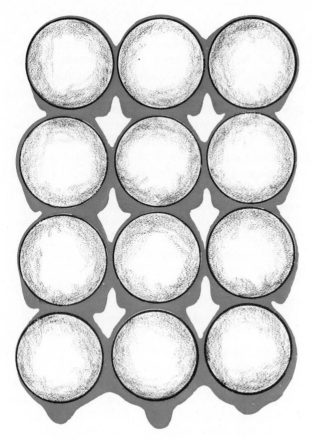

FIG. 14.4. *Diagram showing how water clings to solid particles against the pull of gravity as in the soil zone. (From a photograph by L. J. Briggs.)*

zontal, the water passing downward must also cross the least permeable layers.

Amount and type of vegetation. Plants, and organic matter derived from plants, check the flow of surface water, and therefore more water sinks below the surface. Forests and meadows hold back the runoff, retard evaporation, and increase infiltration.

Atmospheric humidity. If the humidity is low immediately after a shower, much of the rainfall evaporates before it can sink into the earth. This is especially true in arid regions, where even after heavy rains the bulk of the water evaporates and passes again into the atmosphere.

FIG. 14.5. *Diagram showing the distribution of subsurface water.*

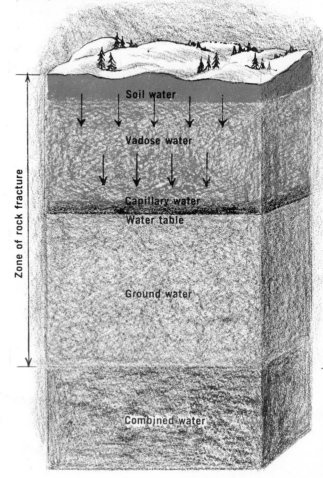

them readily. On the other hand, clays and shales, though very porous, are relatively impermeable.

The quantitative unity of permeability, as measured on a permeameter in a laboratory, is a millidarcy, one-thousandth of a Darcy. Sandstone permeabilities vary from less than 1 to more than 50,000 millidarcys, with many in the range of a few tens to several hundred millidarcys. Tests on natural earth materials by the U.S. Geological Survey show that rocks differ in relative permeability through a range of 1 to 450,000,000, from the least to the most permeable.

Rock structure. Inclined strata allow more water to penetrate the earth than do flat-lying beds. Water passing down inclined beds follows the most permeable layers. However, if the beds are hori-

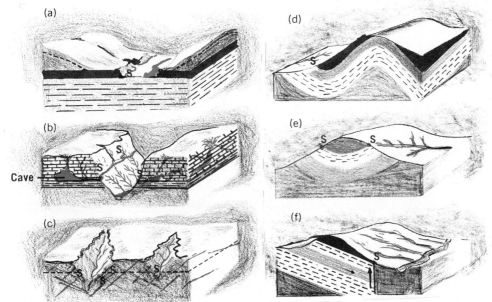

FIG. 14.6. *Diagrams showing various kinds of subsurface rock structures favorable for the formation of springs. Locations of springs are marked by S.*

LEVEL OF GROUND WATER

The terms ground-water level, water table, and plane of saturation are commonly used to describe the upper surface of a zone of saturation within the earth. This saturated zone sometimes is called the *phreatic* zone (Greek *phrear*, a well). Below the ground-water level the openings in rocks are filled with water (Fig. 14.3). The upper limit of this zone of saturation is not a plane but an undulating surface. However, although it tends to follow the undulations of the topography of a region, it is more regular. It generally lies lower below a valley than below a hilltop, but it lies deeper below the surface of a hilltop than below the surface of a valley.

Ground-water level is controlled by several factors, such as the amount of rainfall, the amount of evaporation, and the permeability of the rocks. The general level does not respond immediately to rainfall, because of the time required for the water to percolate downward through the unsaturated materials above the water table. In fact, during a heavy or sustained rainfall a saturated zone may be formed near the surface, constituting a *temporary perched* water table at some distance above the plane of general saturation.

The rise of the water table following a period of rainfall is always less than the number of inches of precipitation, because of runoff, losses through evaporation, absorption by vegetation, and absorption by decomposed rock materials in the unsaturated zone above. The difference in elevation between the top of this zone in a wet year and in a dry year is normally greater under the hilltops than under the slopes and the valleys. Since the water table oscillates with seasonal climatic changes, a certain zone within the earth is above ground-water level in dry periods but below it during wet periods. In moist hilly regions this alternately wet and dry zone may be of considerable vertical extent.

A moist fringe is drawn upward a few inches, by capillary openings, to a few feet above the water table, and some water also is held in the soil by surface tension, in spite of the pull of gravity (Fig. 14.4). Between is the intermittently wet and dry *vadose*, or *aeration*, zone, a zone favorable to leaching and oxidation (Fig. 14.5).

EFFLUENT AND INFLUENT STREAMS

The water table on either side of a river usually slopes toward the stream; contrary to the common belief that ground-water supplies are replenished by rivers, the reverse is more often true. Most rivers are essentially surface streams that receive

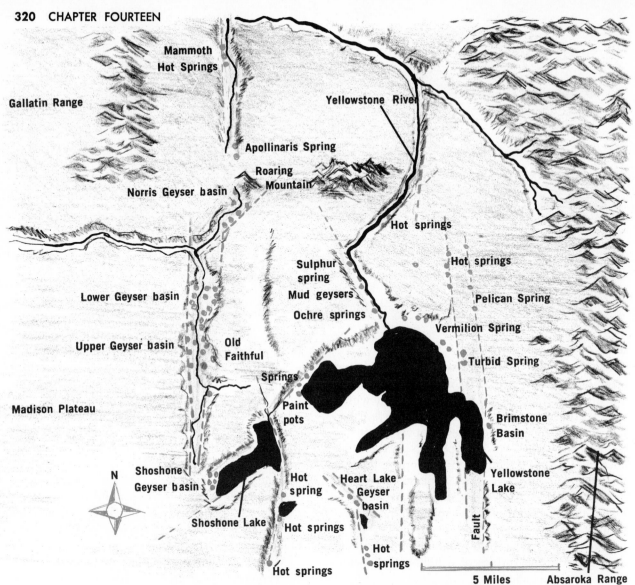

FIG. 14.7. *The Yellowstone Basin, showing the distribution of geysers and hot springs. (After Lobeck, from Atlas of American Geology.)*

ground water from springs and seepage and do not contribute to the zone of saturation. Such rivers, known as effluent streams, lie in troughs on the water table, and the ground water flows toward them. In arid regions, however, the local conditions may be such that the zone of saturation lies below a river and the stream actually loses water into the earth. Such a river, known as an influent stream, lies on a ridge in the water table.

PERCHED WATER TABLE

Under certain conditions a body of water in porous or pervious material may be perched, or suspended, within the zone of aeration above the main water table. These bodies of water are generally found above an irregularly shaped mass of impermeable rock, above basin-shaped beds of clay, or in lenses or wedge-shaped masses of sand

FIG. 14.8. *Old Faithful Geyser in eruption, Yellowstone National Park, Wyoming. (Northern Pacific Railway.)*

and gravel, which catch and hold the downward-percolating water. Perched water tables commonly occur in arid and semiarid regions and may be important sources of water.

In parts of the glaciated region of northeastern North America, where large areas are covered by a thick mantle of clayey glacial drift, many of the lake basins lie above the regional water table. The perched water in such lakes is prevented from percolating downward to the main water table by the impermeable clay layers between the floors of the lakes and the normal regional water table.

MOVEMENT OF GROUND WATER

Above the water table, ground water moves downward without much lateral dispersion. In the zone of saturation the water is not stationary but

tends to migrate slowly along the paths of least resistance through the rocks. If there is a lower outlet along the bottom of a valley, lake, or other basin, the water will move there, even though it may follow a very crooked route before it finds a point where it can issue again at the surface. If the paths of least resistance are downward, the water may sink to great depths before it rises through some permeable formation or fracture which crops out at a point lower than that at which the water first entered the saturated zone. The cause of this movement is gravity, and the water travels from high levels to low ones in proportion to the "hydraulic gradient."

In the zone of aeration. The downward movement of water toward the zone of saturation is termed the vadose, or shallow, circulation. The zone of aeration varies in thickness, since its lower limit is determined by the position of the ground-water level. Near permanent streams or lakes or other bodies of water it is close to the surface. In

FIG. 14.9. *Diagrammatic section illustrating geyser eruption according to the theory of Bunsen. Ground water in fractures and vents below the surface is heated to the boiling point at depth, near the main source of heat, before it reaches the boiling point in the upper part of the vent (see table, page 324). For simplicity only a few fractures are shown.*

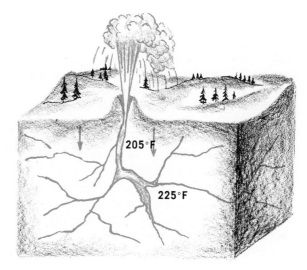

FIG. 14.10. *Travertine deposits named Opal Ter-races at Mammoth Hot Springs, Yellowstone National Park, Wyoming. Hot mineral-spring water carrying calcium carbonate in solution rises to the surface and slowly overflows these shallow pools. Cooling, loss of carbon dioxide, evaporation, and algae cause precipitation of travertine on the bottoms and rims of the pools. The light-colored embankment in the middle distance is a large deposit of similar origin. (Northern Pacific Railway.)*

hilly regions with average rainfall, however, it may lie at depths of a few to several hundred feet. In arid regions, where the amount of rainfall is small and evaporation rapid, the zone of aeration may extend to much greater depths.

In the zone of saturation. Below the water table the circulation of water depends on (1) the relief of the region, or potential head; (2) the number, continuity, spacing, and size of the openings in the rocks; (3) the inclination of the layers of sediments or lava; and (4) possible barriers of clay, shale, or other relatively impermeable rocks. As a rule, the flow of water in this deeper zone is much slower than in the zone of aeration, because the openings are smaller and less numerous. For this reason friction on their walls is greater. In fine-grained rocks the underground circulation becomes exceedingly sluggish, the water moving perhaps not more than a few feet per year.

Below the zone of saturation. The depth to which the surface waters penetrate varies with the character of the rocks. In some rocks, surface waters reach a depth of several thousand feet, whereas in others very little water is collected at depths of more than a few hundred feet. In the copper-bearing rocks of Keweenaw Point, Michigan, shafts have been sunk more than a mile below the surface, and at a number of places the rocks are dry near the lower ends of the shafts.

SPRINGS

Springs are formed wherever underground waters flow to the surface through natural openings in the ground. The rate and manner of flow are regulated by the geological structure of the mantle-rock and of underlying formations (Fig. 14.6). Ground water always flows along the planes or channels of least resistance. At first it percolates and seeps slowly through the rocks, but in time it wears well-defined courses. Springs usually issue upon a hillside or in a valley. An ordinary hillside spring is formed where sand, gravel, sandstone, or other porous strata rest upon impervious beds. Where the water comes to the surface along an escarpment, it "weeps" out in the form of hundreds of small seepage springs. If the strata are inclined, deep-seated fissure springs or artesian springs may issue through points along fault planes that cut the impervious strata. Such fissure springs may discharge fresh water on the floor of the sea, where it rises through the heavier salt water before it mixes with the sea water. Such springs are found along the coast of the Mediterranean Sea. In the Gulf of Argos, Greece, a body of fresh water, estimated to extend over an area 50 feet in diameter, probably represents the exit of a fissure spring, for it discharges fresh water with such force that it forms a convex surface on the sea.

HOT SPRINGS

Hot springs are vents in the earth's crust from which hot water issues. Some hot springs and a considerable number of warm ones are found in areas remote from igneous centers, and it is believed that the water of such springs is normal rain water that has penetrated the ground and moved downward to great depths. The temperature of the earth's crust increases downward at a rate of about 1°F for every 60 feet. Ground water at a depth of 1 mile is about 90°F hotter than the average surface temperature; and if such water were to rise without much dilution, it would be noticeably warmer than surface water. Upward passage is evidently made possible in places by deep-reaching, large-scale fractures called *faults*, along which many hot springs are aligned (Fig. 14.7).

Other hot springs, including the hottest ones, are found in volcanic areas. This association suggests a connection between certain hot springs and igneous rocks which are cooling.

Gases like those which issue from the surface in volcanic areas are present also in many hot springs, and certain vents which emit gases in dry seasons become hot springs in wet seasons. *Boiling springs* are those in which the gases erupt vigorously and agitate the water. *Paint pots* and *ink bowls* are springs that contain rock fragments, particularly oxidized particles of iron, which color the water yellow or red. Algae, which are simple forms of vegetable life, thrive in the warm waters of certain springs. Some of them are brightly colored, and they color the walls of the springs.

GEYSERS

Description. Geysers are intermittently spouting hot springs from which the water is expelled vigorously at intervals. They are much less common than ordinary hot springs, but groups of geysers are situated in Yellowstone Park in the United States (Fig. 14.7), in Iceland, and in New Zealand —all areas of recent volcanic activity. Certain geysers, when they erupt, throw hot water a few hundred feet into the air. In others the water reaches only a few feet above the surface. Most geysers are active at irregular intervals. In some the eruptions occur many days apart; in others the intervals are weeks or months. In general, the water of geysers does not differ from that of other hot springs. In certain geysers, after the activity ceases, some of the water flows back into the vent.

One of the best-known geysers is Old Faithful

FIG. 14.11.   *Two stages of erosion of an area of flat-lying limestone in which underground drainage is developed.   The caves are shown in color. (After A. K. Lobeck, Kentucky Geological Survey.)*

of Yellowstone Park (Fig. 14.8) which for many years erupted regularly at intervals of less than 60 minutes. In recent years this interval has changed somewhat; yet the geyser is still comparatively regular in its eruptions.

The eruption of a geyser is preceded by rumblings and by violent boiling. The water flows over the top of the vent, and soon low columns of spouting water appear. These are followed by strong jets, which are thrown scores of feet into the air.

Explanation of activity. The theory of geyser eruption generally accepted is that of Bunsen, who studied the geysers of Iceland. It is based on the fact that the temperature at which water boils increases with pressure. This temperature is 212°F at sea level, where the pressure on the water is 1 atmosphere, or about 14.7 pounds per square inch. (A column of water 33 feet high has a pressure of about 1 atmosphere; that is, a column of water 1 square inch in cross section and 33 feet

FIG. 14.12. *Fluted and pitted limestone cave, Nakimu Caves, Glacier National Park, British Columbia. (Canadian Government Travel Bureau.)*

FIG. 14.13. *Dendrites of manganese oxide deposited as mosslike growths on walls of narrow fissures, Bavaria, Germany. (B. M. Shaub.)*

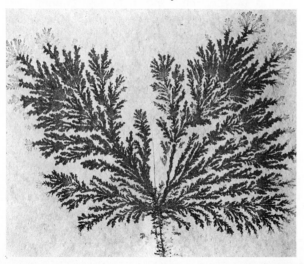

long weighs about 14.7 pounds.) As the depth increases, the weight of the overlying water results in greater pressure, which, in turn, raises the boiling point of water. The relation of boiling points to various pressures is shown in Table 14.1.

TABLE 14.1 *Relation of Boiling Point to Depth and Pressure*

(1) Sample depths, feet	(2) Pressure, atmospheres	(3) Boiling point, °F
0	1	212
33	2	248
295	10	357
787	25	437

The hot water thrown from a geyser is mainly rain water that has soaked into the ground and that has been heated by hot lavas or other igneous rocks. Some of the steam (later condensed to water) and other gases may have come from the magma that formed the cooling igneous rocks.

If the water flows into a fissure, or tube (Fig. 14.9), and becomes warm with depth by absorbing hot gases or by contact with hot rocks, it may remain as water, even though it is much hotter than 212°F, the boiling point of water at sea level. It does not become steam because of the water pressure above it. If water continues to enter the tube, ultimately it will flow over at the surface, and water from below will rise to take the place of the overflow; but the water at great depths is so hot that it would become steam if it were not for the great pressure of the overlying water column.

Finally the temperature rises to such a point that steam does form, even under the great pressure. This steam pushes up the column of water and, mixing with the water above, makes it lighter; soon some of the water spills over at the top and reduces the pressure. Then part of the superheated water flashes into steam, and an eruption follows. Probably the superheating of water at great depths in this manner causes the eruption of some geysers, and the collection of steam and other gases in the high parts of crooked tubes of geysers causes the eruption of others. The crookedness of tubes prevents the convection of heat, thereby hastens local boiling, and prohibits the continuous overflow that characterizes simple hot springs.

DISSOLVED SOLIDS IN SPRING WATER

Even the clearest and most sparkling spring water contains some dissolved mineral matter. As a rule, this consists principally of bicarbonates and sulfates of calcium, magnesium, and sodium, with smaller amounts of chlorides, silicates, and phosphates of these and other elements. Some of these materials are taken into solution through the action of carbon dioxide absorbed by rain from the atmosphere. Other materials are derived from decomposing rock and organic matter in the soil. In areas covered with a mantle of humus, organic acids are abstracted from the soil and help to decompose minerals and to form soluble salts.

The amount of dissolved mineral matter carried in solution by spring waters is enormous. Thousands of tons of gypsum are emitted annually at the springs of Leuk, in Switzerland, and the famous springs at Bath, in England, bring up so much mineral matter in solution yearly that, if it were taken out of the water and made into a monument, it would make a column 9 feet in diameter and 140 feet high. In central Florida, Silver Springs carry about 600 tons of mineral matter daily, and Falls Creek, in Oklahoma, receives water from springs that carry so much lime that a series of natural dams of travertine have been deposited across the stream valley. Most of the mineral matter in waters discharged by seepages and springs, however, is carried by streams to the ocean.

SPRING DEPOSITS

When mineral-laden spring waters emerge from the ground, they are subject to evaporation; to cooling of hot solutions; to loss of carbon dioxide through agitation, release of pressure, or warming of cold solutions; and to the work of bacteria, algae, and other organisms. All these changes tend to cause deposition of the mineral matter.

FIG. 14.14. *Dripstone below a joint crack in the roof of Mayfield Cave, Texas. Its forms include (1) slender, hollow, pendant tubes that resemble soda straws, (2) stouter, iciclelike stalactites, (3) stalagmite mounds on the floor, and (4) continuous columns or pillars where stalactites and stalagmites join. This array, here only about a foot high, shows in miniature the different stages of development that are equally representative of similar features many tens of feet long. (James F. Quinlan, Jr.)*

Calcium carbonate is the salt most abundantly deposited by both hot and cold springs. It frequently forms great beds near the outlets, and at resorts it clogs the pipes that lead the hot water to bathing pools. The calcareous material deposited by springs around their vents is *tufa,* or *travertine,* and because of the long-continued overflow, much of it is in the form of terraces (Fig. 14.10). A banded, crystalline variety, taking a good polish, is "Mexican onyx." Tufa containing fragments cemented together by calcium carbonate is a breccia; some of this material is highly prized as ornamental stone.

Geyserite, or *siliceous sinter,* is a term applied to siliceous hot-spring deposits, particularly to those made by geysers. Where its deposits are abundant, a geyser may build a mound (Fig. 14.8) or a bowllike structure around the orifice. Silica occurs

FIG. 14.15. *Stalactites and stalagmites, some of them joined to form pillars in the Dome Room of Carlsbad Caverns, New Mexico. (Santa Fe Railway.)*

abundantly in many hot waters and is the chief material deposited by the geysers and many of the famous hot springs of Yellowstone National Park.

Other springs deposit such substances as iron hydroxide (ocher), manganese oxide, sodium chloride, sodium carbonate, gypsum, sulfur, and metallic sulfides.

Gradation by Ground Water

SOLUTION

Sinkholes. Water sinks readily into the ground in regions where there are numerous cracks or joints in the rocks. These joints are gradually enlarged by the corrosive work of the descending water. At certain places they become greatly extended parallel to the bedding in rocks having easily dissolved layers (Fig. 14.11). In time these channels become large, so that considerable surface water drains into them. By enlargement of

solution channels along upright fractures or by collapse of the weakened roofs over open underground passages, conspicuous holes form at the surface; these are termed sinkholes, or swallow holes. Such sinks are most commonly found in limestone, gypsum, or salt. Most other rocks have too many insoluble portions to allow cavities to develop.

Occasionally the bottoms of limestone sinks become choked with debris, and so lakes or ponds are formed. Alachua Lake, Florida, is an example. Prior to 1871, the surface drainage of Alachua Prairie emptied into a large sinkhole. That year the outlet of the sink was clogged, and a lake nearly 8 miles long and 4 miles wide was formed. About 20 years later the outlet was opened again, and the lake was drained underground.

Caves. Where pure limestone is attacked, the whole rock is soluble, and therefore nothing remains to fill the space when the strata are dissolved by percolating waters. Thus in the course of time an elaborate system of spacious tunnels and open chambers may be dissolved out of solid rock below the water table (Fig. 14.12).

One of the largest cave systems in the world is that of the Carlsbad Caverns, in New Mexico, located in a region of limestone and gypsum in the Guadalupe Mountains. Because of its enormity and its fantastic display of ornamental deposits of onyx, it was made a national park in 1930. One gallery, the Big Room, is about 4,000 feet long and has a maximum width of 625 feet and a maximum ceiling height of about 300 feet.

Another well-known American cavern is Mammoth Cave, in Kentucky. Some portions of it have been studied and mapped in detail, but many others have never been fully explored. This vast labyrinth consists of several hundred miles of connected galleries, with lakes, rivers, and waterfalls included in the system. These galleries range in height from 1 or 2 feet to more than 100 feet. In some parts of the cave one gallery is located above another. Mammoth Dome, which is an expanded portion of the cavern, is about 400 feet long, 150 feet wide, and 80 to 250 feet high.

Other noted limestone caverns in the United

States are Luray Cave in Virginia, Wyandotte and Marengo Caves in Indiana, Wind Cave in South Dakota, and Marble Cave in Missouri. One of the best-known foreign caverns is at Adelsberg in Italy. Its four great chambers are visited frequently, and festivals are conducted in its grottoes.

Caves in areas having cold winters may contain perennial ice, frozen by intake of heavy, cold air in winter. Popularly known as ice caves, they exhale cool air in summer.

Karst topography. In regions where caves and sinkholes abound, some of the caverns collapse, and a very irregular type of topography is developed. Similarly, portions of the roofs of underground channels and galleries may collapse so as to leave natural bridges. The slopes to the sinkholes and also the slopes of the elevations between them become steep and clifflike. The surface is etched out in a network of numerous short gullies and ravines, which terminate abruptly where they discharge their waters into subterranean channels, and consequently the surface is very rough. Such topography is characteristically developed in the Karst Mountains, northeast of the head of the Adriatic Sea, in an area composed of limestone, and so is classified as karst topography. In the United States somewhat similar topography occurs in the limestone areas of central Tennessee and Kentucky.

The progressive riddling of limestone in a karst area, as sinks and solution basins enlarge to form *solution valleys,* is illustrated in Fig. 14.11.

Residual concentrations. Because of the greater resistance to solution of certain minerals, extensive deposits of economic value have been concentrated at or near the surface by the solution and removal of the valueless minerals associated with them. The extensive residual iron ores of Cuba, of the Appalachian region, and of the Lake Superior region in the United States, together with great deposits of manganese and aluminum ores in various parts of the world, owe their concentration to the solvent action of ground water.

Relatively insoluble substances, such as clays, chert, barite, gold, and many gem stones, also accumulate as residuals.

FIG. 14.16. *The Cave Man, a large stalagmite and other dripstone deposits, Carlsbad Caverns National Park, New Mexico. (New Mexico State Tourist Bureau.)*

DEPOSITION

A considerable portion of the mineral matter taken into solution by ground water is later deposited. Subsurface waters in the zone of leaching (zone of aeration), above the ground-water table,

FIG. 14.17. *Stalactites, stalagmites, and pillars in the caverns of Luray, Virginia. (Luray Caverns Corp.)*

form veins (Figs. 7.14 to 7.18). Vein fillings also are developed when hot magmatic waters or vapors penetrate the rocks. The precipitation is brought about by the cooling effect produced by the fissure walls, by surface waters, or by chemical reactions with the minerals lining the fractures. For example, an acid solution flowing through a fissure in limestone may be neutralized in contact with the calcium carbonate, and the mineral matter in solution may be deposited to fill the fissure, thus forming a mineral vein.

Many of the veins formed by the precipitation of minerals from hot magmatic waters charged with sulfur compounds contain sulfides of metals such as copper, lead, zinc, and silver. Where such ore minerals are present in sufficient quantities, the veins are mined and the metals extracted. Most veins formed from cold meteoric ground waters are filled with quartz and calcite, and some pyrite also may be present.

Mosslike, incomplete fillings of narrow cracks by manganese oxide form *dendrites* (Fig. 14.13).

Cements. The deposition of silica, calcium carbonate, iron oxide, or other mineral matter between the grains of a substance such as sand or gravel serves as cement to convert loose sediments into solid rock (Fig. 9.5).

Concretions. Under certain conditions chemical precipitation takes place about some nucleus, such as animal remains, a leaf, or even a pebble. Deposition, once started, seems to lead to further precipitation on the same surface, and so concentric layers of mineral are built up (Fig. 9.23). Rounded, irregular bodies called concretions are formed in this manner. They are most commonly developed in rather permeable sedimentary rocks. Many coal beds contain concretionary masses of iron sulfide in the form of the mineral marcasite. Concretions are also made of calcite, quartz, gypsum, barium sulfate, calcium phosphate, or other compounds.

Geodes and vugs. Cavities in rocks may become lined with crystals by precipitation from ground water. Geodes are round or egg-shaped examples, generally a few inches in diameter (Fig. 5.11). They have a hollow interior. Larger crystal-lined

are largely acidic solvents, whereas beneath the water table they become alkaline by reaction with the calcium, magnesium, sodium, and potassium of the rocks through which they pass. Such neutralization of acidity, loss of carbon dioxide, or other chemical changes may cause precipitation of dissolved solids.

The principal underground deposits are in the form of veins; cements in sediments; concretions; geodes and vugs; caliche; and stalagmites, stalactites, and other types of dripstone in caves. We have already discussed the mounds, cones, and terraces of travertine and geyserite built by springs and geysers at the surface.

Veins. At places, mineral-bearing waters deposit their loads upon the walls of cracks or joints to

openings, called vugs, are also encountered in some mineral veins. They may yield excellent mineral specimens.

Caliche. In certain semiarid regions capillary action draws lime-bearing waters to the surface, where, by evaporation, a lime-rich deposit called caliche is formed as a cement in the surface debris. In the desert of Chile and Peru the caliche consists of sodium nitrate.

Other evaporites at the surface form *efflorescences,* or if substantial, *alkali spots,* or even *alkali flats.*

Stalactites and stalagmites. When a region is dissected by streams and the water table is lowered to below cave level, deposition in the cave may be caused by water entering the cave from above. Caves opened by solution below the water table may later be filled above the water table by dripstone.

Most of the mineral matter deposited in caves is calcium carbonate. It assumes various forms, among them stalactites, which are attached to the roof of the cavern or to some projecting edge, and stalagmites, which form on the limestone floor of the cavern and build upward to make mounds and cones (Figs. 14.14, 14.15).

Stalactites assume many shapes, determined by the manner in which the water trickles over them and by the amount of water present. Beautiful forms fringed with crystals of calcite, curtainlike draperies hanging from the roofs, grotesque shapes that extend from floor to ceiling, and pillars ornamented with many varieties of filigree may be observed in the same cavern.

Stalactites have their beginning on the damp roof of the cave, where drops of water gather and begin to evaporate and lose carbon dioxide. The drops then become saturated with carbonate and deposit the excess as rings at their margins. Drop after drop lengthens the ring into a long pendant with a hole in the middle, resembling a pipestem. An iciclelike stalactite broken across shows a radial structure, with fibrous crystals around the hole passing across concentric zones of growth. The growing stalactite, kept moist by calcium-bearing water trickling over its surface, is lengthened at

FIG. 14.18. *Cross section of a petrified tree trunk that has been completely replaced by opal (silica and water). The structure of the original woody tissue has been preserved. (American Museum of Natural History.)*

the lower end and thickened from the center of the structure.

Stalactites that reach the floor of the cave become solid stalks, which may thicken into massive *columns* or *pillars.* Many pillars are formed by the union of stalagmites that grow upward from the floor with stalactites that hang from the roof (Fig. 14.16).

Some of the deposits in Carlsbad Caverns, New Mexico, are extensive; Twin Domes, for example,

FIG. 14.19. *A large petrified log in Petrified Forest National Monument, Holbrook, Arizona. (National Park Service.)*

is an enormous stalagmite mass more than 200 feet wide at the base and over 100 feet high. Giant Dome, another stalagmite, is about 16 feet in diameter and 62 feet high.

Luray Cave, in the Shenandoah Valley, Virginia (Fig. 14.17), is famous for its brilliantly colored stalactites, with as many as 40,000 visible from a single point. One celebrated group is that of the Swords of the Titans, composed of eight staffs, 50 feet long, 3 to 8 feet wide, and as much as 2 feet thick.

REPLACEMENT

Where solution and deposition progress simultaneously, one mineral may be dissolved and another may be deposited in its place. This process, called replacement or substitution, produces pseudomorphs and petrified wood, bone, or shell.

Pseudomorphs. A crystal of iron sulfide may be replaced by iron oxide and yet retain the shape of the sulfide crystal. Such a replacement is a pseudomorph (false form). By studying pseudomorphs, we can trace the changes through which a mineral or rock has passed. In some areas an altered sedimentary rock can be traced back to the unaltered sedimentary rock, and the changes can be followed step by step, because the grain, bedding, and other features of the original rock are preserved in the altered rock after metamorphism.

Igneous rocks also are profoundly changed by replacement. Much material is removed, and other material takes its place. Commonly, however, the texture or pattern of the rock is preserved, because the outlines of the original crystals form the outlines of the replacing crystals or of the groups of replacing crystals. By comparing the textures of the fresh and altered rocks, we can see that they were once alike and were formerly parts of the same body.

Petrifaction. If the material replaced is of organic origin, it becomes petrified by the mineral matter that replaces it. Thus, if a log or stump is buried in a bed of sand or volcanic ash that later becomes saturated with ground water, the wood is slowly replaced as it is removed (Fig. 14.18). Eventually a large tree trunk may be converted into a solid mass of silica. The famous petrified logs and forests of Arizona owe their origin to this process. Erosion has again exposed them, so that, at present, silicified stumps and logs occur at the earth's surface (Fig. 14.19).

In addition to wood, bones and shells can be petrified.

Water Supply

WELLS

Prehistoric man used the water from springs, brooks, rivers, and lakes. His villages were built where water was readily obtained at the surface. However, with the growth of civilization, large quantities of water were required in regions where surface water was not available or where it was too polluted for domestic use. Digging or boring for water dates back to very early historic times, especially in China and India. In Babylonia irrigation works were constructed as early as 2000 B.C. In present-day India more land is irrigated from wells than from streams.

Most wells are holes dug or bored into the earth to a point below the water table. They serve as reservoirs into which the ground water percolates. If the water level is near the surface, the wells are shallow. On high plateaus where the water level is as much as several hundred feet below the surface, correspondingly deep wells are required to reach water. Most wells are sunk until they penetrate a permeable rock below the water table. This often means boring through hundreds of feet of impermeable clays or shales that are saturated with water. However, the pore spaces in such rocks are so minute that water cannot flow through them rapidly enough to supply the well adequately.

Even in highly permeable rocks, the removal of water through a well draws the water table down adjacent to the well, so that the water table slopes toward the well (Fig. 14.20). In materials of low permeability such a *cone of depression* is steep and may have a radius of no more than a few hundred feet. In uniformly permeable sands and gravels, however, the cone of depression from one well may extend several thousand feet from the pumping well and interfere with neighboring wells.

ARTESIAN WELLS

Description. Artesian wells received their name from Artois, a province in France, where the water in many wells rises above the surface of the earth, as in a fountain. Today the term artesian well is applied to any deep well from which ground water is obtained under pressure, even though the water does not rise to overflowing.

Causes. Artesian flow takes place because of differences in the pressure under which ground water exists in different parts of a water-bearing stratum. The principle is that water seeks its own level. Gravity is the force causing it to seek that level, and the pressure produced by gravity acting on

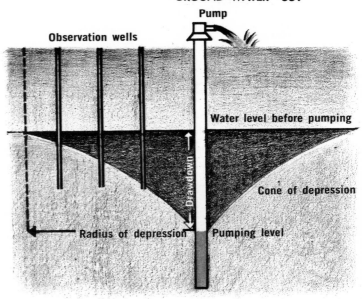

FIG. 14.20. *Diagram showing a cone of depression of the water level around a well that is being pumped.*

water is called *hydrostatic* pressure. Technically, hydrostatic pressure is the property of water which enables pressure to be transmitted equally throughout it in all directions almost instantly. If an object is placed in a body of clear water at rest, hydrostatic pressure may be thought of as the force causing the space occupied by the object to fill up when the object is removed.

In an artesian system the water-bearing bed may be compared to a water-filled tube in which the intake is higher than the outlet. The following conditions are essential for a flowing artesian well (Fig. 14.21) in sedimentary strata:

1. There must be a previous stratum, the aquifer, which water enters and passes through, to function as a conduit.

2. There must be an impermeable bed above the permeable layer to confine the water and prevent it from escaping to the surface in the form of springs.

3. There must be an impermeable stratum below the permeable bed, or else a tightening of the rocks with depth, to prevent the water from escaping downward.

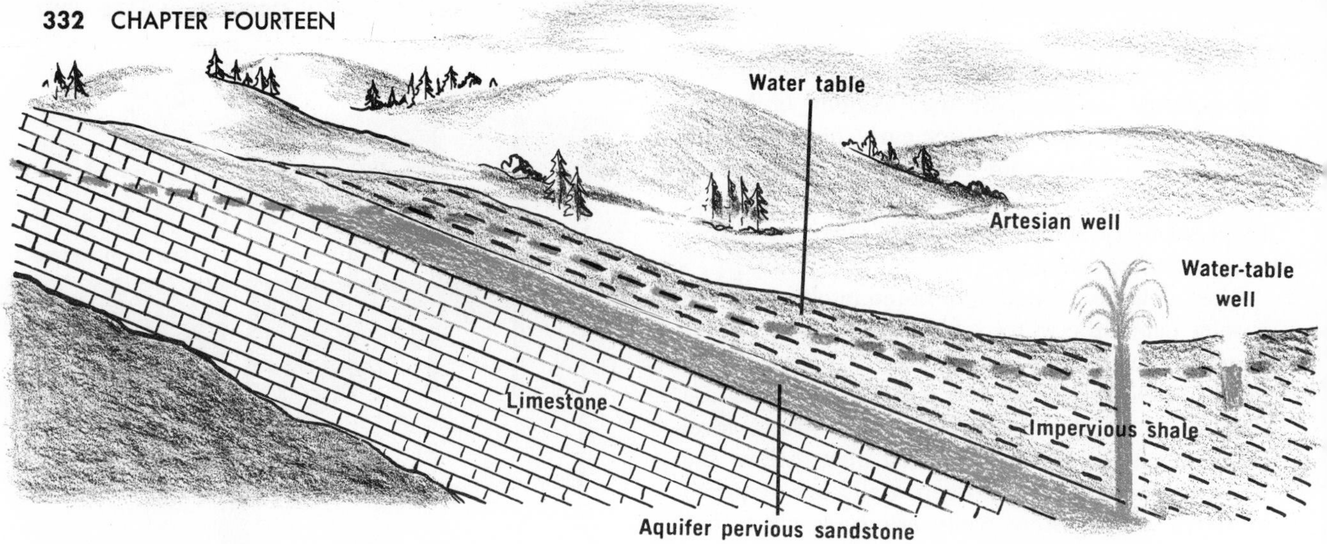

FIG. 14.21. *Diagram showing subsurface conditions favorable for artesian circulation.*

4. There must be an inclination from the horizontal of the permeable bed, so that the place at which the water enters this bed is higher than the surface of the earth at the well. The force of gravity will then cause the water to flow downward. This condition is commonly called "head."

5. The porous stratum either must crop out, so that water may enter it, or, if covered, must lie below permeable material at the intake.

6. There must be adequate rainfall to supply water.

These requirements apply only to sedimentary strata. Artesian flows may be obtained from other kinds of rock, even from unconsolidated sediments, but the structural and textural relations must be such that they contain water under hydrostatic pressure. Artesian flows may be obtained from bedding, cleavage, or shearing planes, from solution passages, from joint and fault fractures, and from contacts of sedimentary with igneous or metamorphic rocks.

At many places the sources of the water in the intake areas are scores or even hundreds of miles distant from the wells. In parts of Arkansas, Alabama, California, and Arizona the principal water supplies for irrigation projects are drawn from artesian wells that derive their water from the foothills of mountainous areas scores of miles away.

Depth. The depth of the porous stratum is determined by the geological structural relations. The Grenelle Artesian in the Paris Basin is 2,000 feet deep; a well near Leipzig, Germany, is 5,735 feet deep; one near Pittsburgh, Pennsylvania, is 4,625 feet deep. Most wells in the famous Dakota sandstone basin are 1,000 feet deep or more. Many flowing wells in the glacial drift are less than 100 feet deep.

WATER RESOURCES

Ground water is a natural resource on which a large part of our population depends. It supplies many municipalities and is widely used in agriculture and industry. Wells and springs are estimated currently to furnish an average of 30 to 35 billion gallons per day, or about one-fifth of the total water used for irrigational, industrial, municipal, and rural (household and stock) purposes. These uses account for 63, 17, 11, and 9 per cent, respectively, of all ground-water withdrawals.

Most ground water comes from unconsolidated mantle-rock, from permeable sedimentary rocks, and from some lava flows. In unconsolidated sediments, most of the water comes from (1) alluvial sands and gravels, (2) glacial outwash, (3) stream terraces and flood plains, and (4) sandy coastal-plain deposits. Among the consolidated rocks the greatest yield may be expected from (1) permeable sandstones, (2) cavernous limestones, (3) closely jointed rocks, such as quartzite and granite, and (4) jointed vesicular or cavernous lavas and basalt. Shattering of solid rocks by faulting or folding—or, artificially, by explosives—is helpful in increasing the ground-water supply.

Few of us in the United States have ever had to think much about our water supply. A fairly high average rainfall throughout most of our country and the presence of many large inland rivers and lakes have deluded us into believing that water is one resource about which we need have little concern. During the past few decades, however, we have been forced to recognize that difficulties with our water supply are increasing and that we must eliminate wasteful practices and adopt conservation measures.

To conserve this vital resource, we can (1) restrict the rate of withdrawal of water by pumping to the natural rate of recharging from rainfall, (2) avoid waste, especially from flowing or leaking wells, (3) prevent salt-water encroachment in coastal areas, (4) reduce losses by evaporation or improper irrigation, (5) assist replenishment by facilitating intake and preventing excess runoff, and (6) return used water (as from industrial cooling, air conditioning, or heat-pump installations) to the ground.

Summary

Nearly all ground water is former rain water. Its infiltration depends on the amount and type of precipitation, the rate of precipitation, the slope of the ground, the porosity and permeability of the rocks, the structure of the rocks, the amount and type of vegetation present, and losses by evaporation.

The top of the saturated zone underground is the water table. Below this level, water moves under the pull of gravity as directed by the hydraulic head and the permeability and structure of the enclosing rocks. Some water emerges as seepage, gravity springs, artesian springs, and geysers. Springs in volcanic and faulted areas may be hot. Some spring waters contain considerable dissolved mineral matter.

Ground water, with the aid of carbonic acid, dissolves limestone and develops karst topography with characteristic sinkholes, caves, and solution valleys. Removal of soluble matter from rocks leaves concentrations of insoluble substances, such as clays and ores of iron, manganese, and aluminum.

Ground water deposits mineral matter underground as veins, cements, concretions, geodes, vugs, and cave deposits (stalactites, stalagmites, pillars, and other dripstone). Aboveground it builds up mounds and terraces of travertine and geyserite. By replacement underground, it makes pseudomorphs and petrifies wood, bone, and shell.

Ground water supplies our dug, bored, and drilled wells. Under favorable structural and topographic conditions, some wells encounter artesian pressures and even overflow. The water requirements for agricultural, industrial, and domestic use are very large. Since ground water is a renewable resource, conservation practices designed to reduce waste and increase recharge are helpful.

We can appreciate ground water for the resource it is, for the caves it carves and adorns, and for the valuable ore veins and mineral concentrations it provides.

Suggestions for Further Reading

Allen, E. T., and A. L. Day: "Hot Springs of the Yellowstone National Park," *Carnegie Inst. Wash. Pub. No.* 466, 1935.

Baker, D. M., and H. Conkling: *Water Supply and Utilization,* John Wiley & Sons, Inc., New York, 1930.

Barth, T. F. W.: "Volcanic Geology: Hot Springs and Geysers of Iceland," *Carnegie Inst. Wash. Pub. No.* 587, 1950. A study of an area famous for its hot springs.

Casteret, Norbert: *Ten Years under the Earth,* The Greystone Press, New York, 1938. A nontechnical work on underground caves and water.

Mohr, C. E., and H. N. Sloane: *Celebrated American Caves,* Rutgers University Press, Rutgers, N.J., 1955. A nontechnical collection of cave-area descriptions, showing more popular cave aspects.

Stefferud, Alfred (ed.): *Water,* Yearbook of the U.S. Department of Agriculture, 1955.

Thomas, Harold E.: *The Conservation of Ground Water,* McGraw-Hill Book Company, Inc., New York, 1951. A book discussing ground water and its effect on man.

Tolman, C. F.: *Ground Water,* McGraw-Hill Book Company, Inc., New York, 1937. Still a good textbook on the subject.

Chapter 15

WIND AS AN AGENT
OF GRADATION

THE EARTH'S ATMOSPHERE is made up of air, and wind is air in motion. Winds usually are regarded as currents of air moving more or less parallel to the earth's surface; but their flow often is turbulent—moving upward or downward and twisting and turning with momentary conditions. Winds are essentially density currents moving from high- to low-pressure areas, although their load of moisture, or dust, may modify their flow. They react to resistances of any kind, and anomalies are numerous.

Wind takes over the work of erosion in arid regions, where stream erosion is slight. However, wind work is not confined to desert areas. In this chapter we shall study the ways in which wind serves as an agent of gradation and the structures which result from its work.

Erosion by Wind

NATURE OF WIND WORK

The energy which causes wind is derived from the heat of the sun. Part of this energy is expended in moving water vapor from the ocean to the land, where it falls as rain, and in shifting the finer rock particles on the earth's surface. Gradation by the wind is the movement and deposition of these rock particles. Since these materials are land-derived, such wind work is more important over the land than over the sea; nevertheless, wind-borne dust and silt may be carried far out

FIG. 15.0. *Wind-blown sand in Death Valley, California. (Frashers, Inc.)*

to the sea and ultimately dropped into the water.

Winds do not have the concentrated thrust and steadiness of the great rivers, so that the work of wind, on the whole, is less important than the work of streams. Wind activity, however, is very important in arid regions, where there is a plentiful supply of fine rock waste and very little vegetation and where stream work is at a minimum. In such areas the wind tends to compensate for the reduction of the work of streams and to supplement their activity. But wind work may be significant in other regions as well, for even the most humid areas have a dry season favorable to wind activity,

FIG. 15.1. *Cave rocks near Sierra La Sal, Dry Valley, Utah. In this wind-swept plain and mesa area wind is a powerful eroding agent. Loose material is carried away by the wind as fast as it is weathered. Note the scoured and grooved section of the bedrock. (Jackson, U.S. Geological Survey.)*

and wind-borne dust may be carried to them despite the prevailing moist climate.

METHODS OF EROSION

In loose, dry materials the impact of the wind itself is sufficient to remove vast quantities of earthy matter by the process of *deflation* (Latin *deflare*, to blow away). Eddies, whirlwinds, and updrafts help the wind to lift and remove its load in this way. Thus many exposed uplands are swept free of loose material as fast as weathering produces it (Fig. 15.1). The remaining particles are the heavy residuals discarded by the wind, which has blown away (deflated) the fine particles that result from the weathering of a rock such as granite.

A more spectacular, but perhaps less important, method of wind erosion is that of *corrasion* and *abrasion* (Latin *abradere*, to scrape off or rub away). In this method, any sand carried by the wind serves as a natural sandblast and operates in much the same manner as the artificially created sandblasts used to clean stone or brick buildings or to carve stone.

EROSION BY DEFLATION

We sometimes see fields of young wheat or corn ruined by the deflation of soil to such an extent that the tender roots are exposed to a withering sun. Fallow land in dry-farming areas is especially subject to this type of damage. In the course of a few days, the wind can blow away an inch or two of soil. The effects of such erosion include deflation basins, lag gravels, and desert pavement.

Deflation basins. The hollows developed by wind erosion in loose or easily deflated material are known as deflation basins (Fig. 15.2). In the Gobi Desert, where solid rock was loosened by weathering, these hollows range from about 300 yards to 30 miles or more in length and from 50 to 400 feet in depth. Since the depths are limited by the position of the regional ground-water level, such hollowed-out areas in very dry regions may extend below sea level.

Lag gravels. Deflation of dust and sand leaves behind coarse particles (granules, pebbles, and larger fragments) as "lag stones" (Fig. 15.2). As these accumulate over a long period of time, they may become so abundant that they form lag gravels, or even a desert pavement, in which the residual fragments touch each other in a nearly continuous layer or mosaic.

Desert varnish. Some lag stones have a thin, shiny, black or brown surface coating of iron-manganese oxide. This is known as desert varnish. The typical desert is a rock plain strewn with lag stones, not a great expanse of sand.

EROSION BY ABRASION

We can also find many examples of wind abrasion, such as the "frosting" and ultimate destruction of glass windows exposed along sandy seashores, the cutting down of telephone poles just above the ground in deserts, the marring of the pyramids in Egypt, and the undercutting of stone building foundations. These examples lead us to place a similar interpretation on many other oddities of wind-swept regions, such as beveled stones, polish, grooves, and various sculpturings.

The sand grains used as tools in the natural sandblast are themselves subjected to wear, so that they become chipped, pitted, and generally reduced in size. Examined with a hand lens, the battered grains may show a "frosted" surface like that of ground glass and concentric percussion cracks like the familiar "moon" texture in glass marbles.

Beveled stones. Some residual stones are beveled by sandblasting to make *einkanter* or *dreikanter*

FIG. 15.2. *Deflation of soft lake beds near Fossil Lake, Lake County, Oregon. Wind erosion of loose material has hollowed out a broad basin, leaving remnants. The highest of these remnants, protected by hard layers or shrubs, is about 6 feet high. In the foreground fragments of hard rock, too heavy to be blown away, remain as lag stones, or residuals.*

(German, one-edged or three-edged) (Fig. 15.3). Einkanter apparently are formed by the cutting of pebbles in a fixed position and with a constant

FIG. 15.3. *Wind-polished and faceted pebbles, or ventifacts, from the Big Horn Basin, Wyoming.*

FIG. 15.4. *Wind-eroded sandstone. The bedding planes of the sandstone have been etched by wind scouring. (Gregory, U.S. Geological Survey.)*

direction of wind. Dreikanter, shaped like brazil nuts, suggest that the pebbles were overturned, perhaps by undermining, so that several facets developed in succession.

Polish. The polish developed on rocks by sandblast or silt blast is generally somewhat dull, but on certain fine-grained hard rocks, such as quartzite, it may be highly lustrous.

Grooves. By means of sand swept along by the wind, solid rock surfaces can be scoured and grooved. In arid regions such grooves are very conspicuous, and where the wind direction varies little, the grooves show a parallel alignment, and their sides become strongly fluted.

Sculpturings. Many odd-shaped landforms are evolved by the combined effects of weathering and wind erosion. These include undercut hills; broad, shallow caves; mushroom rocks; table rocks; pedestals; and similar sculpturings (Fig. 15.4). Small, irregular ridges associated with wind-scoured round-bottomed grooves are called *yardangs*.

Transportation by Wind

METHODS OF TRANSPORTATION

The method by which rock particles are carried by the wind varies according to such factors as the size, shape, and density of the particles. In general, dust particles are carried *in suspension* and sand grains by *traction*, which usually induces *saltation, rolling,* or *creep.*

Suspension. Small angular grains of dust, with relatively large surface areas as compared with their volumes, remain suspended in air better than larger grains or grains with almost spherical smooth surfaces. Light materials are suspended in air more readily than heavy ones. In ordinary winds, sand grains are too heavy to be carried in suspension, so that normally they are moved along the surface of the ground.

For the most part, sand travels within inches of the ground, and rarely more than a few feet from it, although fine sand has been known to rise hundreds of feet and to have been carried in suspension for unusual distances. One example is the uncomfort-

Wind direction

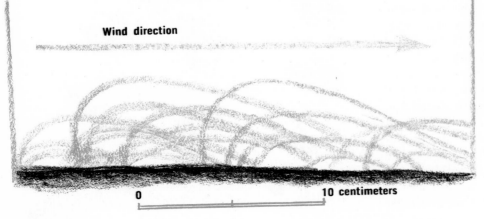

FIG. 15.5. *Lines showing paths of sand grains in saltation over a loose sand surface. (Sketched from a photograph by Bagnold.)*

0   10 centimeters

able blasts of fine sand, carried by strong, turbulent desert winds, that occasionally are encountered by ships passing up and down the Red Sea to and from the Suez Canal.

Traction. Under the traction of the wind, some loose grains of sand merely roll along on the ground. Others are picked up from the surface, carried for some distance forward, and then dropped, only to be picked up and hurled forward again in a series of bounding movements known as saltation (Fig. 15.5). The impacts of the falling grains as they obliquely strike sandy ground urge other grains forward, thus creating a splash effect. These impulses, together with the drag of the wind on the surface over which it flows, cause a forward motion, or creep, of the loose sand.

Saltation and creep, including intermittent rolling, are the most important methods of movement of drifting sand. The buffeted grains, meanwhile, are rounded and reduced by wear, and their surfaces are frosted by the numerous impacts suffered in transit.

VELOCITY AND TURBULENCE

The wind's ability to transport particles is conditioned by its velocity and its turbulence. A light zephyr can carry dust in suspension, and a gentle breeze can roll fine sand. However, a strong breeze, with a velocity of about 25 miles an hour, can move sand grains as much as a millimeter in diameter, and gales and hurricanes can carry sand in suspension to heights of hundreds of feet and can roll pebbles 2 or 3 inches in diameter. Thus the load carried by the wind is a direct function of its velocity.

Most winds are somewhat turbulent, some especially so. Any upward-moving current of air may lift fine particles high above the surface of the ground. A whirlwind (a "dust devil" or "devil wind") is a minor spinning wind of surface origin and upward draft that is characteristic of hot, sunny days. It raises dust and other light materials, which may drift some distance from their origin. The surface effects of such a wind are trivial even over regions where they are common.

A tornado (Fig. 15.6) is a much more violent

FIG. 15.6. *Tornado which occurred near Gothenburg, Nebraska, in the autumn of 1930. Upper left, the tornado cone forming in the clouds; upper right, the fully developed cone approaching the ground; lower left, the cone as it reached the ground; and lower right, the cone striking a farmhouse, which appeared to explode. Although they are terrible to behold, the gradational effects of such temporary winds are slight. (U.S. Weather Bureau.)*

mass of air with much greater lifting power. It originates as a column of whirling air that hangs down from storm clouds and travels with them.

FIG. 15.7. *Beach sand blown inland by wind along coast of California south of Point Sal. Beach sand can be one source of wind's load of material. (Spence Air Photos.)*

It builds up a very high speed of rising air rotating around an axis that may dip down to the ground. Tornadoes, with their great spiral, chimneylike updrafts, have been known to lift heavy objects and to transport them several miles; but since such storms occur infrequently and affect only narrow

FIG. 15.8. *An approaching dust storm in western Oklahoma, 1935. Such storms may carry dust and sand a great distance from their origin. (Pictures, Inc.)*

paths, their gradational effect is slight. Instead, the ordinary winds, which travel more or less parallel to the ground, do nearly all the work involved in large-scale movements of sand and dust.

SOURCES OF LOAD

The sources of the wind's load of dust and sand are varied. The principal source is probably the rock waste formed by weathering and corrasion. Disintegrating sandstones, the flood-plain and sandbar deposits of rivers, glacial moraines, beach sands (Fig. 15.7), and deposits of dried-up lakes commonly serve as immediate sources. In addition, volcanic explosions supply tremendous quantities of light, highly angular rock dust which is well-suited to the capacity of the wind. Although such explosions are infrequent, temporarily they may be of great importance.

EXTENT OF TRANSPORTATION

Dust and fine sand (Fig. 15.8) may be carried to great distances by the wind. Volcanic dust from the explosive eruption of Katmai Volcano in Alaska, in 1912, was spread to such an extent that when the material settled, it formed a deposit 1 foot thick 100 miles leeward from the source, and appreciable quantities were carried as far as Seattle, Washington, about 1,600 miles away. When the volcano Krakatao, in 1883, blew more than 1 cubic mile of its top off and greatly reduced the island on which it stood, dust was carried into the upper atmosphere, causing brilliant sunsets for a period of several months, at first nearby and then, about 2 weeks later, entirely around the globe. Certain ancient deposits of volcanic ash, now consolidated into rock, also testify to the power of wind transportation. Many examples of dust falls and dust-laden rain- or snowstorms are on record. The red snow which fell in Minnesota and Wisconsin in the early spring of 1925 carried reddish silt, apparently derived from the Southwestern states.

Great quantities of dust are transported in the area near the source. Thus in the drier parts of the prairies and plains of North America, often called the Dust Bowl, the air is sometimes so filled with dust that visibility is greatly affected and breathing

FIG. 15.9. *Prolonged drought in a semiarid region in the Southwest has converted topsoil into dust. The wind has removed the dust, partially covering buildings and fences. This type of damage resulted chiefly from farming in areas unsuited to row-crop agriculture, since periodic droughts have been experienced repeatedly in the afflicted areas. (Pictures, Inc.)*

is difficult. Driving an automobile is almost impossible, and lights are required in houses. The dust piles up at fences, even obliterating them, and great dunelike heaps of dust are formed around the buildings (Fig. 15.9). In this region the deflation of topsoil is chiefly the result of introducing farming in a climate little suited to it. Under natural prairie conditions very little of the soil was blown away, although frequent successions of dry years probably occurred far back in the climatic history of the area. Conditions in the Dust Bowl were so discouraging to the inhabitants that during the dry 1930s much farm land was abandoned. After one violent dust storm, observations on the quantity of dust left over the surface indicated that 125 tons per square mile had fallen approximately 500 miles away from its probable source.

Dust storms originating in the Sahara Desert have dropped silt in Italy on the following day and in France, England, and Germany, 200 to 2,500 miles from the source, a day or two later. A 4-day dust storm of this type, in March, 1901, is estimated to have deposited about 1,960,420 tons of dust over Europe, in a sheet about 0.25 millimeter thick, and 1,650,000 tons over northern Africa. Ships in the Middle and South Atlantic Ocean have experienced falls of silt and fine sand, apparently derived from the Sahara Desert, and ships off the coast of Japan have received falls of dust from the interior of China, 1,000 miles away. New Zealand has received dust from Australia, 1,400 miles away.

Mineral fragments of dust-particle size may rise

to great heights and be carried long distances by the wind. The finest of them may remain in suspension for a long period of time.

In general, the history of sand particles is quite different from that of dust. The transportation of sand rolled on the ground is usually limited to distances of a few miles or less. In France, however, sand has been blown inland from the seashore fully 5 miles, and great sand deposits of the Sahara Desert lie on a limestone plateau 100 miles from

FIG. 15.10. *Fifty feet of loess (wind-laid dust deposits), showing a nearly vertical erosional face at Missouri Valley, Iowa. Although the material is loose, the grains are sufficiently angular to uphold a steep face for a time on the sides of a gully or an artificial cut. Eventually weathering and rainwash reduce the slope. (Alden, U.S. Geological Survey.)*

FIG. 15.11.   *Sand dunes, with well-marked ripples, on the east side of the Imperial Valley, California. The steep, advancing front of the dune is marked by its slip face (on right). (Frashers, Inc.)*

the outcrops of the sandstone whose disintegration apparently supplied the sand.

SORTING AND ROUNDING

Since the wind cannot carry in suspension much of the material that it can roll along the ground, the rock particles are separated, depending on the method of transportation. In general, the separation removes clay dust and silt from the larger and heavier sand. The rolling sands themselves may be further sorted on the ground, according to the effective velocities of the wind and the shape of the sand grains. Pebbles generally are too big to move. Sand particles rolled along the ground are subject to considerable wear, so that even very fine grains (0.3 to 0.1 millimeter or less) become well rounded, but suspended dust particles are little changed.

Deposition by Wind

DUST DEPOSITS

The slackening of the wind allows its suspended load to settle slowly out of the air. Rain and snow are even more effective in rapidly clearing the air. "Mud rains" and dust-colored snows sometimes re-

sult. The general haziness of the atmosphere in the Pacific Northwest in the late summer is due to dust and smoke from forest fires, and it disappears when the fall rains begin. Normally the rate of deposition of dust is very slow, except in connection with volcanic outbursts. At Kodiak, Alaska, in 1912, 5 inches of volcanic dust from Katmai fell during a single night.

Although dust deposits are widespread and their total bulk is undoubtedly large, they are without special form, and hence escape much notice. Ancient cities of the Near East were partly buried under a mantle of wind-carried dust, apparently because the regional climate had changed. Wind-blown deposits in general are called *aeolian* deposits. Some deposits of wind-laid dust are of such magnitude as to deserve a special name. Dust composed of volcanic materials, for example, is called volcanic ash. It is derived from explosive volcanic eruptions, and many of its particles are glassy and often sharp.

LOESS

Surface dust, originating chiefly from desiccated glacial outwash, river flood plains, or desert areas, has given rise to deposits called loess (Fig. 15.10). Similar silts of other origin are also sometimes called loess.

Prominent loess deposits occur in the Mississippi Valley, in the Palouse hills of eastern Washington, in the plains of Germany, in the interior of China, in the pampas of Argentina, and elsewhere.

The typical loess of the Mississippi Valley is nonstratified yellowish silt, intermediate in texture between clay and sand. It is composed of many minerals, including quartz, feldspar, hornblende, and calcite, all very slightly weathered. This loess has the physical composition and general appearance of ground-up rock, rather than of chemically weathered material. The deposits range in thickness from a few feet or less to at least 100 feet. When exposed in.the banks of gullies or excavations, the loess reveals the curious property of standing in vertical cliffs, even though the material is not cemented together. This is well shown at Council Bluffs, Iowa. Apparently the grains are sufficiently angular to interlock rather than to roll or slide over each other as most sand grains do.

In general, the thickness of the loess decreases with distance from the source. The more distant loess may have accumulated slowly over grasslands, and the traces of former roots receding upward as the dust thickened probably gave rise to the vaguely defined vertical tubelets, partially filled with calcareous deposit, which are commonly found in the loess and which contribute to its property of standing in vertical cliffs. Many exposures, however, show a prominent vertical jointing that appears to be independent of these depositional features.

Because of its texture and the freshness of the component minerals, loess makes fertile, easily worked soil. One example is the Corn Belt of Iowa and Illinois. The loess of the Mississippi Valley lies principally just beyond or on the outer rim of the glacial deposits of the recent ice age. Presumably the loess was derived from these deposits before vegetation had become reestablished. At the height of the melting season much of the fine rock material, or "rock flour," was probably carried to the outer margin of the glacial outwash. When the cooler season came, the melting diminished, and these marginal muds dried out, forming dust. This material, together with any other fine rock debris available, probably constituted the dust that blew out over adjacent areas and was deposited as loess. Some of the dust deposits appear to be related to the marginal and outward-flowing streams that discharged the melt waters, such as the Missouri and Mississippi Rivers. The dust along these rivers probably had the same origin as that suggested above, but they were carried farther away by these major streams. At the present time strong westerly winds still whip up dust from the periodically dried-up flood plains of these rivers and carry it to the adjacent uplands.

The loess deposits of China are said to reach the enormous thickness of 1,000 feet in Shensi and adjoining provinces. This loess is believed to have accumulated from silt blown in from the deserts of Central Asia by the prevailing westerly winds. It is so easily eroded by wind and rainwash that cer-

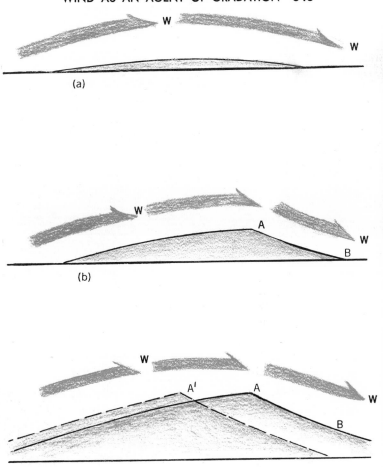

FIG. 15.12. *(a) Longitudinal profile of an early sand-pile stage of a dune, streamlined in the direction of the wind (W) but with little or no distinctive plan. (b) Longitudinal profile of a sand dune with a definite crest (A) and a slip face (A to B) in the wind shadow. (c) Longitudinal profile of a sand dune migrating with the wind (W) from A' to A by transfer of sand from the windward side to the lee slope.*

tain roadways in these deposits, through the wear of centuries of travel, have become depressed into deep, narrow, canyonlike passages. To restrain soil erosion, the loess-covered valley slopes are terraced by the Chinese farmers. Many of these farmers inhabit caves excavated in bluffs of the loess.

FIG. 15.13.   *Sand dunes on the east side of the Imperial Valley, California. Mostly crowded barchans (crescent-shaped dunes), showing the ripple-marked, gentle, windward side and the steep slip face on the leeward side. (Frashers, Inc.)*

DUNES

Wherever loose sand is shifted by the wind, any obstruction, such as a boulder, a tuft of grass, or a shrub, reduces the wind's transporting power and thereby causes deposition of part of its load. Mounds or piles of wind-blown sand heaped up in this manner are called sand dunes (Fig. 15.11).

Dunes are common along sandy seacoasts or lake shores; adjacent to the flood plains of aggrading streams flowing through sandy areas; near some of the sand-covered areas at the margins of Late Pleistocene glaciation; near outcrops of soft, easily disintegrated, geologically young sandstones of parts of the Great Plains; and in sandy desert areas. In fact, wherever loose sand is abundantly available, dunes are likely to be formed, especially if the wind direction is persistent.

In its very early stages a dune is an oval sand pile, with the wind flowing swiftly and freely over it (Fig. 15.12). But almost immediately a lag in wind velocity develops on the leeward side, because of dead air in the protected zone, or *wind shadow*. As the height of the dune increases and the summit of the pile advances faster than the leeward foot, a crest is formed, and a steep slope, the *slip face* (Fig. 15.13), develops, down which the sand grains, dropping out of the retarded wind behind the crest, slide or roll. The lateral margins of the developing dune also may be dragged forward with the wind to produce winglike extensions, or horns, in that direction.

On the windward side of a typical dune (Fig. 15.12) the mid-profile shows a long, gentle slope at an angle of about 5 to 15 degrees from the horizontal, and on the leeward side the slip-face angle is usually from 20 to 30 degrees, though it may range up to the limiting angle of repose of dry sand, about 34 degrees.

Most of the sand sliding down the slip face was previously taken from the front margin of the windward side, swept up the slope, and dropped at the crest. Therefore, the continual transfer produces a slow migration of the dune in the direction of the wind movement. The rate of dune migration varies with local conditions. Usually it does not exceed a few feet a year, but it may be as much as 100 feet or more per year. In a 6-year period slip faces on four large dunes on the Oregon coast advanced at an average rate of about 5 feet per year.[1] As a dune migrates, it may gradually lose part of its sand and thus shrink in size. Unless there is a supply of new material, dunes may eventually be dissipated. However, during their growth and migration they may cover valuable forests (Fig. 15.14) and farm lands. If unhindered, dunes may travel many miles from the original source of the sand and far beyond the obstruction that may have started them.

Dunes are commonly of moderate height and, over large areas, may not greatly exceed 20 to 60 feet; but some reach elevations of hundreds of feet. In the Great Dunes National Monument, Colorado, some dunes are more than 500 feet high. In the Sahara some of the largest dunes approach 1,000 feet.

Dune sands generally are composed mostly of quartz, but there are some exceptions. In Otero

[1] William S. Cooper, "Coastal Sand Dunes of Oregon and Washington," *Geol. Soc. America Mem.* 72, 1958, p. 114.

County, New Mexico, the dunes are composed of grains of snowy white gypsum (Fig. 15.15), those in the Keys off the southwest tip of Florida consist of calcareous algae and foraminifera, those in Bermuda of coral sand, and those in Italy of olivine sand. During the dry years of the thirties, the cultivated topsoil of the Dust Bowl was blown into dunelike deposits over highways, barnyards (Fig. 15.9), and gardens. In fact any loose, dry material of sand size which is exposed to the wind may be blown into dunes. In the polar regions, fine, loose, dry crystals of ice are drifted into dune-shaped piles, as are dry snowflakes or pellets in the common snowdrifts at lower latitudes.

TYPES OF DUNES

Dunes may take several forms, depending on the supply of sand, the lay of the land, the restricting vegetation, and the steadiness of the direction of the winds. The principal types are (1) lee dunes (sand drifts), (2) crag-and-tail dunes, (3) other longitudinal dunes, (4) barchans, (5) seifs, (6) transverse dunes, and (7) complex dunes.

Lee dunes. Lee dunes, or sand drifts, are longitudinal dunes which develop as long, narrow sand ridges in the shape of the wind shadow behind a rocky ledge or behind clumps of vegetation, or as sloping embankments of sand blown over a cliff.

FIG 15.14. *Sand dunes on the Oregon coast encroaching upon a forest. Woahink Lake can be seen in the distance. (National Park Service.)*

FIG. 15.15. *Dunes made of gypsum at White Sands National Monument, New Mexico. Although most dunes consist of quartz grains, there are some exceptions, such as these gypsum dunes. (New Mexico State Tourist Bureau.)*

Crag-and-tail dunes. Crag-and-tail dunes tail out behind a crag. These deposits, and lee dunes, are fixed in position, but, with the addition of great quantities of sand, typical migratory dunes may form and move away from the outer tips of the sand drifts.

Other longitudinal dunes. Longitudinal dunes are elongated in the direction of the effective winds, generally where strong winds blow across areas of scanty sand or where winds have to contest against the holding effect of grass or small shrubs. Occasionally oblique winds are seemingly needed to "shepherd" the sand into ridges. These fluted dunes grade into other forms. Some are blown up the slopes of valley walls.

Barchans. Barchans (Fig. 15.16) form in open

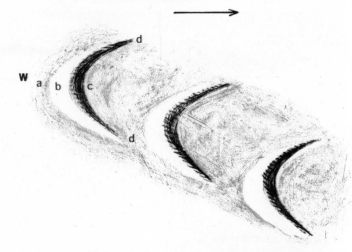

FIG. 15.16. *Outline sketch of barchans such as are found in the Arabian Desert, showing wind direction and the echelon arrangement of dunes. a, windward margin; b, crest; a–b, windward slope; b–c, slip face; d, horns, or points of wings; W, wind direction.*

areas, unrestricted by topographic or vegetational barriers, where the wind direction is fairly constant and the sand supply is limited, particularly over a solid rock base. A typical barchan is crescent-shaped, with the gentle windward slope on the outer curve and with the points, or wings, of the crescent drawn out with the wind on the leeward side, in a streamlined form.

Seifs. A seif is a longitudinal dune considerably modified by quartering winds. One simple variety resembles, in plan outline, an Arabian sword (Fig. 15.17). It is associated with barchans, and conversions of barchans to seifs, and vice versa, are said to occur. Another variety is essentially a lee dune with a knife-edge crest between one rounded windward side and a steeper slip face on the other. A third variety is a huge Saharan sand ridge with a sharp, broadly wavy crest. The forms of seifs, especially their crests, frequently change when the wind shifts from the prevailing direction. Seifs are especially well developed in Arabia, the Libyan Desert, the French Sahara, and the Australian desert.

Transverse dunes. Transverse dunes form where the sand supply is copious and the dry-weather wind direction is constant, as along many seacoasts. The great bulk of sand in such a setting piles up in a ridge or a series of ridges across the wind. Their crests generally are sinuous and uneven, partly from unequal accumulation and partly from wind-swept channels between high points on their summits. Large patches of transverse dunes seem to advance in multiple ranks.

Complex dunes. Complex dunes, lacking clean-cut forms, develop where wind directions are variable, sand is abundant, and, perhaps, vegetation interferes. Barchans, seifs, or transverse dunes locally become crowded and hence overlap, thus losing their characteristic shapes in a confused welter of diverse slopes (Fig. 15.18).

Blowouts. On a grass-covered dune or other area of sand, a break in the sod may become the location of a blowout, where the sand moved out by the

FIG. 15.17. *Outline sketch of seifs such as are found in the Libyan Desert, showing prevailing (solid arrow) and strong secondary (dashed arrow) winds, with the tendency of small dunes to unite into a longitudinal ridge.*

wind is formed into a curved, parabolic dune around the margin of the hollowed-out area. The dune embracing the blowout is usually horseshoe-shaped, with the concavity, or open end, to windward. The cavity excavated may be very irregular, but the slope out of it is more or less continuous with the windward slope of the associated dune, and the rounded front on the outside is the slip face. Blowouts also occur in and among crowded dunes wherever a sag develops that allows air currents to funnel through the sand surface. By this blowout process the complexity of transverse sand ridges and other closely grouped dunes may be increased.

Fixed dunes. Many dunes have become fixed by plants and no longer migrate (Fig. 15.24).

STRUCTURE OF DUNES

A section of an active dune shows a complex internal cross-bedded structure. Thin layers of coarse and fine sand slant at different angles and in various directions within short distances, indicating former winds of differing velocities and directions (Fig. 9.15d). As the windward slope of a dune is sheared off repeatedly during the process of migration, and the sand redeposited, the complexity of cross-bedding tends to increase.

So characteristic is this aeolian type of cross-bedding that, in association with sand grains of fairly uniform size, usually of frosted quartz, it serves as proof of wind-drift origin in sand dunes of all ages. It is as readily recognized in ancient sandstone (Fig. 15.19) of Jurassic age as in an active dune on the south shore of Lake Michigan.

Ripple marks are common on sand dunes (Figs.

FIG. 15.18.   *Sand dunes along the All-American Irrigation Canal in the eastern part of Imperial County, California. Although these dunes are mostly crowded barchans, some of them show a tendency to pass into seifs. Where wind direction is variable and sand is abundant, such complex dunes are apt to occur. (Spence Air Photos.)*

15.14, 15.15) and on the other sand surfaces associated with them. They are formed by frictional waves at the interface of wind and sand under the sorting action of surface creep, the coarsest grains collecting at the crests and the finest in the troughs. They are asymmetrical, like miniature dunes. Variations in wind intensity modify them, continually adjusting and readjusting their crests. Strong winds may obliterate them entirely.

Deserts

Deserts are climatic features and not a special product of any particular geologic process or agent. However, they have an especially close association with the work of the wind.

FIG. 15.19.   *Sandstone, showing aeolian cross-bedding or dune structure. (Lee, U.S. Geological Survey.)*

DEFINITION

Deserts are usually defined as areas that receive less than 10 inches of average annual rainfall. According to this definition, many high mountain tops, polar icecaps, and much of the high-latitude tundra would have to be considered deserts, as well as the almost waterless areas ordinarily meant. But these cold areas may be excluded, since a requirement of a true desert is that the potential evaporation exceed the annual precipitation. Evaporation records, however, are inadequate, whereas precipitation records, though far from complete, are much more extensive. Some climatologists would lower the defining limit to 6 inches of precipitation, the approximate minimum needed to support the most drought-resistant plants.

DISTRIBUTION AND ORIGIN

The seven great tropical deserts lie between Lat. 35°N and 32°S and along the permanent tropical high-pressure belts (and adjacent trade-wind areas), where the descending air is warmed and hence disposed to drying. These deserts are the Sahara, the Thar of western India, the Kalahari of South-West Africa, the Arabian, the Victorian of Australia, the Atacama of South America, and the Sonoran of the Southwestern United States and northwestern Mexico (Fig. 15.20). The Kalahari and Atacama Deserts are favored by cool ocean currents off the adjoining west coasts.

The principal middle-latitude deserts are in the interiors of continents, far from the ocean, the source of water, and in the rain shadow in the lee of mountain ranges. One is part of the great belt, interrupted and more or less surrounded by mountains, that extends eastward from central Iran across Russian Turkestan and the Tarim Basin to the Gobi Desert of Mongolia. Others are the Patagonian Desert of Argentina and parts of the Great Basin of the Southwestern United States.

Adjacent to the true deserts are extensive areas that receive 10 to 20 inches of average annual precipitation. Parts of these areas are popularly thought of as desert also, especially where long dry seasons prevail. These semiarid areas are properly called

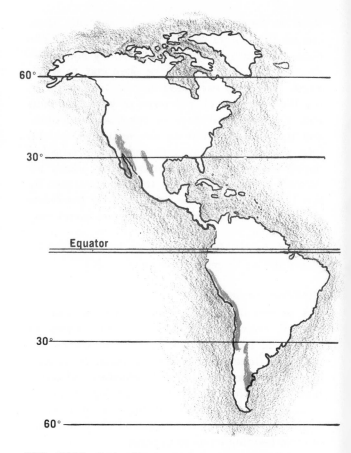

FIG. 15.20. *Left, deserts of the Western Hemisphere. Right, deserts of the Eastern Hemisphere. These deserts are bordered by large areas of semiarid steppes, which raise the total dry lands to more than a third of the continents.*

steppelands. They bear native vegetation of thorny scrub, sagebrush, or short grass and commonly give way to prairies or to sparse woodland wherever the rainfall is increased or better distributed through the seasons. Steppelands are widespread in Asia, Africa, Australia, and the Western United States. The Columbia Plateau and the western Great Plains are examples.

The geographic limits of the dry lands (desert and steppe) are difficult to place because of boundaries that shift from year to year and because of insufficient precipitation data in sparsely settled or unpopulated regions. It is estimated that deserts

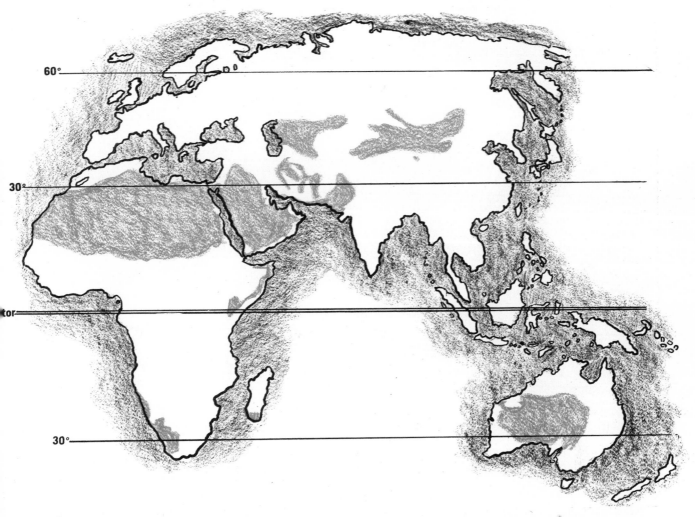

occupy about 12 to 15 per cent of the land area and that the dry lands as a whole cover more than a third of the continents.

CHARACTERISTICS

Rainfall in the desert is not only meager but also irregular and unreliable. Downpours and floods may occur at intervals of a few to many years. The sky is usually clear and sunshine abundant.

Average annual temperatures in tropical deserts are fairly high, but seasonal differences are moderate. Coastal deserts of Kalahari and Chile have cool summers. The middle-latitude deserts of central Asia have cold winters. Because of the clear air,

insolation by day and radiation at night are very effective, so daily temperature changes of 25 to 50°F are common, and extreme variations of 80° or more occur occasionally. The days accordingly are warm to hot, the nights cool.

The relative humidity is low, perhaps 10 to 30 per cent, but at high temperatures the absolute humidity may actually exceed that of many other places.

Fitful and blustery winds are common in the afternoon and evening. Under certain conditions strong winds may persist for several days and nights.

The topography of deserts is varied with moun-

FIG. 15.21. *True desert conditions can be found at Gower's Gulch, eastern Inyo County, California. Barren gullied hills show the erosion pattern in a dry area. (Frashers, Inc.)*

tains, plateaus, and plains, broken in turn by hills and valleys in great variety (Fig. 15.21). The land surfaces likewise differ widely. Some are expanses of solid rock, others are gravel, and still others are sandy. Many lowlands are covered with clay or with salts deposited from temporary playa lakes. Soils are thin or absent.

Mountains and tablelands within the desert areas have cooler and wetter climates, and so their runoff may serve to supply water for irrigation and other purposes. Mining, grazing, and lumbering are also possible in these regions.

The bleakest deserts are nearly lifeless, but most deserts support life in considerable variety. Desert plants and animals are specially adapted to take advantage of moisture when it comes and to conserve it over a long period of time (Fig. 15.22). Many of the animals are nocturnal in habit.

WIND WORK IN THE DESERT

As running water dwindles and finally fails at the edge of the desert, the wind takes over the work of erosion and thus becomes an important agent of desert gradation. In the Peruvian portion of the Atacama Desert, precipitation occurs so seldom that the natives say it never rains. Here the effects of water are almost nil, and so the erosional work is left largely to wind and to mass movement by gravity. The work of the wind, however, is limited to the fine particles.

FIG. 15.22. *Sparse vegetation on the edge of the Mojave Desert, near Thorn, California, consists of joshua trees, creosote bush, and burro bush. Desert plants can store the sporadic moisture for long periods of time.*

Dust storms and sandstorms originating in deserts, sometimes lasting for days and traveling hundreds of miles, testify to the deflationary and transporting powers of the wind in such places.

The sandblast carvings, lag gravels, and desert pavements left behind provide additional evidence. The thick loess deposits of northern China, built up over the centuries from dust transported from the deserts in the interior of Asia, likewise show the cumulative effect of winds.

Contrary to popular conception, only small parts of deserts consist of drifting sands. The Sahara Desert covers 3,500,000 square miles. Less than one-seventh of this area is dune-covered; the remainder has a stony or rocky floor. In the Arabian Desert wind-blown sands cover about 35 per cent of the area; in the Gobi Desert a much smaller percentage is sand-dune and sand-drift surface; and the sun-parched sand dunes in the arid portions of the United States cover even less than 10 per cent of the total desert area. Expanses of relatively barren rock are more characteristic of deserts than are dunes. Desert dunes are limited to areas near special sources of sand, such as dried-up stream beds, toes of alluvial fans (Fig. 15.23), beaches, or areas of disintegrating sandstone, just as are the dunes of humid regions.

FIG. 15.23. *The desert of Death Valley, near Stove Pipe Wells, California. Alluvial fans have accumulated on the left, and seiflike sand dunes can be seen in the foreground. (Spence Air Photos.)*

Even though the wind can export dust and sand entirely beyond a drainage basin and even though its load is measured in enormous tonnages, its effects ordinarily are second to those made by running water. Only locally are the landscape features of the deserts determined primarily by wind; elsewhere rain- and stream-modified topography prevails.

Wind Work and Glaciers

The interiors of continental glaciers exhibit many of the characteristics of deserts, and some geologists are inclined to regard them as such. On an ice-covered area, however, the wind expends its energy chiefly on snow and ice, and so its effects are transient.

During certain seasons, however, the strong winds blowing off a glacier may be dry and may pick up fine, dry rock material at the edge of the ice and later drop it elsewhere to form loess deposits.

The sand of dried-up marginal outwash areas, added to the basal part of the wind, becomes an effective sandblast which cuts and carves exposed rocks and cobbles on the surface of the drift, producing the familiar dreikanter; the sand is carried on and formed into dunes over the borderlands just beyond the source of the wind load. So loess, sandblasted stones, and patches of dunes are not uncommon features in areas previously glaciated by

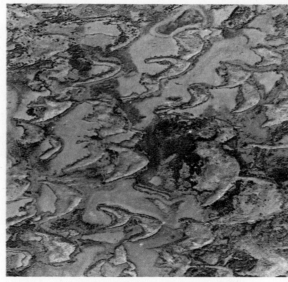

FIG. 15.24. *Barchans pinned down by vegetation near Fort St. John, Peace River District, British Columbia. These dunes were formed by strong winds blowing from the right, probably off a former continental glacier. However, the prevailing wind now is from the left. (Royal Canadian Air Force.)*

ice sheets. In some of these areas (Fig. 15.24), including North America, there are still barchans, now pinned down by vegetation, so arranged in relation to the recently glaciated region that they could have been formed only by a wind blowing off the edge of the ice and in a direction opposite to that now prevailing in the area.

Summary

We have seen that winds erode, transport, and deposit. They erode by deflation and corrasion, developing deflation basins, lag gravels, desert pavement, dreikanter, polished surfaces, grooves, frosted sand grains, and yardangs.

Winds carry dust in suspension and transport sand mainly by traction. They obtain these fine particles from deflation surfaces, weathered sandstones, river flood plains, sand bars, beaches, glacial deposits, dry lake beds, and volcanic explosions. The winds carry dust for thousands of miles, but they rarely transport sand for more than a few tens of miles.

Winds deposit thick sheets of dust (loess), as in the Mississippi Valley, the Palouse area, and China. They build sand hills called dunes—lee dunes, longitudinal dunes, barchans, seifs, transverse dunes, and complex dunes. Blowouts convert some dunes into parabolic shapes. Dune structure and frosted sand grains in certain ancient sandstones prove the aeolian origin of the rock.

Deserts are areas of low precipitation in which

the potential evaporation exceeds the annual rainfall. They occur along the permanent, subtropical high-pressure belts, the interiors of continents, and the lee of mountains. They are bordered by large areas of semiarid steppeland. Wind work is especially effective in these dry lands, as shown by dust storms, sandstorms, sandblast effects, and patches of traveling dunes.

Winds blowing off former ice sheets also formed loess, dreikanter, and local dunes.

Suggestions for Further Reading

Bagnold, R. A.: *The Physics of Blown Sand and Desert Dunes*, William Morrow & Company, Inc., New York, 1942. Although dated, a very good technical study.

Berkey, C. P., and F. K. Morris: *Geology of Mongolia*, American Museum of Natural History, 1927. A technical report on a famous expedition.

Cooper, W. S.: "Coastal Sand Dunes of Oregon and Washington," *Geol. Soc. America Mem.* 72, 1958. A detailed, localized, technical study with maps and illustrations.

Cressey, George B.: "The Indiana Sand Dunes and Shore Lines of the Lake Michigan Basin," *Geog. Soc. Chicago Bull.* 8, 1928.

Gautier, E. F.: *Sahara: The Great Desert*, Columbia University Press, New York, 1935.

Jaeger, E. C.: *The North American Deserts*, Stanford University Press, Stanford, Calif., 1957. A well-known study, although confined geographically.

Sears, Paul B.: *Deserts on the March*, 2d ed., University of Oklahoma Press, Norman, Okla., 1947.

Chapter 16

LAKES AND SWAMPS

THERE ARE many varieties of lakes and swamps, and they are developed in different ways. In the first part of this chapter, lakes are classified according to their origin, and the various types are described. We shall see, however, that lakes undergo modifications after they are formed, that swamps can evolve from lakes, and dry land from swamps. Here, again, we are forced to recognize that the face of the earth is not static, but constantly changing.

The second part of this chapter is concerned with swamps. Swamps cover extensive land areas, and they, too, fall into several categories, depending on origin, geographic location, and climate.

LAKES

General Features

A lake is a natural inland depression or reservoir containing an appreciable amount of water. Most lakes are bodies of quiet or standing water, although some, such as Lake Erie, have definite currents flowing through them. Lakes are due to obstructed surface drainage and are a temporary feature in the erosional history of a land surface. They are more likely to occur in regions where the permanent ground-water level is at or near the surface, but ponds and small lakes may be associated with perched water tables quite above the regional water table, or ground-water level. Some lakes may occur over vadose zones or in areas where the subsoil is only partially filled with water. This type of lake depends mainly on rainfall or the water from melting snows for its water supply, and its basin must therefore be of sufficient size and depth to conserve water from one precipitation period to another.

Lakes vary in size from small ponds to great inland seas, covering many thousands of square miles, such as the Caspian Sea and the Great Lakes. They are widely distributed over the earth's surface, occurring in mountain areas, on plateaus and plains, in valleys, and along seacoasts. They range from low, boggy depressions covered with shallow water to rocky basins containing water over 5,000 feet deep. Soundings in Lake Baikal in Siberia have recorded a depth of 5,618 feet.

Lake waters vary in chemical composition from the soft, fresh water of a mountain lake fed by glaciers to the bitter, concentrated waters of the Great Salt Lake or the Dead Sea. The composition of lakes depends largely on (1) the composition of the rocks which the water sources have passed through or over, and (2) the extent to which the lakes have been concentrated.

FIG. 16.0. *Crater Lake, Oregon, 2,000 feet deep, occupies a caldera formed in the summit of volcanic Mount Mazama when the mountain top collapsed after tremendous ejections of pumice. (Oregon State Highway Commission.)*

Functions

Most lakes have outlet streams that feed rivers. The lake basins act as safety valves for the rivers they feed, for they tend to regulate the discharge volume and thus prevent floods. The floodwaters of inflowing streams spread out over the wide basin of the lake and raise the water level so slowly that only slight damage occurs along the valley of the main outlet. In the same way, during dry seasons, the water from lakes flows out more slowly and aids in preserving the permanent streams. The regulatory effect of lakes on rivers and creeks has been one of the prime reasons for developing artificial lakes or reservoirs to contain the excess rainfall, where no natural ponding occurs, and to prevent the disastrous floods that might be caused by too rapid runoff farther downstream. Artificial lakes also conserve water for irrigation and power generation.

Origins of Lake Basins

Any geologic process which creates a depression upon the surface of the earth or obstructs drainage channels may produce a lake. Most lake basins are the results of gradational processes, but some are due to diastrophic movements or volcanic activity.

A classification of lake basins by origin is given in the following outline:

A. Basins produced by glacial deposition
   1. Irregular deposition of till
   2. Moraine dam
   3. Ice block
      a. In outwash
      b. In till
      c. In esker trough
B. Basins produced by glacial erosion (in bedrock)
   1. Modified preglacial valleys
   2. Cirques
   3. Excavated by differential scour

C. Basins produced by stream erosion and deposition
1. Flood-plain basins
2. Master stream dammed by tributary
3. Tributary dammed by master stream
4. Delta lakes
5. Meander scrolls
6. Oxbow lakes and other abandoned channels
7. Plunge basins

D. Basins produced by ground water (sinkholes and solution basins)

E. Basins that were once segments of larger bodies of water
1. Behind cuspate bars
2. Behind bay bars
3. Segmentation of large lake into two or more separate basins

F. Basins produced by wind
1. Wind-scour basins
2. Basins between and behind dunes

G. Basins produced by mass movement
1. Landslide dams
2. Landslide scars
3. Lows on slides themselves

H. Basins produced by diastrophism
1. By faulting
2. By warping and folding
3. By general subsidence
4. By uplift of an irregular ocean floor as an uneven coastal plain

I. Basins produced by volcanic activity
1. Lava dams
2. Crater and caldera lakes
3. Lakes on and between lava flows

J. Basins produced by infall of meteorites

K. Basins produced by organic agents
1. Beaver-dam lakes
2. Man-made artificial basins
   a. Dams
   b. Abandoned open-pit mines
   c. Quarries

GLACIATION

Lakes generally are numerous in areas recently covered with glacial ice (Fig. 16.1). Some glacial lakes are due to erosion, others to deposition, and still others to a combination of these two processes (Fig. 16.2). Numerous basins in mountain valleys were excavated by glacial abrasion on the high slopes. As the ice receded, rain water and snow melt filled these basins and formed cirque lakes, or tarns (Fig. 16.3).

Continental glaciation is even more prolific in producing basins. Over the surface of the drift sheets covering large areas in northeastern North America and northwestern Europe lakes occur by the thousand. Finland alone has more than 60,000 glacial lakes, and Norway and Sweden are just about as thickly set with them. In North America, Maine, Minnesota, Ontario, Manitoba, and the Northwest Territories rival this European region in abundance of glacial lakes.

A preglacial valley partially blocked by deposition of drift may give rise to a chain of lakes. The deepening of narrow valleys and the deposition of drift across their lower ends have given rise to the famous Finger Lakes of western New York (Fig. 16.4). Glacial abrasion deepened some of these valleys below sea level, and in these areas the present lakes are deep as well as narrow.

FIG. 16.1. *Irregular lakes in glacial-drift basins in terminal moraine, west central Minnesota.*

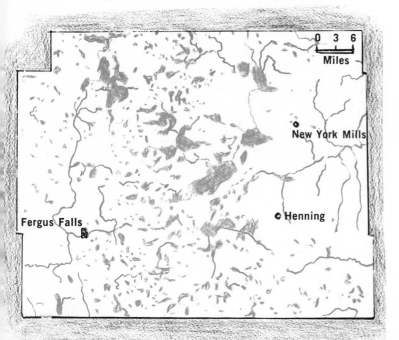

The basins of the Great Lakes of North America are due largely to glacial erosion, drift deposition, and the modification of an older drainage system, much of which was doubtless the ancestral St. Lawrence River. The Great Lakes had an intricate history as marginal lakes along the ice front during the later stages of the great continental glacier of North America. The evidence of this history is preserved in the old shore lines high above the levels of the present lakes and in the old abandoned channels through which the excess water was discharged southward from these higher levels.

STREAMS

Lake basins are formed by both stream erosion and by deposition. At certain places the two processes have been active in the formation of a single depression. Many shallow lakes are formed upon flood plains by streams that wander in meandering loops over the valley flats. Where the stream cuts off a meander, the abandoned part of the channel remains as a crescent-shaped *oxbow lake.*

Numerous irregular lake basins are also formed in the depressions between the natural levees and the outer edges of the flood plains or by rapid sedimentation on the flood plain of the main stream, thus ponding the lower ends of the tributaries. These commonly are referred to as *lateral lakes.*

Still farther down the valley, on the delta surface, the water in the main channel breaks through the levees and forms branching channels, which in turn form still other distributaries. In this way shallow depressions are completely surrounded by delta sediments, and the basins are converted into *delta lakes.* Such basins are now being formed in the deltas of the Nile, Danube, Ganges, and Mississippi Rivers.

Where an excess of sediment is carried to the main stream by a tributary, it is deposited as an obstruction, or dam, in the channel of the main stream, and the water is ponded, forming a *river lake.* This is illustrated strikingly in the Mississippi River above the mouth of the Chippewa River of Wisconsin, where the Mississippi expands over its flood plain and forms Lake Pepin (Fig. 16.5). In the great valley of California, the high-gradient

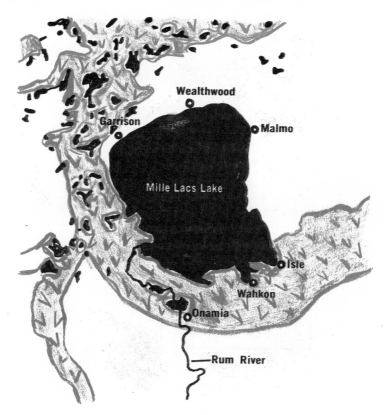

FIG. 16.2. *A lake basin formed by a terminal-moraine dam, east central Minnesota.*

Kings River that flows from the Sierra Nevada Range has built an alluvial fan that obstructs the drainage to such an extent that Tulare Lake is formed above the fan.

Lake San Cristobal in Colorado owes its origin to the Slumgullion mudflow, the lower part of which has built a dam across the valley.

GROUND WATER

Subsurface waters also may lead to the formation of lake basins at the surface. The solution and removal by underground water of large quantities of carbonates of lime and magnesia from regions underlain by limestone lead to the formation of underground cavities and channels. As such cavities increase in size, their roofs may collapse, so that depressions, or sinks, are formed at the surface. If the regional ground-water level later rises, the

FIG. 16.3. *Chasm Lake, a cirque lake, or tarn, in the Rocky Mountains of Colorado. After the glacial ice went away, melting snow and rain filled the glaciated hollow. Longs Peak rises as a 2,000-foot cliff, forming part of the cirque wall. (Denver Tourist Bureau.)*

basins become occupied by lakes. A number of lake basins in Florida were formed in this way, and other examples are found in the limestone-sink, or karst, regions of Tennessee and Kentucky.

WAVES AND SHORE CURRENTS

Sand and gravel bars built by the combined action of wind and waves along the shores of the oceans, seas, and large lakes sometimes create landlocked lakes and lagoons. These lakes are most numerous where bars have been built across the entrances of bays or where they extend from a headland and cut off a curve of the original shore line. Many such lakes occur along the shore of

Lake Ontario and along the Atlantic coast from New York southwest to Panama.

WIND ACTIVITY

Winds transport sand and dust in any region where this type of rock material is available. Such activity, however, is likely to be most obvious in arid and semiarid regions, where it is little interrupted by the effects of running water. Winds are not limited in their gradational work by a base level, nor do they tend to produce a plain. Their downcutting is limited only by the presence of ground water. The fine sand and dust particles picked up at one place may be carried an appreciable distance and deposited in mounds at a higher level than that from which they were removed. This may result in hills or ridges and associated deflation basins.

In dry regions deflation basins are likely to contain water only during wet seasons, and in deserts they may remain dry. But sand dunes and dune topography may occur in humid regions, and the basins among the dunes may be filled with water to form lakes or ponds. Some excellent examples occur in northwestern Indiana near the south end of Lake Michigan. Wind-blown sand may be a material aid in, or the main cause of the formation of either river or coastal lakes where the migration of dunes cuts off portions of an estuary or blocks part of a channel.

MASS MOVEMENT

Mass movements of rock debris, such as mudflows and landslides, may dam a stream course, pond the water, and thus produce a lake. Lakes of this origin are known to have been formed in various mountainous localities in Europe, Asia, and North America. Lake San Cristobal in Colorado, formed by the Slumgullion mudflow, and the small lakes produced by the Gros Ventre landslide in northwestern Wyoming are good examples. The loose slide or flow debris is seldom more than a temporary block to a stream, for such material is rapidly eroded when water spills directly over it. However, if the dam is piled high enough to divert the overflow to some other outlet, it is not exposed to such rapid erosion, and it will serve as a more lasting block.

Other basins produced by gravity can be found as scars caused by landslides and as depressions in the slides.

DIASTROPHISM

The crust of the earth is unstable, and movements of land areas have resulted in the foundation of depressions that retain water.

Warping and folding often are accompanied by the breaking and displacement of rock strata along faults. Differential movement along fault blocks may cause part of a valley to sink, thus producing a lake basin. Downfaulting of a chain of narrow blocks of the earth's crust has formed the Great Rift Valley in Asia and Africa. This rift includes the Jordan River, the Dead Sea, part of the Red Sea, the Upper Nile, and the chain of African lakes including Tanganyika, Leopold, and Nyasa. The basin of Lake Tanganyika extends 1,700 feet below sea level. In the western part of the United States a number of basins have been formed by the same process. Lake Tahoe, on the California-Nevada boundary, is one of the deepest lakes in North America. There an earth block settled several thousand feet to form a lake basin 22 miles long and 12 miles wide.

Displacements or undulations in the earth's surface that developed during earthquakes may produce depressions that later become filled with water. Reelfoot Lake in western Tennessee was formed during the earthquakes of 1811–1812, when there was sinking of numerous adjacent areas in Arkansas, Tennessee, and Missouri.

If, through diastrophism, an irregular ocean floor is raised above sea level, it becomes an uneven coastal plain, dotted with lakes.

VOLCANIC ACTIVITY

Lava, rising from the earth's interior through vents in the surface, may so fill or obstruct a river valley that a lake is formed. Lakes produced in this way once existed on the west slope of the Sierra Nevada, but they have been drained by the erosion of the lava dams.

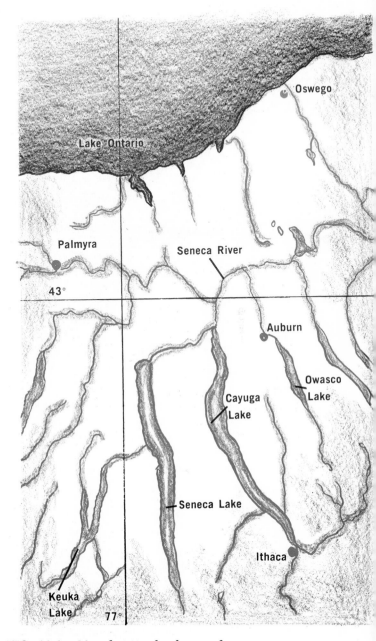

FIG. 16.4. *Map showing the shape and orientation of the Finger Lakes of western New York. These lakes lie in preglacial valleys that were overdeepened by glaciation.*

Lakes also occupy the hollows of extinct volcanic craters (Fig. 16.6), some of which are at considerable altitudes above the surrounding country. Examples are found in Arizona, Nevada, California,

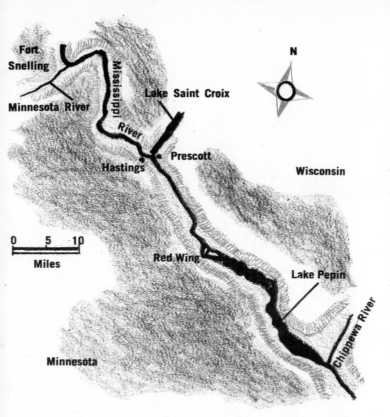

FIG. 16.5. *Lake Pepin, part of the Mississippi River where it has spread out over its former flood plain. The widening of the river is due to the deposition of an excess of sediment brought to the valley by the tributary Chippewa River (lower right).*

and Oregon. Crater Lake (Fig. 16.0), the most renowned of this group, shows such extraordinary geological features that the region it occupies has been declared a national park.

Crater Lake is situated in the Cascade Mountains in southwestern Oregon, at an elevation of 6,239 feet above the sea. About 5 miles in diameter, it is nearly circular, without bays or promontories. The cliffs of dark andesite encircling it rise precipitously to heights varying from 900 to 2,200 feet, and nowhere do they offer an easy means of access to the basin within. There are no streams tributary to the lake, and no visible outlet. The waters probably escape by seeping through the walls and floor, for precipitation in this region exceeds evaporation.

The basin of Crater Lake presumably was formed by the collapse and subsidence of the core of the volcanic mountain, carrying the summit downward as it sank. This was perhaps due to the withdrawal of lava from the mass of the magma deep in the earth beneath the volcano. After the summit of the mountain was removed, the volcano again became active and built a small volcanic cone within the caldera. This cone forms Wizard Island in the present lake.

Lakes can also be formed between lava flows and in depressions on lava flows.

UNUSUAL ORIGINS

Large meteorites striking the earth produce scars, some of which are now filled with water. Chubb Crater, in northern Quebec, is a circular scar of this sort, and it now contains a lake 2 miles across. Others of comparable size are reported to occur in northern Siberia. These, too, are filled with water and are now lakes.

ARTIFICIAL LAKES

Artificial lakes are built by man and by beavers. Both of them obstruct or dam the natural drainage and use the eroded area upstream as the basin for ponding the water. We build dams and artificial lakes for such purposes as water power, water supply for domestic use, irrigation, and flood control. Many of these artificial drainage obstructions merely raise the water level in the river channels above the dam; hence the outline of the quiet water takes on somewhat the dendritic pattern of the stream system, the backwater filling the tributaries to, or slightly above, dam level. In some places the water from one drainage system has been directed to another. This affects the erosional history of both systems, at least temporarily, and perhaps permanently.

Special Types of Lakes

SALINE LAKES

The mineral content of lake water varies greatly. Lakes which have outlets are generally fresh. Lakes in undrained basins also continually receive fresh water, and evaporation takes place from the sur-

FIG. 16.6. *Lakes in former volcanic craters on Paoha Island in Mono Lake, Leevining, California. (Frashers, Inc.)*

bia Rivers into the Pacific Ocean (Fig. 16.9). It left a record of its boundaries in the form of hundreds of miles of shore beaches, terraces, and wave-cut cliffs which it formed along its mountainous shores. At one time Lake Bonneville had a maximum depth of over 1,000 feet. Where the famous Mormon temple now stands in Salt Lake City, the lake was once so deep that if it still existed, the temple would be under 850 feet of water.

ALKALINE LAKES

Lakes containing excessive amounts of alkaline carbonates are commonly called alkaline lakes. They occur at many places throughout the world, including Egypt, Hungary, and Venezuela, and they are merely a special kind of saline lake. Some have lacy and dendritic tufa deposits on their shores. In the United States, they are common along the western part of the Great Basin; Mono Lake in east central California is an example. Its basin lies at the eastern base of the Sierra Nevada, where it covers an area of about 90 square miles. Its size varies with the seasons and, to some extent,

face. The water entering such lakes may carry only small amounts of mineral matter, but since there is no outlet, the minerals become concentrated. The water steadily becomes more salty, and when the point of saturation is reached, salt is deposited (Fig. 16.7). The type of salt that predominates depends primarily on the chemical composition of the rocks in the region of the lake basin and subordinately on the springs that rise in the basin. In some lakes, the salinity is almost that of sea water; in others, alkaline salts predominate; and in several localities, borax salts are abundant.

Some salt lakes are of oceanic origin. The Caspian Sea, which is the largest body of inland salt water known, was cut off from the ocean by the elevation of the intervening land. The most favorable conditions for the formation of terrestrial saline lakes are in regions where mountain streams discharge into interior drainage basins in an arid climate. Such conditions are prevalent over parts of nearly every continent and especially over a large area in the Southwestern states, where Great Salt Lake of Utah is the most notable example.

Great Salt Lake is but a shrunken remnant (Fig. 16.8) of a vast fresh-water lake that once covered an area of 20,000 square miles, mainly to the west and south of the present lake shores. The fresh-water predecessor, known as Lake Bonneville, over-flowed to the north through the Snake and Colum-

FIG. 16.7. *Bad Water, a saline remnant of an ancient lake in the lowest part of Death Valley, California, 310 feet below sea level. The rough, flat area in the middle ground consists of various salts precipitated from the saturated water. Telescope Mountain is in the background. (Frashers, Inc.)*

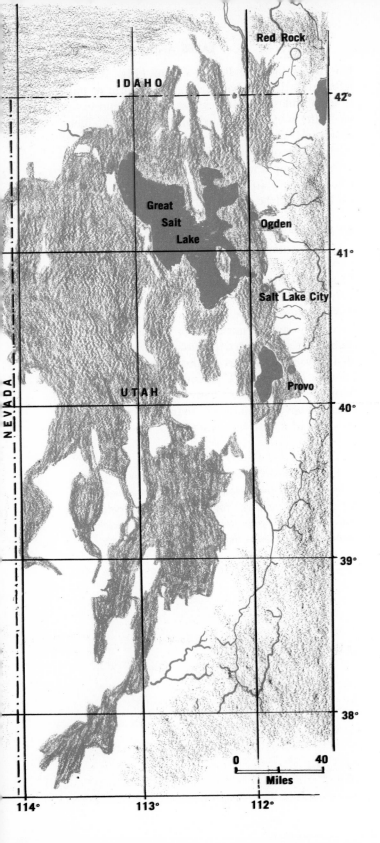

from year to year. This lake, like many others in the Great Basin country, had a much larger ancestor, as is shown by numerous shore features carved on the slopes of its basin (Fig. 16.10). The highest beach line is nearly 700 feet above the present water level. When filled to that beach, the lake covered an area of about 320 square miles.

PLAYA LAKES

Shallow, flat-bottomed depressions in desert areas are flooded by waters from intermittent streams during the wet seasons. When the water supply ceases, the lakes shrink and finally evaporate completely, leaving in their beds deposits of alkali salts that often are as white as freshly fallen snow.

Such ephemeral lakes are characteristic features in the deserts of the Great Basin. In the Black Rock Desert, in northwest Nevada, a lake forms during the winter months that covers an area of 450 to 500 square miles and is seldom more than a few inches deep. Following heavy storms it appears as a vast sheet of liquid mud. In a few days all the water may evaporate, leaving a hard, dry, barren surface showing a reticulate pattern of mud cracks. Similar lakes exist in Arizona, New Mexico, and Sonora. They are found also in the desert areas of other continents.

Modifications of Lake Basins

DESTRUCTION OF LAKES

The shape and capacity of a lake basin depend largely on the forces that operate at the time of its formation. However, the original outline and depth of a basin do not remain the same, for gradation begins immediately and constantly modifies the lake shores, fills the basin with sediment, or drains it by eroding its outlet. Sooner or later most lakes are destroyed by the completion of these proc-

FIG. 16.8. *Map of Great Salt Lake, showing its relation to the vast ancestral lake known as Lake Bonneville (shaded). Lake Bonneville overflowed northward into the Snake River via Red Rock Pass. (After Gilbert, U.S. Geological Survey.)*

esses. In some cases the extinction of lakes is due to evaporation or to the failure of their water supply because of stream diversion. Filling or destroying the basin will terminate a lake, as will cutting off its water supply.

DELTA BUILDING

Lakes are well-suited to the development of deltas, and many lake basins are partially filled by deposits of this sort. Very fine rock materials— grains or flakes of dustlike size—are carried by streams entering the lake. While in the stream, they are held in suspension as cloudlike masses, which produce *turbidity currents* (Fig. 16.11). Such currents still carry part of the original load of sediment acquired by the stream. When the stream enters the lake, the turbidity currents may flow on the surface (overflow) if the lake water is heavier than that of the incoming current; but if the surface water of the lake is lighter, the heavy turbidity current sinks and flows down slope on any submerged surface composed of material of greater density, whether it is a lower mass of water (inflow) or the lake bottom itself (underflow). In this way the extremely fine sediment may be transported to the distant parts of the lake or reservoir. Eventually this fine, dustlike sediment settles out in quiet water, and the outflowing stream from the lake may be quite free from mechanical sediment of any kind. In Lake Mead, the artificial lake behind Hoover Dam, turbidity currents travel the full length (120 miles) of the reservoir and cease only at the dam itself.

Lake deltas are common in many regions throughout the world. The St. Clair River has built a delta filling a large area at the upper end of Lake St. Clair, northeast of Detroit. The flat area on which much of the town of Watkins Glen, New York, is built is a delta, at the head of Seneca Lake, nearly 3 miles long and more than 1 mile wide; the thickness of the fill is 500 or 600 feet, and possibly more. Deltas are especially common in the lakes of Switzerland, since these bodies of water are the settling basins of streams carrying great quantities of sediment brought down from the high mountain area.

FIG. 16.9. *Red Rock Pass in southeastern Idaho, looking southward. This pass lies along the outlet of ancient Lake Bonneville. The bottom of a northeasterly extension of the Bonneville basin, shown in the distance, lies several hundred feet below the surrounding area. The railroad and U.S. Highway No. 91 use the easy grade to their advantage. (Spence Air Photos.)*

GLACIAL FILLING

A special type of basin filling is found in the quiet marginal lakes of glaciated regions where the finest sediment, or rock flour, from the glacial grinding process settled out beyond the turbulence of currents to form well-stratified silt and clay beds. These beds, called varved clays (Fig. 16.12), are discussed in Chapter 12, on glaciation.

ORGANIC FILLING

The remains of animals and plants accumulate on the bottoms and along the margins of lakes. This is especially evident around the edges of small, shallow lakes where vegetation, such as water lilies, grows in the water (Fig. 16.13). Here sediment lodges among the plants, covers up the relics of former living things, and helps to extend the shore line farther into the lake. Many animals and some plants living in lakes secrete calcium carbonate or silica to form their shells or skeletal parts. When such animals or plants die, their hard parts

FIG. 16.10.   *West end of Mono Lake, California, as seen from one of the beaches of a former high-water stage. The water of the lake is highly alkaline. (Frashers, Inc.)*

settle and accumulate as a portion of the bottom sediment of the basin. These remains often form a large part of the lake deposit, and in some places they are so abundant that they constitute the main basin-filling material. In some cases they even form marl, diatomite, or other beds of economic importance.

SWAMPS

General Features

Swamps are a widespread and important feature of the earth's surface. Between 40,000 and 50,000 square miles of the United States, exclusive of Alaska, is rated as swamp- or peat land. Minnesota alone has between 5 million and 6 million acres of such land, and Florida has a similar amount. Swamps, or marshes, are also called peat bogs, or merely bogs, and in some regions the humus soil they contain is loosely referred to as muck.

Swamps are often, but not necessarily, the successors to lakes and sluggish streams. Some cover areas that never contained lakes, and coastal swamps may be the salt marshes of former tidal flats. Swamps are likely to occur wherever there is a wide stretch of relatively flat-lying, poorly drained land and an abundant supply of water. Such conditions generally occur on the poorly drained till plains of recent glaciation, along the flood plains and deltas of major streams, and along the coastal region adjacent to a broad, shallow continental shelf.

Types

MUSKEG

The ground moraine covering large areas of the North Central states and still larger areas of Canada is so flat that water drains from it very slowly. The spongy black soil is made up largely of roots and their fragments, leaves, partly decayed vegetable matter, and fine rock waste. When this material is saturated with water, it becomes a very favorable medium for the growth of plants which need abundant water. The black larch, or tamarack, for example, is a common tree in such areas. Many swamplands are overgrown by sphagnum moss, low shrubs and bushes, or other water plants, often so thickly set and tangled that the region is difficult to penetrate and so wet that it is almost impossible to traverse. Pools of open water are abundant.

These conditions characterize muskeg swamps. They are common in the north central part of the United States, and patches of muskeg may be found at least as far north as Hudson Bay. In some parts of Canada the muskeg is developed directly over smooth, flat glaciated surfaces of the bedrock. Except where shattered by jointing, the rock is so impervious to water that little underdrainage is possible and the swamp lingers on indefinitely. Other marshes partially drain as the outlet is lowered.

ARCTIC

North of the muskeg swamps, there is a gradual transition to the lake and swamp areas of the subarctic and arctic wastelands. In Canada this transition begins near the southern limit of Hudson Bay, where the irregular timber line partly infringes upon areas of permanently frozen subsoil, which generally have a topsoil and vegetation characteristic of the tundras. The arctic lakes and swamps

FIG. 16.11. *Colorado River discharging into the upper end of Lake Mead. The relatively heavy, turbid water of the river is shown plunging downward in gullylike courses to the lake bottom. This is the beginning of a turbidity current that can be traced along the bottom of the lake all the way to Hoover Dam. (Howard Gould.)*

continue northward to the Arctic Ocean. In Europe, Asia, and North America much of this arctic area was covered by the recent continental glaciation. Now ground moraine, with all the topographic features common to that type of drift deposit, covers the surface. In northwestern Canada the drift is locally thin, and some large areas are bare rock (Fig. 16.14), with numerous intervening rock-bound lakes and small patches of moss and lichen. Although these Canadian regions are a definite part of the tundra, they are more frequently referred to as "barrens" and "barren lands."

For the most part the tundras are characterized by a black soil mingled with the partly decayed roots and stems of mosses, lichens, sedges, and small hardy shrubs, which grades upward into a mat

FIG. 16.12. *Varved clays 3½ miles south of Kazabazua, Gatineau County, Quebec. These banded, or varved, clays were deposited in a lake of the glacial period. Each pair of light and dark bands represents a year's accumulation of very fine sediment, with the light layer deposited in summer, and the dark layer in winter. (Geological Survey of Canada.)*

of dead and living plants, the whole constituting the spongy, waterlogged surface. The subsoil over much of the area is little known, except that it is frozen and remains in that condition most of the year. Only the top portion beneath the mat loses part of its frost in summer months. The depth of this surface melting, if any, varies with the length of the summer season and the distance from the outer margin of permafrost. Several feet or only a few inches may be affected by this melting, depending largely on the thickness of the surface mat and the efficiency of its blanketing effect.

FLOOD-PLAIN

The overflow from a river, carrying large quantities of fine sediment, may build the adjacent region into a flood plain of such low relief that the slug-gish stream changes its course frequently and thus abandons parts of its channel. These flat areas are covered by sloughs, oxbow lakes, and secondary channels wandering through a maze of swampland. Since glacial time, the Mississippi River, from Fort Snelling southward, has built a flood plain 90 to 100 feet thick. The river now flows on top of the fill. Its worked-over area exhibits many excellent examples of flood-plain swamps, such as those which can be seen from the highway over the flats at La Crosse, Wisconsin.

Where natural levees are being built, the portion of the flood plain immediately beside the channel becomes raised, and the more distant flat is left as swampland. Much of the farm land along the lower Mississippi lies on the levees near the river and slopes toward the sides of the valley, where the swampy areas are located. Therefore, this farm land drains away from the main stream. The growth of the Mississippi delta is extending these conditions, especially the swamp areas, into the Gulf of Mexico.

COASTAL

Gradational processes, with or without diastrophism, may convert large areas along the seacoast

FIG. 16.13. *Diagram showing marl and peat filling a lake basin*

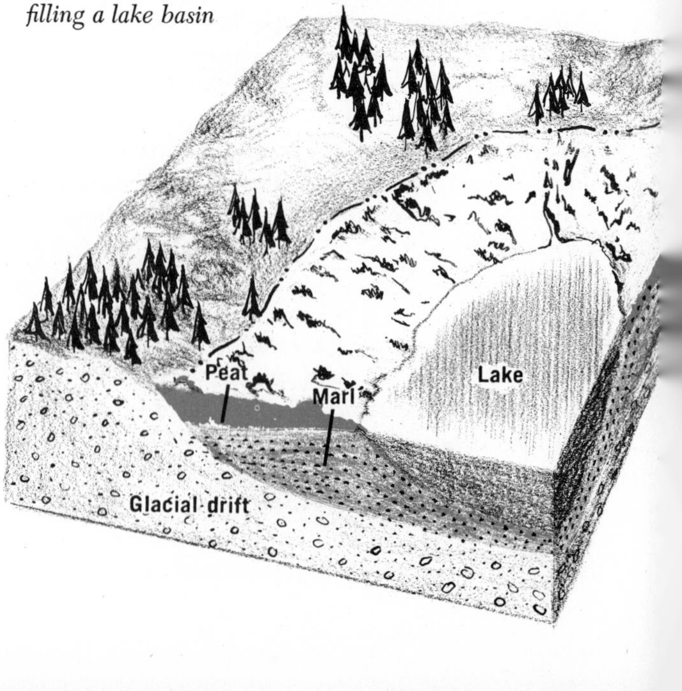

into marshes. These may be partly invaded by the tides, so that their waters are brackish, or flooded by fresh water from the land. Thus they grade from salty tidal flats to fresh-water swamps, and some may even contain shallow lakes in the early stage of marsh or swamp development. Notable examples are the Dismal Swamp, with its Drummond Lake, in southern Virginia; much of the Atlantic coastal area of North Carolina lying adjacent to Pamlico Sound; Okefinokee Swamp, in southern Georgia; the southern tip of Florida; and essentially the whole coast of Louisiana, where shallow lakes and low, soggy lands prevail.

The swampland of southern Florida covers about 6,000 square miles, of which five-sixths is the typical saw grass- or sedge-covered Everglades, with their slight elevations, or "hammocks," bearing hardwood trees. The balance of the marsh area, being more tolerant of vegetable variation, includes cypress swamps, occasional stretches of sandy pineland, and wet prairies and mangrove swamps along the southern and southwestern coastal borders.

In many places along a sandy coast, swampy land lies between beach dunes and the mainland. These areas pass through the same history as other marshy lands and usually become grassy flats.

ALTERATION OF SWAMPS

Ponds, lakes, and shallow embayments may gradually fill and be converted into swamps or marshes by the methods we have just discussed. If improved drainage is developed as erosion proceeds, swamps of any origin may pass into woodlands, meadows, prairies, or dry-land flats.

FIG. 16.14. *Tundra (barren, subarctic or arctic wasteland) as seen from the air north of Great Slave Lake, Mackenzie District, Canada. The bedrock is white, the lakes are dark, and the irregular patches of soggy swampland are light gray. (Royal Canadian Air Force.)*

Others, depressed below drainage level, may be covered by later sedimentation and may preserve for a long time all the evidence of their swamplike character, including the accumulations of vegetable matter, or peat, the shells and shell marl, the diatomaceous earth, and the stratified sands and clays. Eventually the peat may be changed into lignite, or even to coal, and the marl into limestone.

ECONOMIC UTILIZATION

Economically important products are constantly being taken from lake waters or from the sediments that accumulate under the water. Saline lakes furnish salts, and many shallow lakes have extensive deposits of calcium carbonate in the form of a white, chalky marl. This calcium carbonate is used for agricultural purposes and also in the manu-

facture of cement. In some localities the remains of microscopic plants called diatoms, which secrete tiny shells of silica, accumulate to form beds of diatomaceous earth in lake basins. This material is excavated and used in the manufacture of abrasives, refractories, and other products. Extensive deposits of peat have been built up along the shores of lakes and bogs. In many sections of Europe peat cut from the bogs is dried and used as a fuel. Where lake basins have been filled or drained, by either natural or artificial means, the exposed sediments become fertile soils. Large areas of lake soils are being cultivated in the Wheat Belt of North Dakota and western Minnesota, where many thousand square miles of fertile plains represent the drained basin of the extinct Lake Agassiz.

Along the southeastern coast of the United States, and in the Netherlands, many coastal swamps have been drained or filled with sediments, leaving fertile soils with a high humus content. In the Netherlands, much of the former Zuider Zee also has been drained and diked, to reclaim thousands of acres as usable farm lands, called polders. The smaller, fresh-water Ijsselmeer now partly replaces the salty Zuider Zee. Drainage ditches in the Florida Everglades, south of Lake Okeechobee, have lowered the level of ground water about 4 feet and have converted a very large area of swampland into suitable agricultural land. Over that territory sugar-cane plantations and winter truck gardens of great importance have since been developed.

The muskeg and low, soggy tundras of the Far North are suited to reindeer and caribou ranching, and experiments in utilizing them for this purpose are now under way. Certain types of vegetables are also produced, even over areas of permafrost and its boggy soil.

Summary

Lakes occupy enclosed basins which extend below the water table. They regulate stream flow, prevent floods, supply water, and collect deposits.

Lake basins are variously formed by glacial erosion, uneven deposition of till, moraine dams, ice dams, melting of buried ice blocks, abandoned stream channels, uneven stream deposits on valley floors, alluvial dams, solution depressions in limestone, segments of bays and lagoons landlocked by sand bars, deflation of lowlands, depressions between or behind sand dunes, landslide scars, depressions on or behind landslides and mudflows, warping by earth movements, block faulting, lurching from earthquakes, volcanic craters and calderas, lava dams, and meteorite scars.

Salt lakes are either relic seas cut off from the ocean, such as the Caspian Sea, or concentrations resulting from evaporation of large volumes of fresh water, such as Great Salt Lake. Alkaline lakes are strong solutions of alkali carbonates. Playa lakes are shallow, wet-season lakes formed in arid regions, which, upon drying, leave hardened mud and crystalline salts on their flat beds.

Lakes are subject to downcutting of their outlets, evaporation, reduction of water supply, and filling of their basins. They ultimately are destroyed.

Swamps may either succeed lakes or develop independently on poorly drained till plains, river flood plains, or deltas and along seacoasts. Muskeg and tundra are widespread in Canada. Many fresh-water swamps and brackish marshes occur along the Atlantic and Gulf Coasts from Virginia to Texas. Swamps may be drained, filled, or buried. Their principal deposits are peat and muck.

We now see how land can be changed from dry to wet to swampy, and back again, perhaps skipping a few steps, depending on many factors. Lakes and swamps are altered not only by natural methods but also by man. Wet lands can be reclaimed and made usable by drainage and diking. These measures are especially helpful in heavily populated areas. Man also makes economic use of the marl, diatomite, mineral salts, peat, and coal that are formed in lakes and swamps.

Suggestions for Further Reading

Diller, J. S.: "Crater Lake," *U.S. Geol. Survey Prof. Paper* 3, 1902.

Gilbert, G. K.: "Lake Bonneville," *U.S. Geol. Survey Mon.* I, 1890.

Gray, G. B. D.: *Soviet Land*, A. & C. Black, Ltd., London, 1947.

Hutchinson, G. E.: *A Treatise on Limnology*, John Wiley & Sons, Inc., New York, 1957. A scholarly book on all aspects of lakes, with an extensive bibliography.

Lane, F. C.: *The World's Great Lakes*, Doubleday & Company, Inc., New York, 1948.

Russell, I. C.: *Lakes of North America*, Ginn & Company, Boston, 1895. Although out of date, this is still a very important volume on lakes.

Sellards, E. H.: "The Florida Lakes and Lake Basins," *Florida Geol. Survey 3d Ann. Rept.*, pp. 47–76, 1910.

Shaler, N. D.: "Sea-coast Swamps of the Eastern United States," *U.S. Geol. Survey 6th Ann. Rept.*, pp. 353–398, 1885.

Veatch, A. C.: "Formation and Destruction of Lakes of Red River Valley, La.," *U.S. Geol. Survey Prof. Paper* 46, pp. 60–62, 1906.

Williams, Howel: *Crater Lake: The Story of Its Origin*, University of California Press, Berkeley, Calif., 1941.

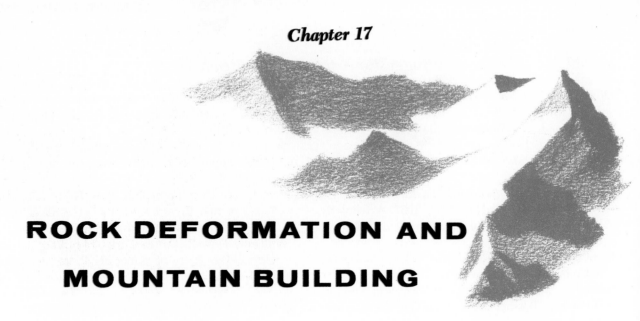

Chapter 17

ROCK DEFORMATION AND
MOUNTAIN BUILDING

ALTHOUGH WE like to think of the earth's surface as strong and stable, this is far from true. Rather, the crust of the earth is constantly moving, and this movement, ranging from a few inches to hundreds of feet, is responsible for our present major topographic features, including the principal mountain ranges. Most alterations of the earth's surface take place very slowly over great periods of time, but in certain circumstances large-scale movements have been completed in a matter of minutes. In this chapter we shall discuss the various types of movement which can take place and their many and varied results.

Deformation Movements

MECHANICAL PRINCIPLES

Because of the ever-present pull of gravity, the rocks of the earth constantly are subjected to forces of varying magnitude. These forces subject the rock to stresses which, in turn, tend to strain and deform it. Such deformation is resisted by the rigidity and strength of the rock formation. The rigidity of a solid is its initial resistance to change of form, and the strength of a solid is its ability to resist deforming forces over a long period of time.

The ability of an object to resist deformation is measured in terms of compressive strength and tensile strength. Compressive strength is the pressure, or force per unit area, required to deform, or crush, an object permanently. Tensile strength is the force required to pull an object apart. Granites have a compressive strength of 20,000 to 30,000 pounds per square inch, but their tensile strength is low, ranging from 600 to 1,000 pounds per square inch.

A viscous fluid, like tar, has no strength; a heavy piece of metal placed on it will eventually sink to the bottom. The chief difference between a fluid and a solid is that a fluid yields continuously under the slightest load or stress. A solid, on the other hand, must be subjected to a definite load or stress before its cohesive strength is overcome and yielding by flow or fracture begins.

The flow or fracture properties of a particular solid under a given stress or load depend on both temperature and pressure. All solids are weaker at high temperatures than at low. If the earth's geothermal gradient is projected to scores of miles beneath the surface, the high temperatures at such depths may allow the rocks to be deformed much more easily by plastic flow under the differential stresses developed there. Furthermore, the plasticity of many solids is markedly increased by confining pressure, and consequently they can be greatly deformed without breaking. Under a pressure of 20,000 atmospheres, a piece of steel can be stretched to 300 times its initial length without breaking. Undoubtedly the effects of temperature and pressure on the flow properties of rocks have played a prominent role in modifying the strength of the earth's crust.

Elasticity. Deformation of any material can be either elastic or plastic. Elasticity is the property of a substance which causes it to resist permanent deformation. It is the ratio of the stress that resists deformation to the strain that is a measure of deformation. Elasticity may be illustrated crudely by pressing a finger against a toy balloon. When the finger is removed, the depressed surface at once assumes its original form. A steel ball responds in like manner to temporary, localized pressure on its surface. Even though such a ball has great rigidity, it yields a little without breaking and without internal flow of the steel. When the

FIG. 17.0. *Mount McKinley, reaching 20,320 feet above sea level, is the highest mountain in North America. It is situated about 125 miles north of Anchorage, Alaska. (Alaska Visitors Association.)*

pressure is removed, the ball instantly resumes its original shape. Thus a steel ball will bounce. So will a pebble of rock, which also is elastic.

Plasticity. Under great and prolonged pressure, however, the bonds among the atoms of steel or rock are broken, the atoms slip past one another, and the material actually flows, although the rate of movement is very slow. Such internal displacements are permanent; a deformed steel ball, for example, will not return to its original spherical form. This latter type of deformation is not elastic, but plastic, and requires a long period of time. Since the rocks of the earth possess both elasticity and plasticity, both types of deformation are possible.

CRUSTAL MOVEMENT

During the earth's geologic past, and even during historic times, the earth's crust has been warped, tilted, and uplifted or depressed, resulting in relative changes of position of the rock formations. Such changes are grouped together under the term diastrophism, which includes all movements of

FIG. 17.1. *Elevated marine terraces in Palos Verdes, California. Five or more distinct terraces can be seen, demonstrating emergence of the land with relation to the sea. (Fairchild Aerial Surveys.)*

parts of the solid earth with reference to other parts. The movements may be in any direction—upward, downward, inclined, or horizontal—and they may be either extremely slow and gradual or sudden and violent.

EVIDENCE OF MOVEMENT

The uplift of the land in relation to the sea may be observed along many coasts. Elevated marine terraces (Figs. 17.1, 17.5) with their associated sea cliffs, sea caves, and chimney rocks lie inland many miles from the present coasts in many parts of the world. They are especially conspicuous along the western coast of the United States.

The nearly flat coastal plains along the Atlantic and Gulf Coasts from New Jersey to Texas also indicate that either the land has been raised or the ocean has withdrawn (Fig. 17.2). However, if the sea had withdrawn, the abandoned shore lines would be at consistent and regular levels at all places behind the present shores, and no such uniformity exists. Nor do the terrace levels here agree with those on other continents. Ancient shore lines, both here and abroad, are higher above the sea at some places than at others. We conclude, therefore, that these coastal areas were uplifted unequally and that they were warped or tilted.

Direct evidence of the change of level also may be seen far inland, where rocks containing the remains of marine shells are exposed high above the present sea level. Such fossiliferous marine

FIG. 17.2. *Map of the United States showing areas that would be submerged if the land sank 100 feet (solid color) and areas that would be submerged if the land sank 500 feet (light color).*

sedimentary rocks compose the high plateaus bordering the Grand Canyon of the Colorado at an altitude of about 7,000 feet. In the Himalaya, marine sediments have been elevated nearly 30,000 feet. Folded beds of similar origin occur in the Appalachian and Rocky Mountains. Such rocks were deposited in the seas as essentially horizontal beds. Where they are high and warped, tilted, or folded, they have been both elevated and deformed.

A classic record of movement in historic time is provided by the ancient Roman public market now known as the Temple of Jupiter Serapis, on the coast near Naples, Italy. The columns have been bored by *Lithophagus* 18 feet above the floor of the temple, and their shells are found in the holes. The temple was built by the early Romans; subsequently the land was submerged, and later it was raised above the sea.

Off the coast of Italy, on the island of Capri, a famous sea cave known as the Blue Grotto was used as a shelter by the Romans (Fig. 17.3). They cut an opening in the roof of the cave to admit more light into the underground retreat. Today the cave is flooded, and the opening in the roof is partly submerged.

Additional evidence of subsidence comes from a coal mine in Illinois, where tree stumps, with their roots spreading out in the position in which they grew, have been found 1,000 feet underground, and 600 feet below sea level.

Irregular shores, such as the rugged coast of New England with its numerous islands, shoals, and drowned valleys, provide still further proof of subsidence. Soundings have shown that there are submarine canyons extending more than 100 miles into the sea. Probably formed in part by rivers, these might indicate that the land once stood at a higher level than it does at present (Fig. 17.4). However, a careful examination of the coastal region of Maine reveals isolated areas of marine sediments which contain shells of various species of marine life that still thrive in the sea. These sediments are more than 100 feet above the present sea level. We must conclude, therefore, that the latest crustal movement in that region was one of up-

lift, although the amount of uplift was much less than the subsidence that preceded it.

Many observations indicate that the earth is sensitive to heavy loads of wide span, at virtually any location. Extensive loads of prolonged application, such as widespread, thick ice sheets, cause the earth's crust to be depressed by plastic flow under the load. When, after thousands of years, the ice melts away, the unloaded region rises by a plastic response. Since the rise is greatest where the ice was thickest, the ultimate result may be an updoming of the surface. Such updoming is recorded by elevated beaches, not only along the northeastern coast of North America and the coasts of Fennoscandia, but also in many other regions that have or had separate icecaps. These include Great Britain, Iceland, Spitsbergen, Patagonia, and New Zealand.

Along the shores of the Baltic Sea in Sweden and Finland the fresh-water marshes and low farm land near shore contain many sea shells identical with those in the Baltic Sea today. Careful measurements by means of rigid monuments set up at various point along the shore have demonstrated that this lowland has risen out of the sea. The present rate of uplift is 3 to 4 feet per century.

FIG. 17.3. *Generalized section of the Blue Grotto on the coast of the island of Capri, Italy, showing evidence of subsidence. (After Von Kuebel.)*

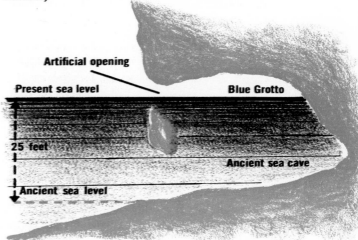

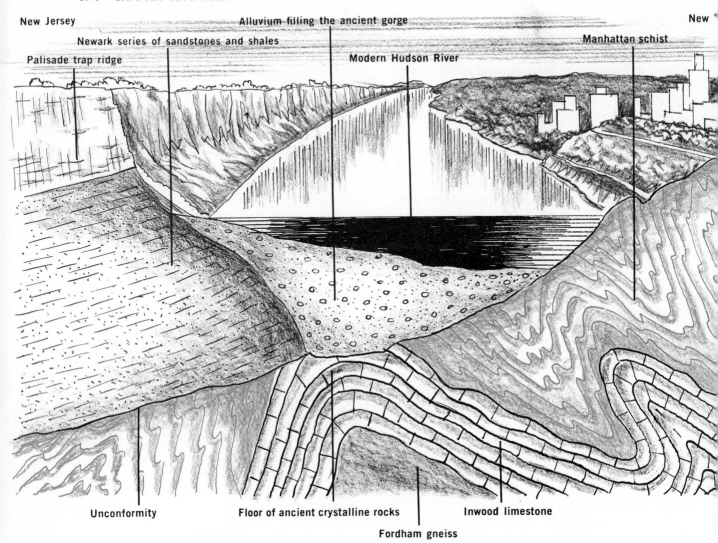

New Jersey
Alluvium filling the ancient gorge
New
Newark series of sandstones and shales
Manhattan schist
Palisade trap ridge
Modern Hudson River

Unconformity
Floor of ancient crystalline rocks
Inwood limestone
Fordham gneiss

FIG. 17.4. *Generalized cross section of the valley of the Hudson River at New York City, showing subsidence and filling of the valley. (After Scott, courtesy of C. P. Berkey.)*

In the region of the Great Lakes, many old shore lines have been mapped which show conclusively that the lake basins have been tilted. North and northeast of the lakes the land has risen as much as several hundred feet, so that the old beaches now slope southward toward the present lakes. The south shores, on the other hand, are marked by drowned valleys or estuaries, such as Keweenaw Bay and the harbors at Ashland, Wisconsin, and

at Marquette, Michigan. Such evidence of submergence is conspicuous also along the south shore of Lake Ontario and along the lower course of the St. Louis River where it discharges into Lake Superior.

RATE OF MOVEMENT

Not all deformation movements are slow. Displacements of the earth's surface during the San

FIG. 17.5. *Elevated and subsequently eroded sea terrace near Brookings, Curry County, Oregon. (Oregon State Highway Commission.)*

Francisco earthquake of 1906 amounted to 21 feet, and during the earthquake in Japan in 1923, the bottom of Sagami Bay moved more than 1,000 feet. However, the latter probably was partly the result of submarine slumping. After a great earthquake in Alaska in 1899, it was found that part of the shore of Yakutat Bay had been raised as much as 47 feet. The earlier beach, with its pebbles and marine shells, is now high and dry above the reach of the highest waves.

TYPES OF MOVEMENT

The movements of the earth are of two types, orogenic and epeirogenic.

Orogenic. Mountain masses are raised by orogenic (mountain-making) movements. Nearly all great mountain ranges are anticlinoria; that is, the dominant folding is upward at the central parts of the folds. Mountains are generally folded because of strong horizontal movements along the circumference of the earth, which result in the folding and crumpling of the strata.

Epeirogenic. By epeirogenic movements, land masses of continental magnitude are raised and lowered with little folding. These movements raise some segments of the earth's surface above the sea where degradation prevails and depress other segments below sea level where aggradation is dominant. Thus the whole trend of geologic events

is changed by such warpings. Most epeirogenic movements are radial, since they take place along the radii of the earth.

TABLE 17.1 *Upwarping of Regions of Complete or Partial Deglaciation*

Area	Maximum uplift, feet
Eastern Labrador	885
Newfoundland	450
Fennoscandia	900
South Island, New Zealand	330
Iceland	390
Scotland	100

SOURCE: R. A. Daly, *Our Mobile Earth*, Charles Scribner's Sons, New York, 1926, pp. 170-210; *The Changing World of the Ice Age*, Yale University Press, New Haven, Conn., 1934, pp. 51-150.

ATTITUDE OF STRATA

The attitude of a rock formation is its position with respect to a horizontal surface and to compass directions. In order to show the position of an inclined surface, such as a bedding plane in sedimentary rock, two observations are necessary: (1) the angle of inclination of the strata from the horizontal and (2) the direction of the intersection of the strata with a horizontal plane.

Dip. The dip of a bed is the angle of inclination,

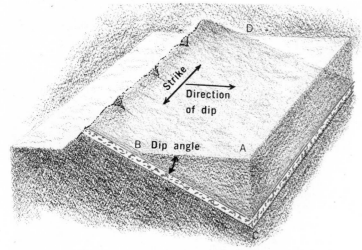

FIG. 17.6. *Diagram illustrating the dip and strike of a tilted stratum. ABC is the angle of dip. BD, a horizontal line, is the direction of strike. The direction of dip is toward the right at right angles to the direction of strike.*

FIG. 17.7. *Rainbow Gardens near Las Vegas, Nevada. Differential erosion of tilted beds of unequal resistance clearly reveals the dip and strike of the resistant rocks. The gentle slopes of the asymmetrical ridges (cuestas) are in the direction of dip of the beds. The strike of the rocks is the geographic direction the longitudinal ridges follow. (Fairchild Aerial Surveys.)*

or the amount that a bed is tilted from the horizontal position. The direction of dip is toward the steepest inclination of the dipping bed and is expressed in terms of the four cardinal points of a compass. For example, a bed may have a dip of 30 degrees toward the northwest. The angle of dip is measured downward from the horizontal plane by an instrument called a clinometer.

Strike. The strike of a bed is the direction of the intersection of the bed with a horizontal plane. The direction of strike is measured by means of a compass with a dial graduated to degrees. Thus, if the line of intersection of the bed and a horizontal plane (*BD*, Fig. 17.6) extends in a direction 40 degrees east of north, the strike is recorded as N40°E. The direction of dip is always measured at right angles to the strike (Fig. 17.7).

Attitude. The compass (Fig. 17.8) used for geological mapping usually contains a clinometer, which is either a pendulum or a mounted level. Thus, the same instrument may be used for determining the direction of strike and the amount of inclination, or the angle of dip. Dip and strike together define the position, or attitude, of a bed with respect to a horizontal surface and to compass directions. Horizontal strata have no dip and therefore can have no strike; both terms apply only to tilted or folded beds.

Deformation Structures

The structures resulting from diastrophic forces may be classed as (1) gentle tilts or warps, (2) folds, (3) joints or fractures without appreciable displacements, and (4) fractures with displacements, called faults.

WARPS

Most large areas of sedimentary strata were originally deposited as horizontal beds. If the sea floor on which they were deposited has not been lifted up uniformly, the rocks are bent into gently sloping structures, such as irregular basins or domes, which may be many miles in diameter. Furthermore, the margins of areas of intensive diastrophism are rarely sharp and distinct. Marginal zones are commonly warped by uplift or depression, and gently inclined or tilted strata are the results of such movements. Uniformly tilted beds are called *homoclines*.

FOLDS

Where rock strata have been subjected to pressures beyond their elastic limit, they may yield slowly, by bending or folding, into more or less symmetrical series of folds with alternating crests and troughs. The principal types of folded structure are monoclines, anticlines, synclines, and domes and basins (Fig. 17.9).

A *monocline* is the flexure connecting horizontal or gently inclined strata on either side of the flexure. Where strata are arched up, as in the crest of an upfold, they form an *anticline*; downfolds, or troughs, are *synclines*. Each of these may have various modifications. In mountainous or formerly mountainous regions, where folds are numerous, nearly parallel anticlines and synclines are common.

The axial plane of a fold is the plane that may be considered to pass through the center of the fold (Fig. 17.10). The axis is the line which the intersection of the axial plane makes with each of the bedding planes of the folded series. If the axis is inclined, the fold is a *plunging* fold (Fig. 17.11). The two sides of a fold are called limbs. If the limbs dip at about the same angle, the fold is said to be *symmetrical*; if one dips at a higher angle than the other, the fold is described as *asymmetrical*. An *overturned* fold is one in which one limb

FIG. 17.8. *Brunton compass, or pocket transit, used by geologists to measure the angle of dip and the azimuth of the direction of strike. (William Ainsworth & Sons, Inc.)*

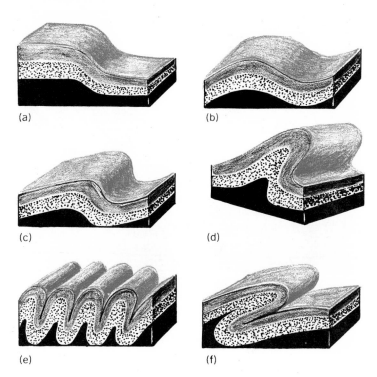

(a) (b)

(c) (d)

(e) (f)

FIG. 17.9. *Diagrams illustrating various types of folds: (a) monocline, (b) symmetrical anticline and syncline, (c) asymmetrical anticline and syncline, (d) overturned anticline, (e) isoclinal folds, (f) recumbent fold.*

FIG. 17.10. *Sketch showing the axial plane of an anticlinal fold.*

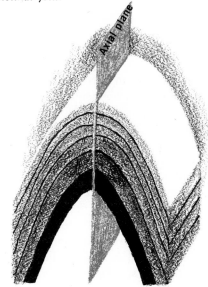

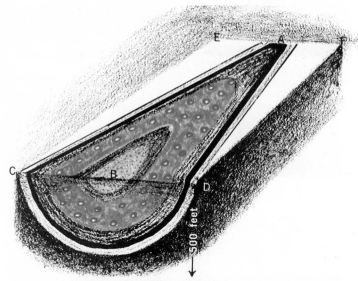

FIG. 17.11. *Block diagram of a syncline plunging toward the southwest. ECDF represents the plane of the earth's surface. At A the formation shown in black is at the surface, but at B, owing to the plunge of the fold, the same formation is more than 300 feet below the surface.*

is, at places, doubled under, so that it lies below the other (Fig. 17.9).

In mapping, it is common practice to map the intersection of the axial plane and the surface of the earth as the axis of the fold, that is, to map the line from which the rocks dip in opposite directions. Such a line is really the surface trace of the axis.

A *recumbent* fold is an overturned fold in which the limbs are essentially horizontal, and an *isoclinal* fold is one in which the two limbs dip equally in the same direction (Fig. 17.9).

An anticline may coincide with a hill and a syncline with a valley. After erosion, however, the anticlines commonly lie in the valleys and the synclines form the hills. We have already discussed this phenomenon in the section on Differential Stream Erosion in Chapter 11.

Many structural features are small enough to be seen at a glance; and in arid mountain regions, where vegetation is scarce, even large structural features may be seen with little difficulty, especially from the air (Fig. 17.12). In general, however, the larger structural features are discovered only by mapping the area (Fig. 17.13).

DIFFERENTIAL-COMPACTION FOLDS

The folds of the earth's surface, in general, are due to compressive stresses acting along the earth's circumference. Certain minor folds, however, are believed to have been formed by the settling of rocks above an ancient irregular surface. Figure 17.14 shows a series of shales and sandstones deposited above a rigid hill. If, as a result of pressure, water is squeezed out of the shales and the shale shrinks 20 per cent, the overlying rocks will be let down above the ancient hill, and the rocks below the summit will be let down more, because the shales are thicker on the sides of the hill than they are at the top. The sandstone will dip away from the center of the hill, forming an anticline. According to certain investigators, some of the minor structural features in the oil fields of Kansas and Oklahoma have been formed by this process, which is commonly referred to as differential compaction.

FIG. 17.12. *Aerial photograph of an eroded plunging fold in North Africa. The anticline in central foreground plunges toward the upper left. Because of the lack of vegetation the structure can be seen easily (United States Air Force.)*

FOLD SYSTEMS

A large system of folds, including both anticlines and synclines, in which the dominant folding is upward is called an *anticlinorium*. A *synclinorium* is a system in which the dominant folding is downward.

The areas of the great mountain folds are characterized by uplifts that extend for hundreds, or even thousands of miles. The axes of the major anticlines of a mountain region overlap each other, and small anticlines are developed on the flanks of larger ones.

During the folding of great mountain ranges, the areas between the mountains are also affected. In the great downfolds, or structural basins, between the mountain ranges, the rocks generally dip away from one mountain range and rise toward another. Between the areas of great mountain folds are smaller folds, and since many of these have axes that are parallel to the greater folds of

FIG. 17.13. *Diagrams showing the relative age and structural relations of strata included in simple folds. A is the oldest bed that crops out at the surface; D is the youngest: (a) symmetrical anticline, (b) plunging anticline, (c) symmetrical syncline, (d) plunging syncline.*

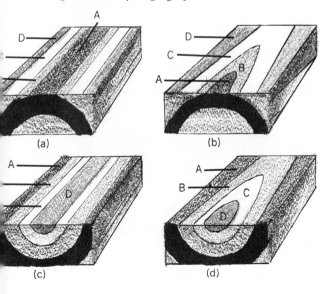

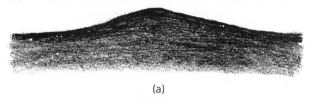

(a)

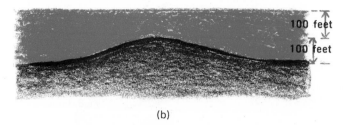

(b)

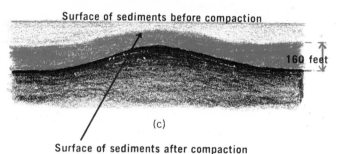

Surface of sediments before compaction

(c)

Surface of sediments after compaction

FIG. 17.14. *Diagrams showing a compaction fold resulting from the settling of sediments over a buried ridge: (a) erosional ridge, (b) same ridge covered by unconsolidated sediment, (c) same but after compaction of sediment. (After Billings.)*

the neighboring mountains, it is believed that they were formed at about the same time and were produced by the same forces.

The arrangement of the minor folds in Wyoming is illustrated by Fig. 17.15, which shows the positions of the major mountain uplifts and of the smaller anticlinal folds around them. Virtually the entire state was involved in the uplifts that formed the Big Horn Mountains, the Shoshone Mountains, the Laramie, and other mountain ranges of Wyoming, and the Black Hills of South Dakota and Wyoming.

SUBSURFACE FOLD RELATIONS

Folded beds commonly lie one above the other, like cards in a flexed pack. If an upper bed, which

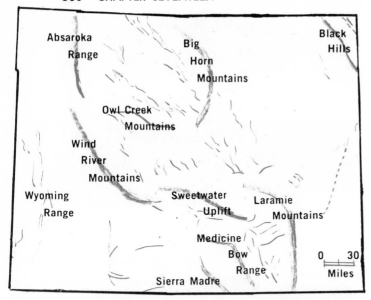

FIG. 17.15. *Sketch of Wyoming, showing axes of major mountain folds (heavy lines) and intermediate minor folds (light lines). (After Hares et al., U.S. Geological Survey, Wyoming Geological Survey.)*

may be seen at the surface, is folded, lower ones also will be folded. The subsurface relations of strata in folds may be depicted by *structure contours,* which, like topographic maps, show the configuration of a surface by lines of equal elevation, with sea level as the datum plane. For a discussion of the methods used in the construction of structural-contour maps, see Appendix A.

CRUSTAL COMPRESSION

The processes of folding involve compression of the earth's crust. This is illustrated by Fig. 17.16, which shows that the bed represented by *AB* was originally 6 miles long but that it measured only 4 miles after folding. In other words, folding decreased its length by one-third. It is estimated that the shortening produced by the crustal folding during the formation of the Appalachian Mountains near Harrisburg, Pennsylvania, including the crystalline belt, amounted to 100 miles and that the compression due to the folding of the Alps

resulted in shortening the earth's visible crust by 125 miles.

DOMES AND BASINS

A dome is a roughly symmetrical upfold in which the beds dip in all directions from a central point (Fig. 17.17). Circular, symmetrical domes are rare, but elongated, oval-shaped domes are very common and occur as parts of many large anticlines (Fig. 17.18). However, there are examples of every gradation between circular and elongated domes. Most domes occur in association with other folds, but in some regions they are isolated structures in areas of horizontal strata. The Black Hills of South Dakota are a single oval dome that rises above the Great Plains and is not connected with other folds. This dome has been deeply dissected by erosion, so that its structure may be readily observed.

A basin is the opposite of a dome. It is a con-

FIG. 17.16. *The upper figure shows a system of horizontal beds as laid down. The lower figure shows same after folding. AB in lower figure is two-thirds as long as AB in upper figure; the shortening is one-third.*

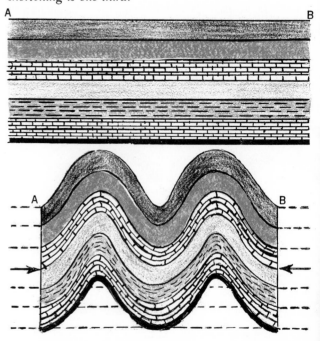

cave structural depression in which the strata dip toward the center from all sides rather than away from it in all directions. In a basin the strata resemble a stack of saucers, each one smaller in surface area than the one next below. The term basin is used also with reference to erosion, and it is necessary, therefore, to distinguish between the basins formed by folding and those produced by agents of erosion. The topography of both may be the same, but the structure may be entirely different.

JOINTS

When subjected to a sufficiently great stress, rocks become strained and eventually yield by deformation, flowage, or rupture. If the yield is by rupture, fractures result. Joints are fractures along which there has been no appreciable displacement parallel to the plane of fracture. The joints are responses to the application of a force such as tension, compression, shear, or torsion (Fig. 17.19).

All rocks are much weaker under tensional stress than under compression, and therefore it is not surprising that tension joints are widely distributed throughout the earth's crust. Undoubtedly many of the irregular fractures are due to the warping and

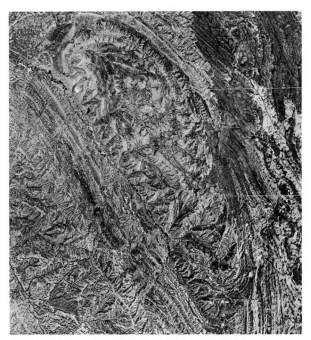

FIG. 17.18. *Aerial photograph of an elongated dome or anticline in the Elk Basin area, Wyoming-Montana. (Fairchild Aerial Surveys.)*

FIG. 17.19. *Block diagram of a simple anticline, showing tension joints along the crest.*

FIG. 17.17. *Aerial photograph of an eroded dome in North Africa. The beds dip outward in all directions from crest of dome at C. The younger beds are exposed at the outer rim of the circle, and the older ones toward the center. (United States Air Force.)*

twisting to which the rocks were subjected during gradual crustal movements. This is true especially in marine sedimentary rocks that were originally deposited below sea level and later elevated by regional uplifts. Such vertical movements would rarely be perfectly uniform over a wide area, and consequently the beds would be subjected to torsional or shearing stresses of such magnitude that they would fracture. Tensional joints also are formed along the crests of anticlines, as a result of the stretching of the rock strata.

Joints are much more numerous in some places than in others. Where they are abundant in sedimentary rocks, they commonly are arranged in intersecting sets at fairly wide angles to each other. In each set, the joints are nearly parallel (Figs. 17.20, 17.21). Such associated sets constitute a joint system, and one set of the system is commonly more strongly developed than the other and extends for long distances across a thick series of beds. A set of this sort is known as a *master joint,*

FIG. 17.20.   *Vertical jointing in portage beds, Cayuga Lake, New York. Note how the sets of joints are parallel and at right angles. (Kindle, U.S. Geological Survey.)*

FIG. 17.21.   *Intersecting joint systems in northern Australia as seen from the air. Joints have been enlarged by weathering and erosion to form gullies. (United States Air Force.)*

as contrasted with a minor fracture, which may be limited to a single stratum.

Joints are also formed by tensional stresses caused by the contraction of cooling magmas in necks, dikes, sills, and lava flows. Columns ranging in diameter from a few inches to several feet form at right angles to the cooling surface, especially in the tabular masses (Fig. 6.9). The Devil Postpile in California, the Devils Tower in Wyoming (Fig. 6.33), and the Giant's Causeway in Northern Ireland are perhaps the best-known and most spectacular examples of such columnar jointing.

In addition to the joints caused by shrinkage due to cooling, many joints and systems of joints in igneous rocks are the products of crustal movements that took place long after the rock had solidified. Such joints are often the results of compressive stresses. A block of granite under compression develops a system of joints nearly at right angles to each other. Many granites and other coarse-grained igneous rocks are regularly jointed into rectangular, more or less cubical blocks or long prisms. The presence or absence of such joints determines not only the method of quarrying but also the size of the blocks that may be quarried. At only a few places are joints sufficiently far apart to permit the quarrying of blocks that can be used in making perfect monoliths as much as 50 to 100 feet in length.

FAULTS

Faults are fractures in the earth's crust along which slipping has occurred, parallel to the surface of the fracture. Faults occur in all types of rock, but they are most easily detected in sedimentary rocks, where the offsetting of definite strata is readily recognized. The amount of displacement may be only a fraction of an inch, or it may be tens of thousands of feet. In either case it is not possible to determine whether one side of the fracture stood still while the other side moved or whether both sides took part in the movement. All that can be observed is that one wall of the fracture has moved in relation to the other (Fig. 17.22).

The surface of the fracture along which displacement took place is called the *fault plane.* This "plane," however, is rarely flat for any considerable distance, and consequently the term *fault surface* would be more appropriate. If a fault could be traced its entire length, it would be found to die out to zero displacement at its two ends. In other words, the amount of displacement is commonly at a maximum near the middle of its length and diminishes toward its extremities. In some regions faults tend to occur in groups, or zones, in which movement takes place along a number of closely spaced fractures, instead of on a single fault surface; and in other districts there are fault zones in which the separate faults are arranged in an overlapping order. Where such overlapping relationships exist, the faults are said to be *en échelon.*

Where the masses of rock involved in faulting are of great size and weight, the enormous pressures keep the faces of the fault blocks in close compressional contact. As a result of the friction between blocks, the fault plane is smoothed or polished to a slick surface, called a *slickenside.* Slickensides sometimes resemble glaciated surfaces, but they are usually more glazed. Fault *striae* are scratches on the walls of faults formed by the abrasion of hard rock or mineral particles scraping against them. On some fault surfaces two sets of striae cross each other, showing different movements at different times. When the fault surface is not clean-cut and definite, the wall rocks may be more or less crushed when the slipping occurs. If the resulting fragmental material is coarse, it is called a *fault breccia;* if it is reduced to a fine powder, it is termed *gouge.* The fragments at a fault surface are made up of the rocks that the fault crosses, and often the fragmental material is a mixture of many kinds of rocks.

Although a few fault surfaces are vertical, most are inclined, so that one wall overhangs the other.

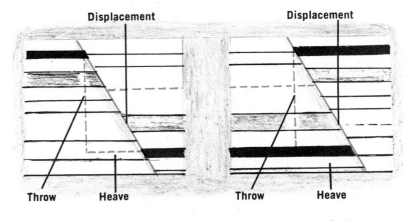

FIG. 17.22. *Diagrams showing cross sections of a normal fault and of a thrust fault. The figures illustrate displacement (dip slip), throw, and heave.*

Displacement   Displacement

Throw   Heave   Throw   Heave

Normal fault   Thrust fault

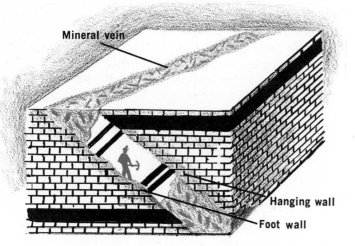

Mineral vein

Hanging wall

Foot wall

FIG. 17.23. *Diagram showing the relation of the hanging wall to the footwall of a fault. The man stands on the footwall, and the hanging wall, which in this instance has moved up, "hangs" above his head. A mineral vein has been deposited along the fault surface.*

It is customary to speak of the rock above the fault plane as the *hanging wall* and that below the fault as the *footwall*. These are mining terms and are applied to both faults and veins. The footwall is the rock on which the miner stands as he works a vein, and the hanging wall is the rock above his head (Fig. 17.23).

The block that appears to have moved up is called the *upthrow side* of the fault, and that which appears to have moved down is termed the *downthrow side*. The striae and grooves on the fault walls do not record the direction of movements. They show only that the movement has taken place in one of two directions, and they do not show which block has moved. On some fault planes there are raised places which are due to hard spots in the rocks. They are worn deeper in the direction from which the movement came. When the hand is passed over the fault surface in the direction of movement of the abrading material, the surface feels smoother than it does when the hand is moved in the opposite direction.

FAULT SCARPS

Many faults break through the surface of the ground, as well as the rocks beneath. Where one side of a fault moves up with relation to the other, it may give rise to a cliff, or fault scarp. The present height or prominence of such a cliff depends not only on the amount of displacement but on its recency in geologic time (Figs. 17.24 to 17.26), for

FIG. 17.24. *Diagrams of a fault cutting horizontal strata: (a) the fracture before displacement, (b) after displacement but before erosion, (c) after erosion of the fault scarp.*

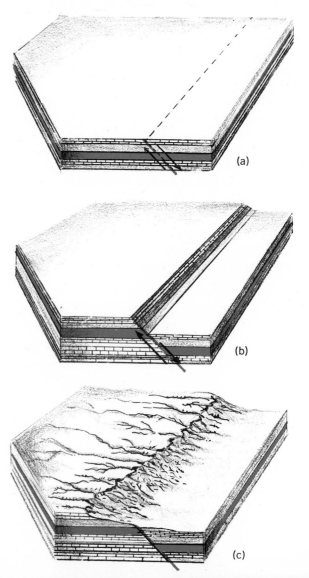

(a)

(b)

(c)

FIG. 17.27. *Chief Mountain in northwestern Montana, an erosional remnant of the Lewis overthrust mass. Ancient Precambrian metamorphic rocks rest here on relatively young Cretaceous sediments.*

FIG. 17.25. *Fault scarp forming shore of Mac-Donald Lake near Great Slave Lake, Mackenzie District, Canada. The faulted block at the upper left has evidently been uplifted with relation to the other block. (Royal Canadian Air Force.)*

FIG. 17.26. *Vertical air view along the San Andreas fault zone in San Luis Obispo County, California. The position of the fault is indicated by the straight, dark furrow between the hills to the right of center. The streams from the mountains at left follow along the fault zone for a few thousand feet before breaking through the opposing fault scarp. (Fairchild Aerial Surveys.)*

at many places erosion has reduced the upthrow block to the same level as that of the downthrow block.

The east side of the Sierra Nevada is a series of fault scarps, several thousand feet high, which serves as the west boundary of the Great Basin of Nevada and Utah. This basin is bounded on the east by the somewhat lower fault scarp of the Wasatch Mountains. Both mountainous escarpments have been made so irregular by erosion that their faulted character is obscured. In the Appalachian Mountains there are many faults but very few fault scarps. There the faulting occurred so long ago that erosion has reduced the upthrow side of the faults to the same level as the downthrow blocks.

RATE OF FAULTING

Along some fault planes, displacements of a fraction of an inch to 20 feet or more have taken place in a few minutes. In Owens Valley, California, in 1872, a slipping occurred along a 40-mile line and resulted in a displacement of 5 to 20 feet. Such sudden movements nearly always produce earthquakes. In some mines, on the other hand, faulting is observed to be taking place continually, but at a very slow rate. If long-continued, the total displacement resulting from such movements may be great, but no surface changes may be detected, since erosion cuts away the upthrow side as fast as it is elevated. If most faulting is assumed to be slow, it follows that a fault with a displacement of

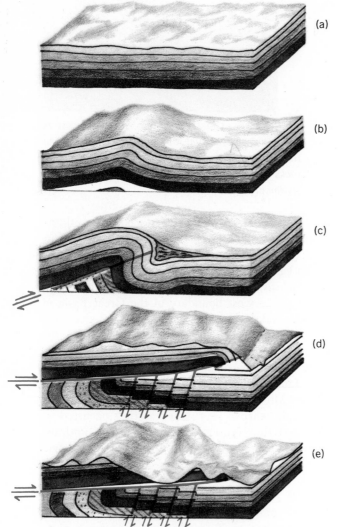

FIG. 17.28. *A series of diagrams showing the probable sequence of events, (a) to (e), in the formation of Chief Mountain in northwestern Montana. Old geologic formations were thrust eastward more than 10 miles along a low-angle fault surface and overrode younger strata, (c) to (e). Chief Mountain, (e), is an erosional remnant of ancient Precambrian rocks resting on and surrounded by much younger Cretaceous strata. (After Hussey.)*

several thousand feet was active for a very long period of time and that the total displacement was accomplished by hundreds of small, sudden slips.

TYPES OF FAULTS

If the hanging-wall block of a fault appears to have moved down, the fault is called a *normal* fault; if it appears to have risen, the fault is a *thrust*, or *reverse*, fault (Figs. 17.27 to 17.30). An *overthrust* fault is an almost horizontal thrust fault, in which the movement has amounted to many miles. Faults that cut across the dip of the beds and lie at right angles to the strike are called *dip* faults (Fig. 17.31); and those which cross both dip and strike are known as *oblique* faults (Fig. 17.32). Dip, strike, and oblique faults may be either normal or reverse.

In the main, reverse faults dip at low angles, usually from 0 to 45 degrees, although some are steeper. Many low-angle faults are ruptured folds broken along an axis of folding (Fig. 17.28).

Great thrust faults are found at many places. Some are traced scores of miles and have horizontal displacements of more than 20 miles. The Lewis overthrust (Chief Mountain) fault of Montana (Fig. 17.27), one of the best-known overthrust faults in the United States, has a displacement of 10 miles or more.

Some faults are neither normal nor reverse; rather, in movement and position, they are merely vertical or horizontal. Still others involve longitudinal movement parallel to a nearly vertical plane, as on the San Andreas fault of California (Fig. 17.26). Such a fault is called a *rift* or *tear* fault.

HORSTS AND GRABEN

A block depressed between two faults is a graben (Fig. 17.33), and a block raised between two faults is a horst (Fig. 17.34). Faulting and the tilting of faulted blocks may go on together, forming parallel ridges, or "saw-tooth" mountains. Such block faulting has taken place on a large scale in the Great Basin area of Arizona, Nevada, and Utah and also in the San Francisco Bay region of California (Fig. 17.35).

Horsts and graben occur in almost every com-

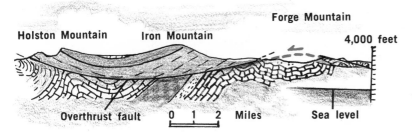

Holston Mountain   Iron Mountain   Forge Mountain   4,000 feet

Overthrust fault   0   1   2   Miles   Sea level

FIG. 17.29. *Generalized cross section from Bristol, Virginia, to Mountain City, Tennessee, showing extensive overthrusting from east to west. (After Butts.)*

plexly faulted area. The Death Valley region has many examples. The Vosges Mountains in France and the Black Forest in Germany are two horsts which face each other across the broad and deep graben of the Rhine Valley. An outstanding example of a large graben structure is the Great Rift Valley of eastern Africa, which consists of a series of downfaulted blocks that are now partially covered by lakes, including Lake Tanganyika, Lake Albert, and Lake Nyasa, which occupy basins produced by the faulting. Lake Tanganyika is more than 4,000 feet deep, and its bottom is 1,600 feet below sea level. Another large graben forms the valley of the Jordan River and the Dead Sea. For much of its length this valley is below the level of the Mediterranean Sea. The surface of the Dead Sea is more than 1,300 feet below sea level.

UNCONFORMITIES

An unconformity is a surface of erosion or non-deposition that separates younger strata from older rocks. Where rocks are laid down one above the other in uninterrupted succession, they are conformable. When one layer of rocks is eroded and submerged before it is covered by another layer, the relationship is an unconformity (Fig. 17.36).

The plane of contact between two such beds or series of beds is called the *plane of unconformity*, but it is commonly an undulating surface.

The relief on the unconformity may amount to hundreds or even thousands of feet. The early Paleozoic sedimentary rocks of the Grand Canyon were deposited on a surface with a relief of more than 800 feet, and the upper Paleozoic rocks around Boston, Massachusetts, rest upon an unconformity with a relief of at least 2,100 feet. If the beds below and above the unconformity plane have the same dip, the relation is an erosional unconformity, or a *disconformity*. If the beds of the lower series were folded or tilted before beds of the later series were laid down, the two series of beds are discordant. The beds dip at different angles, and this relationship is an *angular unconformity* (Fig. 17.37). When an unconformity develops between eroded intrusive igneous rock and a sedimentary bed, it is called a *nonconformity*. An unconformity indicates a long chain of geologic events, and the relation of the beds is highly significant.

Evidences of unconformity. To recognize an unconformity, it is essential to investigate all evidences of erosion that may have taken place between the depositions of the older and the

FIG. 17.30. *Diagrams illustrating a dip fault cutting a syncline vertically. Faulting was followed by peneplaination, so the outcrops are now offset on the map surface.*

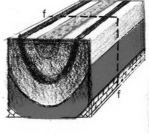
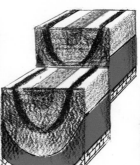
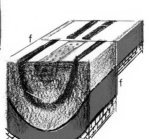

FIG. 17.31.   *Diagram illustrating a normal strike fault: (a) the fracture before displacement, (b) after displacement but before erosion, (c) after erosion of the upthrow side to a flat surface. The outcrop of one bed (black) is repeated.*

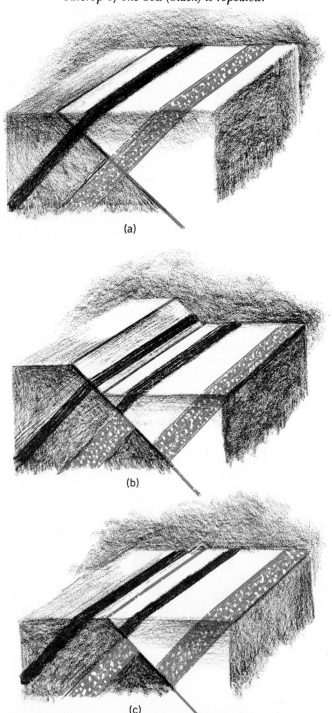

(a)

(b)

(c)

FIG. 17.32.   *Diagrams showing an oblique fault cutting inclined strata. Faulting was followed by erosion. Although the actual movement on the fault was vertical, the apparent displacement is oblique.*

younger series of rocks. Thus, if the dividing surface between the older and the younger series is irregular, this may suggest that the lower layer was once eroded. An ancient soil or weathered zone between two series of rocks shows that there is a buried erosion surface. If the lower series of rocks is more highly folded than the upper one, there is a discordance of bedding, which indicates unconformity (Fig. 17.37). If the lower series of rocks contains many veins or dikes that are absent from

FIG. 17.33. *Diagram of a graben at A. After extensive erosion, block A is reduced to the level of a peneplain at xxx, and the more resistant rock (colored) is removed from the highlands. If the peneplain is rejuvenated, the less resistant rock, w, may be eroded more rapidly than the more resistant rock (colored), so the lowland of block A in the background may become the upland of block B. Block B, though topographically high, is still a graben in structure. (After Lahee).*

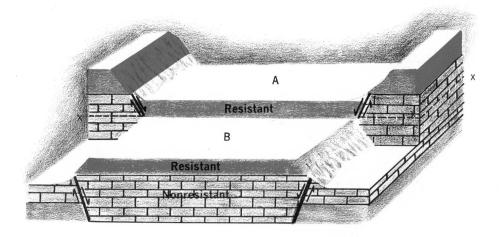

the upper series, an erosion surface may exist between the two strata. If sedimentary rocks lie upon a surface of igneous rock and there are no evidences of intrusive relations, it is probable that the contact is an erosion surface.

An abrupt change in the character of the rocks suggests a change of conditions. Thus, if a conglomerate, which is a near-shore sedimentary rock (and, therefore, evidence of an ancient shore line), contains fragments of the underlying formation, it indicates uplifting and erosion. A basal conglomerate found at the beginning of a new series and containing fragments of different rocks from the older series is particularly significant. Conglomerates are found within formations, and some of

them seem to be made up of fragments of rocks broken by waves during heavy storms. These intraformational conglomerates do not denote unconformities and are to be distinguished from basal conglomerates.

Summary of evidences:

1. Discordance in bedding. The underlying series of beds is more highly folded than the overlying series.

2. Erosion surface. The beds of the upper series rest upon an erosion surface of the older series.

3. Basal conglomerate. The lowest beds of the upper series contain pebbles of the older series.

4. Differences in degree of deformation. The

FIG. 17.34. *Diagram of a horst at A. After extensive erosion, block A is reduced to the level of a peneplain at xxx, and the more resistant rock, h, is removed from the high block. If the peneplain is rejuvenated, a valley may then develop, as shown in block B in the foreground. Thus the lowlands of block A may become the highlands of block B. Block B is still a horst in structure. (After Lahee.)*

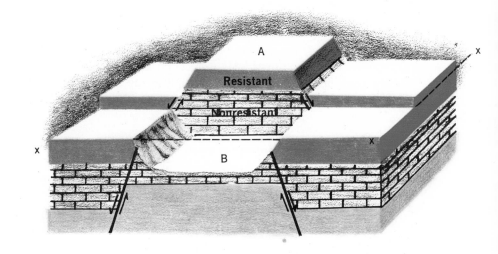

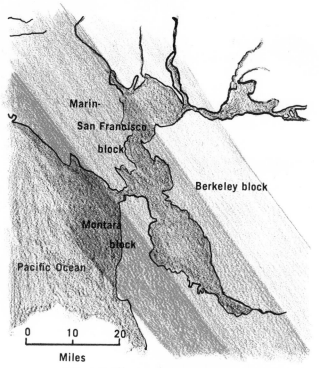

FIG. 17.35. *The system of fault blocks in the San Francisco Bay region. (After Lawson, U.S. Geological Survey.)*

older rocks are faulted, folded, or metamorphosed more than the younger series.

5. Differences in veining and intrusion. The older rocks contain closely spaced dikes and veins that are not present in the younger series.

6. Differences in character of rocks. An intrusive igneous rock that is in contact with sedimentary beds but that does not exhibit intrusive relations was eroded before the upper beds were deposited.

7. Marked differences in fossils occurring in the beds in contact.

Mountain-building Movements

FOLDED MOUNTAINS

The major mountain systems of the world are series of strongly folded ranges which occur as single ridges or as groups of closely associated

FIG. 17.36. *Diagrams illustrating unconformable relations of sedimentary rocks: (a) an angular unconformity with a discordance in bedding, (b) an erosional unconformity or a disconformity with neither series tilted or folded, (c) a disconformity with both series later tilted, (d) a nonconformity where sedimentary beds rest on the eroded surface of plutonic igneous rocks.*

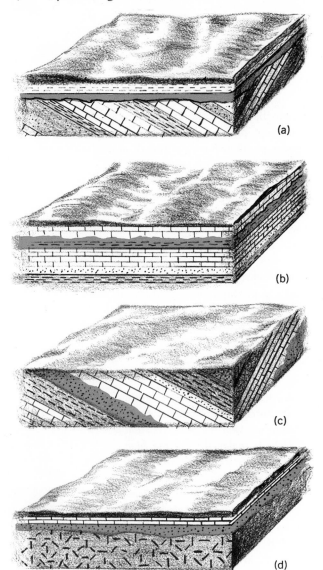

ridges. Such ranges differ from other types of mountains in that they represent a sequence of geologic processes that are distinctive in many respects but comparable in others. A feature common to all is the great thickness of shallow-water clastic sediments contained in the folds—including conglomerates, sandstones, and shales, with subordinate limestone strata (Figs. 17.38 to 17.40).

In eastern North America, to the west of the Appalachian Mountains, the sedimentary rocks are at most a few thousand feet thick. However, in the mountains, rocks of the same age are very much thicker. Furthermore, in the continental interior, the rocks are mainly limestones and dolomites, whereas clastic rocks or their metamorphic equiva-

FIG. 17.37. *Angular unconformity near Socorro, New Mexico. The upper beds were deposited after the lower ones had been tilted and eroded, indicating a gap between the ages of the two series. (Chapman, U.S. Geological Survey.)*

lents predominate in the mountains. This relationship in both thickness and types of rock has been observed in other mountain ranges, such as the Alps, Urals, Andes, and the major ranges of the Western United States (Fig. 17.39).

Further evidence of the shallow-water origin of the clastic sediments in the mountain folds is furnished by the presence of fossils of typical shallow-water marine animals. Such associations occur in the rocks of many mountain ranges, through stratigraphic sections as much as 40,000 feet thick. We can conclude, therefore, that the surface on which the sediments and the remains of animals accumu-

FIG. 17.38. *Mount Robson and Emperor Falls, British Columbia. This mountain was eroded out of many thousands of feet of marine sediments that had been uplifted and warped into broad folds. (Canadian National Railways.)*

FIG. 17.39. *Photograph of a relief map of the United States, showing distribution of mountains. Note the broad, folded belts along the west coast (Rocky Mountain system) and east coast (Appalachian system). (Aero Service Corporation.)*

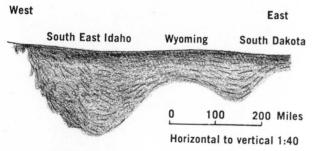

FIG. 17.40. *Cordilleran geosyncline showing the downwarp in southeastern Idaho that filled with sediments prior to the folding of the Rocky Mountains. (After Kay.)*

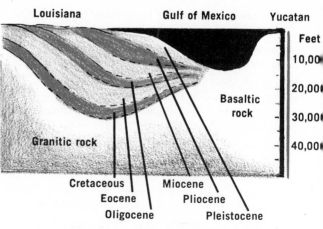

FIG. 17.41. *Diagrammatic section of the geosyncline now in process of formation along the north coast of the Gulf of Mexico. (After Barton et al.)*

FIG. 17.42. *Diagrams showing possible early stages in the history of a complex mountain system: (a) initial downwarping to below sea level, (b) geosynclinal trough developed, with the borderland rising and thrusting toward trough.*

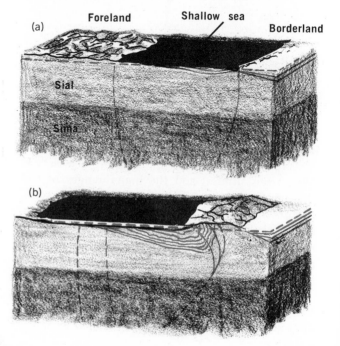

lated was never far below sea level during the long periods of deposition. Presumably, then, the crust in these areas was depressed at a rate approximately equal to that at which the sediments accumulated. Such sediment-filled downwarps of the solid crust are called *geosynclines* (Figs. 17.40, 17.41).

Geosynclinal troughs tend to develop in linear mobile belts at or near the margins of relatively rigid or stable regions, such as the Precambrian shield of north central North America. Such belts consist of a depressed trough of deposition and an adjacent geanticlinal zone, or welt, which tends to rise as the geosyncline is depressed. In the Appalachian region the thickening and coarsening of the sediments toward the east suggest that most of them were derived from a rising land mass to the east of the present mountain folds. Thus the sediments must have come from the piedmont region, the coastal plain that is now covered with younger rocks, or the continental-shelf area that is now submerged by the epicontinental sea, and they were probably derived from all three regions.

The theory of isostasy (page 38) has been used to explain the continued sinking of geosynclinal troughs and the continued rising of the adjacent geanticlinal zones, or welts. However, the theory has two weaknesses: it gives no adequate explanation of the compressive forces that later folded the outer crust, and it does not account for the great uplift that took place after the trough was filled. Obviously, the corrugations which result from folding are partly responsible for the high altitudes of mountains, as may be seen in the Jura. But in the great mountain systems of the earth where folds are now deeply eroded, mountains of extraordinary height would result if the eroded folds were restored. In other words, both uplift and folding have occurred. The uplift may have taken place during the closing stages of compressional folding or long thereafter, arching up the whole mountain system into an elongated bulge.

For many years it was generally believed that both the folding and the uplift were caused by the cooling and consequent shrinking of the earth. The shrinking of the interior, it was argued, obliged the outer crust to wrinkle to accommodate itself to the smaller internal volume. Undoubtedly the earth is slowly losing heat at the surface, as the increase in temperature with depth indicates, but all the heat escaping at the surface probably is of radioactive origin. Furthermore, if cooling is causing the earth to shrink, that shrinking should shorten every great circle of the earth equally. The distribution of folded mountains, however, does not have such a systematic pattern. Shrinkage provides a convenient explanation for the great compressive forces that might have produced folds, but the amount of shrinkage that would have had to take place to explain all the folded mountain ranges, irrespective of their distribution, is far in excess of the amount that could have been caused by the known rate of heat loss.

OROGENIC CYCLES

A surprisingly great deficiency in the force of gravity exists along the front of the arcuate island mountain chains in the East Indies, and similar conditions have been reported in the West Indies. This is interpreted to mean that these narrow zones are not in equilibrium (page 392) with adjoining areas because the mass is far less than it should be. These regions of low density are thought to be belts underlain by rocks whose density is less than is usual at equivalent depths elsewhere. The magnitude of the gravity deficiency indicates that the lightweight crustal rocks extend to depths of 30 to 40 miles. Such isostatically unbalanced conditions may be accounted for by postulating that in these low-gravity belts the upper crust of low density has been forcibly bent or dragged down, by a process somewhat similar to the downwarping of geosynclinal troughs. Most geosynclines, however, are much wider than these belts of negative gravity anomalies.

Various theories have been advanced to explain the mechanics of an orogenic cycle, but none is entirely satisfactory. Figures 17.42 and 17.43 illustrate in a simplified and diagrammatic way four stages in such a cycle. The right half of each diagram represents a "mobile belt," consisting of a zone of deposition and a borderland, or geanticlinal zone. The diagrams represent cross sections which extend downward through the light, granitic sial layer of rock underlying the continents to the

FIG. 17.43. *Diagrams showing later stages in the history of a complex mountain system: (a) the sial is depressed into the hotter sima, and magma is formed and intruded into sediments of trough as folding and faulting continue; (b) vertical uplift and withdrawal of sea, followed by erosion. (After Weeks.)*

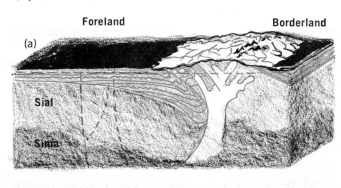

heavy, basaltic sima zone underlying both the ocean basins and the sial layer.

Stage 1 is the initial stage of downward warping to below sea level, with sediments derived from the foreland. Processes of subsidence and fill continue, and at stage 2 a typical geosyncline has developed; the borderland is rising and thrusting toward the geosynclinal trough. We should also note that the low-density sial may be depressed into the denser and hotter sima. The subsiding trough becomes more mobile as it reaches greater depths, and in stage 3 thrust faulting and folding are pronounced, and the borderland' is elevated to supply sediments to the bordering trough. Some of these sediments may be derived from older sediments that were deposited in the trough but later brought to the surface by thrust faulting. At this stage the depressed sial may reach a depth where the temperature is hot enough to melt it and to permit the formation of magma. This magma travels upward into the zone of thrust faulting and folding along the margin of the geosyncline. Granitic batho-

FIG. 17.44. *Beartooth Mountains north of Yellowstone National Park showing the low relief of their flattened summits. They represent an uplifted peneplain or a pediment, partly dissected by later streams and former glaciers. (Northern Pacific Railroad Company.)*

liths are then intruded, and some magma may be poured out as lava flows or hurled out under explosive forces to form volcanic cones.

The magma probably forms because of the accumulation of heat from radioactive disintegration, which is more pronounced in the outer granitic sial shell than in the deeper basaltic sima zone. Starting at the base of the downwarped sial (stage 3), magmatic intrusion proceeds upward. In some mountain systems, volcanic activity at the surface may serve to dissipate the heat and thus to halt the upward progress of batholithic invasion. The sial shell of the earth is known to vary from one region to another, and it is generally thickest beneath mountain chains, where deep "roots" undoubtedly project downward into the basaltic layer.

At a still later stage of an orogenic cycle there is vertical uplift of the entire series of local mountain ranges that were formed by the folding and faulting. This is accompanied by a withdrawal of marine waters as the area of deposition and former downwarping is elevated above sea level (stage 4). Undoubtedly some uplift and concurrent erosion of mountain ranges take place during their folding. The presence of unconformities between sedimentary series that accumulated in the geosyncline and an abundance of coarse clastic sediments in some beds of the outer, gently folded parts of mountain chains testify to such uplifts. Furthermore, in many old mountain ranges the summit uplands have relatively low relief (Fig. 17.44), and the gently sloping surfaces of the upland cut across rocks that vary greatly in composition and structure, which indicates that the area must once have been eroded to a low plain.

The succession of events as outlined in Figs. 17.42 and 17.43 is oversimplified and mostly speculative, though it is in accord with field observations and experimental evidence. Mountain histories are varied and complex, and a simple generalization cannot be made for all parts of any one system, much less for all great systems.

OTHER THEORIES

Geologists long have realized that determining the reason for the compression of the earth's outer crust was the principal problem in explaining folded mountains. One of the older contraction hypotheses visualized the segments under the oceans as wedges which sank because they were heavier than the continents and which, in sinking, exerted a horizontal thrust against the margins of the continents and thus produced folding and thrust faulting of mountainous proportions.

More recent theories, based on slow-moving convection currents within the thick shell of the earth, may hold more promise of reconciling the many hypotheses on mountain building. Such currents might seem impossible, because of the rigidity of the large shell of solid rock, but convection is favored by the low conductivity, low viscosity, and the high temperature at depth. Because the temperature increases downward, the viscosity possibly is very much less near the core of the earth, despite the tremendous pressure that exists there. If the deeper parts of the earth's mantle contain radioactive minerals in amounts equal to those in meteorites, the heat of radioactive disintegration could make the mantle unstable and start a slow convective overturn.

Such a theoretical, subcrustal, convectional circulation is illustrated diagrammatically in Fig. 17.45. The granitic, sial crust supposedly becomes downbuckled into the heavier, sima material of the mantle and thus produces a zone or belt of negative (less than normal) gravity anomalies. This great downfold, called a *tectogene*, may be as much as 30 to 40 miles across and equally deep. It may fill with sediments as it is depressed, and eventually the semiconsolidated sediments may be drawn down into the jaws of the tectogene, where they would be highly compressed and folded (Fig. 17.45). Some of the rocks may be squeezed up and out of the jaws and thrust into overturned folds and faults. Many of the overturned anticlines we now see have sheared-off limbs that are nearly flat-lying. Such sheets are called *nappes* (French) or *Decken* (German) (Fig. 17.46).

According to this theory, the tectogene downfold eventually reaches a depth where the temperature is hot enough to melt its roots. Great volumes of molten rock therefore are forced to rise into the

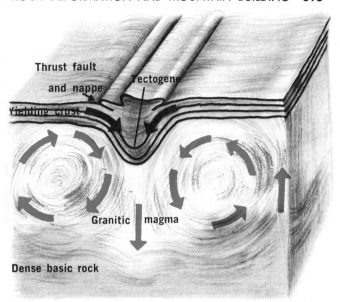

FIG. 17.45. *Diagram showing how orogeny may be induced by subcrustal convectional circulation of magma, which produces a great downwarp or tectogene. (After Griggs.)*

highly folded and metamorphosed sediments above. Such magma forms the great batholiths of granite that make up the cores of many mountain systems (Fig. 17.43). With the cessation of convection currents, a long period of crustal stability may ensue, but eventually the whole trough or geosynclinal belt is warped up to high mountainous altitudes, in the form of a huge anticlinorium. Such an upwarp is presumably the product of isostatic adjustment, induced by the unbalance that resulted

FIG. 17.46. *Generalized section across the Great Smoky Mountains and adjacent foothills showing overthrust faults in the southern Appalachians. (After King.)*

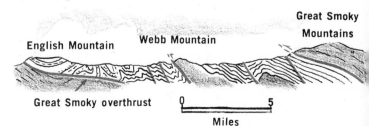

when the downfolded tectogene carried lightweight rocks excessively deep into the heavier basic rock of the mantle.

Although the evidence now available is abundant, it is still not sufficient to permit accurate interpretation of the unseen mechanism of mountain building. However, even intelligent guesses may have real value, for they suggest tests and the reexamination of evidence, and these, in turn, may modify or validate earlier concepts.

THRUST-FAULTED MOUNTAINS

Complex folding usually is accompanied by fracturing. Where the rocks are broken by continuous fractures, displacement or faulting may take place as deformation continues. Most intensely folded mountain structures show that both folding and faulting were involved in their formation. Thrust faulting is a very common structural feature in mountains formed by compressional forces. The Highlands of Scotland are an example of mountains built by a shortening of the earth's crust through a series of distributive overthrust faults.

In the United States, both the southern Appalachians (Fig. 17.46) and the northern Rockies show overthrust faulting on a large scale. In northern Montana the Front Range is represented by the Lewis and the Clark Ranges. Both ranges have high, craggy peaks reaching altitudes of 6,000 to 10,000 feet. The whole structure is a synclinal block, each limb cut off by a steep outer face. The two ranges are formed by the upturned edges of the strata, dipping 5 to 30 degrees toward the central trough. The entire block of earth constituting the ranges has been thrust eastward by one of the greatest faults known. Ancient dolomites, quartzites, and argillites which make up the mountains have been pushed eastward over the younger Cretaceous shales of the plains. The thrust plane is nearly horizontal. It can be traced 7 miles in the direction of thrusting, but the extent of the thrust was greater, for the overthrust block has been reduced by erosion. Field evidence shows that the thrust extended at least 10 miles horizontally, and possibly more (Fig. 17.28). Chief Mountain, an erosion remnant in northern Montana, is a mass of

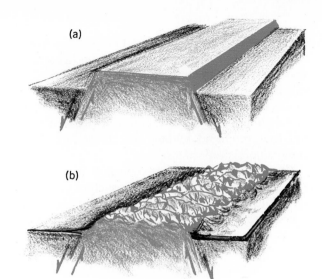

FIG. 17.47. *Diagrams showing the mode of origin of block mountains: (a) the earth's crust is fractured and faulted; (b) erosion has sculptured the high block into mountainous topography.*

Precambrian rock standing on Cretaceous formations 8 miles east of its origin. A similar contact penetrated in drilling on the plains of Alberta indicates that the eastward thrust may have been 25 miles in that area.

BLOCK-FAULTED MOUNTAINS

Where faulting occurs on a large scale, mountains may be produced by differential movement of adjacent blocks along fractures in the earth's crust. This may be accomplished by an elevation or a depression that takes place along one side of a fracture, leaving the other block of the earth in its original position, or by a combination of the two types of movement. Where there are great systems of intersecting or parallel fractures along which there has been differential movement, mountains known as fault, or block, mountains are produced (Fig. 17.47). In most cases block mountains represent segments of the earth which probably have maintained their positions while the adjoining blocks have broken away and subsided.

The most notable examples of this type of mountain structure are found in the Great Basin area in the southwestern part of the United States. This region, bordered on the east by the Wasatch Range and on the west by the lofty Sierra Nevada, extends for nearly 800 miles north and south and for 500 miles east and west. The basin area is traversed by numerous, approximately parallel mountain ranges, with their axes somewhat irregular but generally extending north and south. Many of the ranges rise 3,000 to 5,000 feet above their bases and are outlined by the slightly eroded escarpments of normal downthrow faults. Such faults result from lateral tension rather than compression.

The abrupt change from valley floor to mountain slope, together with the uniform slopes of the mountainsides, is a striking characteristic of basin and range structure. In the more arid portions of the Great Basin area the slopes range from 20 to 90 degrees. In the southern part of the basin many of the fault blocks have been so deeply dissected by erosion that their original form has been almost completely destroyed. In this region many of the intermontane depressions are so filled with rock waste deposited by intermittent streams that some of the mountains are partly buried by alluvial cones and talus slopes of debris derived from the weathering of the fault escarpments.

Faulting and crustal warping of great magnitude resulted in the formation of the Sierra Nevada, on the eastern border of California. These mountains form a continuous range about 75 miles wide and nearly 400 miles long. They represent a huge block of resistant rock uplifted by faulting and tilted toward the west. For this reason, the crest of the range is near its eastern margin, and the eastern slope is steep and clifflike. Where the crest line is highest, the average eastward slope from crest to foot is more than 1,000 feet per mile. In contrast to the steep eastern front, the gentle westward slope descends gradually from 9,000 feet on the east to 1,000 feet above sea level at the margin of the central valley of California. Along the crest of the range, Mount Whitney rises to 14,495 feet, the highest elevation in the United States, excluding Alaska. All structural features of the east front of the range indicate that it is a huge fault scarp. The displacement did not take place along a single fracture but, rather, along a zone with numerous compound faults, which have left spurs and offsets in the present topography.

The Vosges and Black Forest mountains, which form the walls of the Rhine Valley, are also fault scarps. These mountains have escarpments that face each other across the valley. Before the valley was formed, the two ranges probably were welded together as a broad anticlinal ridge composed of a core of ancient crystalline rocks overlain by younger sedimentary strata. Faulting caused the crest of the arch to subside, forming a troughlike valley by the depression of a series of small fault blocks.

DOMED MOUNTAINS

In a number of mountainous regions where the mountains occur as irregular groups the central area of the group is composed of intrusive rock, such as granite, around which sedimentary rocks dip in all directions away from the igneous core. The structure of the strata indicates that they once formed a continuous roof over the igneous mass. One of the ways in which such formations are produced is by magma being injected into the earth's crust in such quantity that the surface strata are lifted into domelike structures, or laccoliths. Erosion removes the strata from the top of the dome, and irregular hills and mountains are carved from the exposed igneous core. In other mountain groups ancient igneous bodies, such as granite masses, were laid bare by erosion and subsequently covered by sedimentary beds.

The Black Hills, in southwestern South Dakota and the adjoining portion of Wyoming, are mountains which rise several thousand feet above the level of the surrounding plain (Fig. 17.48). They are carved from a domelike uplift that is nearly 100 miles long and approximately 50 miles wide. However, this dome is not laccolithic in origin and is not related to any other known intrusions. Before the sedimentary rocks were removed from the top of the dome, it must have risen at least 6,000 feet above the plains. The exposed ancient core of the dome is composed of granite that has been eroded to form many ridges and peaks, culminating in Harney Peak, which rises to more than 7,000 feet above sea level. Around the base of the igneous

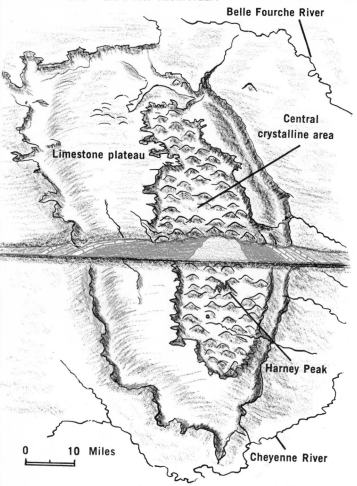

FIG. 17.48. *Diagram of the Black Hills of South Dakota, a group of mountains formed by the dissection of a domal uplift.*

tains formed from such a dome are indistinguishable from typical laccolithic mountains.

The Henry Mountains, in southern Utah, are typically domed structures. They stand singly or in clusters upon a desert plain that has an altitude of over 5,000 feet. They are a group of five individual mountains, the highest of which is Mount Ellen, climbing more than 11,000 feet above sea level. The domes show considerable diversity in the amount of erosion. Some are still partially or completely capped by overlying sedimentary strata. In others, the intruded igneous rock is exposed on

FIG. 17.49. *Map of the western Pacific, showing island arcs (dashed lines), sea trenches (solid black), and active volcanoes (triangles). (After H. H. Hess.)*

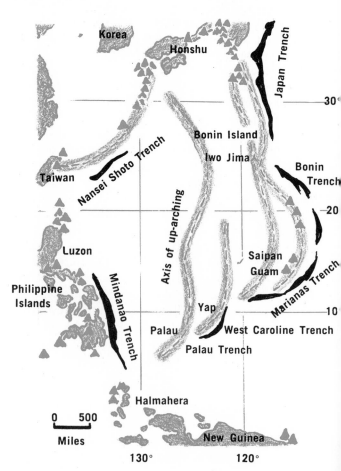

core is a ridge of limestone, younger than the granite, with a steep escarpment facing inward toward the center of the hills. Beyond the limestone outcrops are hogback ridges of sandstone, which constitute the outer rim of the domelike structure.

Not all mountains domed by intrusions have simple laccolithic structures. Some are produced by stocklike, cylindrical intrusive masses of igneous rocks that cut across the strata at depth but, nearer the surface, have bent and pushed the sedimentary rocks upward into symmetrical domes similar to those produced by laccoliths. Until erosion uncovers and removes much of the intrusive rock, the moun-

the crest of the structure, and the sedimentary strata appear in hogbacks or cuestas that encircle the uplift.

The intrusive masses responsible for the domelike structure of the Henry Mountains are not simple laccoliths but, rather, concordant tongues extending outward from a central, trunklike stock. In form they are somewhat like the semicircular lenticular fungus growths that develop on trees and make radial patterns around the trunks. In some instances dikelike ridges on the roofs of the intrusive masses trend away from the stocks.

SUBMARINE MOUNTAINS

Conspicuous mountain ranges are known to exist on the floor of the sea. The greatest of these is the Mid-Atlantic Ridge, which winds down the middle of the Atlantic Ocean from Iceland almost to Antarctica. It is thought to be the greatest single mountain system on earth. It is at least 10,000 miles long and 500 miles wide, more than twice the width of the Andes, and with many peaks loftier than most continental mountains. Its summits lie 1 mile or more below the surface of the sea throughout most of its length, but the highest peaks form some of the scattered islands of the Atlantic, such as Ascension Island, the Rocks of St. Paul, and the Azores. The highest of all, Mount Pico of the Azores, towers 7,613 feet above the surface of the sea and extends 20,000 feet below the surface. Possibly only the peaks are true mountains, and the remainder of the system a submerged platform. Granite, however, occurs on some of the islands and probably makes up the bulk of the ridge.

The island arcs of the western Pacific represent zones of sharp mountain folds, and great ocean deeps occur along the outer side of the arcs. These zones include a series of widely spaced geanticlines, such as the Marianas, Iwo Jima, and the Caroline and Palau Islands. The islands represent high points, many of which are active volcanoes, along the crests of the geanticlinal arches (Fig. 17.49).

Summary

Although rocks are strong and rigid, they do yield by fracture and flow under certain conditions. However, the exact conditions of deep-seated movement within the earth are still in doubt. Rocks fracture mostly in the outer part of the earth's crust. They can be deformed within their elastic limits at all depths. At great depths, where pressure and temperature are high, they yield by plastic flow (though remaining in a solid state) and are bent into folds.

Evidence of former earth movements include elevated and warped sea terraces, marine beds at high elevations, folds, displacements along faults, drowned valleys, tilted glacial-lake shores, and actual measurements in historical time.

Most earth movements are slow, but sudden faulting movements of tens of feet have been known to occur. The major types of movement are orogenic and epeirogenic.

Deformed rocks exhibit tilts (homoclines), warps, folds (monoclines, anticlines, synclines, domes, basins), anticlinoria, synclinoria, joints, and faults.

In terms of relative movement, faults may be normal, reverse, or rift. In position, they are vertical, horizontal, or inclined. According to their orientation, they are classified as dip, strike, or oblique. Fault movements may be in any direction along the fault plane. Many faults show slickensides, striae, and grooves along the fault surface, and fault breccia or clayey fault gouge between the footwall and the hanging wall. Great low-angle thrust faults are associated with intensely folded mountain ranges. Geologically young, high-angle faults of large throw have caused high fault scarps at the surface. An elevated block bounded by faults is a horst; a fault trough is a graben.

An unconformity is a buried surface of erosion or of nondeposition between younger beds and older rocks. It ranges in type from a simple disconformity, through angular unconformity, to a nonconformity on plutonic rocks.

Many mountain ranges have been formed by

intense folding, thrust faulting, batholithic intrusion, and uplift of great thicknesses of geosynclinal sediments. Extensive overthrust faults, marginal to former geosynclines, characterize the Scottish Highlands, the southern Appalachians, and the northern Rocky Mountains. Block-faulted mountains prevail in the Great Basin. Domed mountains are exemplified by the Black Hills of South Dakota and the Henry Mountains of Utah. The latter, formerly thought to be simple laccoliths, have complex intrusive cores. The Mid-Atlantic Ridge also is mountainous, as the island arcs in the western Pacific.

In this Chapter we have seen that folds and faults in rocks are indicative of the tremendous changes that have taken place in the geologic history of an area. Although mountains often appear to be much alike superficially, they may differ greatly in origin and internal structure. In addition to its general cultural value, a study of the structure of an area has practical application in the search for mineral resources and in the selection of efficient methods of obtaining them.

Suggestions for Further Reading

Billings, M. P.: *Structural Geology*, 2d ed., Prentice-Hall, Inc., Englewood Cliffs, N.J., 1954. An excellent study of rock faults and other earth structures.

Daly, R. A.: *Strength and Structure of the Earth*, Prentice-Hall, Inc., Englewood Cliffs, N.J., 1940. Although dated, this is still one of the standard textbooks on the subject.

De Sitter, L. U.: *Structural Geology*, McGraw-Hill Book Company, Inc., New York, 1957. This is an advanced textbook, with much information on rock deformation and mountain building.

Donn, W. L., and J. A. Shimer: *Graphic Methods in Structural Geology*, Appleton-Century-Crofts, Inc., New York, 1958. Descriptive geometry as applied to geology.

Jaeger, John C.: *Elasticity, Fracture and Flow with Engineering and Geological Applications*, John Wiley & Sons, Inc., New York, 1956.

Nevin, C. M.: *Principles of Structural Geology*, John Wiley & Sons, Inc., New York, 1949. A very good basic structural geology textbook.

Russell, W. L.: *Structural Geology for Petroleum Geologists*, McGraw-Hill Book Company, Inc., New York, 1955. The types of rock structures important in the search for oil.

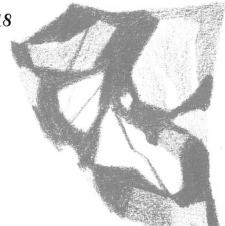

Chapter 18

METAMORPHISM

AND METAMORPHIC ROCKS

IN PRECEDING CHAPTERS we have studied the three dominant geologic processes—vulcanism, gradation, and diastrophism. Any or all of these processes bring rocks into new environments, and with a change in environment, rocks may alter in mineral composition, structure, and texture. Such transformed rocks are classified as metamorphic. In this chapter we shall discuss the causes of metamorphism and its effects on various types of rock.

Metamorphism

Every rock is the product of a definite environment in which the significant factors are temperature, pressure, and chemically active fluids, vapors, and gases. Rocks that are in stable equilibrium under one set of conditions may become unstable under another set, and their adjustment to a different environment may result in the formation of new minerals and rocks. Rocks that have been subjected to this process belong to the third great division of rocks, called metamorphic, and the fact that they are the products of transformation, or recrystallization, implies that they are formed from older, preexisting rock formations. Thus metamorphism may be defined as the sum of the processes that transform rocks and minerals.

Some minerals, however, are stable under a wide range of con-

FIG. 18.0. *Closely folded rocks that were recrystallized to schist by metamorphism at great depth and are now exposed at the surface, Black Hills, South Dakota. (Tieje.)*

ditions. In certain circumstances, moreover, the transformation may proceed so slowly that a rock never attains a condition of complete equilibrium with its surroundings, because environmental conditions may change again before the transformation is completed. Eventually some rocks may become so profoundly altered that little or no trace of their original structure and mineral association remains.

CHANGES PRODUCED

The most evident changes in metamorphic rocks include an increase in grain size (Fig. 18.1), a partial reorganization of the chemical components to form a new mineral assemblage, and the development of new structural patterns, particularly those showing a parallel arrangement of minerals.

The textures of most metamorphic rocks are different from those of igneous and sedimentary rocks, primarily in the way in which the minerals fit together. In igneous rocks, which crystallize in a more or less orderly sequence, the minerals are interlocked, the last minerals to form fitting into the spaces remaining after previously developed minerals have crystallized. In coarse-grained sedimentary rocks, such as sandstone, we can readily see that the grains are in simple contact and that the spaces between them are filled by some cementing material such as quartz, carbonate, iron oxide, or other bonding substance. In metamorphic rocks, on the other hand, the minerals often fit together without interlocking and without introduced cement. The exceptions are some marble, certain types of quartzite, many gneisses, and some schist.

The textural pattern of a given metamorphic rock is determined by such variable factors as the nature of the original material, the metamorphic processes involved, and the intensity with which they have operated. If material is removed or introduced, it is transported as either a liquid or a gas or even by the migration of ions or atoms through diffusion.

CAUSES

Rocks may be brought into new environments by any of the dominant geologic processes—vulcanism, diastrophism, and gradation. They can be subjected to the heat and pressure of volcanic intrusions; or they can be more deeply buried by accumulating sediments or by deep folding. Formerly deep-seated rocks can be exhumed by erosion. The conditions to which the rocks have been subjected determine the kind of metamorphic changes that take place.

Pressure. Pressure, one of the most important factors in metamorphism, is of two types: (1) static, or balanced, pressure, which is caused by the weight of the overlying rock and which increases with depth, and (2) dynamic, or unbalanced, pressure, which results from, and accompanies, diastrophic movements. When the term metamorphism is used without qualification, it generally refers to recrystallization induced by pressure and the movement resulting from this pressure.

Heat. Since a rise in temperature accelerates

most chemical reactions, heat is a potent factor in metamorphism. The heat may come from hot intrusive magmas, or it may be the ordinary heat that prevails at depth. In regions where diastrophism is active, heat may result from the friction of movement within the rock that is being deformed. Hot liquids, vapors, and gases aid in the transfer of atoms to produce new mineral compounds. In fact, a certain critical temperature must be reached before an interchange of atoms begins and new minerals can form. Superheated water, under great pressure, is able to attack many minerals and produce new products of crystallization that will not form in an environment of dry heat. Laboratory experiments demonstrate that vapors under great pressure will transfer atoms of metals from one compound to another. Furthermore, rocks which require a temperature of 2500°F to melt in dry heat will melt at 750°F when water is present as either a liquid or a vapor. Thus, by lowering the melting point, hot solutions increase the plasticity of the minerals and thereby lower the pressure necessary to deform the rock masses in which they occur.

Mineralizers. Liquids and vapors given off from magmas at high temperatures penetrate far into the country rock that is being invaded. Thus metamorphic changes are induced hundreds, or even thousands, of feet from the contact between magma and country rock. Such liquids and vapors are called mineralizers. They consist mainly of steam, chlorine, fluorine, and boric acid intermixed with other chemically active agents. The extent of their influence depends on the amount and kind of magmatic emanations, the pressure under which they react, and the porosity of the rock invaded.

TYPES

Metamorphic processes may be classified as (1) geothermal, (2) hydrothermal, (3) igneous, or contact, and (4) dynamic, or kinetic. Since metamorphism may be caused by a single agent or by several, it follows that metamorphic rocks may show one or more gradations, representing intermediate stages of transformation, depending on the factor or agent that exercised the greatest influence

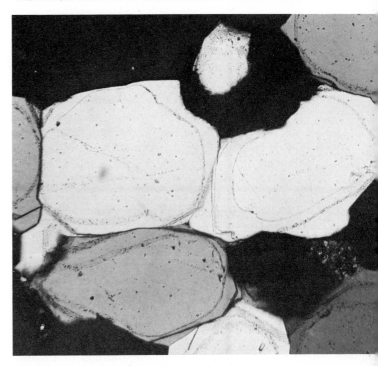

FIG. 18.1. *Photomicrograph (x 40) of a thin section of quartzite showing deposition of silica on sand (quartz) grains. The rounded shape of the original sand grains is indicated by the concentric, dusty outlines within the white grains. If the silica had been deposited from hot ground waters, the quartzite would be considered metamorphic.*

during metamorphism. Furthermore, rocks may pass through more than one cycle of metamorphism, and each may produce distinctive characteristics.

Geothermal. Geothermal metamorphism is so called because it is produced by the earth's heat alone, without the intervention of heat from magmatic sources. It refers to the changes brought about by the high temperatures existing at considerable depths beneath the surface. Rocks formed at the surface may become deeply buried and depressed in the crust under a heavy load of overlying rocks. In the Appalachian Mountains, where a geosyncline, filled with 30,000 feet of sedimentary rocks, was folded, uplifted, and eroded, rocks are now exposed that were once buried at a depth of nearly 6 miles. At these depths former muds have been changed to shales. Some minerals in these shales are unstable at the surface and, from laboratory experiments, are known to form at temperatures of 900 to 1800°F.

Other examples, such as the potassium salt deposits of Germany, show similar changes. These salt beds were deposited on the floor of an evaporating lake, and later the floor of the basin in which they accumulated subsided and became filled with 15,000 to 20,000 feet of younger sedimentary rocks. In this environment of deep burial, with its accompanying higher temperature, the salts were unstable; recrystallization took place, and many new and rare minerals were formed.

Hydrothermal. The terms hydrothermal metamorphism and hydrothermal alteration refer to the changes produced by hot magmatic waters. Magmatic heat also makes ground water of atmospheric origin much more active chemically, either as a liquid or as a vapor. Metamorphism of this type is often accompanied by the addition or removal of substances, and sometimes by both. Ferromagnesian minerals are commonly altered to serpentine or soapstone, and orthoclase is altered to the fine-grained white mica called sericite. Many igneous rocks are changed so much that they are difficult to recognize. In such metamorphism, replacement

FIG. 18.2. *Diagram showing the changes produced by intrusion of a granite mass into various types of sedimentary and igneous rocks.*

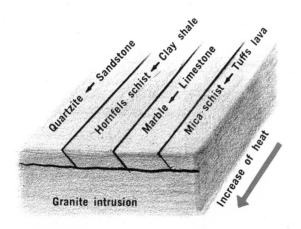

is common and is often accompanied by the deposition of metallic ores. A well-known example of hydrothermal metamorphism is seen at Butte, Montana, a copper-mining city built on granite. The waters that deposited the copper ores altered the granite so thoroughly that practically no unaltered rock is found in the vicinity of the ores.

The rocks near the springs and geysers in Yellowstone National Park have been softened and bleached by the hot waters, and no doubt the action still continues at depth.

Igneous, or contact. The changes brought about in the invaded, or country, rock by intruding magmas and their emanations are classed as igneous, or contact, metamorphism. The high temperatures and pressures under which magmatic solutions come out of intrusive magmas account for the pervasive character of this type of metamorphism. The changes are greatest near the contact with the intruded rock and become progressively less intense outward from the contact (Fig. 18.2).

Extrusive flows only slightly affect the rocks or soils over which they move. They may melt or bake a thin layer of the older rock, but such changes rarely extend more than a few inches into the older rock.

Along small dikes and sills the invaded rocks are not changed very greatly, nor do the changes extend very far from the igneous body. However, beds of coal have been converted into coke by sills injected along bedding planes near them, and beds of clay have been "fired," or burned into a hard, red brick-like rock, by dikes that intersect them.

The most extensive metamorphic changes accomplished by contact action are found around batholiths, particularly in the invaded rocks near the stocklike masses of the upper parts of these structures. In such environments all rocks are changed—limestones, shales, sandstones, and any older igneous rocks that may be present. The most profound changes are generally in limestone and calcareous shales.

The alterations are caused by heat, mainly hot fluids, from the intruding rock, and not by readjustments due to pressure. The altered contact zones around the intrusion have sometimes been found to be 100 feet wide and sometimes as much as 1 mile wide. At many places, however, there is no altered zone.

The material present in the invaded rock is generally utilized in making up its metamorphosed equivalent. If the limestone contains magnesium, a magnesium mineral like pyroxene is formed; if clay or some other aluminous material is present in the limestone, the new minerals, such as pyroxenes and garnet, also will be aluminous. However, in most contact zones much new material is added, such as silica and iron.

If the vapors and gases given off by the magma contain metals, particularly if they have appreciable amounts of iron, zinc, lead, or copper, ore deposits of the metals may form in the invaded rocks (Fig. 18.3). Such deposits are formed most commonly in limestones and calcareous shales, but they may occur in any type of invaded rock.

At great depths the environments associated with igneous intrusions are characterized by very high temperature and intense pressure. In some of the rocks formed under such conditions, the effects of igneous and metamorphic activity cannot be clearly distinguished. This is true especially along orogenic belts where sedimentary rocks subsided or were dragged to great depths by diastrophic forces. Some granitic rocks now exposed in the cores of folded mountains appear to have acquired their present characteristics while they were still far below the mountain folds.

Granitic rocks that retain evidence of former sedimentary bedding have undergone a process known as *granitization*. Such granitized rocks may constitute a wide aureole around an intrusive granite batholith, with no definite contact between wall rock and granite. The granite grades gradually into the wall rock, which it appears to have replaced or transformed by the addition of gaseous or liquid emanations or by the upward migration of ions through diffusion. Field evidence from a number of areas indicates that various types of igneous, sedimentary, and metamorphic rocks have been transformed into granite or granitelike rock by such metamorphic processes.

Dynamic, or kinetic. Dynamic metamorphism refers to changes induced by strong unbalanced or directed pressures, without the aid of a notable increase in temperature. It is characteristically associated with zones of intensive folding at relatively

FIG. 18.3. *Diagram showing a contact-metamorphic zone of garnet rock and ore in the garnet zone.*

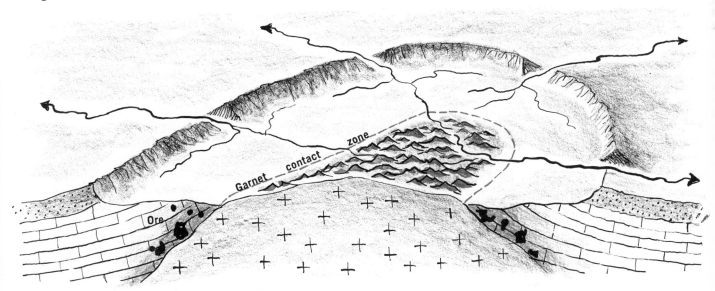

FIG. 18.4. *Conglomerate schist with elongated pebbles, squeezed in the zone of rock flowage. This schist has evidently been formed by dynamic metamorphism under conditions of high pressure and high temperature. (F. J. Pettijohn.)*

shallow depths. The differential stresses cause strata to be folded, crumpled, crushed, stretched to the tearing point in some places, and mashed together in others. The pebbles in Fig. 18.4 are drawn out into thin lenses. Under such conditions, minerals are sheared and flattened. If water is present, the atoms composing the minerals are rearranged, and new mineral compounds are formed. Such a finely granular mosaic of fragments is called a *cataclastic structure.*

Although all dynamic metamorphism implies movement, rocks move differently in different parts of the lithosphere. The earth's outer shell may be divided into (1) an outer zone near the surface, called the *zone of fracture,* where consolidated rocks break when under great stress, and (2) a deeper zone, called the *zone of flowage,* where, under the prevailing pressures, even the stronger rocks are unable to keep their shape or to hold spaces open.

Rocks differ greatly in their response to pressure. Wet muds do not fracture, but they flow at the very surface of the earth; and soft shales will flow at shallow depths. Quartzites and igneous rocks are strong enough to hold fractures open even when there is a weight of several miles of rock above them. At greater depths, even stronger rocks yield by flowage. In experiments conducted by Adams

and Bancroft a cylinder of marble was placed in a hollow cylinder of steel. After great pressure was applied on the pistons, as shown by the arrows in Fig. 18.5, it was found that the rock had changed its shape by flowage. The flowage of rocks under these conditions is not like that of a liquid, nor do the rocks become malleable like some metals. The movement takes place very slowly by the formation of minute fractures and gliding planes, by shearing, by crushing, and by recrystallization.

Where the pressures result in strong differential movement along thrust-fault zones, the rocks near the fault surfaces are likely to be pulverized and the fragments strung out in the direction of movement along the fault. This type of mechanical disturbance produces a streaky, compact rock called a *mylonite,* which is a strongly coherent mass of microscopic mineral grains, produced by the mashing of the original rock grains. In general, fault gouge and breccia form near the surface of the earth, where the confining pressures are comparatively small, whereas mylonite forms at greater depths, where the confining pressure forces the rocks to retain their coherence even though they are pulverized. A mylonite, therefore, may be thought of as a microbreccia that maintained its coherence during deformation.

DEGREES

Some metamorphic rocks are more intensely altered than others. In the transformation of shale to slate, comparatively little recrystallization takes place. But when slate is transformed to phyllite, to mica schist, and finally to garnetiferous schist or gneiss, each succeeding rock represents a higher degree, or rank, of metamorphism. The chemical composition of the original shale and that of the end product of intensive metamorphism, the garnetiferous schist or gneiss, may be nearly identical, but their general appearance and mineral composition are vastly different. The degree, or rank, of metamorphism attained is determined by the intensity of action of the agents and by other factors in the environment. In general, slates and phyllites, which are low-rank metamorphic rocks, are formed near the surface, whereas schists and gneisses, both

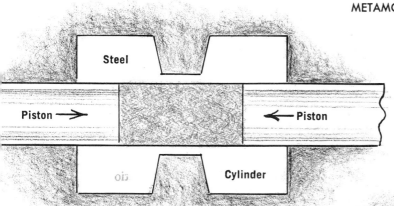

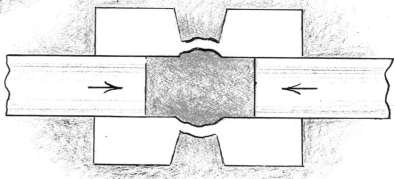

FIG. 18.5. *Diagrams illustrating the deformation of marble by great pressure. The upper figure shows a section of a hollow cylinder in which a small cylinder of marble is fitted. The lower figure shows the same after great pressure has been applied by movement of the pistons. Plastic deformation took place slowly, resulting in shortening and bulging out of the marble cylinder and the confining steel jacket. The rock is deformed, but it is not crushed. (After Adams and Bancroft.)*

FIG. 18.6. *Garnet metacrysts in schist, Stikeen River, Alaska. Garnetiferous schist is an intensely metamorphosed rock. (American Museum of Natural History.)*

high-rank metamorphic rocks, are formed at greater depth or near the margins of intrusive masses of magma.

An intensely metamorphosed rock, such as a garnetiferous schist, may be transferred by diastrophism into a new position, which may have a different environment. At its new location the conditions of stability may be those which produce slates and phyllites. Thus the schist may return to the low-rank state of a phyllite. Such metamorphism has occurred in many mountainous areas where refolding and faulting of older metamorphic rocks have taken place.

Structures and Textures of Metamorphic Rocks

Metamorphic rocks are classified, on the basis of their structure and texture, into foliated and nonfoliated groups. Many metamorphic rocks are more

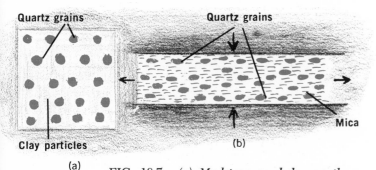

Quartz grains

Quartz grains

Clay particles

Mica

(a)

(b)

FIG. 18.7. *(a) Mudstone or shale, greatly enlarged, consisting of fine quartz sand and of smaller clay particles; (b) the same rock metamorphosed by pressure to form slate. The quartz grains are broken and flattened, and the fragments and minute lenses of quartz are oriented so that their long axes lie parallel to the direction of least pressure. The clay particles recrystallize to tiny mica flakes arranged parallel to the direction of least pressure also. This alinement of grains makes slate readily cleavable.*

or less foliated, or arranged in bands. This structure is due to the parallel arrangement of their constituent minerals or to the elongation of bands, layers, or lenses of granular material. The rocks will split more readily on planes that run parallel to the planes of foliation than on planes that cross them. The planes of foliation are often highly irregular and undulating. In a coarse-grained metamorphic rock, like gneiss, the planes are poorly defined, whereas in a fine-grained rock, like slate or schist, they are well-defined and closer together.

The property of a rock that causes it to split, or break, in certain directions more easily than in others is called *rock cleavage*. If the minerals are arranged so that their long dimensions are parallel, the rock breaks in such a way that the minerals separate on planes parallel to the long dimension of the grains. This type of cleavage is called *schistosity*, and the rocks that possess it are schists (Figs. 18.6, 18.10, 18.11). Nonfoliated rocks are massive and do not cleave readily.

When a mud or shale is examined under the microscope, it is found to consist of small particles of quartz mingled with finer particles of clay. Under great pressure the quartz grains are broken and are rotated so that their long axes lie in the direction of least pressure; the finer clayey material is recrystallized, and new minerals, such as mica and amphiboles, are produced. These new minerals are formed so that their long dimensions are parallel to the direction of least pressure, as is illustrated by Fig. 18.7, in which (*a*) represents an unaltered shale, greatly magnified, and (*b*) shows the same rock after dynamic metamorphism. The direction of greatest pressure is indicated by the long arrows and the direction of least pressure by the short horizontal arrows. If free to move, the material of the rock tends to lengthen in the direction of least pressure and to become shorter in the direction of greatest pressure. Because the mineral fragments are strung out at right angles to the lines of greatest pressure and because the flaky or fibrous minerals that are formed are aligned in that direction, the rock usually will break, or cleave, in planes parallel to the long minerals. Thus a slaty cleavage is developed. Bedded rocks that are greatly compressed by folding tend to take on a slaty cleavage, so that they often break across the beds, particularly at the axes of the folds (Fig. 18.8).

FIG. 18.8. *Diagram of folded beds converted to slate with slaty cleavage developed across the bedding.*

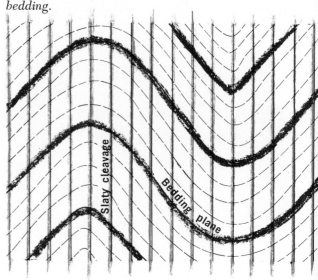

Slaty cleavage

Bedding plane

Most slates are formed from muds and clays. Shales are very readily changed to slates and schists, not only because they are weak, but also because they usually contain aluminum, potash, and iron, from which flaky minerals may form. If much potash is present, mica usually will be abundant in the product. Pure limestone and pure quartzite, on the other hand, do not form schists, because they do not contain the materials for the formation of the platy minerals.

Foliated Metamorphic Rocks

The most common foliated rocks are those composed mostly of micas and chlorite. These platy minerals are easily cleavable. A rock containing a large number of platy grains, parallel to each other, will split readily in the direction parallel to that of the cleavage of the mineral grains. The most abundant foliated rocks are the slates, phyllites, schists, and gneisses.

SLATES

A slate is a homogeneous, fine-grained rock which will split into thin or thick sheets with relatively smooth surfaces. The chief minerals are not readily distinguished by the naked eye. Because of their finer grain, slates generally have smoother surfaces than schists. Some slates, however, have crumpled and folded cleavage surfaces. The cleavage is often parallel to the bedding, but at many places it intersects the bedding at high angles (Figs. 18.8, 18.9). The original bedding planes may appear as streaks, often more or less plicated and running at any angle to the slaty cleavage.

Slates range in color from gray, through red, green, and purple, to black. The gray and black colors generally are due to carbonaceous material in the original rock, the carbon compounds having changed to graphite. The red and purple shades are due to iron and manganese oxides, and the green to ferrous iron silicates. Slates commonly are named from the predominant color or most conspicuous mineral. There is no sharp boundary

FIG. 18.9. *An outcrop of slate in Deep Creek Canyon, Montana, showing the platy character of the cleavage. (Walcott, U.S. Geological Survey.)*

between shales and slates or between slates and phyllites.

Slates are a valuable roofing material. Uniform platy cleavage is the characteristic most desired in commercial slates. A good slate splits in one direction only and divides into flat sheets with smooth surfaces, as thin as $\frac{1}{16}$ inch. The market value of a roofing slate also depends on its color and on the

FIG. 18.10. *A porphyry changed to schist by pressure. The white spots are former phenocrysts that range in size up to about 1 inch. (Keith, U.S. Geological Survey.)*

permanence of the color. Some slates fade or discolor rapidly, whereas others retain their original color for many years.

Slate granules are used to surface asphalt shingles, and slabs of slate are used for blackboards, table tops, and switchboards. Georgia, Vermont, Pennsylvania, and New York are the main sources of slate.

PHYLLITES

A phyllite is a foliated, finely micaceous rock of nearly uniform composition. It is coarser and more lustrous than slate but too fine-grained to be classed as a schist. In phyllites, the mica flakes are generally large enough to be distinguished by the naked eye, but most of the other material is very fine-grained. Phyllites represent a degree of metamorphism greater than that of slates but less than that of schists. They may grade into either of these rocks.

SCHISTS

The mineral grains in schists are generally large enough to be seen with the naked eye. The individual leaves are not of uniform thickness but are flattened lenses, often bent and curving, with their platy surfaces in parallel planes (Figs. 18.10, 18.11). At right angles to these planes, schists break with great difficulty, leaving irregular frayed edges.

Schists generally are classified on the basis of their mineral composition. If micas are prominently developed, the rock is *mica schist*. If hornblende is the mineral responsible for the foliation, the rock, which is generally dark green to black with a silky luster, is *hornblende schist*. Schists rarely have abundant feldspar. Most schists are formed from shales, but some are formed by the metamorphism of fine-grained igneous rocks, such as felsites and basalts.

Schists and phyllites are generally too weak along the cleavage to be employed in construction.

GNEISSES

A gneiss is a banded, coarsely textured metamorphic rock with a rough foliation (Fig. 18.12). The alternating bands, or layers, are commonly of unlike mineral composition. In most gneisses feldspar is a prominent constituent; often the presence of large feldspar crystals serves to distinguish a gneiss from a schist.

During movement under great pressure, the feldspar crystals of a granite may rotate so that they lie with their long axes aligned in the direction of

TABLE 18.1 *Some Common Minerals of Crystalline Schists*

Generally without marked elongation	Generally elongated in two dimensions, platy or tabular	Generally elongated in one dimension, needlelike
Quartz	Muscovite	Actinolite
Garnet	Biotite	Tremolite
Pyrite	Chlorite	Hornblende
Magnetite	Talc	
Staurolite		

least pressure (Fig. 18.12). Micas also are recrystallized, and these lie with their leaves parallel to the long axes of the crystals. These changes are brought about much less readily than the change from shale to slate, because the granite is a stronger rock; yet at great depths the granite may act as a somewhat plastic mass, and its minerals rotate in much the same way as the minerals involved in the formation of schist. Gneisses also have been formed from arkose sands by the granulation and cementation of the fragments of feldspar and other minerals that make up the sands.

Certain granite gneisses appear to have been formed by movement during the consolidation of the granite, probably just after the granite had cooled to a pasty mass but had not yet become completely solid. In such granites the feldspar and mica crystals are drawn out and arranged in lines, so that the structure of the gneiss is much like that of a granite gneiss formed by metamorphism. Such texture is known as *flow banding*, and the rock is called a *primary gneiss*. Recent work has shown that primary gneisses are more common than was formerly supposed and that they should not be classified as metamorphic rocks.

Where granitic batholiths are injected into slates and schists, many sill-like injections of granite occur parallel to the foliation of the invaded rock. Near the margin of the batholiths the amount of granite may be as great as the amount of foliated rock. The "sills" range in thickness from a small fraction of an inch to several feet, and the rock between them is completely recrystallized by the high temperature and the great pressure of the injected magma. The resulting composite rock has a gneissic, laminated appearance and is called an *injection gneiss,* or granitized schist. Such rocks are common in the roof pendants of batholiths and around the cupolas that extend upward into the invaded rock (Fig. 6.29). Many injection gneisses are so intricately folded and convoluted that we must conclude that both the granite and the host rocks were in a mobile state at the time the folding occurred.

Gneiss sometimes is substituted for granite in construction, but the blocks must be laid with the foliation flat, and not on edge.

FIG. 18.11.   *Complex folding and crumpling in quartzose schist on Boardman Hill, Clarendon, Vermont.   The hammer handle is 15 inches long. (Dale, U.S. Geological Survey.)*

Nonfoliated Metamorphic Rocks

Not all metamorphic rocks have a foliated structure. Some are massive like igneous rocks but can be distinguished from them by their mineral composition. Many nonfoliated metamorphic rocks are the products of hydrometamorphism in environments where solutions at either high or low temperatures were the dominant factors in producing the mineral alterations.

MARBLE

Marble is a crystalline calcareous rock formed by the metamorphism of limestone. The principal mineral is either calcite or dolomite. Marbles range in texture from fine to relatively coarse varieties, in which the grains are clearly visible to the unaided eye. Marble is more compact than limestone, its porosity having been reduced by pressure and recrystallization. Pure marble is white, but impurities may give it a great variety of colors. Red, yellow, and brown marbles, many of which are very attractive when polished, owe their color to varying proportions of compounds of iron. Carbonaceous organic matter produces gray and black colors, and the green color is due to the presence of serpentine and chlorite.

FIG. 18.12. *Banded gneiss, near Embry Lake, Manitoba. The crinkled bands are vertical as a result of pressures applied horizontally at great depths within the earth. (Geological Survey of Canada.)*

Marble, mainly used as ornamental stone, is quarried extensively in Vermont, Tennessee, and Georgia.

TABLE 18.2 *Sedimentary Rocks and Their Metamorphosed Equivalents*

Unconsolidated	Consolidated	Metamorphosed
Gravel	Conglomerate	Conglomerate schist
Sand	Sandstone	Quartzite, quartz schist
Mud, clay	Shale, argillite	Slate, phyllite, mica schist
Calcareous ooze	Limestone	Marble, calcareous schist
Peat	Lignite, bituminous coal	Anthracite coal, graphite

TABLE 18.3 *Igneous Rocks and Their Metamorphosed Equivalents*

Igneous rocks	Metamorphosed equivalents
Granite	Granite gneiss
Syenite	Syenite gneiss
Diorite	Diorite gneiss
Gabbro	Gabbro gneiss
Peridotite	Serpentine
Rhyolite	Mica schist
Andesite	Hornblende schist
Basalt	Hornblende schist, biotite schist, chlorite schist

QUARTZITE

Quartzite is formed from sandstone that was thoroughly cemented by quartz brought into the rock in solution and deposited around the sand grains. A broken surface of quartzite shows a glassy luster and a splintery or conchoidal fracture. Impure sandstones, especially those containing clayey minerals, form quartzose schists when subjected to dynamic forces due to earth movements. Thus sandstones may show various degrees and types of metamorphism. Quartzites formed by simple deposition of quartz from cold ground waters are not considered metamorphic rocks.

Pure quartzite, containing more than 97 per cent silicon dioxide, as at Baraboo, Wisconsin, is used to make silica firebrick and other refractories. Because of its high silica content, such quartzite, if crushed and ground, may be used in fillers and abrasives as a substitute for quartz taken from sedimentary rocks. The cost of preparing it, however, is generally too high to make this feasible.

SOAPSTONE

Soapstone is a rock composed essentially of talc but commonly containing some mica, tremolite, chlorite, and quartz as accessory minerals. The rock is light bluish gray or grayish green in color and has a greasy feel. It is a product of hydrothermal alteration and consequently contains various hydrous silicates.

Cut in thin slabs, soapstone is used for table tops, electrical switchboards, laboratory sinks, laundry tubs, and refractories.

COAL

Coal is formed by the consolidation and induration of plant remains, which, as subjected to progressively greater pressure during metamorphism, successively form (1) peat, (2) lignite, (3) bituminous coal, (4) anthracite coal, and (5) graphite. Each substance in this series contains more carbon and less gas and water than the preceding substance. At many places coal-bearing formations may be followed from the plains, where they lie nearly flat, to mountains, where they are highly folded.

As the amount of folding increases, the character of the coal changes. In the Western plains, where the beds lie nearly horizontal, only lignite is present; toward the mountains the lignite has changed to bituminous coal, and where the coal beds have been more intensely folded, the coal has become anthracite.

Summary

We have seen how metamorphism transforms the composition, texture, and structure of minerals and rocks in response to changes in their environment. Such alterations are caused by increases in pressure and temperature and by the introduction of hot fluids.

Geothermal metamorphism produces general recrystallization of susceptible rocks, such as sediments, to make coarser textures and different mineral combinations.

Hydrothermal metamorphism changes feldspars to sericite or clay minerals, olivine to serpentine and talc, biotite to chlorite, and pyroxenes and amphiboles to chlorite and serpentine. It generally softens and bleaches the altered rocks.

Contact metamorphism alters the rocks around the periphery of stocks and batholiths by heating them and introducing hot solutions. Limestone coarsens its grain to marble, and sandstone changes to quartzite. The hot solutions may carry silica, iron, copper, gold, and other substances in sufficient quantity to make ore deposits. Where large quantities of magmatic juices are introduced into schists in the contact zone, the end product may be a granitelike rock or an injection gneiss.

Dynamic metamorphism, resulting from deep-seated earth movements, operates by granulation, shearing, alignment of particles, solid flow, and recrystallization. Slate and phyllite are low-rank metamorphic products; schist and gneiss are formed by intense, long-continued, high-rank metamorphism.

Because of the parallel arrangement of their cleavable minerals, slate, phyllite, schist, and gneiss are foliated and display rock cleavage. Lacking such alignment, the nonfoliates, such as marble, quartzite, soapstone, and anthracite, do not have cleavage.

Suggestions for Further Reading

Fenton, C. L., and M. A. Fenton: *Rocks and Their Stories*, Doubleday & Company, Inc., New York, 1951. A well-illustrated nontechnical book.

Fyfe, W. S., F. J. Turner, and J. Verhoogen; Metamorphic Reactions and Metamorphic Facies, *Geol. Soc. America Mem.* No. 73, 1953. This is an advanced study of metamorphism.

Grout, F. F: *Kemp's Handbook of Rocks,* . Van Nostrand Company, Inc., Princeton, N.J., 1952.

Harker, Alfred: *Metamorphism: A Study of the Transformations of Rock-Masses*, Methuen & Co., Ltd., London, 1932. Although dated, this is a standard textbook on metamorphism.

Ramberg, Hans: *The Origin of Metamorphic and Metasomatic Rocks*, University of Chicago Press, Chicago, 1952. An advanced discussion of the subject.

Turner, F. J., and J. Verhoogen: *Igneous and Metamorphic Petrology*, McGraw-Hill Book Company, Inc., New York, 1951. A detailed study of metamorphism, especially its physical chemistry.

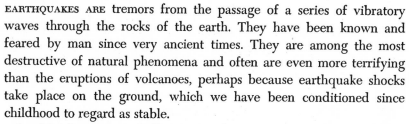

Chapter 19

EARTHQUAKES AND THE INTERIOR OF THE EARTH

EARTHQUAKES ARE tremors from the passage of a series of vibratory waves through the rocks of the earth. They have been known and feared by man since very ancient times. They are among the most destructive of natural phenomena and often are even more terrifying than the eruptions of volcanoes, perhaps because earthquake shocks take place on the ground, which we have been conditioned since childhood to regard as stable.

In this chapter we shall examine the causes and effects of earthquakes and consider some measures that may be adopted to minimize their danger to man. In addition, we shall see that the study of earthquakes has given us important insights into the internal structure of the earth.

Examples of Earthquakes

LISBON, PORTUGAL

On All Saints' Day, Nov. 1, 1755, thousands of persons were congregated in the cathedrals of Lisbon, Portugal, when, at 9:40 A.M., the city was struck by a violent earthquake. This earthquake, only 6 or 7 minutes long, virtually destroyed the churches and other buildings of the city and killed tens of thousands. Some of the survivors, many of them seriously injured, sought refuge on a new marble quay at the waterfront, but a second shock, about 20 minutes after the first one, plunged the quay and the people into the water. A third severe earthquake at noon added to the havoc.

As a result of the impact, the waters of the Atlantic Ocean first left the harbor and then, about 10 A.M., sloshed back on land as a great wave, variously estimated at from 16 to 50 feet high, which reached inland ½ mile. When the wave retreated, it washed ships, buildings, bridges, and people out to sea. Three other such waves, each about 16 feet high, returned in the next 4 hours.

Altogether, about half the city was destroyed. The aftershocks of the quake continued for several months. The earthquake was felt over an area of at least 1,250,000 square miles. The shock disturbed lakes and rivers over much of Western Europe. For about 1½ hours, Loch Lomond, Scotland, 1,220 miles from Lisbon, rocked back and forth every 10 minutes in seiche (oscillation) waves about 2 feet high.

NEW MADRID, MISSOURI

A little after 2 A.M. on Dec. 16, 1811, a major earthquake struck the region of New Madrid, Missouri. Before dawn, there were 27 aftershocks, followed by a declining series of shocks for days afterward. On Jan. 23, 1812, a second great earthquake struck, and on Feb. 7, 1812, there was a third, the most severe of all. In 3 months' time a total of 1,874 shocks were noted at Louisville, Kentucky, 200 miles away, and chimneys were toppled in Cincinnati, Ohio, 400 miles away. The alluvial fill on the Mississippi River flood plain was thrown into waves and cracked; parts of it were elevated, and an area of about 5,750 square miles, including the newly created basin of Reelfoot Lake, Tennessee, sank several feet; and the course of the river was changed (Fig. 19.1). The affected area displayed an array of newly formed fissures, sand dikes, sand extrusions, elevated domes, landslides, sunken ground, lakes, and swamps. The earthquake was felt from the Rocky Mountains to the Atlantic coast and from Canada to the Gulf of Mexico. The American seismologist Perry Byerly regards the New Madrid earthquake as the greatest on record in the United States. A

FIG. 19.0. *Damage to stores (ground floor) and public auditorium (above), resulting from the severe earthquake near Bakersfield, California, on July 21, 1952. (U.S. Coast and Geodetic Survey.)*

repetition of it would cause prodigious damage because of the subsequent growth of population and cities within its potential reach.

CHARLESTON, SOUTH CAROLINA

On Aug. 31, 1886, a violent earthquake shook the city of Charleston, South Carolina, for about 70 seconds. Buildings on filled-in ground were heavily damaged, roads and railroads were twisted about, air and water spurted out of the ground, and sand mounds were built up at many places. The earthquake was felt over most of the eastern part of the United States, from Boston to Milwaukee to New Orleans. The intensity of the shock decreased with distance from the source. Aftershocks continued for more than a year. This quake is noteworthy for its occurrence in a region generally free from shocks, the wide range of the area in which it was perceptible, and the moderate damage and loss of life occasioned by a shock of such intensity.

ASSAM, INDIA

At about 5:15 P.M., June 12, 1897, an earthquake severely shook the region of the province of Assam in eastern India. Inasmuch as nearly all buildings over an area of about 30,000 square miles were destroyed or seriously damaged and inasmuch as the acceleration was great enough to overcome gravity and project stones vertically off the ground, this earthquake may be the most severe ever recorded, although relatively few persons were killed.

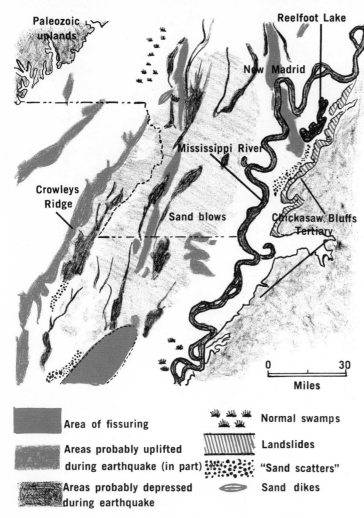

Paleozoic uplands

Reelfoot Lake

New Madrid

Mississippi River

Crowleys Ridge

Sand blows

Chickasaw Bluffs Tertiary

0   30
Miles

Area of fissuring

Normal swamps

Areas probably uplifted during earthquake (in part)

Landslides

"Sand scatters"

Areas probably depressed during earthquake

Sand dikes

FIG. 19.1. *Map of part of region affected by the earthquakes of 1811 near New Madrid, Missouri. (After Fuller, U.S. Geological Survey.)*

The shock started great landslides, opened fissures, displaced alluvial soils, ruined forests and rice fields, and produced visible waves on the ground. Several thousand aftershocks were noted in the next 2 years.

Another unusually severe shock occurred in Assam in 1950.

SAN FRANCISCO, CALIFORNIA

On Apr. 18, 1906, California was shaken by the most severe earthquake in the history of the state. About 700 persons were killed, buildings were de-

stroyed, and in a fire that followed the earthquake a large part of San Francisco was burned. Piers in nearby harbors were destroyed, and landslides occurred. The first snap, or movement, of the earth was recorded at the observatory of the University of California and was found to be 3 inches in a horizontal direction and 1 inch in a vertical direction. The first snap was quickly followed by rebounds over the greatly disturbed area on both sides of a fault line (the San Andreas fault). These movements, or "temblors," brought down chimneys and towers. The shocks were felt from Coos Bay, Oregon, to Los Angeles and were recorded at Washington, D.C.; at Potsdam, Germany; Irkutsk, Siberia; and other places.

The San Andreas fault (Fig. 19.7), which caused the California earthquake, is almost vertical, and the movement along it was approximately horizontal. In general, the effects were most severe nearest the fault, although they varied considerably with the character of the rock. Buildings on rocky hills were little damaged, whereas those on loose ground collapsed. Where foundations were laid on piles driven into the ground, the destructive effects were generally slight, even in areas of man-made ground. The buildings most affected by the shocks were on raftlike foundations on the loose mantle-rock or fill.

SAGAMI BAY, JAPAN

On Sept. 1, 1923, a great earthquake destroyed Yokohama and a large part of Tokyo, Japan. At 11:58:44 A.M., a violent shock shook the houses and other structures. Other shocks followed, and fire was kindled at scores of places. Because of the bursting of water mains the fire could not be extinguished. At 4 P.M., a high wind swept the city. By nightfall 1 million persons in Tokyo were left homeless. Sea waves destroyed shipping along the shores. More than 100,000 persons were killed, many as a result of the fire. The bottom of Sagami Bay, which is about 1 mile deep, had been mapped by soundings before the earthquake; and when it was mapped again after the earthquake, it was found that at some places the movements of the sea bottom, partly upward but mostly downward, amounted to hundreds of feet, probably because of the shifting of loose sediments on the floor of the bay.

LONG BEACH, CALIFORNIA

At Long Beach, California, there was a shock on Mar. 10, 1933. At short distances away it was not a strong shock, as recorded by seismographs, but it was severe locally. Since there is deep alluvium over much of the area, there were heavy damage and some loss of life. The point of origin was a little offshore. There was neither a sea wave nor a notable disturbance of water, although vessels nearby felt the tremors.

HELENA, MONTANA

Some earthquakes consist of a large number of small shocks. These are called *swarm earthquakes*. At Helena, Montana, from Oct. 18, 1935, to Jan. 1, 1936, there were nearly 1,300 shocks; strong shocks on Oct. 18, Nov. 28, and Dec. 31 were destructive. At least 40 houses were ruined, 200 were considerably damaged, and 80 per cent of the houses in the city suffered some damage. In mines nearby the shock was felt strongly, but no damage was done.

ARVIN-TEHACHAPI, CALIFORNIA

The strongest California earthquake since 1906 struck the Arvin-Tehachapi area, at the south end of the San Joaquin Valley, on July 21, 1952. It had a maximum intensity of XI (see Modified Mercalli Intensity Scale below), but since the area was thinly settled, only 14 lives were lost. It was followed by numerous aftershocks, including seven strong ones within a few weeks, one of which, on Aug. 22, damaged Bakersfield. The series of shocks did extensive damage to wells, pipelines, irrigation reservoirs, ditches, roads, railroad tunnels, and other structures, mainly because of the lurching of alluvium. The quakes were started by movement on the White Wolf fault near the base of Bear Mountain (Fig. 19.7). Numerous fractures and scarplets were formed in the alluviated lowland (Fig. 19.2); on the higher slopes fissures formed in solid rocks, and several landslides broke loose.

FIG. 19.2.   *Irregular "mole track," showing location of fractures in alluvium caused by movement on White Wolf fault near the base of Bear Mountain, Kern County, California. This movement took place during the Arvin-Tehachapi earthquake on July 21, 1952. (California Division of Mines.)*

ORLEANSVILLE, ALGERIA

At 1:07 A.M., Sept. 9, 1954, a severe earthquake occurred at Orleansville, in northern Algeria, wrecking much of the city and killing more than 1,000 out of a population of 32,500. The earth fractured, and open fissures appeared for 60 miles around. The major shock was followed by a series of minor quakes that continued throughout the following week.

HEBGEN, MONTANA

At 11:47 P.M., on Aug. 17, 1959, a strong earthquake struck the vicinity of Hebgen Lake a short distance north of West Yellowstone near the Montana-Wyoming border. It was followed by hundreds of aftershocks of slight to moderate intensity and was felt over an area of about 550,000 square miles between the Dakotas, Puget Sound, and Nevada. Property damage was greatest between West Yellowstone and Butte.

The earthquake cracked the dam at Hebgen Lake, disrupted or blocked paved roads at many places, and started numerous slides. One huge slide, 4,000 to 5,000 feet wide, 300 to 400 feet high, and containing 30 to 50 million cubic yards of rock, dammed up a new lake in the Madison River canyon about 7 miles below Hebgen Dam. This slide buried about 20 people encamped near the river.

Vertical scarps 10 to 20 feet high broke the ground for 15 miles along the side of the valley. The movement tilted the block of ground under Hebgen Lake enough to depress the north shore and to raise the south shore several feet. Consequently the lake itself slopped about in its basin. The circumstances clearly demonstrated that subsurface block faulting had caused the earthquake.

OTHER EARTHQUAKES

References to earthquakes appear in ancient and medieval writings of Greece, Italy, and other countries, as well as in modern records. It has been estimated that, in 10 great shocks since A.D. 1,000, more than 1.5 million persons have lost their lives and that, in the last 4,000 years, more than 13 million persons have been killed in earthquakes.

Some outstanding earthquakes are listed in Table 19.1.

Features

INTENSITY

The intensity of an earthquake is measured by its effects on man, its damage to buildings and other structures, and the changes it produces in rock and soil at the earth's surface. The intensity

TABLE 19.1   *Other Examples of Destructive Earthquakes*

Year	Place	Remarks
1450 B.C.	Cimini, Italy	City engulfed in Lake Cimini
224 B.C.	Rhodes, eastern Mediterranean	Colossus, bronze statue of Apollo, 105 feet high, one of the Seven Wonders, at harbor entrance, destroyed
811	Rome, Italy	Basilica of St. Paul's destroyed
1170	Sicily	15,000 lives lost
1303	Alexandria, Egypt	Pharos, 370-foot first lighthouse, another of the Seven Wonders, 1,500 years old, destroyed
1456	Naples, Italy	60,000 lives lost
1693	Naples, Italy	93,000 lives lost
1731	Peking, China	100,000 lives lost
1891	Mino-Owari, Japan	Horizontal and vertical movements on faults readily apparent
1899	Yakutat Bay, Alaska	Seacoast uplifted as much as 47 feet, and glaciers affected
1906	Colombia, Ecuador	One of the largest of the last century
1908	Messina, Italy	125,000 lives lost
1911	Tien Shan Mountains, Asia	Of large magnitude
1920	Kansu, China	100,000 lives lost, mainly by landslides of loess
1922	Chile	Of great severity; great sea wave in the Pacific
1927	Murchison, New Zealand	Vertical faulting of 14 feet, great landslides, and a seismic sea wave
1929	Grand Banks, off Newfoundland	12 transatlantic cables broken, submarine slides started, 50-foot sea waves set up
1931	Hawkes Bay, New Zealand	Originated offshore; damaged cities and harbors; coast uplifted several feet
1939	Turkey	40,000 lives lost
1950	Assam, India	Of unusually high magnitude

differs not only from place to place but also at the same place, because of differences in the stability of the foundations, the manner of construction, and other variables. Macelwane states that destructivity depends on the geological character of the ground; the size and shape of the structures, their design and workmanship, and the materials used in their construction; and the acceleration of the earthquake wave, its period, its velocity, and its duration.

In a severe earthquake, buildings are shaken down, cornices fall off, chimneys topple, bridges collapse, pavement is broken, roads and railroads are buckled and twisted (Fig. 19.3), telephone and telegraph wires and cables are broken, power lines are downed, fires are started, water towers and tanks give way, and gas and water mains are severed—in other words, the life of an urban community is almost completely disrupted.

MODIFIED MERCALLI INTENSITY SCALE

The Mercalli scale, as modified by Wood and Neumann in 1931, is the intensity scale most used in the United States. An abridged form of it is as follows:

I. Not felt, except by a very few in especially favorable circumstances.

II. Felt only by a few persons at rest, especially on upper floors of buildings. Delicately suspended objects may swing.

III. Felt quite noticeably indoors, especially on upper floors of buildings, but not recognized by many people as an earthquake. Standing motor cars may rock slightly. Vibration like that caused by a passing truck. Duration can be estimated.

IV. During the day, felt indoors by many, outdoors by few. At night, some awakened. Dishes, windows, doors are disturbed; walls make cracking sound. Sensation like that of heavy truck striking building. Standing motor cars are rocked noticeably.

V. Felt by nearly everyone; many awakened. Some dishes and windows broken; a few instances of cracked plaster; unstable objects overturned. Disturbances of trees, poles, and

FIG. 19.3. *Rails of track twisted by the Arvin-Tehachapi earthquake, July 21, 1952, at east entrance to Tunnel No. 3, Southern Pacific Railroad, near Bealville, California. (U.S. Coast and Geodetic Survey.)*

other tall objects sometimes noticed. Pendulum clocks may stop.

VI. Felt by all; many frightened and run outdoors. Some heavy furniture moved; a few instances of fallen plaster or damaged chimneys. Damage slight.

VII. Everybody runs outdoors. Damage *negligible* in buildings of good design and construction; *slight to moderate* in well-built ordinary structures; *considerable* in poorly built or badly designed structures; some chimneys broken. Noticed by persons driving motor cars.

VIII. Damage *slight* in specially designed structures; *considerable* in ordinary substantial buildings, with partial collapse; *great* in poorly built structures. Fall of chimneys, factory stacks, columns, monuments, walls. Panel walls thrown out of frame structures. Heavy furniture overturned. Sand and mud ejected in small amounts. Changes in well water. Persons driving motor cars disturbed.

IX. Damage *considerable* even in specially designed structures; well-designed frame struc-

FIG. 19.4. *Map showing isoseismal lines of earthquake centered in west central Nevada, December 16, 1954. The earthquake was felt over an area of about 200,000 square miles in five states. A maximum intensity, X, was reached near the source, where fault displacements reached 20 feet vertically and 12 feet horizontally. (After map by U.S. Coast and Geodetic Survey.)*

tures thrown out of plumb; *great* in substantial buildings, with partial collapse. Buildings shifted off foundations. Ground cracked conspicuously. Underground pipes broken.

X. Some well-built wooden structures destroyed; most masonry and frame structures destroyed along with foundations; ground badly cracked. Rails bent. Landslides considerable from riverbanks and steep slopes. Shifted sand and mud. Water splashed (slopped) over banks.

XI. No structures remain standing, except pos-

sibly a few masonry buildings. Bridges destroyed. Broad fissures in ground. Underground pipelines completely out of service. Earth slumps and land slips in soft ground. Rails bent greatly.

XII. Damage total. Waves seen on ground surfaces. Lines of sight and level distorted. Objects thrown into the air.

The intensities at different places are rated by trained seismologists on the basis of field surveys and returned postcard questionnaires distributed by the U.S. Coast and Geodetic Survey or by local collaborators.

The intensity of each locality is plotted on a map, and *isoseismal lines* are then drawn at the boundaries of areas of different intensities (Fig. 19.4). Such an isoseismal map shows the area of maximum damage, surrounded by more or less concentric belts of progressively less damage. Its principal value is to call attention to areas of poor geologic foundations, unstable methods of construction, or other hazards which need to be taken into account in planning to reduce destruction in future earthquakes.

FIG. 19.5. *Alluvium cracked by earthquake near Arvin, California, July 21, 1952. The house was shifted off its foundation and severely damaged structurally. (California Division of Mines.)*

GEOLOGIC EFFECTS

The foregoing accounts of specific earthquakes mention some of their geologic effects—fissuring of the ground, sunken ground, raised hummocks, slumping, earthslides, mudflows, eruptions of water and sand, seismic sea waves, and seiches (oscillation waves) on lakes (Figs. 19.2, 19.3, 19.5, 19.6). In addition, there may be disturbances of the ground-water circulation, which muddy the waters of wells and springs, stop some springs, and initiate others. Earthquakes may also start avalanches of snow, release icebergs from tidewater glaciers, and perhaps affect glaciers in other ways.

It will be seen that these effects are relatively superficial, largely local, and generally of minor geological consequence. In spite of their destructiveness, earthquakes are comparatively unimportant as geologic agents. However, they do give important clues to the internal structure of the earth.

CAUSES

Earthquake waves may be caused by (1) the *fracture* of rocks in faulting or volcanic explosions; (2) *percussion*, or sudden blows, from an explosion (quarry blast, atom bomb, volcanic eruption), from traffic (trucks, tanks, trains), or from rockfalls (from cliffs, waterfalls, caverns, or mines); or (3) the *rubbing* together of two uneven surfaces in faulting, landslides, avalanches, and submarine slumping of sediments.

Faulting. The principal cause of earthquakes is faulting, either the initiation of a new fault or repeated movement on an existing fault. Nontectonic causes are responsible only for local and mostly minor tremors. Most volcanic explosions, even the giant firecracker outbursts of Krakatao in 1883 and of Katmai in 1912, have only small, local, shallow, and weak effects.

The association of earthquakes with faulting was especially well shown by the California earthquake of Apr. 18, 1906, when the San Andreas fault moved over a length of at least 270 miles (Fig. 19.7). The fault is vertical, but the movement was almost entirely horizontal and parallel to the trend

FIG. 19.6. *Landslide scars in Sycamore Canyon, Kern County, California, after the Arvin-Tehachapi earthquake of July 21, 1952. The mountain in the background is Bear Mountain. The White Wolf fault zone, along which movement took place, causing the earthquake, lies a fraction of a mile to the left (northwest). (Robert C. Frampton.)*

of the fault. The block on the southwest side shifted northward with reference to the opposite side (Fig. 19.8). The maximum measured displacement of 21 feet was found by the offset of a road near the head of Tomales Bay, northwest of San Francisco.

Similarly, in connection with the Imperial Valley earthquake of California in 1940, roads and row crops were offset horizontally at least 15 feet. In Sonora, Mexico, a 35-mile fault associated with an 1887 earthquake showed 26 feet of vertical displacement. In 1897, the Chedrang fault in Assam, India, had a vertical displacement of 35 feet. In Japan, in 1891, the displacement on the Mino-Owari earthquake fault, several tens of miles long, was 13 feet horizontally and 20 feet vertically. These faults, it must be remembered, were the *causes* of

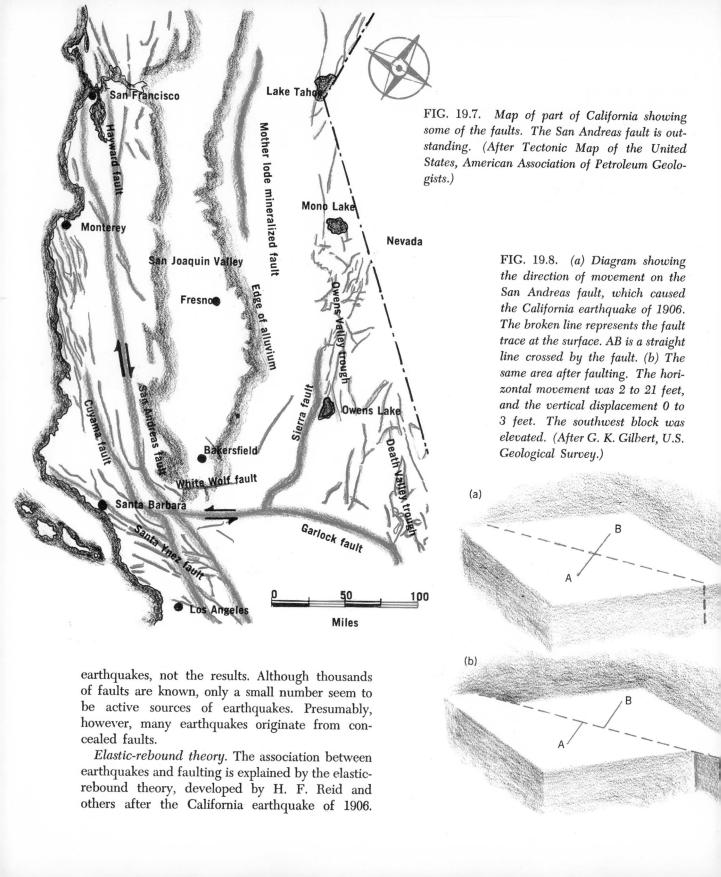

FIG. 19.7. *Map of part of California showing some of the faults. The San Andreas fault is outstanding. (After Tectonic Map of the United States, American Association of Petroleum Geologists.)*

FIG. 19.8. *(a) Diagram showing the direction of movement on the San Andreas fault, which caused the California earthquake of 1906. The broken line represents the fault trace at the surface. AB is a straight line crossed by the fault. (b) The same area after faulting. The horizontal movement was 2 to 21 feet, and the vertical displacement 0 to 3 feet. The southwest block was elevated. (After G. K. Gilbert, U.S. Geological Survey.)*

(a)

(b)

earthquakes, not the results. Although thousands of faults are known, only a small number seem to be active sources of earthquakes. Presumably, however, many earthquakes originate from concealed faults.

Elastic-rebound theory. The association between earthquakes and faulting is explained by the elastic-rebound theory, developed by H. F. Reid and others after the California earthquake of 1906.

According to this theory, the rocks beside the fault, held tightly together, are able to undergo gradually accumulating strain by changing shape, until their elastic limit is finally reached. Then they suddenly snap, and much of the pent-up energy is released in earthquake waves. The rocks resume their original shapes, but in faulted, or different, relative positions, and then the process may be repeated.

The process of elastic rebound is illustrated diagrammatically in Fig. 19.9. The point O lies on the fault, and A and B are points on opposite sides. In stage 1, before any strain has accumulated, the line AOB is straight. In stage 2, after strain has accumulated but before an earthquake, A and B have been displaced in opposite directions, and the line AOB is bent. The situation here is somewhat analogous to that of a bent steel spring. In stage 3, after an earthquake, the points formerly adjacent to O have shifted to O' and O'', faulting has occurred, the segments AO' and $O''B$ are straight, and the strain is relieved.

Careful surveying many years prior to, and just after, the California earthquake of 1906 showed that points on the northeast side of the San Andreas fault were displaced 2 to 5 feet south (depending on their nearness to the fault) and that points on the southwest side had shifted 6 to 10 feet north. Thus the elastic-rebound theory was confirmed. Two subsequent surveys have shown that the differential displacement is taking place again at a rate of about 2 inches a year. How long can this go on before the fault snaps loose again?

GEOGRAPHIC DISTRIBUTION

Although earthquakes are transmitted over the entire earth, they originate in limited areas. The most violent earthquakes (Figs. 19.10, 19.11) take place in two main belts: (1) the circum-Pacific belt, extending through Chile, Peru, Central America, two loops in the Carribbean-Antillean area, Mexico, California, the Puget Sound, Vancouver and Queen Charlotte Islands, the Aleutian Islands, Kamchatka, Japan, the Philippines, Indonesia, New Zealand, and certain of the associated arcuate island groups; and (2) the Alpine-Mediterranean-trans-Asiatic belt, including northern Africa, Spain,

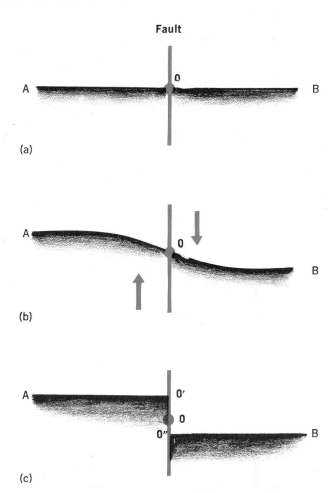

(a)

(b)

(c)

FIG. 19.9.   *Elastic rebound: (a) before strain has accumulated; (b) after strain has accumulated, but before earthquake; (c) after earthquake, strain relieved. (After Reid.)*

Italy, Greece, Turkey, Iran, northern India, and Burma. The fact that these two belts almost coincide with the volcanic belts of the earth suggest that both phenomena may be related to a common cause. Minor belts lie along submarine ridges in the Arctic, Atlantic, and Indian Oceans, and in the rift zones of eastern Africa and east central Siberia.

Gutenberg and Richter state that, of several thousand major shocks occurring between 1904 and 1946, about 80 per cent of the shallow shocks (those originating at depths of less than 37 miles),

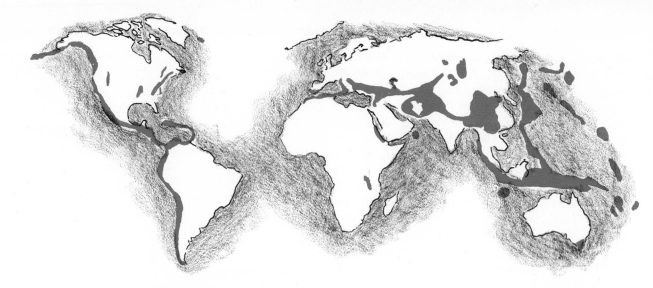

FIG. 19.10. *Map of world showing distribution of earthquake areas. (Base map, University of Chicago Press.)*

90 per cent of the intermediate shocks (those originating at depths between 37 and 186 miles), and all deep shocks (those originating below 186 miles) occurred in the circum-Pacific zone. The Alpine-Mediterranean-trans-Asiatic belt accounted for most of the other major shallow and intermediate shocks. Obviously, then, the circum-Pacific zone is the principal source of shocks.

The major earthquake zones consist mostly of regions where young mountains have been uplifted

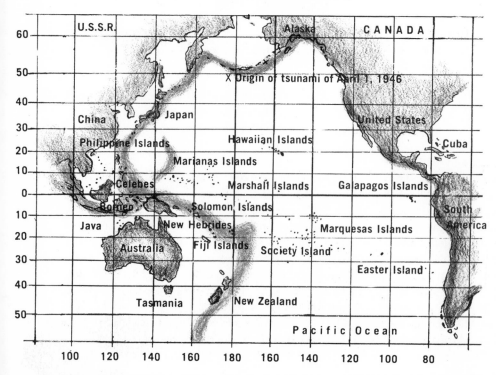

FIG. 19.11. *Map of the Pacific Basin showing the position of the Hawaiian Islands, the place of origin of the seismic sea wave of April 1, 1946, and the distribution of seismically active belts around the Pacific. (After Macdonald, Shepard, and Cox.)*

in late geologic time, where steep slopes exist on the earth's crust, or where rift faulting prevails. Apparently the areas where the high segments and the low segments of the earth come together are zones of weakness and the zones of the greatest and most deep-seated movement. In contrast, the interiors of the geologically old areas of east central Canada, Brazil, Scandinavia, part of Siberia, much of Africa, southern India, and western Australia, except in rift zones, are comparatively, but not wholly, free from earthquakes. The interior of the Pacific Basin, outside the Hawaiian Islands, also is nearly inactive.

Not all earthquakes, however, are in the great deformation belts of the earth. Some are situated in areas remote from present-day volcanoes and late mountain building. New Madrid, Missouri, is far from volcanic centers and far from high mountains, and so is Charleston, South Carolina. Some minor earthquakes occur in areas of delta building, presumably because of loading of the earth's crust, and others in areas of recent continental glaciation, presumably because of unloading by removal of the ice sheets.

FREQUENCY

Since earthquakes occur somewhere on the earth every few minutes, the earth is said to be in a state of "perpetual tremor." Severe shocks come every week or two. Large numbers of minor shocks attend volcanic activity on the island of Hawaii (Fig. 19.12). According to Gutenberg and Richter, the annual average for the whole earth is about 2 great shallow shocks and 17 other major shocks, of which 5 are of intermediate origin and 1 of deep origin. As a rough estimate, it may be said that, for each shock of intensity VII, there are 10 of intensity VI, 100 of intensity V, and so on, in increasing numbers down the scale. Earthquakes are a common and frequent occurrence, but many of them are so slight as to be negligible.

RECURRENCE

Earthquakes recur, but apparently not in any regular cycle. Even though we know, for example, that elastic strain has been accumulating along the San Andreas fault in California since 1906, we are unable to tell when the limit will be reached. So we cannot predict the year, much less the day or hour, when another shock may be expected.

There is some evidence that full moon, high tides, heavy rainfall, sharp changes in barometric pressure, and, especially, another earthquake elsewhere act as "triggers" for earthquakes. However, detailed studies by seismologists, especially in quake-ridden Japan, have failed so far to make

FIG. 19.12.   *Earthquake frequency on the volcanic island of Hawaii, January, 1943, to September, 1949. During the period shown, earthquakes averaged several tens a month and had a maximum of about 90. Unrest continues between eruptions. (From Macdonald and Orr, U.S. Geological Survey.)*

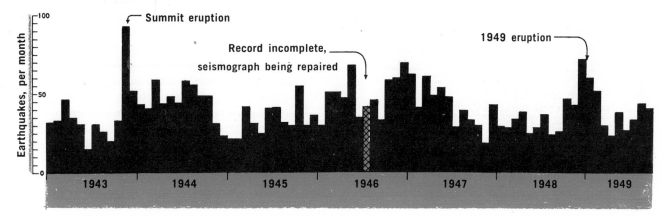

useful predictions possible. We can be sure only that earthquakes come again and again and that buildings should therefore be constructed to withstand the shocks.

PROTECTION

In many earthquake regions, nearly every house in the shock-originating areas suffers damage, and many are destroyed. The destructive effects result from the falling of roofs and chimneys and from the breaking of foundations and walls. A so-called earthquake-proof house, according to Milne, should be constructed with rafters running from ridgepole to floor sills and with iron straps and sockets replacing mortises and tenons. Light roofs and chimneys are recommended.

Potentially dangerous are heavy cornices, parapet walls, unnecessary ornaments (especially over doorways), old lime mortar, unanchored roofs and roof trusses, unanchored brick veneer, loose shelving and partitions, unreinforced chimneys, unstiffened elevator shafts and frames, unreinforced stair well, party walls in adjoining buildings of different size, poorly supported water, gas, steam, and sewer pipes, free-standing elevated water tanks, and similar structures subject to rupture by differential movement.

Examination of the ruins of the San Francisco earthquake of 1906 showed that many of the bricks had been laid dry in mortar. They were poorly bonded and had clean surfaces, and the mortar showed little adhesion. Walls laid in cement with wet brick stood the test of the earthquake better. Reinforced-concrete buildings have proved relatively stable, but wood, steel, and reinforced-masonry structures can be earthquake-resistant if well designed and well built, with adequate reinforcements and appropriate ties, bracing, struts, and anchor bolts. The most secure structure is one that will move as a unit.

Bridges and tall buildings require special consideration of their weight (to obtain a low center of gravity), resistance to horizontal forces, "free period" (to avoid harmonic resonance with an earthquake), and internal balance. For large structures soft ground should be avoided. River bluffs and sites near deep excavations are also undesirable.

SEISMIC SEA WAVES

The seismic sea waves or *tsunamis* (Japanese), which accompanied the Lisbon earthquake of 1775 have already been mentioned. At an average speed of about 400 miles an hour, these waves swept 3,540 miles across the Atlantic Ocean to Antigua, in the southeastern West Indies, where they were 12 feet high.

On Aug. 13, 1868, the west coast of South America was shaken from Guayaquil, Ecuador, to Valdivia, Chile. The shock was most violent in the neighborhood of Arica, a city on the west coast, where many buildings were destroyed. A few minutes after the destructive shock the sea slowly receded from the shore, and ships anchored in 42 feet of water were left dry. Later the water returned as a great wall, caught up the ships, and swept them inland as if they had been chips of wood. The United States steamer *Wateree* was carried inland ¼ mile, with little damage, and left ashore.

In 1877, another earthquake in Chile set up a succession of sea waves which traveled across the Pacific to Japan, where for several hours the water rose and fell a maximum of 8 feet at intervals of about 20 minutes. Great sea waves also followed the earthquake accompanying the eruption of the volcano Krakatao in August, 1883. The waves were 100 feet high and destroyed towns along the coasts of Java and Sumatra.

In 1896, a series of waves as much as 98 feet high dashed up on the shores of Japan and destroyed thousands of houses and tens of thousands of lives. The waves crossed the Pacific in about 10½ hours at an average velocity of 450 miles an hour. In 1923, great sea waves accompanied the disastrous earthquake of Sagami Bay, Japan.

In connection with the Messina earthquake of 1908, seismic sea waves rose 25 to 35 feet above the still-water level, flooded many villages, and greatly added to the destruction.

Another tsunami on Apr. 1, 1946, originating in the Aleutian area, destroyed a lighthouse at Dutch

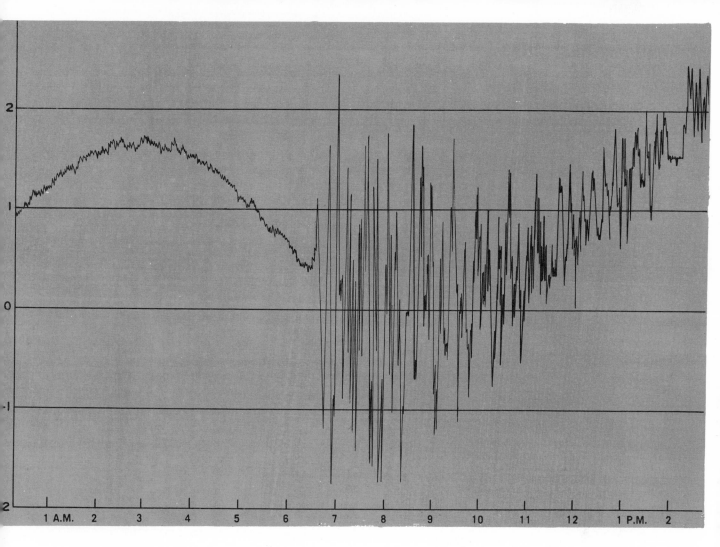

FIG. 19.13. *Record produced on the tide gauge in Honolulu Harbor by the seismic sea wave of April 1, 1946. (From Macdonald, Shepard, and Cox, Pacific Science.)*

Cap, Alaska, about 100 feet above sea level, and crossed 2,300 miles of ocean to the Hawaiian Islands at an average speed of 470 miles an hour (Figs. 19.11, 19.13). At sea the waves were only a few feet high and 90 miles long, but near shore they rose 10 to 20 feet and in places were funneled to elevations of 30 to 50 feet above sea level. Such walls of water did great damage to buildings, roads, railroads, bridges, piers, breakwaters, and ships. The total property damage in the Hawaiian Islands was estimated at 25 million dollars.

Seismic sea waves are characterized by their great length, moderate height, high velocity, and great potential destructivity. They are not to be confused with *seaquakes*, which are short-period tremors of the water itself that result from refraction of earthquake waves from the rocks underneath. Seaquakes merely shake ships, stun and kill fish, and ripple the surface of the sea.

Instrumental Studies of Earthquakes

SEISMOGRAPHS

The instrument used to record earthquakes is called a seismograph. It consists of (1) a vibrating system, or seismometer, and (2) a recording device.

The vibrating element must be well anchored, ordinarily on solid rock, so that it moves with the ground. It usually is damped either mechanically by a plunger in a fluid or magnetically or electromagnetically by a copper vane in a magnetic field.

Vibrating systems are of many kinds. One variety uses a simple horizontal pendulum, free to move in a fixed direction, north-south or east-west (Fig. 19.14). Since the mass of the pendulum may be either very heavy or relatively light and either damped or undamped, the natural periods, sensitivities, and magnifications of these instruments differ considerably. The Milne-Shaw seismograph is a much-used, simple, light, compact horizontal-pendulum instrument.

Another type (Galitzin) also uses a pendulum, but coils of fine wire are wound around it, and strong permanent magnets are attached to the framework. When the pendulum swings through the magnetic field, the motion of the coil generates an electric current in the coil in proportion to the movement. Wires lead from the coil to a recorder. In a third type (Wood-Anderson) the pendulum

is a small copper cylinder suspended off center by a very fine vertical wire. When the ground underneath it moves, the cylinder is twisted back and forth (Fig. 19.15). This torsion pendulum has a natural period of about 1 second, is quite sensitive, and may be used to give high magnification of the real movement. Hence it is not well adapted for use in a strong-earthquake area but finds its principal place outside the main earthquake belts, where it is used to obtain records of distant earthquakes or of nearby earthquakes of moderate intensity and short period.

A different type of instrument, without a pendulum, has been set up at Pasadena, California, to measure the changes that occur, during the passage of an earthquake, in the linear strain in the ground between two points about 20 meters apart.

The instruments described above measure only the horizontal components of the earthquake waves. The vertical component is more difficult to determine, mechanically, and its amplitude ordinarily is small. A heavy inverted pendulum on springs may be used, and the Galitzin galvanometric device may be adapted to the purpose. In the Benioff vertical-component seismograph a large, heavy horseshoe

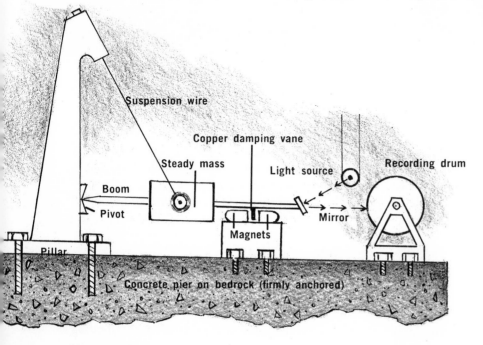

FIG. 19.14. *Sketch of the main elements of a horizontal-pendulum seismograph. The suspension of the steady mass resembles a sagging gate, free to swing horizontally as the earth moves underneath it. It is damped magnetically and restored by gravity. The swing of the mirror attached to the end of the boom is recorded photographically on the revolving drum. Many variations and adjustments are possible.*

permanent magnet is suspended as a vertical pendulum from a spiral spring at a distance of about 1 millimeter over a soft iron bar attached to the ground. Coils of wire are wound around the pole pieces of the magnet. When an earthquake moves the iron bar vertically toward or away from the pole pieces, the magnetic flux is changed accordingly, so that a current is generated in the coils. The resulting current is conducted by wires from the coils to a galvanometer.

The recorder may use mechanical, optical, or electromagnetic devices, or combinations of them, to transfer the vibrations to paper clamped on a revolving drum driven by a synchronous motor. The earliest recorders used a pen on a clock-driven drum. In some modern designs a point of light is reflected, from a mirror attached to the seismometer, directly upon photographic paper. In another and very sensitive design (the Galitzin type) the electric current initiated by movement of a coil on a pendulum set in a strong magnetic field actuates a galvanometer to which a tiny mirror is attached. Thus light is reflected to the photographic paper. The movement of the drum is such that, in the absence of an earthquake, the light describes a fine line in the form of a helix around the drum, because the drum moves a short distance longitudinally as it rotates. When an earthquake occurs, the moving mirror transfers the motion to the recording paper as a seismogram (Figs. 19.16, 19.19).

Magnification of the movement is accomplished either mechanically, by levers, or optically, by increasing the distance from the mirror so that the point of light swings through a larger arc. Instruments vary in the degree of magnification they provide, but those commonly used give magnifications in the range of a few hundred to several thousand times the actual movement.

Since exact timing of the record is very important, an arrangement is made to put a break, or jog, in the recording line once a minute, based on radio time signals, such as those from the U.S. Naval Observatories. Drum speeds differ, but the usual speed is about ¼ inch to 1 or 2 inches per minute.

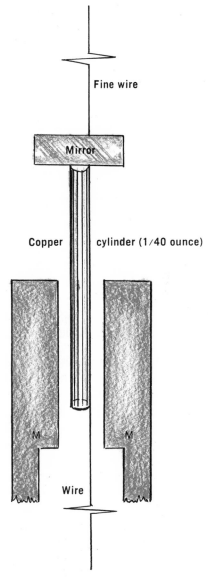

FIG. 19.15. *Sketch of a Wood-Anderson torsional seismograph. Horizontal movement of the ground causes the cylinder and attached mirror to twist on the fine-wire suspension. Damping is done by means of an adjustable magnet, M. A point of light reflected from the mirror to photographic paper on a revolving drum records the twist as the mirror swings back and forth with an earthquake. A slightly inclined suspension allows control both by torsion and by gravity.*

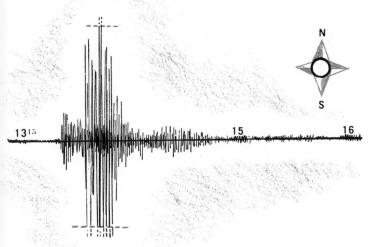

FIG. 19.16. *Seismograph of the San Francisco earthquake of 1906, registered by a horizontal-pendulum seismograph at Irkutsk, Siberia. The oscillations recorded are made by earthquake waves that have passed deep into the earth. (After California Earthquake Commission.)*

It should be noted that there is no universal seismograph. Some instruments are very sensitive, others are sluggish; some give low magnifications, others high; and so on. Different instruments meet different needs at different places. A strong-motion accelerograph, for instance, is a special type constructed to begin recording only when started by a movement of large, predetermined amplitude and to continue operating only for a fixed period of, say, 60 to 70 seconds, unless the motion lasts longer. It will supply a record in a strong-earthquake area when more delicate instruments may have been thrown out of commission by a heavy shock. For obvious reasons, its light and power sources are independent of public utilities.

EARTHQUAKE WAVES

Seismograms show that earthquakes consist of the passage of a series of waves. Near the earthquake the amplitudes of these waves may be large, but at a distance they are so small as to require magnification. In the Imperial Valley earthquake of May 18, 1940, at El Centro, California, the maxi-

mum horizontal movement was about 15 inches in somewhat less than 3½ seconds and the maximum vertical motion about 4 inches in ·2½ seconds—exceptionally large ranges of movement.

Earthquake waves are of three main types: (1) *P*, or *primary* (fast), waves, which are transmitted by alternate push-pull changes of volume (dilatation), or by compression and rarefaction in the direction of propagation; (2) *S*, or *secondary* (slow), waves, which shake, shear, twist, and distort by changes in shape; (3) *L*, or *long* (last), waves, which are complex sinuous or undulatory gravity waves that travel along the surface of the earth (Figs. 19.17, 19.18).

The P waves resemble sound waves, but they are far below audible frequencies. Most of them vibrate only once in 2 or 3 seconds, and the longest ones only once in 25 seconds or more. Those of shortest frequency vibrate only about 10 times a second; in contrast, the frequency of middle C on a piano is 256 per second.

The L waves include Raleigh waves, vibrating

FIG. 19.17. *Diagram showing difference in the times of arrival of various types of seismic wave at a seismograph station. (After N. H. Heck.)*

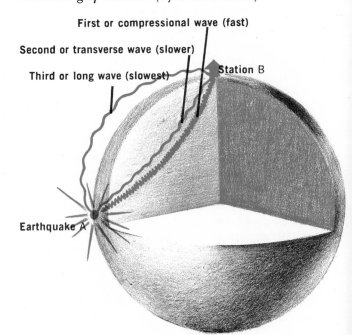

First or compressional wave (fast)

Second or transverse wave (slower)

Third or long wave (slowest)

Station B

Earthquake A

vertically in the direction of propagation, and transverse Love waves, vibrating horizontally. These waves lengthen out to periods of 2 or 3 per minute in traveling one-quarter of the way around the earth and to periods of 1 per 3 minutes in going entirely around it.

The P waves travel at velocities of about 3.4 to 8.6 miles per second, increasing with depth; the S waves, 2.0 to 4.5 miles per second; and the L waves, about 2.5 to 2.7 miles per second. Because of their different velocities and different routes of travel, the three sets of waves arrive at a seismographic station at different times, and so a simple record of a not too distant earthquake is a threefold set of signals. Thus, if there is an earthquake at A (Fig. 19.17), a station at B will record (1) the time of arrival of the fast longitudinal P wave, (2) the time of arrival of the slower transverse S wave, and (3) the time of arrival of the L wave that passes around the earth. Since the interval between the arrivals of P and S waves increases proportionately with the distance, the time lag (S minus P) may be used to compute the distance to the source (Figs. 19.18, 19.19).

When the travel times of the different waves are plotted against the surface distances from the source, we find that the travel times of the L waves are almost directly proportional to the surface distances—hence the inference that they follow the surface. They do, however, travel at slightly different rates in areas of different kinds of rock, and they travel somewhat faster in the rocks beneath the oceans than they do under the continents. On the other hand, the travel times of the P and S waves decrease, and the velocities increase, as the surface distances from the source become greater. Therefore we infer that these waves travel not along surface arcs, but along paths within the earth and that their velocities increase (within limits) as their paths reach greater depths. Seismograms indicate that the travel of waves within the earth is greatly complicated by refraction, reflection, diffraction, and dispersion. Very complex wave patterns result, but professional seismologists are able to identify and classify most of them.

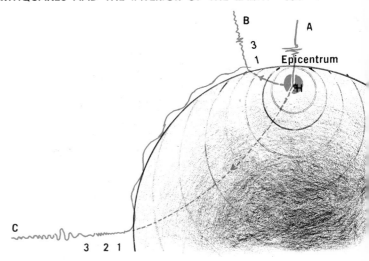

FIG. 19.18. *Diagrammatic section of part of the earth's crust showing the direction of propagation of elastic waves from the focus of an earthquake (dotted lines). The wave fronts are not spherical because the impulse travels more rapidly with depth. The nature of the vibrations at the epicentrum (or epicenter) are shown at A, those not far distant are indicated at B, and those which have traveled a great distance are recorded at C. (After Sieberg.)*

FOCUS AND EPICENTER

The point of origin of an earthquake is its *focus*, and the point on the surface directly above the focus is its *epicenter*. Since the intensity of an earthquake dies out inversely as the square of the distance from the source, the depth of focus may be computed from the records of intensities at different places.

At least 75 per cent of all earthquakes—and some seismologists say more than 90 per cent—originate within about 30 miles of the surface. The depth of focus of most of these is less than 5 miles. The remainder, the intermediate- and deep-focus types, originate at depths of 30 to 435 miles.

The existence of deep-focus earthquakes was discovered from the early arrival of P waves on the opposite side of the earth and from discrepancies

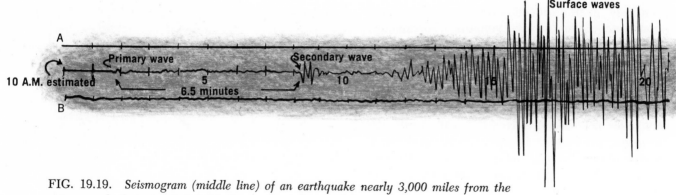

FIG. 19.19. *Seismogram (middle line) of an earthquake nearly 3,000 miles from the seismograph that recorded it. A shows the undisturbed line 1 hour before the quake; B is a record of the minor waves still arriving 1 hour after the quake. (Harvard University Press.)*

in the arrival times of P and S waves, which made the estimated epicentral distances disagree, even by hundreds of miles. The weakness or the lack of surface waves is also an indication of a deep-source earthquake. From a deep focus the waves not only follow the usual direct courses through the earth but also travel up to the surface, from which they are reflected back to the receiving station. The extra time, ranging from a few seconds to about 1 minute, required by the roundabout route is a measure of the depth of the focus. Earthquakes originating at depth show that the rocks of the earth are highly rigid, can accumulate strain, and can fracture even at great depths. Such earthquakes are confined to the margins of the Pacific Basin.

DISTANT EPICENTERS

The geographic location of distant epicenters is generally determined by the three-circle method. First, the epicentral distances from three stations are calculated by the interval between the arrival times of P and S waves at each station; then a circle is drawn about each station, preferably on a globe, with the radius appropriate to each. The point at which the three circles intersect indicates the location of the epicenter (Fig. 19.20).

The position of distant earthquakes can also be computed from known travel-time curves, provided that there is an accurate record of the arrival times

of the P waves at several stations. This method works best where pairs of stations show nearly identical arrival times.

The direction to the source also may be indicated at a single station if the record is good enough to show the first push or pull. This direction and the epicentral distance obtained from the S-minus-P arrival times give at least an approximate location of the source.

SCALE OF MAGNITUDES

The scale of earthquake magnitudes, originated by Richter in 1935, is based on the common logarithms of the maximum amplitudes traced on a seismogram by a standard Wood-Anderson seismograph of specified free period, magnification, and damping, at a distance of 100 kilometers from the epicenter. Corrections are made for other instruments and for other distances. On this scale, earthquakes range in magnitude from 0 (barely recorded) to about 8.5 (for the world's greatest shocks).

MICROSEISM

The records of many sensitive seismographs of high magnification commonly show tiny quivers from earth waves of small and irregular motion. These waves are termed microseisms. They come and go, but they usually continue for hours or even days at a time and become a nuisance. They have been ascribed to the pounding of the surf on seacoasts; to hurricanes, typhoons, and other storm centers; and to monsoons and trade winds. The microseisms recorded at specially equipped stations enable us to locate a hurricane at sea. However, we still do not know how a hurricane propagates these earth waves. Storms on land seem to have little comparable effect.

SEISMIC PROSPECTING

Small artificial earthquakes are used to probe the structure of the outer part of the earth's crust, especially in the search for petroleum. Small charges of explosives are detonated in shallow holes especially bored for the purpose, and the resulting waves are picked up by a series of geophones carefully spaced along the line of a traverse. Recording equipment is housed in an accompanying truck. Timing of the record must be very precise, and relatively high drum speeds are used.

The rates of travel of the waves underground differ in different kinds of rock; so the travel times suggest at least the general character of the underlying rocks. Greater emphasis is placed, however, upon the reflections and refractions which the waves undergo, because these changes in the direction of wave travel serve as clues to the positions of underground contacts between different bodies of rock, especially layered ones (Fig. 19.21). From a series of shots it is possible to compute the depth of a reflecting or refracting layer at different places and thus to work out the structure of the rocks below the surface.

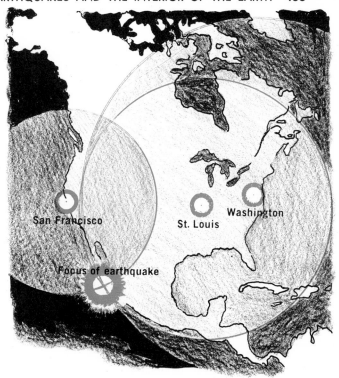

FIG. 19.20. *Map showing the method of locating the focus of an earthquake from seismograph records at three stations. The distances from San Francisco, St. Louis, and Washington are determined from the time elapsed between the arrival of the first and second seismic waves. Using the calculated distances as radii of circles drawn about the stations (preferably on a globe), they intersect near the coast of Lower California.*

The Interior of the Earth

DISCONTINUITIES

The velocities at which earthquake waves travel at various depths are shown in Fig. 19.22. These travel times show sharp changes in velocity at certain depths within the earth. The buried surfaces where these changes occur are called discontinuities. The principal ones lie at depths of (1) 6 to 9 miles on land; (2) 19 to 25 miles, the Mohorovičić discontinuity; and (3) 1,800 miles, the Dahm

discontinuity. Less abrupt discontinuities occur at 250 miles and at 435 miles.

These discontinuities indicate that the earth is made up of a series of concentric shells, of different material or of different state, surrounding a central core. Each of these shells has a different earthquake conductivity. Since the velocities depend on the elastic properties and the density of the material through which the waves pass, the changes in velocity at various depths presumably result from the waves' encountering a combination of different

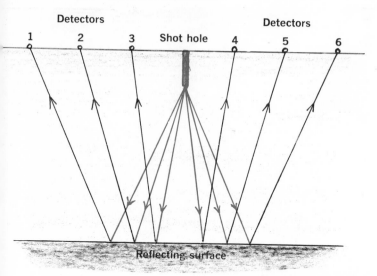

FIG. 19.21. *Diagrammatic sketch of the reflection method of seismic prospecting. Waves spreading out from the shot point are reflected from an underground surface (where velocities change abruptly) back up to a series of carefully spaced detectors at the surface. Comparisons of the records of the first arrivals by direct horizontal routes and of the reflections received later, plotted as time-distance curves, indicate the depth and slope (if any) of the reflecting surface.*

composition, different density, and possibly different state, especially in the core.

MANTLE AND CORE

That part of the earth which lies at depths between 18 and 1,800 miles is called the *mantle*. The velocities of P waves in this zone increase from about 5 miles per second at its top to about 8 miles per second at the bottom.

Below a depth of 1,800 miles is the *core*. Its surface is a remarkable discontinuity, where P waves are easily reflected and sharply refracted and where their velocity drops abruptly from about 8 miles per second to about 5 miles per second. The fact that S waves, incapable of transmission through liquids, are not known to pass through the core suggests that the core may be liquid, in spite of the high pressure prevailing there. There are also

indications of differences within the core itself at a depth of about 3,100 miles.

The extensive reflections and refractions of P waves caused by the core leave a ring-shaped *shadow zone*, 3,000 miles wide, between 105 and 142 degrees (7,000 to 10,000 miles) from the epicenter (Fig. 19.23).

Combining our knowledge of densities with this picture of the earth's layered internal structure, we may envision a model of the composition of the earth. A model (Fig. 19.24) which fits the known facts consists of (1) the atmosphere and ocean; (2) the granitic layer of the continents; (3) the basaltic substratum; (4) an outer and an intermediate mantle of heavier, more basic rocks, ranging in composition from peridotite on the outside to pallasite (a mixture of the minerals of basic

FIG. 19.22. *Diagram showing the velocities of seismic waves in the interior of the earth. P = compressional waves, S = transverse waves. (After Gutenberg and Richter, 1935.)*

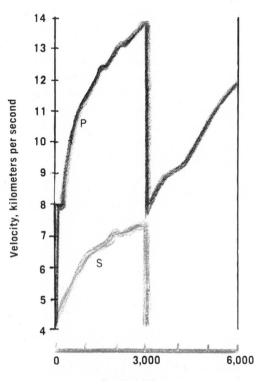

rocks and metallic iron) at greater depths; and (5) a core of metallic iron or iron and nickel, possibly partly in a liquid state. Such a model is consistent with inferences based on the earth's equatorial bulge, its body tides, its moment of inertia about its axis of rotation, and the composition of meteorites.

DISTRIBUTION OF DENSITIES

Since the mass of the earth is 5.98×10^{27} grams and its volume is 1.083×10^{27} cubic centimeters, its average specific gravity (mass divided by volume) is 5.52 times that of water, not far from the figure obtained by Lord Cavendish in his famous experiment of 1799 in weighing the earth.

Inasmuch as the familiar rocks of the earth's crust generally have densities of only 2.6 to 3.0, it follows that rocks at depth must have much greater densities, in order to give the average density of 5.52. Volume relations are important. The core, with a diameter only about half that of the earth as a whole, has a volume of only about one-eighth that of the earth. To help meet the density requirements, we infer (partly by analogy with meteorites) that the core is composed mostly of iron (or iron and nickel) and that the density of the iron, normally 7.8 at the earth's surface, may be increased by compression to about 10 or more. Even so, a great deal of the extra weight must be in the mantle, because of its large volume. So we infer that the rocks of the mantle are composed of heavy peridotite and pallasite and that their densities, somewhat increased by the weight of the overlying load, range from about 3.0 on the outside to about 8.0 just above the core. When adjusted in this way, the model of the earth seems reasonable (Fig. 19.25). The density of the crust is thought to range from about 2.65 (granite) at the surface to about 3.3 (peridotite) at a depth of 18 miles.

STRUCTURE OF THE CRUST

The earth's crust consists of two layers. The P waves in the top layer travel about 3½ miles per second. Partly because this rate corresponds to the rate found by experiment to be characteristic of granite and partly because granite is observed to

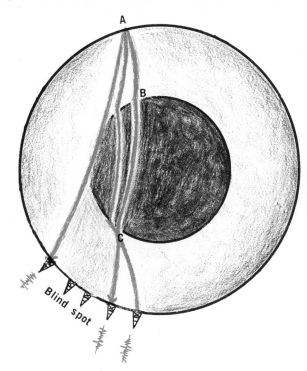

FIG. 19.23. *Diagrammatic section showing how the earth's dense core changes the direction of travel of seismic waves. Vibrations set off below the surface at A are refracted at B and C. Seismic stations in the "blind-spot" area do not receive penetrating waves. (After Lynch.)*

be abundant at the earth's surface, this outer layer, generally 6 to 9 miles thick, is called the *granitic layer*. This includes the sedimentary film, although velocities in most sedimentary rocks are slightly less than those in granite.

The inner layer of the crust, extending to a depth of 18 to 25 miles, corresponds to basalt in its density and earthquake velocities, and so it is called the *basaltic substratum*. Velocities of P waves in this layer range from about 4 miles per second near the top to about 5 miles per second near its base.

This two-layer concept of the crust is oversimplified. As Birch[1] reminds us, it is probably more ac-

[1] Francis Birch, "Physics of the Crust," in "Crust of the Earth," *Geol. Soc. America Spec. Paper* 62, p. 103, 1955.

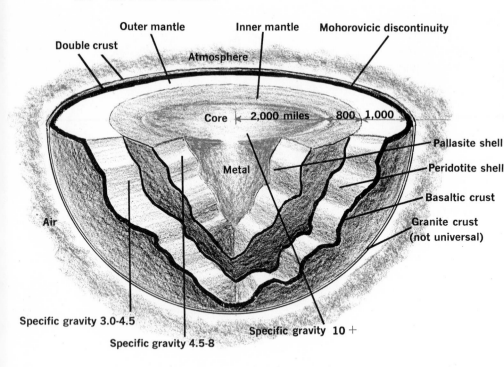

Outer mantle   Inner mantle   Mohorovicic discontinuity

Double crust

Atmosphere

Core ◂ 2,000 miles ▸ 800 1,000

Metal

Air

Pallasite shell

Peridotite shell

Basaltic crust

Granite crust
(not universal)

Specific gravity 3.0-4.5

Specific gravity 4.5-8

Specific gravity 10 +

FIG. 19.24. *Sketch showing the inferred composition of the interior of the earth. The ocean is too shallow to be shown at this scale.*

curate to think of the crust as a "mosaic of intrusions of different kinds, metamorphosed sediments and volcanics, even to depths of 10 km or more in places, of unmetamorphosed sediments—all of this faulted and broken into blocks of various shapes and sizes." Observations of the actual outcrops (especially in shield areas), of gravity differences, and of minor variations in earthquake velocities support the mosaic idea.

CONTINENTS AND OCEAN BASINS

The speed of surface seismic waves indicates that the granitic layer of the crust is absent from the Pacific Ocean Basin and is thin or missing in the other ocean basins. Presumably, therefore, the continents owe their existence primarily to the fact that their masses are composed of relatively light platforms of granite.

MOUNTAIN ROOTS

It has been found that P waves traveling in the basaltic substratum from an epicenter in western California are not received on seismographs in Owens Valley, immediately east of the Sierra Ne-

vada. Hence, the Sierra Nevada must have deepseated "roots," or downward extensions of granitic rocks, which cut off these waves. In other areas, too, the granitic layer is found to be thicker beneath mountains and plateaus than it is under lowlying plains. Under the Colorado Plateau, however, the crust is only 18 miles thick, about the usual amount, and not the expected 40 miles.[2]

TEMPERATURE

It is known that the interior of the earth is hot, for hot materials are expressed from it. Thermometer measurements of the temperatures in mines and oil wells show that the temperature of the earth's crust increases steadily with depth. In regions of hot springs, the increase is as high as 1°F per 30 or 40 feet. In mines that have been opened for some time, where the rock is cooled by air circulation, the increase is much less rapid. The average increase is about 1°F per 60 feet.

If this increase continued to a depth of 60 miles, the temperature would be about 5300°F, which

[2] Howard E. Tatel and Merle E. Truve, "Seismic Exploration of a Continental Crust," *ibid.*, p. 47.

is far above the melting points of ordinary rocks at the earth's surface. However, because of the pressure, the rocks are mainly in a solid state. Very little is known of temperatures deep within the earth. It is improbable that they increase downward at a uniform rate. Most estimates for the temperature at the center of the earth range between 4000 and 7500°F. It is certain that the greater part of the earth is essentially solid, for most of it transmits earthquake waves of a character that do not pass through liquids. If, by compression or radioactivity, parts of the earth become molten, it is probable that some of this hot material rises toward the surface and carries heat with it. It is not unlikely that the outer part of the earth has a relatively high temperature as a result of this process.

PRESSURE

The pressures within the earth are very high because of the weight of the overlying rocks. Since the densities of rocks are known, these pressures can be calculated. At the center of the earth, the pressure is more than 3 million atmospheres, or more than 20,000 tons per square inch.

MAGNETISM

The earth is a gigantic magnet. If a magnetized needle is mounted so that it is balanced on a pin, it will be acted upon by the earth's magnetism, orient itself parallel to the earth's magnetic field, and point to the earth's magnetic pole. A needle so mounted is known as a magnetic compass, and it is used to indicate directions on land and sea. At the magnetic poles the magnetic needle points directly downward. The magnetic poles are not points but small areas.

The earth's magnetic poles do not coincide with the north and south axial poles (Fig. 19.26). The magnetic pole in the Northern Hemisphere is located among the islands of northern Canada and is approximately at 70°5'N and 96°46'W.

The variations of the compass in general are well known (Fig. 19.27), so that when it is used for finding directions, allowances are made for the declination or the variations which result in part

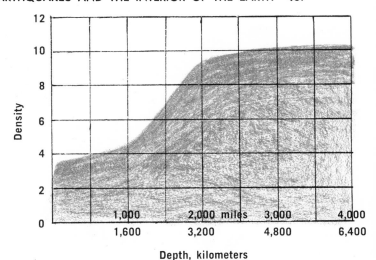

FIG. 19.25.   *Diagram showing the density of the earth at various depths. (After Adams and Williamson.)*

from differences in the earth's geographic and magnetic poles. The south magnetic pole is at about 72°40'S and 152°30'E. Since the magnetic and geographic poles do not coincide, the needle does not

FIG. 19.26.   *Diagram showing the relative positions of the magnetic and planetary poles of the earth. (After Black and Davis.)*

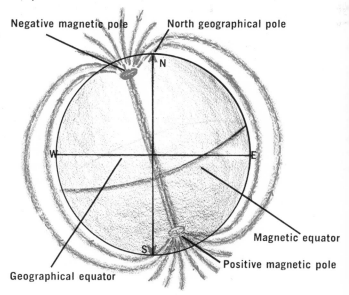

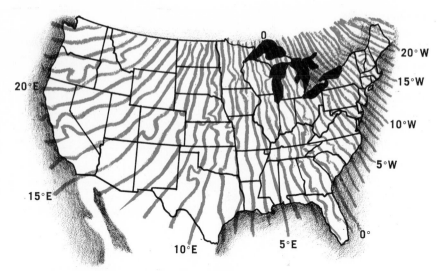

FIG. 19.27. *Isogonal lines showing the declination of the magnetic needle throughout the United States. East of the zero line the north end of the compass needle points to the west of north; west of that line it points east of north. (After U.S. Coast and Geodetic Survey.)*

point to true north or south. In mapping (from any particular location) the angle the needle makes with the geographic meridian is known as the *angle of declination.*

In the magnetic compass the needle is mounted to swing horizontally, and the compass box is graduated in a 360-degree circle. Other needles, called dip needles, are mounted to swing in a vertical arc, and this arc also is graduated to read 360 degrees.

The magnetic needle is a very useful instrument for the mariner and for the geologist, although at places it is unreliable, owing to local magnetic attraction. The dip needle shows great variation. Thus a needle will read different intervals on the arc on different days and at different times during the same day. The dip needle is used for locating magnetic masses near the surface of the earth. Some of these magnetic bodies are valuable ores. Certain beds that contain small quantities of a magnetic substance may be followed by dip-needle readings, which indicate the positions of the various rocks and thus make it possible to determine the geologic structure of an area, even where most of the beds are concealed by mantle-rock. Reconnaissance magnetometer surveys now can be made rapidly from airplanes.

The iron-nickel in the core of the earth and in the pallasite zone presumably is the main seat of the earth's magnetism, but the polarization is unexplained. Movements in the core may be responsible for the gradual changes in the earth's magnetic field.

ISOSTASY

If a plumb bob is hung from a string suspended above an extensive flat plain, it points approximately toward the center of the earth. If the plumb bob is hung above a plain near a great mountain range, it is deflected from the vertical, though only slightly, by attraction to the mass of the mountain nearby. In Peru, India, and elsewhere, however, it has been found that the deflection is less than the value should be as computed from the known size, shape, and density of the mountains. Therefore, we infer that mountains stand high because they are the upper portions of masses of relatively light rocks and, conversely, that ocean basins are low because they are underlain by comparatively heavy rocks.

The pendulum also may be used for measuring the pull of gravity at various places on the earth's surface. The period of a pendulum of a given length depends on the pull of gravity, which varies with the mass of material below the pendulum. The stronger the pull, the faster the pendulum vibrates. The vibrations are recorded by a clock. If the pull is abnormally strong, the pendulum vibrates faster, and the clock gains time; if the pull is abnormally weak, the pendulum vibrates more slowly, and the clock loses time. By allowing the clock to run over long periods, even small differences in the pull of gravity can be measured. Gravity observations have been recorded at stations established at many places over the earth's surface

Thousands of measurements of gravity both on land and from a submerged submarine at sea tend to confirm the suspected distribution of mass in the earth's crust. These observations show a deficiency of mass, not only in or below mountains, but in and under continents as well. Although there are gravity anomalies, that is, departures from the computed values, they tend to cancel out when areas of a square degree or more are considered.

In explanation of these relations, the theory of isostasy ("equal standing" or "equal weight") holds that different masses of the earth's crust stand in equilibrium with each other at some depth within the earth, where the weights of all columns of rocks of equal area are the same, regardless of whether there are mountains or plains, shallow or deep seas at the surface. If the equilibrium is disturbed, as by the long-continued erosion of a continent, the loss of mass is presumably countered by the plastic flow of heavier material into the area underneath it. Such a process is called *isostatic compensation*.

The theory of isostatic compensation is illustrated by Fig. 19.28. The three columns represent three prisms of the earth. In one, the surface of the ground is above sea; in another, it is at sea level; and in the third, it is below sea. The three prisms are of equal mass and weight; the longest is made of the lightest material, and the shortest is of the heaviest material. The line on which the blocks rest is called the *level of compensation*. It is a theoretical plane, or zone, and the rock columns above it are supposed to be of equal weight. Below the bases of the three columns, the earth is solid, but, because of the great pressures, it is believed to yield easily, as does a plastic or a highly viscous liquid.

An isostatic condition is illustrated in Fig. 19.29. Blocks of various materials of different densities are immersed in quicksilver, which has a density 13.6 times that of water (specific gravity, 13.6+). The blocks weigh the same and have the same cross section, but they differ in length. The densities of

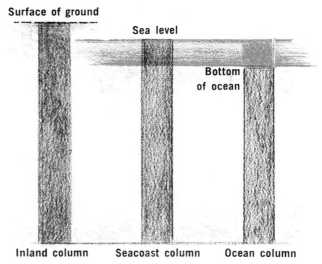

FIG. 19.28. *Diagrams showing three columns of rock, one extending above sea level, another to sea level, and a third to the bottom of the sea. According to the interpretation of isostatic compensation, the weights of all three columns (including sea water on the third) are equal. (After Hayford and Bowie.)*

the materials are shown on the blocks. The blocks of the lighter materials extend higher above the surface of the mercury than those of heavier materials. In Fig. 19.30, all the blocks are of copper (specific gravity, 8.9) but are of different lengths. The longer ones sink deeper and also extend farther upward than the short ones. If material is taken from the top of a high block and added to a low one, the base of the high block will rise and the base of the low one will sink. Adjustment follows the movement of the mercury from the bottom of the depressed block to the bottom of the elevated block.

According to the hypothesis of Pratt, the bottoms of the columns are even, and the level of compensation is uniform, as in Fig. 19.29. If so, the depth of compensation would be 35 to 60 miles. According to the hypothesis of Airy, the light masses float freely in the heavier substratum; so each column displaces a quantity equal to its own mass, as in Fig. 19.30. Thus, high columns (continents and mountains) would have deep extensions down-

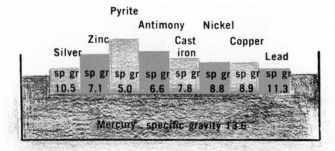

FIG. 19.29. *Ideal illustration of the isostatic assumption that differences in altitude of large parts of the earth's crust are compensated by differences in density. The blocks are equal in cross section and in total weight and thus sink to equal depth. (After Bowie.)*

ward, low columns (ocean basins) would have short ones, and the level of compensation would be uneven. The Airy concept fits the geologic record fairly well and is consistent with the behavior of surface seismic waves.

How well isostatic compensation works is a debatable question. It is certain that the earth is rigid and can accumulate strains over many eons. It tends, however, to assume a shape in accord with the theory, but perhaps it does so imperfectly. That it accumulates stresses through long periods without important adjustments is shown by peneplains developed by erosion. Peneplains are common features and have formed again and again in the

FIG. 19.30. *Diagram showing seven copper blocks of equal cross sections but of different heights; all are immersed in mercury. The longest blocks rise highest and also extend to the greatest depths. According to the theory of isostasy, high mountains are underlain by lighter material than low ones, and both are in balance. (After C. R. Longwell.)*

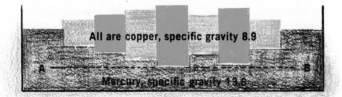

geologic past. If the earth's surface responded quickly and perfectly to changes of load, a peneplain could not readily form. As soon as a mass of rock was eroded from a high area, that area would rise again and be subjected to renewed erosion. If peneplaination occurs despite such an isostatic adjustment, the quantity of rock to be removed in producing a peneplain is increased about tenfold.

A greater difficulty is posed by the rejuvenation of peneplains. Old erosion surfaces have lain low for a long time and then have been uplifted hundreds, or even thousands, of feet. How does compensation work then?

Notwithstanding these difficulties, the earth does seem to respond to great load stresses by subsurface adjustment, though its strength and rigidity are perhaps great enough to resist at least minor changes in equilibrium.

PHASE-CHANGE THEORY

The phase-change theory proposes that the Mohorovičić discontinuity at the base of the earth's crust marks a phase change rather than a change in chemical composition.[3] A phase change is the conversion of one mineral to another by a rearrangement of its component atoms in accordance with the surrounding pressure and temperature conditions. An example is the artificial change of graphite or other carbonaceous matter to diamond at sufficiently high temperature and pressure. Conceivably, the Mohorovičić boundary may be a zone where the earth's crust gives way to an underlying denser rock that is identical chemically but different mineralogically, because of the high pressure and high temperature prevailing at that depth.

The theory would explain such problems as the contrasting thicknesses of the crust beneath continents and ocean basins, the existence of roots under major mountain systems, the persistence of continents despite long-continued erosion, the subsidence of geosynclinal troughs, and the uplift of peneplains to form plateaus as the result of differences

[3] George C. Kennedy, "The Origin of Continents, Mountain Ranges, and Ocean Basins," *Amer. Scientist*, vol. 47, pp. 491-504, December, 1959.

in the earth's temperature gradient from place to place. The variations in temperature would determine the different depths of the reversible phase transformations, but the details are too involved to be discussed here. Although more laboratory experiments and more detailed seismic work are needed to confirm or refute the phase-change theory, the outlook is promising.

CONCLUSIONS

We *know* that the interior of the earth is (1) hot, (2) heavy, (3) solid (except, perhaps at the core), (4) highly elastic, (5) magnetic, (6) under great pressure, (7) different at different depths and zoned, or layered, according to elasticity, (8) responsive to tides, (9) radiating heat very slowly, (10) overlain by light rocks at the surface, (11) composed of columns of different density at different places, and (12) isostatically balanced.

We *infer* that (1) the temperature gradient declines rapidly, (2) the zoning is caused by changes in composition and density, (3) the thin outermost shell is granite, (4) most of the crust is basalt, (5) the bulky mantle is peridotite and pallasite, (6) the core is nickel-iron, (7) the central density is about 10, and (8) the deep-seated solid rocks yield isostatically, mainly by plastic flow. We also believe that earth heat is caused principally by compression and radioactivity and that magma forms in an otherwise solid earth when and where the heat, pressure, and steam are sufficient to produce it.

Summary

The earth is a constant victim of earthquake shocks. These tremors are transmitted as waves by the rocks of the earth. Historical examples show a variety of effects. The intensity of an earthquake is rated on a modified Mercalli scale of I to XII, according to the effects felt and the damage done.

The geologic effects of earthquakes include fissuring of the ground, sunken ground, hummocks, slumping, earthslides, mudflows, eruptions of mud and sand, seismic sea waves, lake seiches, disturbances of ground-water circulation, avalanches, calving of icebergs from tidal glaciers, and other local and superficial consequences.

Earthquake waves are started by fracture, percussion, or rubbing, especially by the breaking and rubbing of rocks along faults. Periodically repeated earthquakes associated with the same fault result from elastic rebound.

We have seen that earthquakes are most frequent in the circum-Pacific and Alpine-Mediterranean-trans-Asiatic belts. Many thousands occur every year, but only a few tens of these shocks are severe. Unfortunately, we cannot predict the time of their recurrence, but we can reduce their disastrous effects by means of earthquake-resistant construction.

Earthquake waves are recorded by various types of seismograph. The three main sets of waves are labeled P (primary), S (secondary), and L (long) waves. The differences in their travel times and their routes through or around the earth enable us to locate the centers and epicenters of earthquakes and to study the internal structure of the earth.

Artificial earthquakes are used in seismic prospecting, because their underground reflections and refractions can provide clues to hidden structures, especially in oil fields.

Seismic records show that the earth's crust consists of a granitelike rock, 6 to 9 miles thick, under the continents and of a basaltlike rock, 18 to 25 miles thick, under both land and sea. This two-layer crust overlies the mantle, which is nearly 1,800 miles thick. The central core below the mantle is about 2,000 miles in diameter. The several depth zones are separated by sharp discontinuities, which presumably are caused by differences in the composition, the density, and, perhaps, the physical state of the various zones. With the possible exception of the core, or part of it, the interior of the earth is solid. Its average density is 5.52. We also know that it is zoned, hot, elastic, and magnetic.

Continents, ocean basins, and smaller areas within them, which are underlain by rocks of different density, show only local gravity anomalies, and therefore seem to be isostatically balanced.

Although our knowledge of the interior of the earth is still incomplete, the study of earthquakes has given us more than an inkling of its hidden depths.

Suggestions for Further Reading

Bates, D. R.: *The Earth and Its Atmosphere*, Basic Books, New York, 1958. Essays on pp. 31 and 48 give information on movements within the earth.

Birch, Francis: *Elasticity and Constitution of the Earth's Interior, Jour. of Geophys. Research*, vol. 57, pp. 227–286, 1952.

Bullen, K. E.: *An Introduction to the Theory of Seismology*, Cambridge University Press, New York, 1953. A rather technical study.

Byerly, Perry: *Seismology*, Prentice-Hall, Inc., Englewood Cliffs, N.J., 1942.

Gutenberg, Beno: *Internal Constitution of the Earth*, Dover Publications, New York, 1951.

Gutenberg, Beno, and Charles F. Richter: *Seismicity of the Earth and Associated Phenomena*, Princeton University Press, Princeton, N.J., 1954.

Heck, N. H.: *Earthquakes*, Princeton University Press, Princeton, N.J., 1936.

Heck, N. H., and H. O. Wood: *Earthquake History of the United States*, U.S. Coast and Geodetic Survey Serial No. 609, 1957 and 1951. Technical information.

Jeffreys, H.: *Earthquakes and Mountains*, Methuen & Co., Ltd., London, 1950.

Jeffreys, H.: *The Earth*, Cambridge University Press, London, 1952. A technical study of the earth, its history, and its composition.

Leet, L. D.: *Causes of Catastrophes Earthquakes, Volcanoes, Tidal Waves, and Hurricanes*, McGraw-Hill Book Company, Inc., New York, 1948. A general study.

Leet, L. D.: *Practical Seismology and Seismic Prospecting*, Appleton-Century-Crofts, Inc., New York, 1938. A well-known textbook.

Lynch, J. J.: *Our Trembling Earth*, Dodd, Mead & Company, Inc., New York, 1940. By a well-known seismologist.

Newmann, F.: *Earthquake Intensity and Related Ground Motion*, University of Washington Press, Seattle, Wash., 1954. An advanced study.

Poldervaart, Arie (ed.): "Crust of the Earth (a Symposium)," *Geol. Soc. America Spec. Paper* 62, 1955.

Richter, Charles F.: *Elementary Seismology*, W. H. Freeman & Company, San Francisco, 1958. A very interesting, elementary textbook, covering both technical and nontechnical aspects of earthquakes.

TOPOGRAPHIC AND STRUCTURAL MAPS

Topographic Maps

TOPOGRAPHIC MAPS show the configuration of the land surface—the size and shape of the hills and valleys, as well as their location with respect to each other. The term *relief* refers to the difference in elevation of features within the map area. The *elevation* of a feature is its vertical distance above the datum plane selected to denote the level of zero elevation. In practically all the maps of the U.S. Geological Survey, mean sea level is used as the datum plane. The term *height* has a different meaning. It designates the vertical distance between the base and the top of a feature. A hill 500 feet high might stand on a coastal plain which itself has an elevation of 300 feet. The top of the hill, then, would have an elevation of 800 feet, and the base of the hill would have an elevation of 300 feet. A similar hill, 500 feet high, might stand on the surface of a plateau which has an elevation of 5,000 feet above sea level. In this case the elevation at the top of the hill would be 5,500 feet, and the elevation at the base of the hill would be 5,000 feet. The height of the hill is 500 feet in either case.

To map relief on a flat surface, any one of four methods may be used: (1) color, (2) shading, (3) hachures, and (4) contours (Figs. A.1 to A.4). The contour method is the most common and the most nearly accurate. A contour line on a map represents an imaginary horizontal line that passes through all points in the area that have the same elevation above a given datum—usually sea level. The lines are drawn to indicate a certain regular difference in elevation, and this difference is called the contour interval. Figure A.1 represents a con-

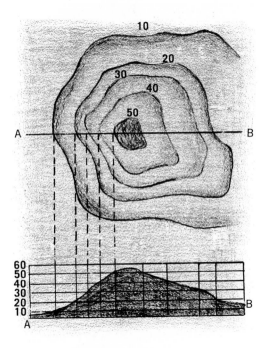

FIG. A.1. *Diagram showing a contoured hill. The contour interval is 10 feet. The lower diagram is a profile of the hill along the line AB.*

toured conical hill. The contour interval is 10 feet. Contours bend, or "loop," upstream in valleys. They are closely spaced on steep slopes and widely spaced on gentle slopes. They encircle conical hills and are paired on opposite sides of parallel ridges. The contours near the crests of hills are relatively short, closed curves.

443

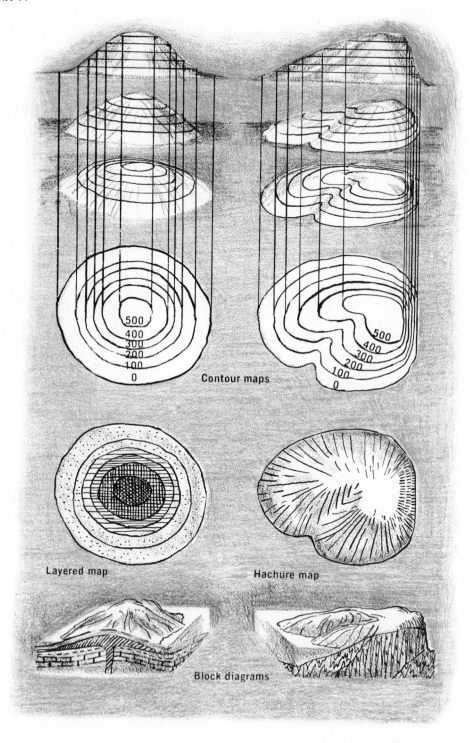

FIG. A.2. *Methods of showing relief. (After Lobeck.)*

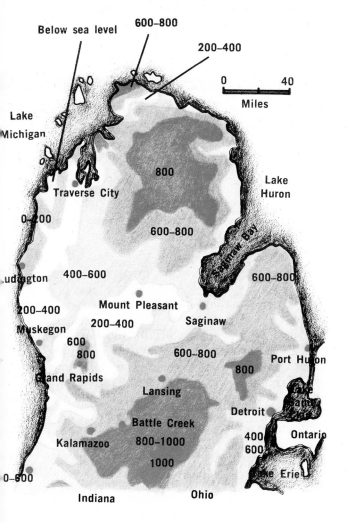

FIG. A.3. *Relief map of the bedrock surface of the Southern Peninsula of Michigan; contour interval 200 feet. (After Michigan Geological Survey.)*

0   2
Miles
Contour interval, 20 feet

FIG. A.4. *Topographic map showing the contrast between low hills with gentle slopes (lower right) and high ridge with steep slopes (upper right) near New York–New Jersey boundary. (U.S. Geological Survey.)*

Structural Contour Maps

In making a structural contour map, the surface chosen is that of the top or bottom of some easily recognized bed that is persistent over a large area and is not too far below the surface of the land. The elevation of this key bed, or datum, above sea level is obtained in the field at as many points as possible, both at actual outcrops and from the

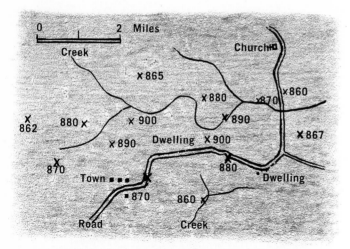

FIG. A.5. *Sketch map showing elevation of the same stratum at different points, marked by crosses. (After Gardner.)*

FIG. A.6. *Sketch map showing elevation of same stratum at different points marked by crosses, as in Fig. A.5. The structure contours connect points of equal elevation, thus outlining an elongated dome. (After Gardner.)*

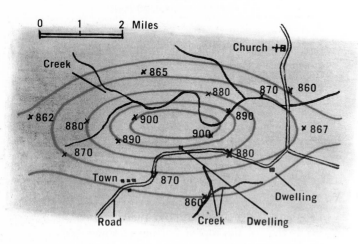

records of drill holes. At some locations, rocks above the key bed are exposed. If the thickness of the intervening strata is known, the depth to the key bed may be calculated. Likewise, if the rocks exposed lie below the surface that is being contoured, it is possible to determine the position of the key bed before it was removed by erosion.

These data are plotted at their proper locations on a map of the region, and lines are drawn through points of equal elevation (Figs. A.5, A.6). Such structural contour lines show the approximate position of the key bed below the surface at all points over the entire area of the map. Since the other beds included in the folds lie parallel to it, the contour map will show the position of all beds of

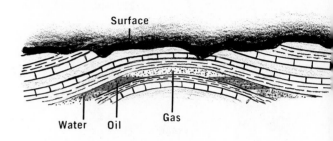

FIG. A.7. *Lengthwise section of elongated dome shown in Fig. A.6; vertical scale greatly exaggerated. (After Gardner.)*

the series. A section through the contoured area is shown in Fig. A.7.

Since most of the world's petroleum is found in such subsurface structural highs as anticlines and domes, the mapping of oil-bearing areas by structural contours is a great aid in the search for petroleum. Structural contour maps are also used in explorations for coal, iron ore, phosphate rock, and other valuable beds.

MAP SYMBOLS, COLUMNAR SECTIONS, AND STRUCTURE SECTIONS

TO REPRESENT specific rocks on geological drawings, certain symbols are in general use (Fig. B.1). Groups of beds make up the geological formations, and groups of formations make up the rock systems. From this information, a standard geologic column can be constructed to show the relative ages of the rocks. The younger rocks appear above the older ones in the table (Fig. B.2).

After the age relations have been established, a structure section can be constructed (Fig. B.3).

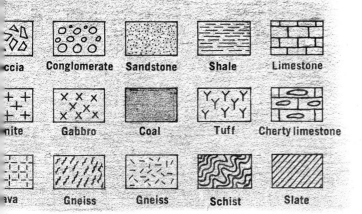

FIG. B.1. *Conventional symbols used in geological cross sections. Those shown in the upper row are used very generally to show the rocks listed. The other symbols are used with less uniformity.*

FIG. B.2. *A columnar section showing the chronological succession of the Mississippian rock formations in the Ste. Genevieve County, Missouri. (After Stuart Weller.)*

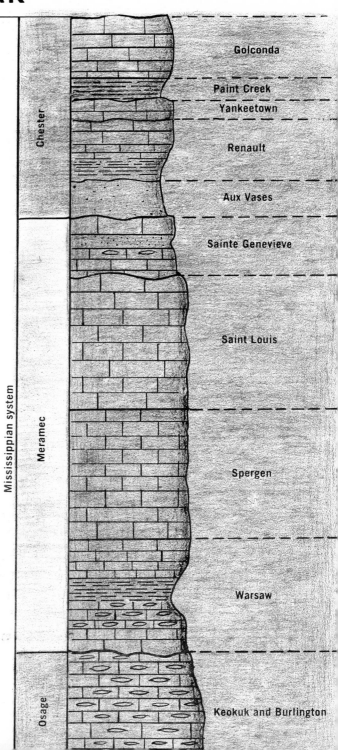

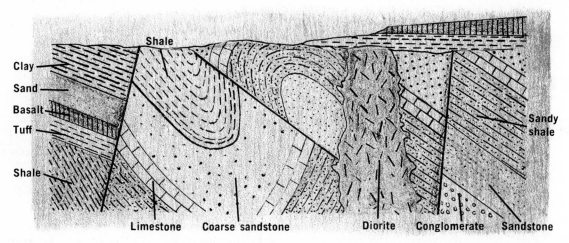

Clay
Sand
Basalt
Tuff
Shale
Shale
Sandy shale
Limestone   Coarse sandstone   Diorite   Conglomerate   Sandstone

FIG. B.3. *A geologic cross section showing the subsurface structural relations of the rock formations. (After Krauskopf.)*

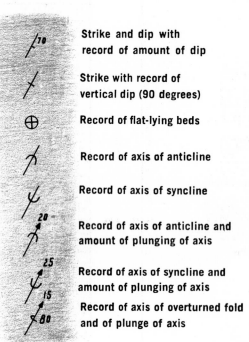

Strike and dip with
record of amount of dip

Strike with record of
vertical dip (90 degrees)

Record of flat-lying beds

Record of axis of anticline

Record of axis of syncline

Record of axis of anticline and
amount of plunging of axis

Record of axis of syncline and
amount of plunging of axis

Record of axis of overturned fold
and of plunge of axis

FIG. B.4. *Conventional signs used on geological maps.*

KEY TO 52 CHEMICAL SYMBOLS

Alphabetically by name				Alphabetically by symbol			
Al	Aluminum	Mn	Manganese	A	Argon	Mg	Magnesium
Sb	Antimony	Hg	Mercury	Ag	Silver	Mn	Manganese
A	Argon	Mo	Molybdenum	Al	Aluminum	Mo	Molybdenum
As	Arsenic	Ne	Neon	As	Arsenic	N	Nitrogen
Ba	Barium	Ni	Nickel	Au	Gold	Na	Sodium
Be	Beryllium	N	Nitrogen	B	Boron	Ne	Neon
Bi	Bismuth	O	Oxygen	Ba	Barium	Ni	Nickel
B	Boron	P	Phosphorus	Be	Beryllium	O	Oxygen
Br	Bromine	Pt	Platinum	Bi	Bismuth	P	Phosphorus
Cd	Cadmium	Ra	Radium	Br	Bromine	Pb	Lead
Ca	Calcium	Rb	Rubidium	C	Carbon	Pt	Platinum
C	Carbon	Se	Selenium	Ca	Calcium	Ra	Radium
Cl	Chlorine	Si	Silicon	Cd	Cadium	Rb	Rubidium
Cr	Chromium	Ag	Silver	Cl	Chlorine	S	Sulfur
Co	Cobalt	Na	Sodium	Co	Cobalt	Se	Selenium
Cu	Copper	Sr	Strontium	Cr	Chromium	Si	Silicon
F	Fluorine	S	Sulfur	Cu	Copper	Sn	Tin
Au	Gold	Te	Tellurium	F	Fluorine	Sr	Strontium
He	Helium	Th	Thorium	Fe	Iron	Te	Tellurium
H	Hydrogen	Sn	Tin	H	Hydrogen	Th	Thorium
I	Iodine	Ti	Titanium	He	Helium	Ti	Titanium
Fe	Iron	W	Tungsten	Hg	Mercury	U	Uranium
Kr	Krypton	U	Uranium	I	Iodine	V	Vanadium
Pb	Lead	V	Vanadium	K	Potassium	W	Tungsten
Li	Lithium	Zn	Zinc	Kr	Krypton	Zn	Zinc
Mg	Magnesium	Zr	Zirconium	Li	Lithium	Zr	Zirconium

KEY TO THE IDENTIFICATION OF ROCKS

IGNEOUS ROCKS

Pyroclastic or fragmental in texture

Loose	Consolidated
Volcanic ash or dust (mostly small particles of glass or pumice and occasional mineral or rock grains)	Tuff
Lapilli, pumice pebbles, cinders, bombs	Volcanic breccia
Fragments of lava (aa)	Flow breccia
Coarse blocks (near vents)	Agglomerate

Glassy (noncrystalline); may show flowage lines

Description	Name
All glassy and compact	Obsidian
Glassy but finely vesicular	Pumice
Glassy but coarsely vesicular	Scoria
Glassy with occasional phenocrysts	Vitrophyr
Partly glassy and partly crystalline	Banded stony and glassy lava

Crystalline but dense (fine-grained, aphanitic, generally extrusive)

Acidic ←--→ Basic			
Light-colored or red		Medium gray	Dark gray to black
With quartz	No quartz	Andesite	Basalt (abundant)
Rhyolite	Trachyte		

Each of these may be porphyritic, vesicular, amygdaloidal, or even partly glassy. Examples are porphyritic andesite, amygdaloidal basalt, and scoriaceous basalt. Flow structure is common.

Coarsely crystalline (coarse-grained, phaneritic, intrusive)

Acidic ←			→ Basic	
Usually light-colored or red		Gray	Usually dark-colored or green	
Rich in feldspars (especially orthoclase and sodium-rich plagioclase)		Contains intermediate plagioclase, usually with hornblende	Contains calcium-rich plagioclase and augite	Contains no feldspar; all olivine, pyroxene, or hornblende
With quartz	No quartz			Peridotite, pyroxenite, hornblendite, dunite
Granite (abundant)	Syenite (rare)	Diorite	Gabbro	

Varietal names may be used—for example, biotite granite, quartz diorite, and olivine gabbro.

Each of these may be porphyritic—for example, porphyritic granite.

Unusually coarse-grained (pegmatitic) rocks are named by the minerals present or the nearest rock type—for example, quartz-mica pegmatite and granite pegmatite.

"Graphic" intergrowth appears occasionally.

Ultrabasic rocks may contain notable amounts of chromite, magnetite, or ilmenite.

SEDIMENTARY ROCKS

Clastic sediments of mechanical origin

Loose, unconsolidated	Consolidated (by compaction, cementation, or recrystallization)
Blocks, such as talus	Breccia
Boulders	Boulder conglomerate (or breccia)
Cobbles	Cobble conglomerate
Pebbles	Pebble conglomerate
Granules	Granule conglomerate, grit
Sand (many varieties)	Sandstone (many varieties)
Greensand, glauconite	Glauconitic sandstone
Grüs (feldspar, quartz, mica, etc.)	Arkose, graywacke
Silt (including loess) ⎫	
Clay (adobe, gumbo, ⎪	Siltstone ⎫ Mudstone, shale
china clay, ⎬ Mud when wet	Claystone ⎭ (if laminated)
fire clay, and ⎪	
fuller's earth) ⎭	
Volcanic ash or dust	Tuff
Lapilli, cinders, and bombs	Volcanic breccia
Till, glacial drift	Tillite

Precipitates from water solutions (textures: earthy, dense, granular, fossiliferous, oölitic, and crystalline)

Name	Description
Limestone ($CaCO_3$) (many varieties) Chalk, marl, oölite, coral limestone, coquina (shell limestone), travertine (usually porous)	Hardness of 3 or less; generally light-colored but variable; soluble in cold dilute HCl with effervescence of CO_2
Dolomite [$CaMg(CO_3)_2$]	Hardness 3.5; weathers buff or pink; soluble only in hot or strong acid
Chert, flint, jasper (SiO_2)	Very hard; dense; chert white or any color, flint black, jasper red; insoluble
Geyserite, siliceous sinter	White or gray; porous; hard (abrasive) but crumbly
Diatomite, diatomaceous earth	White if pure; lightweight; incoherent; sonorous if blocks are rubbed gently

Name	Description
Rock phosphate, phosphorite	Brown to black; granular or dense; stinks if rubbed hard
Hematite rock	Heavy; red
Limonite rock, bog iron ore, yellow ochre	Heavy; yellow, brown, black
Siderite rock, "ironstone"	Heavy; light brown
Pyrite or marcasite rock	Heavy; brassy, metallic
Saline deposits, mostly evaporites	Nearly all are white or nearly so
Rock gypsum ($CaSO_4 \cdot 2H_2O$)	Hardness of 2
Anhydrite rock ($CaSO_4$)	Hardness of 3
Rock salt ($NaCl$)	Salty to taste
Borates, nitrates, and caliche	

Organic remains, residues, and derivatives

Peat, lignite, subbituminous, and bituminous coal

Guano (as in caves and on desert islands in the Pacific)

Bone beds

Petroleum, natural gas, natural asphalt, waxes, etc.

METAMORPHIC ROCKS

Description	Name
Foliated, banded, or cleavable	
Coarsely crystalline	
Banded with feldspar	Gneiss (e.g., granite-gneiss)
Banded with carbonate	Banded marble (impure)
Schistose with mica, hornblende, talc, or chlorite (may contain metacrysts of garnet, staurolite, cyanite, and andalusite—for example, garnetiferous quartz-mica schist)	Schist (e.g., biotite schist)
Graphitic	Graphitic schist, graphite
Mixed silicates and carbonates	Banded contact rocks
Dense or amorphous	
With platy cleavage (thin slabs ring when struck)	Slate, phyllite
Carbonaceous	Anthracite, graphite, graphitic slate
Dark and cleavable (resembling impure quartzite)	Graywacke, graywacke slate
Nonfoliated, massive, homogeneous, noncleavable	
Coarsely crystalline	
Hydrous silicates predominant, usually greenish	Serpentine, soapstone, or steatite (talcose), greenstone (chloritic), propylite (hydrothermal)
Siliceous; original sand grains more or less visible	Quartzite
Calcareous or dolomitic	Marble
Mixed calcite-dolomite-serpentine rocks	Ophicalcite, verd antique
Hornblendic	Amphibolite
Quartz-mica aggregate	Greisen
Mixed silicates, carbonates, and/or ores	Tactite, contact rocks, impure marble
Dense	
Greenish hydrous silicates apparently abundant	Serpentine, soapstone, steatite, greenstone
Siliceous	Quartzite, novaculite, graywacke
Calcareous or dolomitic	Crystalline limestone, fine-grained marble
Carbonaceous	Anthracite, natural coke (rare)
Sericitic (hydrothermally altered)	Sericite rock
Various minerals, sugary-grained, more or less vitreous in appearance (baked)	Hornfels

GLOSSARY

Aa. Basaltic lava flow with rough, clinkery surface.

Ablation. The surface wastage of glacial ice by melting and evaporation.

Abrasion. The wearing away of rocks and minerals by rubbing or friction, with the aid of sand or other particles.

Abyssal. Pertaining to the great depths of the sea. The oceanic deeps below 1,000 fathoms (6,000 feet).

Acicular. Slender or needle-shaped.

Acidic rock. An igneous rock that contains more than 66 per cent silicon dioxide.

Adjusted stream. A stream which tends to flow parallel to the strike of a rock formation.

Adobe. Pertaining to the clay and silt deposits in the desert basins of southwestern North America that are used for sun-dried brick.

Aeolian. Related to, formed by, or deposited from wind (from Aeolus, the god of the winds).

Agate. A waxy quartz or opal in which the colors are arranged in bands or distinct groups.

Agglomerate. Angular volcanic fragments. A coarse volcanic breccia.

Aggrade. To deposit sediments on a stream bed or valley floor.

A horizon. The uppermost zone in a soil profile, in which organic matter has accumulated and from which soluble salts and colloids have been leached; topsoil.

Alabaster. Compact, fine-grained gypsum.

Albite. A high-soda plagioclase.

Alluvium. Any type of detritus deposited by streams.

Alpha particle. A helium atom that lacks two electrons and therefore has a double positive charge.

Alpine. Like the Alps or any lofty mountains.

Amber. A fossil resin from prehistoric coniferous trees.

Amorphous. Pertaining to rocks and minerals having no definite crystalline form and no orderly arrangement of atoms.

Amphibole group. A group of silicate minerals containing iron and magnesium. A common example is hornblende.

Amygdale. A vesicle or vapor cavity in volcanic rock which has become filled with secondary minerals. The diminutive form is *amygdule.*

Amygdaloid. A rock with numerous amygdules.

Anchor ice. Ice formed on the bottom of a stream (also called "ground ice" or "bottom ice").

Andesite. A fine-grained igneous rock composed essentially of andesine plagioclase but also containing ferromagnesian silicates.

Angle of repose. See *Repose, angle of.*

Angstrom unit. A unit of length equal to one hundred-millionth of a centimeter (10^{-8} cm).

Anhydrite. A sulfate mineral similar to gypsum, but free of water. Composition: anhydrous calcium sulfate ($CaSO_4$).

Anorthite. One of the plagioclase feldspars, high in calcium.

Antecedent stream. A stream that maintains, during and after uplift, the course it had established prior to uplift.

Anthracite. Hard coal.

Anticline. A fold or arch of rock strata dipping outward in opposite directions from an axis.

Anticyclone. An atmospheric condition of high barometric pressure over an area from which air flows spirally outward.

Apatite. A group of mineral phosphates.

Aphanite. A dense, fine-grained igneous rock in which the crystalline mineral grains are too small to be distinguished by the naked eye.

Aqueous. Pertaining to or containing water, as an aqueous solution.

Aquifer. A permeable rock formation or subsoil through which ground water moves more or less freely.

Arctic. The region within the Arctic Circle (66°30′N).

Arenaceous. Pertaining to rocks that contain sand.

Arête. A narrow, rugged ridge formed by glacial plucking on opposite sides of the ridge.

Argillaceous. Pertaining to a rock containing considerable clay.

Arkose. A clastic sedimentary rock composed of sand-sized grains of quartz and orthoclase. Generally formed from the disintegration of granite.

Arroyo. A vertical-walled, flat-floored channel of an intermittent stream, in the semiarid Southwest.

Artesian basin. A subsurface geologic structural feature in which water is confined under hydrostatic pressure.

Asbestos. Highly fibrous minerals such as chrysotile, a variety of serpentine. Also some amphiboles, such as actinolite and tremolite.

Asphalt. A brown to black semisolid bituminous substance occurring in petroleum.

Assay. An examination of a mineral or ore to determine the amount of certain of its constituents. Not a complete analysis.

Atoll. A ringlike coral island encircling or nearly encircling a lagoon.

Atomic number. The number of positive charges on the nucleus of an atom.

Atomic weight. Average relative weight of the atom of an element with reference to the atomic weight of oxygen, which is standard at 16.000.

Atoms. The extremely minute particles of which all matter is composed. They contain protons, neutrons, and electrons.

Augite. An abundant ferromagnesian silicate mineral (a pyroxene); commonly found in some basic igneous rocks.

Avalanche. A large mass of snow or ice that falls from higher to lower parts of mountains.

Axis. The linear trend of the crest of an anticline or the trough of a syncline.

Backwater. Water in lagoons between shore and offshore bars.

Badlands. Topography characterized by an intricate maze of ravines and sharp divides.

Bajada. A compound alluvial fan that merges with a valley floor.

Banded. Designating the structure of rocks having thin and nearly parallel bands of various minerals, textures, or colors.

Bar. A sand embankment built on the floor of the sea by waves and currents. May also occur on stream beds.

Barbed tributary. A tributary entering the main stream in an upstream direction.

Barchan. A crescent-shaped dune with horns pointing in the direction of wind movement.

Barite. An orthorhombic mineral composed of barium sulfate ($BaSO_4$).

Barometer. An instrument for measuring atmospheric pressure.

Barrier beach. Offshore bar. A sand ridge parallel to shore, slightly above high-tide level. Commonly separated from shore by a lagoon.

Barrier reef. A coral reef parallel to shore and beyond a lagoon.

Basal conglomerate. A conglomerate formed over an old erosion surface, such as the near-shore deposits of a slowly advancing sea.

Basalt. A fine-grained, black to medium-gray igneous rock with a high percentage of ferromagnesian minerals. Common in lava flows.

Base. A substance capable of accepting protons and of combining with silica in a rock. Lime and potash are common examples.

Base level. The base that limits downward erosion by streams. A level inclined slightly toward sea level.

Basic rock. An igneous rock in which the dominant minerals are comparatively low in silica and rich in metallic bases, as in the ferromagnesian minerals.

Batholith. A huge intrusive body of igneous rock that flares outward with depth and is thought to be "bottomless," with an area of exposure exceeding 40 square miles.

Bathyal. Pertaining to the deeper parts of the ocean; the "deep" sea; specifically, the submarine continental slope.

Bauxite. The principal ore of aluminum. Composed essentially of aluminum hydroxides.

Bay-head bar. A bar built a short distance out from the shore at the head of a bay.

Beach cusps. Beach deposits of sand and gravel in the form of a succession of ridges with sharp points facing the water.

Beach drifting. The movement of beach sediments parallel to the beach.

Bedding. Planes dividing sedimentary beds, or layers, of the same or different kinds of rocks.

Bedrock. Any solid rock exposed at the surface or underlying soil, sand, or any type of mantle-rock.

Beheaded stream. The lower section of a stream from which water has been diverted by stream piracy.

Benthos. The deep part of the sea. Also, the life dwelling on the bottom of the sea.

Bergschrund. A deep, arcuate crevasse or series of crevasses between the glacial ice and the cirque wall of a valley glacier.

Beta radiation. The emission of either an electron or a positron by an atomic nucleus.

B horizon. The soil zone that lies below the *A* horizon in the soil profile. Colloids, soluble salts, and fine mineral particles from near the surface accumulate in this zone.

Bicarbonate. A salt containing a metal and the radical HCO_3, such as $Ca(HCO_3)_2$.

Biogenic. Pertaining to nonclastic sediments resulting from the physiological activities of organisms.

Biotite. Black mica. A common ferromagnesian silicate mineral with one perfect cleavage, yielding very thin, translucent, flexible sheets or scales.

Bitter lakes. Lakes with a high content of dissolved sulfates and alkaline carbonates, as distinct from salt lakes.

Bitumen. A tarry hydrocarbon mixture soluble in carbon disulfide.

Bituminous coal. Soft coal, containing about 80 per cent carbon and 10 per cent oxygen. Despite its name, it contains no bitumen.

Black sands. Sands in which heavy black minerals have been concentrated by wave and current action. Common minerals are magnetite, ilmenite, tourmaline, rutile, and hornblende.

Blowout. A shallow, saucer-shaped hollow formed by wind erosion on a preexisting dune or other aeolian deposit.

Blue mud. A variety of deep-sea mud, consisting mainly of land-derived fine silt and clay. Turns red when oxidized.

Bog. A swamp or tract of wet land commonly covered with peat.

Bombs, volcanic. Ellipsoidal or spindle-shaped masses of viscous lava ejected from a volcano. They range in size from a fraction of an inch to several feet.

Bore. A tidal wave moving upstream in a river or estuary.

Bottomset beds. The layers of sediment on the bottom of a delta.

Boulder clay. Unsorted glacial drift with embedded rock fragments of boulder size; till.

Braided stream. A stream choked with sand bars that divide it into an intricate network of interlacing channels.

Breaker. A wave that drags on the shallow bottom of the sea and breaks on or near the shore.

Breccia. A fragmental rock resembling conglomerate but having angular, instead of rounded, fragments.

Brownstone. A ferruginous sandstone in which the grains are coated and cemented with iron oxide.

Bulb glacier. A valley glacier that spreads out into a fan or bulb shape where its terminus descends to the piedmont slope.

Butte. A conspicuous isolated hill with precipitous sides and a small crest. Commonly an erosion remnant.

Calcareous. Containing varying amounts of calcium carbonate.

Calcite. A mineral composed of calcium carbonate, the principal constituent of limestone.

Caldera. A large, basin-shaped volcanic depression, with a diameter much greater than its depth, produced by either collapse or explosion.

Caliche. Desert surface debris cemented by porous calcium carbonate.

Calving. Wastage of ice from terminus of a floating glacier; the breaking off of huge masses that usually float away as icebergs.

Carbon 14. A radioactive isotope of carbon with atomic weight 14. Useful in determining age of carbonaceous material younger than 38,000 years.

Carbonaceous. Pertaining to or composed for the most part of carbon.

Carbonate. A salt or mineral containing the radical CO_3.

Carbonation. A chemical process during weathering that converts basic oxides into carbonates.

Cataract. A cascade or waterfall of great volume.

Catchment area. The intake area of an artesian basin.

Cation. An ion that would move toward a cathode. Synonymous with positive ion.

Cementation. The deposition of minerals around grains in rocks by precipitation from solution. Quartz, carbonates, and iron oxides are common cementing materials.

Centrosphere. The central, highly metallic core of the earth.

Chalk. A variety of unindurated limestone composed of tests of microorganisms.

Chert. A compact, fine-grained, siliceous rock composed of chalcedonic silica. Flint is a variety.

Chloride. A compound of chlorine with an electropositive element.

Chlorite. A complex group of platy, blackish-green hydrous magnesium aluminum silicates containing iron.

C horizon. The weathered zone under the *B* horizon in the soil profile. It grades downward into the unweathered rock.

Cinder cone. Volcanic cone composed of gravel-sized and coarse-sand-sized cinders.

Cinders. Volcanic-glass fragments of gravel sizes and coarse-sand sizes.

Cirque. A steep, blunt, bowl-shaped valley head in a mountainside at high elevation, formed by glacial plucking and frost action.

Clastic sediments. A textural term applied to sediments and rocks composed of fragmental material derived from preexisting rocks.

Cleavage. In minerals, the tendency to break or split so that smooth plane surfaces are produced, which parallel a possible crystal face; in rocks, splitting along closely spaced, parallel planes.

Cobble. A rock fragment larger than a pebble and smaller than a boulder. Between 64 and 256 millimeters in diameter.

Col. A saddle on a divide, such as a pass through a glaciated mountain ridge.

Cold front. The edge of an advancing cold air mass that pushes under warm air like a wedge. Commonly produces a rise in barometric pressure and a fall in temperature.

Columnar jointing. Vertical fractures in igneous rocks formed by contraction during cooling. The fractures bound columns, many of which are hexagonal.

Compaction. Decrease in volume of sediments due to compression by overlying strata.

Conchoidal fracture. The curved, shell-like form of a surface produced by the fracture of brittle minerals and rocks, such as quartz and volcanic glass.

Concretion. A variously shaped mass or nodule with concentric structure developed by the deposition of material from solution about a nucleus.

Cone-in-cone. Referring to a series of small, nesting, concentric cones with wrinkled and fluted surfaces.

Cone of depression. A conical depression in the water table that develops around a well as it is being pumped.

Confluence. The point where two streams flow together to form one stream.

Conformable. Designating beds, or strata, that lie upon one another in an unbroken and parallel order.

Conglomerate. A clastic sedimentary rock composed of gravel or boulders cemented together.

Connate water. Water trapped in the pore spaces of a sedimentary rock when the sediment was deposited.

Consequent stream. A river whose course was determined by the original slope and irregularities of the surface on which it developed.

Contact metamorphism. Alteration of rocks that takes place near their contact with magma or lava.

Continental shelf. The margin of a continental mass submerged by the sea. It slopes gradually from the coast line to a depth of about 70 fathoms (420 feet).

Contour line. A line connecting points of equal elevation above or below a datum plane, such as sea level.

Coquina. A variety of limestone made up chiefly of coarse shell fragments.

Corrasion. Mechanical erosion performed by running water or other moving agents of erosion using rock particles as tools.

Correlation. The establishment of the equivalence in geologic age and stratigraphic position of two or more sedimentary units in separated areas.

Corrosion. Erosion accomplished by chemical solution.

Corundum. A hexagonal mineral, Al_2O_3. Ruby and sapphire are gem varieties.

Cove. A small bay or baylike recess in the coast.

Crag-and-tail. Designating a rock cliff or crag which has superficial deposits, such as dune sand, banked up against it in the form of a long sloping "tail."

Crater. Funnel-shaped pit at the summit or on the flanks of a volcano.

Creep. The slow downward movement of soil and rock fragments on a slope.

Crevasse. A large and deep gaping crevice or fissure in glacial ice.

Cross-bedding. The structure of sedimentary beds characterized by parallel laminations lying at an angle to the planes of general stratification.

Crust. The solid rock of the outer part of the earth to a depth of 18 to 25 miles.

Crystal. A solid with an orderly atomic arrangement. It commonly is bounded by plane surfaces.

Cuesta. An asymmetric ridge with one long, gentle, plainlike slope along the dip of the rock and one steep slope across it.

Cuspate bar. A crescent-shaped bar attached to shore at one end.

Cycle of erosion. The succession of events involved in the reduction of a region from its youthful stage to base level through normal processes of erosion.

Cyclone. An area of low air pressure around which winds blow in a counterclockwise direction in the Northern Hemisphere and in a clockwise direction in the Southern Hemisphere. It may cause precipitation.

Dacite. The fine-grained equivalent of a quartz diorite.

Débouchure. The mouth of a river. Also the point of issuance of an underground stream, as from a cave.

Debris. The material resulting from the disintegration and decay of rocks.

Decomposition. Chemical weathering of minerals and rock.

Deflation. The removal of fine clastic materials by wind.

Degradation. The process of lowering the land surface by erosion. To degrade is to wear down.

Delta. The accumulation of sediment where a stream empties into a body of quiet water, resulting in the building out of the shore line.

Dendrite. A branching pattern resembling a shrub or tree.

Dendritic drainage pattern. Treelike pattern of tributaries of a main stream.

Denudation. The removal of surface materials by erosion.

Desert. A region with little rainfall and sparse vegetation.

Desiccation. Evaporation of water in unconsolidated sediments, resulting in shrinking and compaction. Tension cracks may form during the process.

Detrital. Clastic particles derived from former rocks.

Detritus. Accumulations arising from the waste or disintegration of preexisting rocks.

Diabasic. Designating the texture of certain basic igneous rocks.

Diamond. An isometric mineral composed of the element carbon. The hardest naturally occurring substance known.

Diaspore. An aluminum hydroxide mineral.

Diastrophism. All movements of the earth's crust resulting in relative vertical or horizontal changes of position and in the deformation of rocks.

Diatomaceous earth. An earthy siliceous deposit consisting mainly of the shells of diatoms.

Differential weathering. Unevenly weathered rock surface due to differences in the character of the constituent rocks. Such forms as isolated stacks, buttes, and flutings are the results of such weathering.

Dike. A tabular mass of igneous rock intruded in a crack or fissure.

Diorite. A coarse-grained igneous rock composed chiefly of medium plagioclase and ferromagnesian minerals.

Dip. The angle at which a stratum, vein, dike, or sill is inclined from the horizontal.

Discharge. Volume of stream flow, per unit of time, through a given cross section of the stream.

Disconformity. An unconformity in which the beds on opposite sides of the surface of unconformity are parallel.

Discontinuities. Zones in the earth where rapid velocity changes in earthquake waves occur because of changes in the elasticity and density of the rock.

Discordance. A lack of parallelism between contiguous strata.

Dismembered river system. A drowned stream valley which, as a result of flooding, has its former tributaries enter the sea by separate mouths.

Dissection. The work of erosion on flat upland areas that cuts them into rugged hills, valleys, and ravines.

Distributary. An outflowing branch of a river that does not rejoin it. Characteristically occurs on a delta.

Diverted stream. In stream piracy, the stream that was diverted from the beheaded stream and that flows to the pirate stream.

Dolomite. A mineral composed of both calcium and magnesium carbonates, $CaMg(CO_3)_2$. Also applied to those rocks that approximate the mineral dolomite in composition.

Dome. A roughly symmetrical upfold, the beds dipping in all directions from the crest of the structure.

Dreikanter. Three-faceted pebbles shaped by sandblasting.

Drowned valley. A valley whose lower end has been inundated by the sea and thus converted into a bay or estuary.

Drumlin. A small, smooth, oval hill of glacial till with its long axis parallel to the movement of the ice.

Drumlinoid. A hill similar to a drumlin, but less regular in shape and less symmetrically arranged.

Druse. A crust of small crystals lining a cavity.

Dune. Hillock of wind-blown sand.

Dust well. A small pit in glacier ice, produced where tiny rock and mineral particles on the ice absorb heat from the sun's rays and sink down into the ice.

Dynamic metamorphism. Textural and mineral changes produced largely by rock deformation.

Earthquake. A group of elastic waves in the solid earth, generated by a disturbance of the elastic equilibrium, which causes rocks to break or slip along preformed fractures.

Effusive. Designating igneous rock formed from lava poured out or ejected at the earth's surface.

Einkanter. One-faceted pebbles shaped by sandblasting.

Ejecta. Rock material hurled out of the earth by a volcano.

Elastic rebound. The springing back of rocks, after rupture, to a position of no strain.

Electron. A subatomic particle, negatively charged, that revolves around the nucleus of an atom.

Element. A substance which cannot be decomposed into other substances by ordinary chemical methods.

Emanations. Vapors and gases given off by a magma.

End moraine. Terminal moraine. An accumulation of glacial drift at the end or margin of a glacier.

Entrenched meander. A meandering stream in a deeply incised valley. Entrenched during uplift.

Epeirogenic movements. The raising or lowering of land masses of continental magnitude with little, if any, folding.

Epicenter. The area on the earth's surface directly above the focus of an earthquake.

Epicontinental sea. Shallow sea that lies far in upon a continental mass.

Erratic. A large rock fragment different from the

bedrock on which it lies, generally transported by glacier ice.

Escarpment. A steep slope or cliff separating gently sloping areas.

Eskers. Winding ridges of irregularly stratified sand and gravel that occur in the area of ground moraine.

Estuary. The portion of a stream valley influenced by the tide of the body of water into which it flows.

Eustatic. Relating to a world-wide rise or fall of sea level, caused by melting or accumulation of continental glaciers.

Evaporite. A sediment deposited from solution as a result of extensive evaporation of the solvent.

Exfoliation. Process by which concentric sheets or scales peel off from bare rock surfaces.

Exposure. An outcrop of rock exposed at the surface of the earth.

Facet. A plane surface abraded on a rock fragment.

Faceted spur. The end of a ridge which has been truncated by erosion or faulting.

Facies. Rock features reflecting the environment in which the rock was formed.

Fan. Detrital material deposited in the shape of a fan, as an alluvial fan.

Fault. A fracture in the rock along which there has been movement.

Fault block. A unit of rock bounded by faults.

Fault scarp. A cliff formed by faulting.

Feldspars. A group of minerals classed as aluminosilicates.

Felsites. Fine-grained, light-colored igneous rocks.

Ferromagnesian. Pertaining to certain dark-colored minerals and rocks containing iron and magnesium.

Fiord. The seaward end of a glaciated, steep-walled valley that is partly submerged.

Firn. Compacted, granular snow. Also called névé.

Fissure. An extensive break, crack, or fracture in the rocks.

Flint. A tough, fine-grained form of silica. Breaks with conchoidal fracture. Commonly occurs as nodules in limestone.

Float. Pieces of rock separated from the parent beds or ore veins by agents of weathering and erosion.

Floe ice. Floating pieces of sea ice.

Flood plain. Portion of a stream valley bordering the channel, built of sediments brought there by the stream during time of flood.

Flow breccia. Fragments of solidified lava welded or cemented by lava, as at the top of a lava flow.

Flow cleavage. Rock cleavage caused by parallel alignment of minerals, as in schists.

Flowing well. A well from which water or oil flows at the surface without pumping. Hydrostatic pressure lifts the fluid to the surface.

Fluorite. A mineral composed of calcium fluoride, an ore of fluorine.

Focus. The center from which earthquake waves are propagated.

Foliation. A structural lamination produced during metamorphism. Schists are foliated.

Fool's gold. The mineral pyrite, composed of iron sulfide.

Footwall. The mass of rock beneath a fault plane or vein of ore.

Foreset beds. Inclined strata dropped by river currents on the frontal slope of a delta or a channel bar.

Fossils. Remains or traces of plants or animals preserved in the rocks.

Fracture cleavage. A system of closely spaced parallel fractures, along which a rock breaks readily.

Fuller's earth. Fine, claylike earth possessing the property of decolorizing oils and fats.

Fumarole. A vent in volcanic areas from which fumes issue.

Gabbro. A coarse-grained basic igneous rock composed for the most part of pyroxene and calcic plagioclase.

Galena. A mineral composed of lead sulfide. The principal ore of lead.

Gangue. The nonvaluable minerals associated with ore minerals in a vein.

Garnets. A group of silicate minerals used as gems and abrasives.

Geochemistry. All parts of geology that involve chemical changes.

Geode. A thick-walled, rounded or egg-shaped rock cavity lined with crystals.

Geoid. The figure of the earth considered as a mean sea-level surface extended through the continents.

Geomorphology. The origin and development of the topography of the continents.

Geophysics. The physics of the earth.

Geosyncline. A long troughlike belt of sediments within a continent that has warped down during the long period of accumulation.

Geothermal gradient. The change in temperature of the earth with depth.

Geyser. An intermittently eruptive hot spring.

Geyserite. The siliceous deposits formed around hot springs.

Glacial milk. Melt water from glaciers, colored by suspended particles of clay and silt.

Glacial retreat. The recession of the frontal margin of a glacier.

Glacial striae. Glacial scratches on smoothed rock surfaces.

Glacier table. A large block of stone supported by a column of ice on the surface of a glacier.

Glauconite. A green, granular mineral composed of hydrous potassium iron silicate.

Gneiss. Coarse-grained, imperfectly foliated feldspathic rock, usually metamorphic.

Gossan. A ferruginous residue forming a superficial cover on a sulfide vein.

Gouge. Crushed and abraded material occurring between the walls of a fault.

Graben. A fault trough or a fault block downthrown relative to both margins.

Gradation. The processes that tend to bring the earth's surface to grade through erosion and deposition.

Graded bedding. A gradation in grain size within a sedimentary layer, from coarse below to fine above.

Graded stream. A stream in which the long profile is in equilibrium. It neither degrades nor aggrades.

Gradient. Any departure from the horizontal.

Granite. A coarse-grained, intrusive igneous rock composed of orthoclase, quartz, and a ferromagnesian mineral.

Granitoid. Designating the texture of a coarsely crystalline, igneous rock.

Graphite. A mineral composed of carbon.

Gravity fault. A normal fault. The hanging wall appears to have moved downward relative to the footwall.

Graywacke. A gray, clastic sedimentary rock composed of fragmental granite debris and other rock and mineral fragments in a muddy matrix.

Greensand. Highly glauconitic sand.

Grit. Very coarse-grained sand.

Groundmass. The fine-grained or glassy matrix of a porphyritic igneous rock.

Ground moraine. A moraine with low relief, consisting mainly of unsorted till, deposited as a widespread veneer over a bedrock surface.

Ground-water level. The upper surface of the zone within the earth below which the openings in the rocks are filled with water.

Guano. Deposits of excrement of bats and birds.

Gumbo. Soils that yield a very sticky mud when wet.

Gypsum. A common mineral, consisting of hydrous calcium sulfate. Varieties are called satin spar, selenite, and alabaster.

Hade. The angle of inclination of a vein or fault measured from the vertical.

Halite. Rock salt. A common mineral consisting of sodium chloride and formed as an evaporite.

Hanging valley. A valley in which the floor is notably higher than the floor of the trunk valley into which it leads.

Hanging wall. The mass of rock above a fault plane, vein, or bed of ore. The opposite of a footwall.

Hardness. The resistance of minerals and rocks to abrasion or scratching.

Headland. A bold cape or promontory projecting into the sea.

Headward erosion. The lengthening of the upper end of a valley by the water that flows in at its head, as illustrated by gullies gnawing back into slopes.

Hematite. The principal ore of iron, consisting of iron oxide.

Hogback. A resistant ridge produced by the erosion of highly tilted strata.

Homogeneous. Of the same nature; consisting of similar parts; opposite of heterogeneous.

Hook. A hook-shaped spit.

Horn. A high pyramidal peak with steep sides formed by the intersecting walls of several cirques. (Term derived from the Matterhorn in the Swiss Alps.)

Hornblende. The dark, aluminous variety of the amphibole group of minerals.

Hornblendite. A coarse-grained basic igneous rock composed of hornblende.

Hornfels. Dense, finely granular metamorphic rock. A product of contact metamorphism formed at temperatures above 1200°F.

Horst. A block of the earth's crust, generally long compared to its width, that has been uplifted along faults relative to the rocks on either side.

Hurricane. Violent cyclonic winds around an area of low atmospheric pressure.

Hydration. The chemical combination of water with another substance.

Hydraulic gradient. A gradient due to hydrostatic pressure.

Hydrocarbon. A compound containing only carbon and hydrogen, such as petroleum.

Hydrogenic sediments. Precipitates from solution in water.

Hydrologic cycle. The water cycle, in which water is evaporated from the sea, then precipitated from the atmosphere to the surface of the land, and finally returned to the sea by rivers and streams. Some water is evaporated again before it reaches the sea.

Hydrology. The science that relates to the water of the earth.

Hydrosphere. The water portion of the earth.

Hydrostatic pressure. The pressure exerted by water at any point in a body of water at rest.

Icecap. A small ice sheet.

Ice foot. A fringe of ice frozen to the shore along the coasts of polar seas.

Ice jam. Fragments of broken river ice lodged in a narrow of a river channel.

Iceland spar. A transparent variety of calcite that has double refraction.

Ice rampart. Ridge of sand, gravel, and boulders that parallels a lake shore. Results from expanding ice overriding low shore zone.

Ice sheet. Glacier forming continuous cover over a large land surface and moving outward in many directions.

Igneous rock. Rock formed by cooling and solidification of hot, mobile mineral material called magma.

Impervious. Applied to rocks, such as clays and shales, that do not allow the penetration of solutions, oil, or gases.

Inclusion. A fragment of older rock enclosed in an igneous rock.

Induration. Hardening of sediments by compaction through pressure, cementation, or heat.

Infiltration. The percolation of water into soil and rock through pores. Also, the deposition of mineral matter by the permeation of water carrying it in solution.

In situ. In its natural position or original place.

Insolation. The action of the sun's heat upon the rocks at the surface, or the solar radiation received by the earth.

Intercalated. Pertaining to material interbedded with another kind of material.

Intermediate rock. Rock that is intermediate between acidic and basic. Containing between 52 and 66 per cent silica.

Intermittent stream. A stream that flows only part of the time. One that has not cut its valley below the water table.

Interstitial water. Water contained in the pores between grains of rock.

Intrusive rock. Rock consolidated from magma beneath the earth's surface.

Ion. An atom or group of atoms with an electric charge.

Ionosphere. The highest layer of the atmosphere; the zone in which ionization takes place.

Isoclinal fold. A fold with parallel limbs.

Isomorphous. Having similar crystalline form.

Isopach. On a geologic map, a line drawn through points of equal thickness of a given formation or stratigraphic unit.

Isoseismals. Imaginary lines on the surface of the earth connecting points of equal seismic disturbance.

Isostasy, theory of. The hypothesis that different masses of the earth's crust stand in gravitational equilibrium with each other at some depth within the earth.

Isotherm. An imaginary line connecting points of equal temperature.

Isotopes. Atoms of the same element which differ in atomic weight because of differences in nuclear structure.

Jasper. A variety of very fine-grained quartz, red to dark brown in color.

Joint. A fracture in a rock formation along which there is no evidence of displacement.

Joint chasms. Deep indentations formed along coasts where joints have been quarried out by the waves.

Joint system. Two or more sets of joints which may have characteristic patterns.

Kame. A conical hill of stratified glacial drift deposited as an alluvial cone or fan against the outer margin of an ice sheet by a melt-water stream from the ice.

Kame terrace. A terrace along a glaciated valley wall formed from stratified drift deposited along the margin between the ice and the bounding rock slope of the valley.

Kaolinite. China clay. A common clay mineral consisting of hydrous aluminum silicate. Has a greasy feel and is plastic when wet.

Karst topography. Rough topography etched out in a network of numerous short gullies and ravines which terminate in sinkholes produced by the solution of limestone strata. (Named from Karst Mountains, northeast of the head of Adriatic Sea.)

Kettle. A depression in a drift sheet, made by the melting of a mass of glacial ice that had been either wholly or partly buried in the drift.

Labradorite. A calcic plagioclase feldspar.

Laccolith. A lens-shaped intrusive body that has domed up the overlying sedimentary beds and that has a floor, which is generally horizontal.

Lag gravel. Residual material of coarser fragments, from which finer particles have been blown away.

Lagoon. The quiet water on the landward side of an offshore bar.

Lamination. Thin bedding, less than 1 centimeter in thickness, in a sedimentary rock or in unconsolidated sediments.

Land breeze. A light wind blowing from the land over a lake or sea because of unequal cooling of land and water areas.

Landslide. Large masses of earth and rock that slide bodily down a slope.

Lapilli. Volcanic ejecta ranging from 4 to 32 millimeters in diameter.

Lateral moraine. A moraine built along the edge of a valley glacier and composed of angular rock fragments that had fallen on the glacier from the valley wall.

Laterite. A residual product of weathering in hot, humid climate. It is composed of iron and aluminum hydroxides and occurs as a red, porous, concretionary veneer over bedrock.

Lava. Fluid rock material that issues from a volcano or a fissure in the earth's surface. Magma that reaches the surface.

Lava cone. A volcanic cone built almost entirely of lava flows.

Leaching. The process by which the more soluble mineral compounds are removed in solution by percolating ground waters.

Leeward. The direction toward which the prevailing wind is blowing.

Lignite. Low-rank, brown coal with a woody appearance.

Limestone. A sedimentary rock consisting chiefly of calcium carbonate.

Limonite. Brown, hydrous iron oxide. An important iron ore.

Lithification. The complex processes that convert unconsolidated sediments into solid rock.

Lithosphere. The solid portion of the earth.

Littoral zone. The zone along the coast between

the average extent of the highest flood tide and the average recession of the lowest ebb tide.

Load. The quantity of material being transported by a current of water, wind, or glacial ice.

Loess. Nonstratified, yellowish silt deposited primarily by the wind. Consists of fresh, sharp-cornered particles of quartz, feldspar, calcite, and numerous other minerals mingled with some clay.

Longshore drift. Sediment transported by currents parallel to the shore.

Lopolith. A large, floored intrusive that is centrally sunken into the form of a basin.

Magma. Hot, fluid rock material generated within the earth and capable of intrusion or extrusion. When cooled and solidified, it forms igneous rocks.

Magmatic differentiation. Process by which different types of igneous rocks are derived from a single mass of magma.

Magmatic water. Water that exists in, or which is derived from, magma.

Magnesite. A mineral consisting of magnesium carbonate.

Magnetic declination. The angle between the direction of the magnetic and geographic meridians.

Magnetite. A magnetic, black mineral consisting of iron oxide. An important ore of iron.

Mantle-rock. Unconsolidated rock debris that overlies the bedrock surface.

Marble. A metamorphic rock composed essentially of granular calcite or dolomite. A product of the recrystallization of limestone.

Marsh gas. Methane. Abundant in natural gas and derived from the partial decay of plant tissue. Called "fire damp" by coal miners.

Mass movement. Surface movement of earth materials induced by gravity.

Matterhorn. See *Horn.*

Meander. One of a series of looplike bends in the course of a stream.

Medial moraine. A ridge of drift formed by the joining of adjacent lateral moraines below the junction of two valley glaciers.

Mesa. A low, flat-topped mountain or tableland bounded on at least one side by a steep cliff.

Metamorphic rock. A rock that has been changed in texture and/or composition by heat, pressure, or chemically active solutions.

Meteor. A small fragment of interplanetary matter heated to incandescence by friction when traveling through the earth's atmosphere. Commonly called a "falling" star.

Meteoric water. Water which occurs in, or is derived from, the atmosphere.

Meteorite. A meteor that reached the earth's surface before being consumed by the heat of friction in the atmosphere.

Meteorology. The science dealing with the atmosphere, with special reference to weather.

Millidarcy. One-thousandth of a Darcy. A measure of permeability.

Mineral. A naturally occurring, homogeneous, inorganic, crystalline substance.

Monadnock. A mountainlike mass such as a butte, standing above a peneplain as a remnant of erosion.

Monocline. A succession of beds dipping in one direction or folded in a steplike bend from an otherwise horizontal position.

Monzonite. A coarse-grained igneous rock containing equal amounts of orthoclase and plagioclase feldspar.

Moraine. Glacial drift or till deposited chiefly by direct glacial action.

Moulin. A circular depression on the surface of a glacier and the underlying well into which melt waters plunge.

Muck. A substance similar to peat but containing more soil minerals.

Mud volcano. A mud geyser, commonly formed by the eruption of bituminous mud from a central vent.

Muscovite. White mica, a member of the mica group of minerals.

Muskeg. A moss-covered bog or marsh.

Nappe. A large body of rock that has moved a great distance from its original position, either by overthrusting or by recumbent folding.

Narrows. A steep-walled narrow part of a wide valley.

Native. Designating the state of an element that occurs in nature uncombined. Commonly applied to metals, as native silver, native copper.

Natural levee. A long alluvial ridge built up on either side of a stream by muddy floodwaters.

Neap tides. The tides that have the least rise and fall.

Needle. A prominent, sharp, rocky pinnacle or spire in mountainous topography. A product of differential erosion.

Neritic zone. The portion of the sea floor extending from the low-tide line to a depth of 400 to 600 feet.

Neutron. A fundamental particle of matter having no electric charge and a mass approximately equal to that of a proton.

Névé. Snow converted into granular ice. Also called firn.

Nonconformity. An unconformity where the older rocks are of plutonic origin.

Normal fault. A fault in which the hanging wall has moved downward relative to the footwall.

Nunatak. Mountaintop projecting above the surface of a snow and ice field.

Oblate spheroid. A spheroid flattened or depressed at the poles. The shape of the earth.

Obsidian. Volcanic glass. Characterized by glassy luster and conchoidal fracture, with composition close to that of rhyolite and granite.

Ocean currents. Nontidal oceanic circulation, such as that of the Gulf Stream and equatorial currents.

Offlap. A relationship of strata that develops where a shore line has retreated seaward and progressively younger strata have been deposited in layers offset seaward.

Oil shale. A shale with abundant organic material that yields oil when distilled slowly.

Olivine. A green, rock-forming mineral composed mainly of magnesium silicate.

Onyx. A banded variety of cryptocrystalline quartz. Mexican onyx is translucent banded calcite.

Oölite. A rock consisting of sand-sized, spheroidal grains of calcareous material—or, less commonly, ferruginous, siliceous, or phosphatic material—in concentric layers around a nucleus, generally of quartz.

Ooze. Fine-grained deep-sea deposits containing more than 30 per cent of organic residues.

Opal. An amorphous form of hydrous silica. A solidified silica gel.

Orbit. The path described by a celestial body in its revolutions around another body—for example, the moon's path around the earth.

Ore. A mineral deposit from which a metal or nonmetal can be extracted at a profit.

Orogeny. The processes of folding and faulting that result in the formation of mountain ranges.

Orthoclase. A mineral of the feldspar group composed of potassium aluminum silicate. An essential mineral of granite.

Outcrop. That part of a rock formation which appears at the surface.

Outwash. Stratified drift deposited by melt-water streams beyond the margin of glaciers.

Overlap. In stratigraphy, the extension of one formation beyond another or over the beveled edge of another.

Oxbow lake. A crescent-shaped lake formed in an abandoned river bend by a meander-neck cutoff.

Oxidation. The process of combining with oxygen.

Pack ice. Floating ice blocks driven closely together in irregular ridges and covering a large area.

Pahoehoe. Basaltic lava flows with a billowy or ropy surface. A Hawaiian term.

Paleobotany. The study of plant fossils.

Paleontology. The science that deals with the life of past geologic ages.

Palisade. A bold cliff exposing basalt columns.

Parasitic cone. A cinder cone on the flank of a larger volcano.

Parting. The separation of crystals along planes that are not true cleavage planes.

Patterned ground. A land surface characterized by the polygons, circles, and stripes that form in unconsolidated surface materials subjected to prolonged, intense frost action.

Peat. A dark-brown, spongy residue produced by

partially decomposed vegetative tissue in swamps and bogs.

Pediment. Gently sloping rock plain eroded at the foot of steep slopes or cliffs.

Pegmatite. Very coarse-grained granite that occurs in dikes. Some pegmatites contain rare minerals and gems.

Pelagic. Pertaining to free-swimming and -floating communities of marine organisms.

Peneplain. A land surface worn down by erosion to a nearly flat or broadly undulating plain.

Perched boulder. A glacial boulder deposited in an unstable position on the top of a hill.

Perched water table. Ground water that lies above the regional ground-water table and is separated from it by impervious strata.

Peridotite. A coarse-grained basic igneous rock composed of olivine.

Perlite. Volcanic glass having numerous concentric cracks formed by contraction during cooling.

Permafrost. Permanently frozen subsoil.

Permeability. A rock's capacity for transmitting a fluid.

Pervious rock. A stratum or formation that contains voids through which water will move under ordinary hydrostatic pressure.

Petrifaction. The conversion of organic matter into stone.

Petrology. The study of the natural history of rocks.

Phaneritic. Designating igneous rocks with a coarse-grained texture.

Phenocryst. A relatively large and conspicuous crystal in a porphyritic igneous rock, surrounded by much smaller grains.

Phosphate rock. A sedimentary rock containing nodular and irregular masses of concretionary calcium fluorophosphate.

Phyllite. A slaty metamorphic rock with fine mica crystals that give the cleavage surfaces a silky sheen.

Piedmont. Lying or formed at the foot of a mountain. Examples are piedmont alluvial plains and piedmont glaciers.

Pillow lava. A lava exhibiting an ellipsoidal, pillow-shaped structure. Most common in basaltic flows extruded into water.

Piracy. The diversion of the upper part of a stream by the headward growth of another stream.

Pitted plain. A glacial outwash plain with numerous small kettle holes.

Placer deposit. An alluvial deposit containing particles or nuggets of gold, platinum, tin, or other stable, valuable minerals derived from the weathering of rocks or veins.

Plagioclase. A group of rock-forming feldspar minerals.

Plastic deformation. A permanent change in the shape of a solid that occurs without fracturing or rupture.

Playa lake. A flat-floored, shallow desert basin containing a temporary lake.

Plug. See *Volcanic neck.*

Plunge pool. See *Pothole.*

Pluton. A great body of intrusive igneous rock that formed beneath the surface by the cooling and consolidation of magma.

Podsol. A highly bleached soil that is low in iron and lime.

Polygon ground. See *Patterned ground.*

Porphyritic. Designating a rock texture in which large phenocrysts (crystals) are set in a finer groundmass.

Pothole. A cylindrical hole worn into the solid rock at rapids or at the foot of waterfalls.

Precipitation. The fall of water from the atmosphere as rain, snow, sleet, or hail.

Proton. A fundamental particle of matter with a positive electric charge.

Pseudomorph. A false form. A mineral having the proper crystal form of another mineral, which it has replaced.

Pumice. A cellular, volcanic froth of glassy texture. Sufficiently buoyant to float on water.

Pyrite. A brass-yellow mineral composed of iron sulfide. It has cubic crystals and is commonly striated. Popularly called fool's gold.

Pyroclastic. Designating detrital volcanic materials that have been ejected explosively.

Pyroxenes. A group of ferromagnesian minerals.

Pyroxenite. A coarse-grained basic igneous rock composed of pyroxene.

Quartz. A mineral, composed of silicon dioxide,

with six-sided crystals tapering to pyramids at the ends. Colorless or white when pure, but commonly tinted. Without cleavage.

Quartzite. Quartz sandstone thoroughly cemented by silica deposited in optical continuity around the sand grains.

Quicksand. Sand supersaturated with water and easily movable, or "quick." Will not support a heavy object.

Radioactivity. Radioactive disintegration. A natural breakdown of atomic structure that results in one atom's changing into another by the emission of charged particles from its nucleus.

Radiolarian ooze. Siliceous ooze composed of skeletons of radiolaria which accumulate on the floor of the deep sea.

Range line. In public-land surveys, a boundary line of a township extending in a north-south direction.

Recessional moraine. A ridgelike accumulation of drift deposited by a glacier along its outer margin, back from the position of its maximum advance.

Reconstructed glacier. Ice blocks that have cascaded or fallen from a hanging valley and reunited to form a glacier at the base of the plunge.

Recumbent fold. A fold in which the axial plane is approximately horizontal.

Reduction. The process of removing oxygen from a compound.

Reef atoll. A ring-shaped coral reef enclosing a body of water.

Regional metamorphism. Large-scale recrystallization of rocks without the intervention of heat from magmatic sources.

Rejuvenate. To stimulate, as by uplift, the erosive activity of a stream.

Repose, angle of. The slope on which any given deposited material will come to rest or remain at rest.

Residual clay. A clay deposit formed by the decay of rock in place.

Reverse fault. A fault plane along which the hanging wall appears to have moved upward relative to the footwall.

Rhyolite. A fine-grained equivalent of a granite.

Ria shore line. A shore line formed by the partial submergence of a land mass dissected by numerous river valleys.

Rift valley. An elongated valley formed by the depression of a block of the earth's crust between two parallel faults. Also called a graben.

Ring dike. An arcuate dike with a steep dip.

Rip current. Seaward-moving water that returns the water previously carried landward by waves.

Ripple marks. Small undulations produced on the surface of unconsolidated materials by waves or by currents of wind or water.

Roche moutonnée. Sheepback rock. A rounded hummock of rock smoothed by glacial abrasion.

Rock. A mineral or an aggregate of minerals forming an essential part of the earth's crust.

Rock flour. Fine-textured rock particles, resulting from glacial abrasion, transported and deposited by melt-water streams.

Rock glacier. Talus glacier. A tongue-shaped mass of angular boulders that creeps slowly from high, rugged terrain with the aid of interstitial ice.

Rock terrace. Terrace cut into solid rock rather than alluvium. More resistant horizontal beds are worn back from the valley wall less rapidly than beds above them.

Runoff. The discharge of water through surface streams.

Salinity. A measure of the total concentration of dissolved solids in water.

Saltation. The process whereby a particle is picked up by a turbulent current and carried forward by leaps and bounds.

Salt dome. A domelike, subsurface structure resulting from a roughly cylindrical mass of common salt being pushed upward through surrounding sediments.

Sandstone. A sedimentary rock composed of sand-sized grains of minerals and rock fragments cemented together.

Saucer lake. A lake that occupies a shallow basin between a natural levee and a valley wall.

Scarp. An escarpment or cliff.

Schist. Metamorphic rock which has a foliated structure. Micaceous minerals are prominent.

Scoria. Volcanic glass characterized by vesicularity

resulting from expanding gases. The frothy texture is retained.

Scour and fill. The process of cutting and refilling channels in sediments deposited by an aggrading stream. Associated with variations in flow velocity, as with rising and ebbing floods.

Seamount. A submarine mountain rising several hundred fathoms above the sea floor.

Sedimentation. The process by which mineral and organic matter is deposited to make sediments.

Seepage. The infiltration and percolation of water through or out of openings in rocks.

Seiche wave. An oscillation wave on the surface of a lake, caused by an earthquake.

Seismic sea wave. Tsunami. A long-period wave generated by a submarine seismic disturbance. Commonly misnamed "tidal wave."

Seismograph. Instrument for detecting and recording earthquake waves.

Seismology. The science of earthquakes.

Serpentine. A common rock-forming mineral composed mainly of magnesium silicate.

Shale. A laminated, detrital sedimentary rock in which the particles are predominantly of clay size. Shales, however, are not limited to clay minerals but may contain silt-sized fragments of quartz, feldspar, calcite, dolomite, and other minerals.

Sheet erosion. Erosion caused by a continuous sheet of surface water.

Shield. A deeply eroded area of the earth's surface that has been sufficiently stable to allow it to be peneplained and warped upward like the profile of a shield.

Shield volcano. A gently sloping volcanic cone built chiefly of overlapping and interfingering basaltic lava flows, as on Hawaii.

Shingle. Beach gravel composed of smooth, generally flattish pebbles and cobbles of roughly the same size.

Sial. A thick zone of rock underlying continental areas. The term is derived from the symbols for silicon (Si) and aluminum (Al) and refers to rocks relatively high in silica.

Siderite. A mineral composed of iron carbonate.

Silica sand. Sand high in quartz (silicon dioxide).

Siliceous sinter. Geyserite. Hydrated varieties of silicon dioxide deposited from waters of hot springs and geysers.

Silicification. Replacement of the original hard parts of an animal or plant by silica. Also the impregnation or replacement of a rock with silica.

Silt. Clastic sediment in which the particles are coarser than clay and finer than sand, that is, between $\frac{1}{16}$ and $\frac{1}{256}$ millimeter in diameter.

Sima. The basic outer shell of the earth under the ocean basins and under the sial layer of the continents. The term is derived from the abbreviations for silicon (Si) and magnesium (Ma).

Sinkhole. A funnel-shaped depression in the surface that occurs where rocks such as salt, gypsum, or limestone have been dissolved and the roof of the solution cavern has collapsed.

Slate. A fine-grained metamorphic rock possessing a well-developed secondary cleavage which allows it to break into sheets that have smooth surfaces.

Slickenside. A polished and scratched surface that results from friction along a fault plane.

Slip face. The steep face on the lee side of a sand dune.

Slumping. See *Creep.*

Soapstone. A massive, impure variety of talc.

Soil profile. A vertical section of the soil from the surface downward through all of its horizons into the parent material.

Solifluction. Soil flow. See *Creep.*

Solfatara. Volcanic fissure from which steam and sulfurous vapors are emitted.

Spatter cone. A steep-sided mound or small hill of spatter built by a lava fountain.

Specific gravity. The ratio of the mass of a body to the mass of an equal volume of water at a temperature of 4°C.

Specularite. Crystalline hematite (iron oxide) occurring in disk-like crystals with metallic luster.

Spheroidal weathering. Production of rounded, residual boulders by chemical weathering of rock along fractures.

Spit. A narrow, ridgelike sand bar projecting into a body of water from a promontory.

Spring. A current of ground water issuing through

a natural opening where the water table intersects the surface.

Spring tide. The tide which is highest and lowest from the mean sea level.

Stack. An isolated, steep-sided rock mass standing as a small island in front of the cliff line or off the end of a promontory along the coast.

Stalactite. Icicle-shaped pendants of dripstone hanging from the roof of a cave.

Stalagmite. Cone-shaped posts of dripstone growing upward from the floor of a cave. Stalactites and stalagmites often meet, forming a pillar from floor to roof.

Steppes. Subarid to arid plains and brushlands. A Tartar term applied to the vast plains of northeastern Russia and northern Siberia.

Stock. An intrusive rock mass, covering less than 40 square miles, that has steep contacts and no determinable floor.

Stoss. The side of a glacially shaped hill that faces the direction from which the glacier came.

Stratification. The deposition of layers, or strata, of sediments as tabular units.

Stratigraphy. The study of the sequence and correlation of stratified rocks.

Stratosphere. A zone of the earth's atmosphere, beginning about 6 miles above sea level, that is constantly cold and dry.

Strato-volcano. A large volcanic cone built of alternating layers of lava and pyroclastic debris, hence a stratified cone.

Stratum. A single layer of sedimentary rock, regardless of thickness.

Streak. The color of the powder of a mineral.

Striae. Minute grooves or scratches on fault surfaces or on rock over which glacial ice has moved.

Strike. The direction, or compass bearing, of the outcrop of an inclined stratum, dike, or vein on a level surface. It is always perpendicular to the direction of the dip.

Sublimate. A solid deposited by a gas or vapor.

Subsequent stream. A stream that adjusts its course to fit belts of weak structure.

Subsidence. A sinking of part of the earth's crust.

Superimposed drainage. A drainage system that, because of the erosion of the strata in which it was established, has been imposed on the older, underlying rocks, which have a different structure.

Surf zone. The area between the outermost breaker and the limit of wave uprush.

Swash. The rush of water up onto the beach following the breaking of a wave.

Syenite. A coarse-grained igneous rock consisting essentially of orthoclase and hornblende or biotite.

Symmetrical fold. A fold in which the axial plane is essentially vertical, so that the limbs are of equal length and the dips at similar angles.

Syncline. A downfold or trough in which the strata dip inward from both sides toward the axis. The opposite of an anticline.

Synclinorium. A broad regional synclinal trough on which minor folds are superimposed.

Taconite. A granular ferruginous chert containing varying amounts of magnetite, hematite, siderite, and hydrous iron silicates. An ore of iron in the Lake Superior region.

Talc. A very soft mineral with a greasy or soapy feel. A magnesium silicate.

Talus. An accumulation of coarse rock waste at the base of a cliff. Also known as scree.

Tarn. A small mountain lake which occupies a cirque.

Tectogene. A large downfold within a geosyncline beneath an orogenic belt.

Tension fault. A fault produced by tension.

Terminal moraine. A rugged ridge or belt of unsorted till marking the outermost margin of a glacier.

Terminus. The end, or outer, margin of a glacier.

Terrace. A level-topped surface bordered by a steep escarpment. May be composed of alluvium or of solid rock.

Test. The external shell of many small invertebrates.

Throw. The vertical component of the net slip of a fault.

Thrust fault. A fault along which the hanging wall appears to have been raised relative to the footwall. Generally characterized by a low angle of inclination. with reference to the horizontal. Commonly called a reverse fault.

Tide. The response of large bodies of water to the gravitative attraction of the moon and the sun, resulting in the rising and falling of the surface of the water.

Tidewater glacier. A glacier which discharges into the sea.

Tied island. See *Tombolo.*

Till. Nonstratified glacial drift.

Tillite. A rock composed of indurated and cemented till.

Tombolo. A sand bar connecting an island with the mainland or with another island. The result is called a tied island.

Topset beds. The layers deposited horizontally on top of a delta. See also foreset and bottomset beds.

Trachyte. The fine-grained equivalent of syenite.

Traction load. The bottom load, or bed load, of a stream, carried by rolling, sliding, or saltation.

Trade winds. Winds which blow from the subtropical high-pressure belts toward the equator.

Travertine. A somewhat porous or cellular variety of calcium carbonate, deposited from solution in surface and ground waters. Deposited also as stalactites and stalagmites in underground caverns.

Trellised drainage. A drainage pattern that parallels deeply eroded, folded strata. Pattern resembles a garden trellis. Also called grapevine drainage.

Truncated spur. The cutoff or steepened end of a divide between the tributaries of a glaciated valley, resulting from the widening of the main valley by glacial erosion.

Tsunami. See *Seismic sea wave.*

Tufa. A porous spring deposit composed of calcium carbonate or silica.

Tuff. Consolidated volcanic ash. Fragments are generally less than 4 millimeters in diameter.

Tundra. A treeless plain or swampland in the arctic region, generally developed over regions of permafrost.

Turbidity current. A current due to differences in density produced by suspended clays and silt in the water.

Typhoon. A tropical cyclone over the western Pacific Ocean.

Unconfined ground water. Water that is not confined under an impervious cap rock, and is thus able to establish a normal water table.

Unconformity. An old erosion surface that separates younger strata from older rocks.

Underclay. A layer of clay under a bed of coal. Represents the soil in which the plants that formed the coal once grew.

Underground water. Water occupying the pore spaces in the mantle-rock and solid rock below the surface of the ground. Also called ground water and subsurface water.

Undertow. Conjectural return of surf water beneath waves. See *Rip current.*

Uraninite. A mineral composed essentially of uranium oxide. An ore of uranium.

Vadose water. Subsurface water in the zone of aeration or leaching, above the zone of saturation.

Valley train. A long, narrow body of glacial outwash deposited downstream beyond the terminal or recessional moraine of a glacier.

Varve. An annual pair of thin sedimentary beds, one coarse and one fine, deposited as glacial-lake sediment, the coarse laid down during the summer, the fine during the winter.

Vein. A crack or fissure filled with mineral matter deposited from underground-water solution.

Ventifact. Designating pebbles or boulders shaped by the abrasive action of wind-blown sand.

Vermiculite. A platy, micalike mineral that expands markedly when heated.

Vesicle. A small cavity in a fine-grained or glassy igneous rock, formed by a bubble of gas during the solidification of lava.

Viscosity. The internal friction of a fluid that offers resistance to flow.

Vitreous. Having the luster of broken glass; noncrystalline; amorphous.

Vitrophyr. A consolidated, glassy igneous rock, containing occasional phenocrysts.

Volcanic ash. Uncemented volcanic ejecta consisting of fragments mostly under 4 millimeters in diameter.

Volcanic breccia. An indurated pyroclastic rock consisting mainly of angular fragments more than 32 millimeters in diameter.

Volcanic glass. Natural glass produced when lava cools too rapidly to permit crystallization. Examples are obsidian, pitchstone, pumice, and scoria.

Volcanic neck. A roughly cylindrical mass of igneous rock that represents the filling of the vent of an extinct volcano. Volcanic necks range in diameter from a few hundred yards to a mile or more.

Volcano. A mountain which has been built up by lava and pyroclastic fragments ejected from the interior of the earth through a vent. Also, the vent itself.

Vug. A cavity in rock, usually lined with crystals of different composition from that of the surrounding rock.

Vulcanism. The generation and migration of magmas and lavas and the formation of their products.

Warm front. The boundary between advancing warm air and the mass of colder air over which the warm air rises.

Warping. A gentle bending of the crust of the earth that does not result in the formation of pronounced folds or faults.

Water gap. In a stream that flows across tilted or folded strata, the narrows, or pass, developed where the valley crosses the more resistant beds.

Watershed. A term used loosely to mean both drainage basin and drainage divide.

Water table. The upper surface of the zone of saturation.

Wave-built terrace. An embankment built along or near the shore by the aggradational work of waves.

Wave-cut terrace. A leveled rock bench produced by the retreat of a sea cliff through wave erosion. Also called wave platform, shore platform, and plain of marine abrasion.

Wave of translation. A wave in which there is a pronounced forward movement of the water.

Weathering. The complex set of natural processes, both chemical and mechanical, involved in the breaking up and decay of rocks.

Wind gap. A notch in a ridge associated with an abandoned water gap.

Winnowing. The process by which the wind separates fine particles from coarser or heavier ones.

Xenolith. An inclusion or rock fragment broken from the wall or roof of a magma chamber and found embedded in the igneous rock mass.

Yazoo-type tributary. A tributary stream that parallels the main channel in the back-swamp area because high levees prevent it from entering the main stream. Named from the Yazoo River in Mississippi.

Zeolite. A secondary mineral occurring in the cavities of a lava flow.

Zigzag ridges. Ridges looping back and forth, formed by resistant layers in deeply eroded series of alternating plunging anticlines and synclines.

Zone of aeration. The portion of the ground in which the pore spaces in permeable rock are not filled with water. The zone that lies above the zone of saturation.

Zone of flowage. That part of the earth's crust in which rocks are deformed by solid flow, because pressures are such that openings cannot exist.

Zone of fracture. The zone near the surface of the earth's crust in which rocks are deformed by fracture.

Zone of saturation. That part of the ground within which all openings are filled with water. Its upper surface is the water table, and it extends as far down within the earth as connected openings can exist.

INDEX

Page references in **boldface** type indicate illustrations